PREFACE

The British Catalogue of Music is a record of new music —with the exception of certain types of popular music— published in Great Britain. In addition, it records foreign music available in this country through a sole agent and books about music. It is based on the works deposited at the British Museum where copies of all new publications must be sent by law and is the most complete list of current British music available.

Hints for tracing information

The Catalogue is presented in three sections:
Classified Section
Composer and Title Index
Subject Index

The purpose of the Classified Section is to arrange works according to the various voices, instruments, and combinations for which they are written. It is not essential to understand the system of classification. To find information, first consult the Composer and Title Index, which makes it possible to find details of which the composer, title, arranger, or any similar fact, is known. The Subject Index provides an alphabetical index of instruments, musical forms, etc., appearing in the Classified Section.

Composer

When the composer or author of a work is known, look under his name in the Composer and Title Index. The information given here, including the publisher and price, will be adequate for most purposes. If, on the other hand, the fullest information about a work is required, turn to the entry in the Classified Section. This may be found by means of the class symbol (group of letters) at the end of the composer or author entry. In tracing class symbols which include ( ) "brackets" or / "stroke", it should be borne in mind that these signs precede letters in the arrangement.

Thus:

	A
is followed by	A(. . . .)
which is followed by	A/ . . . .
which is followed by	AA
which is followed by	AB
which is followed by	B, etc.

Titles, series, editors and arrangers

Entries are made in the Composer and Title Index under the titles of all works, so that, if you do not know the composer or author, a work can be found by looking up its title in the Composer and Title Index.

If you do not know either the composer or the title, it may still be possible to trace the work if the name of the editor or arranger is known and, in the case of vocal works, the author of the words.

Instrument, musical form and character

While the Classified Section displays the works systematically according to the instrument or combination for which a work is written, the Subject Index lists the principal musical forms and musical character and it shows by means of the class symbol where works having such forms or musical character are to be found in the Classified Section. For example, in the Subject Index under the word Sonatas the following entries may be found:

Sonatas: Arrangements for 2 pianos	QNUK/AE
Sonatas: Organ	RE
Sonatas: Piano duets, 4 hands	QNVE
Sonatas: Piano solos	QPE
Sonatas: Violin solos, Unaccompanied	SPME

It will be seen that this group of entries enables you to assemble all the works in sonata form no matter for what instrument the music is, or was originally, written.

Under the word Violin the following may be found:

Violin	S
Violin: Accompanying female voices: Choral works	FE/S
Violin: Books	AS
Violin & orchestra	MPS
Violin & string orchestra	RXMPS

This group directs you first to the place S in the Classified Section, where music for the violin is found, including works composed originally for other instruments and arranged for violin. It also directs you to works in which the violin figures in combination with other instruments.

It thus provides at one and the same time the link between an instrument and its place in the Classified Section and an exhaustive guide to all the works in which that particular instrument figures.

Musical literature

Books about music which normally appear in the *British National Bibliography* are also included in this catalogue. They occur in the sequences lettered A and B. They are indexed in exactly the same way as musical works in the Composer and Title Index and are designated by the qualification "Books" in the Subject Index. Thus, in the second group above, the entry Violin: Books, directing you to AS, indicates that books about the violin will be found at that place.

Prices

Prices given are those current at the time of the first recording of an entry in this catalogue. In a few cases prices of parts are not given but can be obtained on application to the publisher.

Abbreviations

Most of the abbreviations used in describing musical works are self-explanatory. The size of a musical work is indicated by one of the following conventional symbols: *8vo* for works up to $10\frac{1}{2}$ in. in height, *4to* for works between $10\frac{1}{2}$ and 12 in. in height, and *fol.* for works over 12 in. in height. The abbreviation *obl.* (oblong) is added to show when a work is of unusual proportions, and a single sheet is designated by the abbreviations *s.sh.* The abbreviations used for the description of books in the sections A and B are those in use in the *British National Bibliography*.

THE
BRITISH CATALOGUE
OF MUSIC
1974

THE
BRITISH CATALOGUE
OF MUSIC
1974

A record of music and books about music recently published in Great Britain, based upon the material deposited at the Copyright Receipt Office of the British Library, arranged according to a system of classification with a Composer and Title Index, a Subject Index, and a list of music publishers

LONDON: THE BRITISH LIBRARY BIBLIOGRAPHIC SERVICES DIVISION

© 1975   The British Library

ISBN 0 900220 49 X

The British Catalogue of Music,
The British Library Bibliographic Services Division,
Store Street, London, WC1E 7DG

APRIL 1975

Printed in Great Britain by William Clowes & Sons, Limited, London, Beccles and Colchester

OUTLINE OF THE CLASSIFICATION

The following outline is given for general information only. Users are advised to consult the Subject Index to discover the exact location of required material in the Classified Section.

MUSICAL LITERATURE

A	General works
	Common sub-divisions
A(B)	Periodicals
A(C)	Encyclopaedias
A(D)	Composite works, symposia, essays by several writers
A(E)	Anecdotes, personal reminiscences
A(K)	Economics
A(M)	Persons in music
A(MM)	Musical profession
A(MN)	Music as a career
A(P)	Individuals
A(Q)	Organisations
A(QT)	Terminology
A(QU)	Notation
A(R)	Printing
A(S)	Publishing
A(T)	Bibliographies
A(U)	Libraries
A(V)	Musical education
A(X)	History of music
A(Y)	Music of particular localities
A/AM	Theory of music
A/CC	Aesthetics
A/CY	Technique of music
A/D	Composition
A/E	Performance
A/F	Recording
A/FY	Musical character
A/G	Folk music
A/GM	Music associated with particular occupations
A/H	Dance music
A/HM	Ballet music
A/J	Music accompanying drama
A/JR	Film music
A/KD	Music to accompany social customs
A/L	Religious music
A/LZ	Elements of music
A/R	Harmony
A/S	Forms of music
A/Y	Fugue
AB	Works on vocal music
AC	Works on opera
ACM	Works on musical plays
AD-AX	Works on music for particular vocal or instrumental performers, enumerated like D–X below
B	Works on individual composers (including libretti and other verbal texts of particular musical works)
BZ	Works on non-European music

MUSIC (SCORES AND PARTS)

C/AY	Collections not limited to work of particular composer, executant, form or character
C/AZ	Collections of a particular composer not otherwise limited
C/G-C/Y	Collections illustrating music of particular form, character, etc., enumerated like A/G-A/Y above
CB	Vocal music
CC	Opera. Vocal scores with keyboard
CM	Musical plays. Vocal scores with keyboard
D	Choral music
DC	Religious choral music
DF	Liturgical music
DH	Motets, Anthems, Hymns
DTZ	Secular choral music
DX	Cantatas
DW	Songs, etc.
E	Choral music with instruments other than keyboard
EZ	Choral music unaccompanied
F	Choral music. Female voices
G	Choral music. Male voices
J	Unison vocal works
K	Vocal solos
L	Instrumental music
M	Orchestral music
N	Chamber music
PVV	Music for individual instruments and instrumental groups
PW	Keyboard instruments
Q	Piano
R	Organ
RW	String instruments
S	Violin
SQ	Viola
SR	Cello
SS	Double bass
TQ	Harp
TS	Guitar
U	Wind instruments
V	Woodwind
VR	Flute
VS	Recorder
VT	Oboe
VU	Saxophone
VV	Clarinet
VW	Bassoon
W	Brass
WS	Trumpet
WT	Horn
WU	Trombone
WX	Bass tuba
X	Percussion instruments
Z	Non-European music

CLASSIFIED SECTION

This section contains entries under subjects, executants and instruments according to a system of classification, a synopsis of which appears in the preliminary pages. The key to the classification and to this section is found in the Subject Index at the end of this volume, which is followed by a list of music publishers and their addresses.

The following are used in giving the sizes of musical works:—

8vo for works up to 10½″ in height.
4to for works between 10½″ and 12″ in height.
fol. for works over 12″ in height.
obl. indicates a work of unusual proportions.
s.sh. means a single sheet.

A — MUSICAL LITERATURE
Abraham, Gerald
The tradition of western music / [by] Gerald Abraham. — London [etc.] : Oxford University Press, 1974. — [6],130p : music ; 22cm.
Index.
ISBN 0-19-316324-1 Pbk : £1.00

(B74-22802)

Cecily, *Sister, OP*
Lámhleabhar ginearálta don cheoltóir / [le] an tSuír Cecily ; léaraídí le Priscilla Kavanagh; Diarmuid Breathnach a d'aistrigh ... — Baile Atha Cliath [Dublin] : Folens, 1973. — 133p : ill, music, ports ; 25cm.
Bibl.: p.132-133.
ISBN 0-902592-58-0 Pbk : £0.48

(B74-11047)

A(B) — Periodicals
Music & Man : an interdisciplinary journal of studies on music. — [London] : Gordon and Breach.
Vol.1, no.1- ; 1973-. — 1973-. — 1 ill ; 23cm.
Four issues a year. — [78]p. in 2nd issue.
Pbk : £3.50 (yearly) (£10.15 yearly to libraries and institutions)

(B74-14306)

A(C) — Encyclopaedias
Ammer, Christine
Harper's dictionary of music / by Christine Ammer ; drawings by Carmela M. Ciampa and Kenneth L. Donlon. — New York [etc.] ; London (28 Tavistock St., WC2E 7PN) : Barnes and Noble, 1973. — xiii,414p : ill, music ; 21cm. — (Everyday handbooks)
Originally published: New York: Harper and Row; London: Hale, 1972.
ISBN 0-06-463347-0 Pbk : £1.60

(B74-09865)

A(C/XM71) — Encyclopedias. History, 1900-1970
Vinton, John
Dictionary of twentieth-century music / edited by John Vinton. — London : Thames and Hudson, 1974. — xiv,834p : music ; 25cm.
Originally published: as 'Dictionary of contemporary music'. New York : Dutton, 1973.
ISBN 0-500-01100-1 : £9.50

(B74-24905)

A(D) — Essays
Kodály, Zoltán
The selected writings of Zoltán Kodály / [edited by Ferenc Bónis; translated from the Hungarian by Lili Halápy and Fred Macnicol; photographs by László Vámos]. — London [etc.] : Boosey and Hawkes, 1974. — 239p,[16]p of plates : ill, map, music, ports ; 25cm.
Translations from: 'Visszatekintés', I-II. Budapest : Zenemükiadó, 1964. — Index.
ISBN 0-85162-021-3 : £3.95

(B74-21534)

A(P) — Wagner, Cosima. Biographies
Sutherland, Douglas
Twilight of the swans / by Douglas Sutherland. — London : New English Library, 1974. — 285p,[12p] of plates : ill, ports ; 22cm.
Originally published: 1973. — Bibl.: p.283-285.
ISBN 0-450-01876-8 : £3.00

(B74-11051)

A(QU) — Notation
Cole, Hugo
Sounds and signs : aspects of musical notation / by Hugo Cole. — London [etc.] : Oxford University Press, 1974. — vi,162p : ill, facsim, music ; 22cm.
Index.
ISBN 0-19-317105-8 Pbk : £1.50

(B74-02414)

Read, Gardner
Music notation : a manual of modern practice / by Gardner Read. — 2nd ed. — London : Gollancz, 1974. — xi,482p : music ; 22cm.
Second ed. originally published: Boston, Mass.: Allyn and Bacon, 1969. — Index.
ISBN 0-575-01758-9 : £3.50

(B74-08076)

A(T) — Bibliographies
Olmsted, Elizabeth H
Music Library Association catalog of cards for printed music, 1953-1972 : a supplement to the Library of Congress catalogs / edited by Elizabeth H. Olmsted. — Totawa, N.J. ; London (2 Rugby St., WC1N 3QU) : Rowman and Littlefield, 1974. — 2v. (vii,575p;iii,557p) ; 29cm.
ISBN 0-87471-474-5 : £33.35

(B74-13898)

A(U/BC/YC) — Libraries. Directories. Great Britain
Long, Maureen W
Music in British libraries : a directory of resources / compiled by Maureen W. Long. — 2nd ed. — London : Library Association, 1974. — 154p ; 21cm. — (Library Association. Research publications ; no.14)
Previous ed.: 1971. — Index.
ISBN 0-85365-287-2 Pbk : £3.00 (£2.40 to members)

(B74-19811)

A(VC) — Teaching
Choksy, Lois
The Kodály method : comprehensive music education from infant to adult / [by] Lois Choksy. — Englewood Cliffs ; London [etc.] : Prentice-Hall, 1974. — xi,221p : ill, music ; 23cm.
Index.
ISBN 0-13-516757-4 Pbk : £2.60

(B74-23950)

A(VC/QU) — Teaching. Notation
Szönyi, Erzsébet
Musical reading and writing / [by] Erzsébet Szönyi ; [translated from the Hungarian by Lili Halápy ; translation revised by Geoffry Russell-Smith]. — London [etc.] : Boosey and Hawkes.
Vol.1. — 251p : ill, music ; 25cm.
Translation of: 'A zenei írás-olvasás módszertana', 1. Budapest : Zenemükiadó, 1954.
ISBN 0-85162-011-6 : £2.95

(B74-25493)

A(VG) — Primary schools
Hart, Muriel
Music / by Muriel Hart. — London : Heinemann Educational, 1974. — x,150p : ill, music ; 20cm. — (Activity in the primary school)
Bibl.: p.148-150.
ISBN 0-435-80606-8 Pbk : £0.80

(B74-15369)

Keetman, Gunild
Elementaria : first acquaintance with Orff-Schulwerk / [by] Gunild Keetman ; [drawings by Ottmar Frick; photographs by Peter Keetman; translated from the German by Margaret Murray]. — London (48 Great Marlborough St., W1V 2BN) : Schott and Co. Ltd, 1974. — 202p : ill, music ; 23cm.
Originally published: in German. Stuttgart : Klett, 1970. — List of films: p.195. — List of gramophone records: p.195-197. — Bibl.: p.197-199. — Index.
ISBN 0-901938-04-1 : £4.50

(B74-13706)

A(VJ) — Middle schools
Glynne-Jones, Marjorie Lilian
Music / [by] M.L. Glynne-Jones. — London [etc.] : Macmillan, 1974. — 176p : ill, music ; 23cm. — (Basic books in education : schooling in the middle years)
Bibl.: p.153-155. — Index.
ISBN 0-333-12252-6 : £2.60

(B74-21533)

A(VK) — Secondary schools
Morrish, Donald James
Basic goals in music. — [New ed.] / [by] D.L. [i.e. D.J.] Morrish. — London [etc.] : McGraw-Hill.
Previous ed.: / by Earle Terry, Lloyd H. Slind, Frank Churchley. Toronto [etc.] : McGraw-Hill Ryerson, [1973?].
1. — 1974. — [12],102p : ill(some col), music ; 23cm.
ISBN 0-07-094430-x Pbk : £1.10

(B74-22799)

2. — 1974. — x,118p : ill(some col), music ; 23cm.
ISBN 0-07-094431-8 Pbk : £1.20

(B74-22800)

A(VK/YDJC/XQG4) — Secondary schools. Northwest England, 1967-1970
North West Regional Curriculum Development Project
Creative music making and the young school leaver / The North West Regional Curriculum Development Project. — Glasgow [etc.] : Blackie, 1974. — [5],122p : ill, music ; 22cm.
Bibl.: p.89.
ISBN 0-216-89673-8 Pbk : £1.40

(B74-20922)

A(X) — History
The **new** Oxford history of music. — London [etc.] : Oxford University Press.
In 11 vols.
Vol.10 : The modern age, 1890-1960 / edited by Martin Cooper. — 1974. — xix,764p,[1],ix p of plates : ill, facsims, music ; 26cm.
Bibl.: p.701-733. — Index.
ISBN 0-19-316310-1 : £9.50

(B74-22160)

Young, Percy Marshall
A concise history of music : from primitive times to the present / [by] Percy M. Young. — London [etc.] : E. Benn, 1974. — 168p : ill, music, plan, ports ; 23cm.
Index.
ISBN 0-510-37312-7 : £2.00

(B74-13103)

A(XB) — Historiology
Westrup, *Sir* **Jack Allan**
An introduction to musical history / [by] Sir Jack Westrup. — 2nd ed. — London : Hutchinson, 1973. — 176p ; 22cm. — (Hutchinson university library)
Previous ed.: 1955. — Bibl.: p.160-165. — Index.
ISBN 0-09-031591-x : £1.50
ISBN 09 031592 8 Pbk: £0.80

(B74-04792)

A(XM46) — History, 1900-1945
Bray, Trevor
Twentieth century music, 1900-1945 / prepared by Trevor Bray for the Course Team. — Milton Keynes : Open University Press, 1974. — 115p : ill, music, ports ; 30cm. — (Arts, a third level course : the development of instruments and their music ; units 23-25) (A304; 23-25)
Bibl.: p.112-113. — List of gramophone records: p.113-114.
ISBN 0-335-00866-6 Pbk : Unpriced

(B74-21535)

A(XM71) — History, 1900-1970
Salzman, Eric
Twentieth-century music : an introduction / [by] Eric Salzman. — 2nd ed. — Englewood Cliffs ; London [etc.] : Prentice-Hall, 1974. — xiii,242p : ill, music, ports ; 24cm. — (Prentice-Hall history of music series)
Previous ed.: 1967. — Bibl. — Index.
ISBN 0-13-935015-2 : £4.70
ISBN 0-13-935007-1 Pbk : £2.35

(B74-24208)

A(XM73) — History, 1900-1972
Hellewell, David
The new music : an introduction and general survey for the non-specialist / [by] David Hellewell. — Bournemouth (57 Lansdowne Rd, Bournemouth, Hants. BH1 1RN) : Apollo Contemporary Music, [1973]. — [2],17p ; 21cm.
ISBN 0-9503225-0-4 Sd : £0.50

(B74-06501)

A(XPK24) — History, 1950-1973
Nyman, Michael
Experimental music : Cage and beyond / [by] Michael Nyman. — London : Studio Vista, 1974. — [6],154p : ill, facsims, music, ports ; 26cm.
Bibl.: p.149-151. — Index.
ISBN 0-289-70182-1 : £3.75

(B74-23495)

A(Y) — MUSIC OF PARTICULAR LOCALITIES
A(YB/XDXJ151) — Europe, 1550-1700
Donington, Robert
The interpretation of early music / by Robert Donington. — New version. — London : Faber, 1974. — 766p : ill, music ; 26cm.
Previous (i.e. 2nd) ed.: 1965. — Bibl.: p.673-728. — Index.
ISBN 0-571-04789-0 : £10.00

(B74-21536)

A(YC/WE/Q) — Great Britain. Festivals. Organisations
British Federation of Music Festivals
Year book / the British Federation of Music Festivals (incorporating the Music Teachers' Association). — London (106 Gloucester Place, W1H 3DB) : The Federation.
1974. — 1974. — [5],123p,plate : ports ; 21cm.
ISBN 0-901532-05-3 Sd : £0.60

(B74-12386)

A(YDB/W) — Promenade concerts. London
Orga, Ateş
The Proms / [by] Ateş Orga. — Newton Abbot [etc.] : David and Charles, 1974. — 192p : ill, facsims, ports ; 26cm.
Bibl.: p.184. — Index.
ISBN 0-7153-6679-3 : £3.95

(B74-24907)

A(YDFR) — Cornwall
Combellack, Myrna May
A survey of musical activities in Cornwall / [by] Myrna M. Combellack. — Redruth (Trevenson House, Pool, Redruth, Cornwall) : Institute of Cornish Studies, 1974. — 16p ; 21cm. — (Institute of Cornish Studies. Special reports ; no.1)
ISBN 0-903686-05-8 Sd : £0.30

(B74-22803)

A(YT/X) — United States. History
Hitchcock, Hugh Wiley
Music in the United States : a historical introduction / [by] H. Wiley Hitchcock. — 2nd ed. — Englewood Cliffs ; London [etc.] : Prentice-Hall, 1974. — xvii,286p : ill, music ; 24cm. — (Prentice-Hall history of music series)
Previous ed.: 1969. — Bibl. — Index.
ISBN 0-13-608398-6 : £3.65
ISBN 0-13-608380-3 Pbk : £2.10

(B74-28313)

A(Z) — MUSIC IN RELATION TO OTHER SUBJECTS
Bray, Trevor
Music and society today / prepared by Trevor Bray and Richard Middleton for the Course Team. — Milton Keynes : Open University Press, 1974. — 33p ; 30cm. — (Arts, a third level course : the development of instruments and their music ; unit 30) (A304 ; 30)
ISBN 0-335-00869-0 Sd : Unpriced

(B74-24207)

Honigsheim, Paul
Music and society : the later writings of Paul Honigsheim / edited, with additional material and bibliographies, by K. Peter Etzkorn ; foreword by J. Allan Beegle. — New York ; London [etc.] : Wiley-Interscience, 1973. — xxi,327p ; 24cm.
Bibl.: p.233-320. — Index.
ISBN 0-471-24680-8 : £8.50

(B74-07432)

A(Z/D) — Music - in relation to the physically handicapped. Conference papers
Joint Study Conference on Music and the Physically Handicapped, *London, 1970*
Report of Joint Study Conference on Music and the Physically Handicapped, held on April 6th, 1970, at the Goldsmiths' Hall, London, E.C.2 ... / [organised by] Disabled Living Foundation [and the] National Council of Social Service. — London (346 Kensington High St., W.14) : Disabled Living Foundation, 1970. — 63p ; 22cm.
ISBN 0-901908-02-9 Sd : £0.50

(B74-16560)

A(ZE) — Music - expounded by postage stamps
Peat, Sylvester
Music on stamps / by Sylvester Peat. — Chippenham (Citadel Works, Bath Rd, Chippenham, Wilts. SN15 2AA) : Picton Publishing.
Part 3 : G-L. — 1973. — [6],58p : chiefly ill, music, ports ; 21cm.
ISBN 0-902633-20-1 Sd : £0.60

(B74-17382)

A/AM — Theory of music
Jones, George Thaddeus
Music theory / by George Thaddeus Jones. — New York [etc.] ; London ([28 Tavistock St., WC2E 7PN]) : Barnes and Noble, 1974. — xvii,310p : ill, music ; 21cm. — (College outline series)
Bibl.: p.305-306. — Index.
ISBN 0-06-460137-4 Pbk : £1.95

(B74-25492)

A/B — PHYSICS OF MUSIC
A/C — Appreciation
Reimer, Bennett
The experience of music / [by] Bennett Reimer, Edward G. Evans, Jr. — Englewood Cliffs ; London [etc.] : Prentice-Hall, 1972. — xiv,434p,8p of plates : ill(some col), music ; 22x24cm.
Bibl. — Index.
ISBN 0-13-294553-3 : £6.00

(B74-16180)

A/CC — AESTHETICS
Whone, Herbert
The hidden face of music / [by] Herbert Whone ; with
illustrations by the author. — London : Gollancz, 1974. — 128p :
ill ; 24cm.
Index.
ISBN 0-575-01739-2 : £3.00

(B74-12385)

A/D — COMPOSITION
Cone, Edward T
The composer's voice / [by] Edward T. Cone. — Berkeley [etc.] ;
London : University of California Press, 1974. — ix,184p : ill,
music ; 23cm. — (The Ernest Bloch lectures)
Index.
ISBN 0-520-02508-3 : £5.50

(B74-28312)

A/D(YB/M) — Composers. Europe
Borge, Victor
My favourite intervals / by Victor Borge and Robert Sherman ;
drawings by Thomas Winding. — London : Woburn Press, 1974.
— 189p : ill ; 23cm.
Originally published: as 'My favourite intermissions'. Garden City, N.Y. :
Doubleday, 1971.
ISBN 0-7130-0126-7 : £2.25

(B74-09227)

Rowland-Entwistle, Theodore
Famous composers / [by] Theodore Rowland-Entwistle and Jean
Cooke. — Newton Abbot [etc.] : David and Charles, [1974]. —
128p ; 23cm. — (Brief biographies)
ISBN 0-7153-6375-1 : £2.50

(B74-09226)

A/E — PERFORMANCE
A/E(YTF/XQM2) — New York, 1972-1973
Porter, Andrew
A musical season : an English critic in New York / [by] Andrew
Porter. — London : Gollancz, 1974. — [6],313p ; 23cm.
'All the essays in this book originally appeared in "The New Yorker"' - title
page verso. — Index.
ISBN 0-575-01950-6 : £4.00

(B74-30189)

A/EC(P) — Beecham, Sir Thomas. Biographies
Procter-Gregg, Humphrey
Sir Thomas Beecham, conductor and impresario, as remembered
by his friends and colleagues / compiled and edited by Humphrey
Procter-Gregg. — [Windermere] ([3 Oakland, Windermere,
Cumbria]) : [H. Procter-Gregg], [1973]. — [10],206p : 1 ill, port ;
20cm.
Bibl.: p.202-203.
ISBN 0-9503649-0-8 : £3.50

(B74-23498)

A/EF — Aural training
Kliewer, Vernon Lee
Aural training : a comprehensive approach / [by] Vernon L.
Kliewer. — Englewood Cliffs ; London [etc.] : Prentice-Hall,
1974. — xii,499p : music ; 24cm.
ISBN 0-13-053231-2 Pbk : £4.15

(B74-24904)

A/FD — RECORDED MUSIC
A/FD(T/WT) — Bibliographies. Lists
Foreman, Ronald Lewis Edmund
Discographies : a bibliography of catalogues of recordings, mainly
relating to specific musical subjects, composers and performers /
[by] Lewis Foreman. — London (10e Prior Bolton St., N.1) :
Triad Press, 1973. — 65p ; 30cm. — (Triad Press bibliographical
series ; no.1)
Index.
ISBN 0-902070-08-8 Sp : £1.60

(B74-03642)

A/FD(U) — Recorded music. Librarianship
Foreman, Lewis
Systematic discography / [by] Lewis Foreman. — London :
Bingley, 1974. — 144p : facsims ; 23cm.
Bibl.: p.129-135. — Index.
ISBN 0-85157-161-1 : £3.00

(B74-25104)

A/FD(WM) — Trade lists. Columbia Broadcasting System
Columbia Broadcasting System
Main alphabetical & numerical catalogue : including CBS, CBS
Harmony Series, Embassy, Epic, Monument, Mums, Philadelphia
International / [Columbia Broadcasting System]. — London (28
Theobalds Rd, WC1X 8PB) : CBS Records.
1974-75. — [1974]. — 158p : ill ; 28cm.
'This catalogue incorporates all LP discs and tapes which at the time of
going to press had been announced for release up to and including 27th
September 1974'.
ISBN 0-904456-01-3 Pbk : Unpriced

(B74-30308)

A/FD(WM) — Trade lists. Decca
Decca Group records & tapes, main catalogue (alphabetical &
numerical). — London : Decca Record Co.
1974: up to and including September 1973. — 1974. — 672p in various
pagings ; 26cm.
ISBN 0-901364-05-3 : Unpriced

(B74-13392)

A/FD(WM) — Trade lists. Phonogram
Phonogram Limited
Phonogram complete alphabetical and numerical catalogue. —
London (Stanhope House, Stanhope Place, W2 2HH) : Phonogram
Ltd.
1974 : containing full details of all long playing 33 1/3 rpm records,
musicassettes, and 8-track cartridges issued up to and including December
1973. — 1974. — [5],116,49,368,46p,[3] leaves ; 25cm.
ISBN 0-904400-00-x : £5.00

(B74-12650)

A/FD(WT) — Lists
The **art** of record buying : a list of recommended microgroove
recordings. — London : E.M.G.
1974. — [1974]. — [2],318p : map ; 23cm.
ISBN 0-900982-05-5 : £2.60

(B74-02648)

A/FH — MECHANICAL MUSIC
A/FM(EM) — Fair organs. Illustrations
Fair Organ Preservation Society
Organ parade / [Fair Organ Preservation Society]. —
[Manchester] (c/o K. Redfern, 3 Bentley Rd, Denton, Manchester
M34 3AZ) : Fair Organ Preservation Society, [1973]. — 108p :
chiefly ill ; 25cm.
Index.
ISBN 0-9502701-1-3 Sd : £1.50 (Free to members)

(B74-07436)

A/FY — MUSICAL CHARACTER
A/G — Folk music
Nettl, Bruno
Folk and traditional music of the Western continents / [by] Bruno
Nettl ; with chapters on Latin America by Gérard Béhague. —
2nd ed. — Englewood Cliffs ; London [etc.] : Prentice-Hall, 1973.
— xiii,258p : ill, music ; 24cm. — (Prentice-Hall history of music
series)
Previous ed.: 1965. — Bibl. — Lists of records. — Index.
ISBN 0-13-322941-6 : £4.70
ISBN 0-13-322933-5 Pbk: £2.60

(B74-16181)

A/G(BC) — Folk music. Yearbooks. Directories
Folk directory / English Folk Dance and Song Society. — London :
The Society.
1974 / edited by Tony Wales. — 1974. — 188p : ill, ports ; 22cm.
Index.
ISBN 0-85418-096-6 : £1.25 (£0.75 to members)
ISBN 0-85418-095-8 Pbk: £0.60 (£0.30 to members)

(B74-13106)

A/G(WJ) — Folk music. Catalogues
Vaughan Williams Memorial Library
The Vaughan Williams Memorial Library catalogue of the English
Folk Dance and Song Society : acquisitions to the library of
books, pamphlets, periodicals, sheet music and manuscripts from
its inception to 1971. — London : Mansell Information
Publishing, 1973. — xiv,769p ; 29cm.
ISBN 0-7201-0368-1 : £25.00

(B74-06945)

A/G(YDL/B) — Folk music. Scotland. Periodicals
Sandy Bell's Broadsheet. — Edinburgh (Forrest Hill Bar, Forrest
Rd, Edinburgh) : John Barrow.
Issue no.1- ; Aug. 20, 1973- . — 1973-. — ill ; 31cm.
Fortnightly. — [6]p. in issue no.20.
Sd : £0.03

(B74-16726)

A/G(YDM/XA1909) — Folk music. Ireland. To 1909
O'Neill, Francis
Irish folk music : a fascinating hobby, with some account of allied
subjects including O'Farrell's treatise on the Irish or Union pipes
and Touhey's hints to amateur pipers / by Francis O'Neill. — [1st
ed. reprinted] ; with a new introduction by Barry O'Neill. —
Wakefield : EP Publishing, 1973. — xii,359p,[24] leaves : ill,
music, ports ; 24cm.
Facsimile reprint of: 1st ed., Chicago : Regan Printing House, 1910. —
Index.
ISBN 0-85409-910-7 : £3.00

(B74-12387)

A/G(YSW) — Folk songs. North America
Adams, Pamela
There was an old lady who swallowed a fly / illustrated by Pam
Adams. — Purton (Restrop Manor, Purton, Wilts.) : Child's Play
(International) Ltd, 1973. — [16]p : chiefly col ill ; 30cm.
ISBN 0-85953-021-3 : £1.00
ISBN 0 85853 018 3 Pbk: £0.60

(B74-05270)

A/GB — Popular music
Taylor, Derek
As time goes by / [by] Derek Taylor. — London (30 Gray's Inn Rd, WC1X 8JL) : Abacus, 1974. — 182,[12]p of plates : ports ; 20cm.
Originally published: London : Davis-Poynter, 1973. — Index.
ISBN 0-349-13381-6 Pbk : £0.75

(B74-27796)

Top pop scene. — Maidenhead : Purnell.
[1974]. — 1974. — 4-61p : chiefly ill(some col), ports(some col) ; 28cm.
ISBN 0-361-02840-7 : £0.70

(B74-22801)

A/GB(Q/YC) — Popular music. Great Britain. Organisations. Apple Corps Ltd
DiLello, Richard
The longest cocktail party / [by] Richard DiLello. — London (37 Soho Sq., W.1) : Charisma Books, 1973. — x,325p : ill, ports ; 23cm.
Originally published: Chicago : Playboy Press, 1972. — List of gramophone records: p.309-322.
ISBN 0-85947-006-7 Pbk : £1.90

(B74-18700)

A/GB(WE/YC) — Popular music. Festivals. Great Britain
Sandford, Jeremy
Tomorrow's people / [by] Jeremy Sandford, Ron Reid. — London [etc.] (47 Catherine Place, S.W.1) : Jerome Publishing Co. Ltd, 1974. — 128p : ill(some col), ports(some col) ; 30cm.
ISBN 0-904125-05-x Pbk : £1.95

(B74-14305)

A/GB(XQG4) — Popular music, 1967-1970
Fong-Torres, Ben
The 'Rolling Stone' rock 'n' roll reader / edited by Ben Fong-Torres. — Toronto [etc.] ; London : Bantam, 1974. — xv, 783p ; 18cm.
'All material previously appeared in "Rolling Stone"' - title page verso.
ISBN 0-552-67483-4 Pbk : £0.75

(B74-15523)

A/JR(YT/XNJ43) — Films. United States, 1929-1971
Thomas, Tony
Music for the movies / by Tony Thomas. — New York : A.S. Barnes ; London : Tantivy Press, 1973. — 270p : ill, ports ; 26cm.
List of music: p.221-264. — Index.
ISBN 0-900730-63-3 : £4.50

(B74-02980)

A/LZ — ELEMENTS OF MUSIC
A/M(XDS) — Theory, 1517
Ornithoparchus, Andreas
[Musice active micrologus]. A compendium of musical practice / Ornithoparchus, Dowland; with a new introduction, list of variant readings and table of citations of theorists by Gustave Reese and Steven Ledbetter. — New York : Dover Publications ; London : Constable, 1973. — xxx,212p : ill, music ; 26cm. — (American Musicological Society. Reprint series) (Music Library Association. Reprint series)
'Complete facsimile reproductions of the second 1517 edition of "Musice active micrologus" by Andreas Ornithoparchus and the 1609 translation "Andreas Ornithoparchus his micrologus; or, Introduction, containing the art of singing" by John Dowland ...' - book jacket.
ISBN 0-486-20912-1 : £7.00

(B74-11735)

A/PN/PF — Twelve note music. Tonality
Forte, Allen
The structure of atonal music / [by] Allen Forte. — New Haven ; London : Yale University Press, 1973. — ix,224p : ill, music ; 26cm.
Bibl.: p.213. — Index.
ISBN 0-300-01610-7 : £4.95

(B74-11052)

A/R — Harmony
Forte, Allen
Tonal harmony in concept and practice / [by] Allen Forte. — 2nd ed. — New York ; London [etc.] : Holt, Rinehart and Winston, 1974. — ix,502p : music ; 25cm.
Previous ed.: New York : Holt, Rinehart and Winston, 1962. — Index.
ISBN 0-03-077495-0 : £6.95

(B74-14970)

AB — MUSICAL LITERATURE. VOCAL MUSIC
AB/EBE — Bel canto. Singing
Manén, Lucie
The art of singing : a manual / [by] Lucie Manén. — London (38 Russell Sq., WC1B 5DA) : Faber Music Ltd, 1974. — 46p : ill, music ; 25cm.
Gramophone record (2s. 7in. 33 1/3 rpm.) in pocket.
ISBN 0-571-10009-0 Pbk : £2.20

(B74-21538)

AB/FD — Recorded music
Steane, John Barry
The grand tradition : seventy years of singing on record / [by] J.B. Steane. — London : Duckworth, 1974. — xii,628p : ports ; 25cm.
Bibl.: p.611-612. — Index.
ISBN 0-7156-0661-1 : £10.00

(B74-15525)

AC — MUSICAL LITERATURE. OPERA
AC/E(YC/Q) — Opera. Great Britain. Organisations
National Operatic and Dramatic Association
Year book / National Operatic and Dramatic Association. — London (1 Crestfield St., WC1H 8AU) : The Association.
1974. — [1974]. — [1],336,A23p : ill, map ; 19cm.
Index.
ISBN 0-901318-06-x Pbk : Unpriced
ISSN 0547-8030
Also classified at 792'.0222'06242

(B74-29672)

AC/E(YC/QB/X) — Sadlers Wells Opera Company. History
English National Opera Limited
A history of Sadler's Wells Opera : an illustrated booklet, published in the centenary year of Lilian Baylis's birth, to mark the change of the Company's name to the English National Opera / written and edited by Richard Jarman. — [London] ([London Coliseum, St Martin's La., WC2N 4ES]) : [English National Opera Ltd], [1974]. — [68]p : ill, facsims, ports ; 30cm.
ISBN 0-9503681-0-5 Sd : £1.00

(B74-26029)

AC/FD — Recorded music
Harris, Kenn
Opera recordings : a critical guide / by Kenn Harris. — Newton Abbot : David and Charles, 1973. — 328p ; 23cm.
Index.
ISBN 0-7153-6362-x : £3.95

(B74-00871)

ACM — MUSICAL LITERATURE. MUSICAL PLAYS
ACMBN — Musical plays. Stories
Drinkrow, John
The vintage musical comedy book / [by] John Drinkrow ; illustrated from the Raymond Mander and Joe Mitchenson Theater Collection. — Reading : Osprey Publishing, 1974. — 146p,16p of plates : ill, ports ; 20cm.
List of gramophone records: p.140-146.
ISBN 0-85045-103-5 : £1.95

(B74-04045)

AD — MUSICAL LITERATURE. CHORAL MUSIC
AD(YB/M/XM) — Composers. Europe, from 1900
Twentieth century composers. — London : Weidenfeld and Nicolson.
In 5 vols.
Vol.4 : France, Italy and Spain / [by] Frederick Goldbeck ; edited by Nicolas Nabokov and Anna Kallin ; with an introduction by Nicolas Nabokov. — 1974. — [9],147p : ill ; 23cm.
Bibl.: p.140-142. — Index.
ISBN 0-297-76793-3 : £4.50

(B74-29004)

AD/EC(P/D) — Hughes, John. Essays
Hughes, Hugh John
Gŵr wrth gerdd : John Hughes, 1896-1968 / golygydd H.J. Hughes. — Llandysul : Gwasg Gomer, 1973. — 85p ; 22cm.
ISBN 0-85088-217-6 : £0.90

(B74-04044)

AD/LD(YD/D) — Church music. England. Essays
English church music : a collection of essays. — Croydon (Addington Palace, Croydon CR9 5AD) : Royal School of Church Music.
1974. — [1974]. — 3-60p,[2] leaves of plates : 1 ill, music, port ; 22cm.
ISBN 0-85402-057-8 Pbk : £1.12

(B74-20190)

ADT(ZF) — Plainsong - influenced by folk song
Chambers, George Bennet
Folksong - plainsong : a study in origins and musical relationships / by G.B. Chambers ; preface by Ralph Vaughan Williams. — 2nd ed. — London : Merlin Press, 1972. — viii, 120p : music ; 22cm.
Previous ed.: 1956. — Bibl.: p.106-108. — Index.
ISBN 0-85036-195-8 : £3.00

(B74-20191)

ADW(YD/XE101) — Songs, etc. England, 1600-1700
Spink, Ian
English song, Dowland to Purcell / [by] Ian Spink. — London : Batsford, 1974. — 5-312p,[8]p of plates : ill, music, ports ; 23cm.
Bibl.: p.261-288. — Index.
ISBN 0-7134-0756-5 : £5.50

(B74-06503)

ADW/G(YT/P) — Folk songs. United States. Carter family.
Biographies
Atkins, John
The Carter family / edited by John Atkins. — London (33
Brunswick Gardens, W8 4AW) : Old Time Music, 1973. — 63p :
ill, facsims, ports ; 30cm. — (Old Time Music booklet; 1)
List of gramophone records: p.36-59. — Bibl.: p.61-62.
ISBN 0-904395-00-6 Sd : £0.60

(B74-12389)

ADW/GB — Popular songs
Rock file. — St Albans : Panther. — (Panther rock series)
2 / [edited by Charlie Gillett]. — 1974. — 169p,[16]p of plates : ill, ports ;
18cm.
ISBN 0-586-04087-0 Pbk : £0.50

(B74-18933)

ADW/GB(P) — The Beatles. Songs. Words
Beatles, The
The Beatles lyrics complete / with an introduction by Jimmy
Savile. — [London] (49 Poland St.,) : Futura Publications Ltd,
1974. — [4],186p ; 18cm.
Originally published: in 2 vols as 'The Beatles illustrated lyrics'. London :
Macdonald and Co., 1969.
ISBN 0-86007-052-2 Pbk : £0.40

(B74-20924)

ADW/GB(YT/M) — Popular songs. United States. Composers
Wilk, Max
They're playing our song : from Jerome Kern to Stephen
Sondheim - the stories behind the words and music of two
generations / [by] Max Wilk. — London [etc.] : W.H. Allen,
1974. — [1],xv,295p ; 24cm.
Originally published: New York : Atheneum, 1973.
ISBN 0-491-01530-5 : £3.50

(B74-11736)

ADW/GB/E(M/XPM22/EM) — Popular singers, 1952-1973.
Illustrations
Peellaert, Guy
Rock dreams / [by] Guy Peellaert, Nik Cohn. — London : Pan
Books, 1974. — [146]p : chiefly col ill, col ports ; 30cm.
ISBN 0-330-24008-0 Pbk : £1.95

(B74-07429)

ADW/KC(YD) — Songs. Sea. England
Ashton, John, b.1834
Real sailor songs / [collected and edited by] John Ashton. — [1st
ed. reprinted] ; introduced by A.L. Lloyd. — London (15
Mortimer Terrace, N.W.5) : Broadsheet King, 1973. — xi,[290]p :
ill ; 35cm.
Facsimile reprint of: 1st ed. of this collection, London: Leadenhall Press,
1891.
ISBN 0-902617-10-9 : Unpriced

(B74-02415)

ADW/KJWX(T) — Anti-war songs. Bibliographies
Denisoff, R Serge
Songs of protest, war and peace : a bibliography & discography /
[by] R. Serge Denisoff. — Revised ed. — Santa Barbara ; Oxford
(30 Cornmarket St., Oxford OX1 3EY) : ABC-Clio Inc., 1973. —
xvi,70p ; 23cm. — (War-peace bibliography series)
Previous ed.: Los Angeles : Center for the Study of Armament and
Disarmament, California State College, 1970. — List of records: p.47-54. —
Index.
ISBN 0-87436-121-4 Pbk : £1.45
Also classified at ADW/KMP(T); ADW/KJWX/FD(WT);
ADW/KMP/FD(WT)

(B74-16447)

ADW/KJWX/FD(WT) — Anti-war songs. Recorded music. Lists
Denisoff, R Serge
Songs of protest, war and peace : a bibliography & discography /
[by] R. Serge Denisoff. — Revised ed. — Santa Barbara ; Oxford
(30 Cornmarket St., Oxford OX1 3EY) : ABC-Clio Inc., 1973. —
xvi,70p ; 23cm. — (War-peace bibliography series)
Previous ed.: Los Angeles : Center for the Study of Armament and
Disarmament, California State College, 1970. — List of records: p.47-54. —
Index.
ISBN 0-87436-121-4 Pbk : £1.45
Primary classification ADW/KJWX(T)

(B74-16447)

ADW/KMP(T) — Patriotic songs. Bibliographies
Denisoff, R Serge
Songs of protest, war and peace : a bibliography & discography /
[by] R. Serge Denisoff. — Revised ed. — Santa Barbara ; Oxford
(30 Cornmarket St., Oxford OX1 3EY) : ABC-Clio Inc., 1973. —
xvi,70p ; 23cm. — (War-peace bibliography series)
Previous ed.: Los Angeles : Center for the Study of Armament and
Disarmament, California State College, 1970. — List of records: p.47-54. —
Index.
ISBN 0-87436-121-4 Pbk : £1.45
Primary classification ADW/KJWX(T)

(B74-16447)

ADW/KMP/FD(WT) — Patriotic songs. Recorded music. Lists
Denisoff, R Serge
Songs of protest, war and peace : a bibliography & discography /
[by] R. Serge Denisoff. — Revised ed. — Santa Barbara ; Oxford
(30 Cornmarket St., Oxford OX1 3EY) : ABC-Clio Inc., 1973. —
xvi,70p ; 23cm. — (War-peace bibliography series)
Previous ed.: Los Angeles : Center for the Study of Armament and
Disarmament, California State College, 1970. — List of records: p.47-54. —
Index.
ISBN 0-87436-121-4 Pbk : £1.45
Primary classification ADW/KJWX(T)

(B74-16447)

ADX(YH/XF71) — Secular cantatas. France, 1700-1770
Tunley, David
The eighteenth-century French cantata / by David Tunley. —
London : Dobson, 1974. — xv,272p,[8]p of plates : ill, facsims,
music, ports ; 23cm.
Bibl.: p.262-267. — Index.
ISBN 0-234-77070-8 : £6.00

(B74-25495)

AELDW(YD/XCQ) — With instrument. Songs, etc. England, 1400
A **fifteenth** century song book : Cambridge University Library
Add.MS 5943 / made in facsimile by Leslie Hewitt ; with an
introduction by Richard Rastall. — Leeds (5 Albert Grove, Leeds
6) : Boethius Press, 1973. — [35]p : chiefly music ; 23cm. —
(Early music in facsimile ; 1)
ISBN 0-904263-01-0 : £4.60

(B74-04046)

AK — MUSICAL LITERATURE. VOCAL SOLOS
AK/E(M/XM71) — Singers, 1900-1970
Pahlen, Kurt
Great singers from the seventeenth century to the present day /
[by] Kurt Pahlen ; translated [from the German] by Oliver
Coburn. — London [etc.] : W.H. Allen, 1973. — [6],266p,16p of
plates : ports ; 24cm.
Translation of: 'Grosse Sänger unserer Zeit'. Gütersloh: Wien [Vienna]:
Bertelsmann Sachbuchverlag, 1971. — Index.
ISBN 0-491-01361-2 : £4.75

(B74-00870)

AKDW(XEXK301) — Songs, etc., 1650-1950
Osborne, Charles, b.1927
The concert song companion : a guide to the classical repertoire /
by Charles Osborne. — London : Gollancz, 1974. — 285p ; 23cm.
Bibl.: p.247. — Index.
ISBN 0-575-01825-9 : £4.00

(B74-24211)

AKDW/GB/E(M) — Popular songs. Singers
Gray, Andy
My top pop book / by Andy Gray. — London [etc.] : Hamlyn,
1974. — 2-47p : chiefly ill(some col), ports(some col) ; 33cm.
ISBN 0-600-37073-9 : £0.85

(B74-30606)

AKDW/GB/E(M/XPK19) — Popular songs. Singers, 1955-1973
Soul, pop, rock, stars, superstars. — London : Octopus Books,
1974. — 2-255p : ill(chiefly col), ports(chiefly col) ; 31cm.
Cover title: Story of pop. — '... adapted from "The story of pop"' - title
page verso. — Index.
ISBN 0-7064-0409-2 : £3.95

(B74-29003)

AKDW/GB/E(M/YT/XN54) — Popular songs. Singers. United
States, 1920-1973
Pleasants, Henry
The great American popular singers / [by] Henry Pleasants. —
London : Gollancz, 1974. — 3-384p : ill, ports ; 24cm.
Index.
ISBN 0-575-01774-0 : £3.75

(B74-28316)

AKDW/GB/E(P) — Dene, Terry. Biographies
Wooding, Dan
I thought Terry Dene was dead / by Dan Wooding. — London
[etc.] : Coverdale House, 1974. — 160p,[8]p of plates : ill, ports ;
18cm.
ISBN 0-902088-55-6 Pbk : £0.50

(B74-25498)

AKDW/GB/E(P) — Dylan, Bob. Books
McGregor, Craig
Bob Dylan : a retrospective / edited by Craig McGregor. —
Sydney ; London [etc.] : Angus and Robertson, 1973. — [6],169p ;
22cm.
Originally published: New York : Morrow, 1972.
ISBN 0-207-12675-5 Pbk : £0.75

(B74-17386)

AKDW/GB/E(P) — Essex, David. Biographies
Tremlett, George
The David Essex story / [by] George Tremlett. — London (49
Poland St., W1A 2LG) : Futura Publications Ltd, 1974. — 144p,
[16]p of plates : ill, ports ; 18cm.
ISBN 0-86007-092-1 Pbk : £0.40

(B74-26609)

AKDW/GB/E(P) — Jagger, Mick. Biographies
Scaduto, Anthony
Mick Jagger / [by] Anthony Scaduto. — London : W.H. Allen,
1974. — [6],290p,[32]p of plates : ports ; 23cm.
Ports on lining papers.
ISBN 0-491-01122-9 : £3.50

(B74-23497)

AKDW/GB/E(P) — Pallandt, Nina, Barones van. Biographies
Pallandt, Nina, *barones van*
Nina / [by] Nina van Pallandt. — London : Hale, 1974. — 221p,
[16]p of plates : ill, ports ; 23cm.
Originally published: New York : Walker, 1973.
ISBN 0-7091-4586-1 : £2.80

(B74-17384)

AKDW/GB/E(P) — The Rolling Stones
Greenfield, Robert
Stones Touring Party : a journey through America with the
Rolling Stones / [by] Robert Greenfield. — London : Joseph,
1974. — [11],337p,[16]p of plates : ports ; 23cm.
Also published : as 'STP : a journey through America with the Rolling
Stones'. New York : Saturday Review Press, 1974.
ISBN 0-7181-1249-0 : £3.00

(B74-25497)

AKDW/GB/E(P) — The Rolling Stones. Biographies
Tremlett, George
The Rolling Stones story / [by] George Tremlett. — London (49
Poland St., W1A 2LG) : Futura Publications Ltd, 1974. — 190p,
[16]p of plates : ill, ports ; 18cm.
ISBN 0-86007-128-6 Pbk : £0.40

(B74-25496)

AKDW/GCW(P) — Cash, Johnny. Biographies
Wren, Christopher, *b.1936*
Johnny Cash - winners got scars too / [by] Christopher S. Wren.
— London : Abacus, 1974. — 221p,[24]p of plates : ports ; 20cm.
Originally published: as 'Winners got scars too', New York : Dial Press,
1971; and as 'Johnny Cash - winners got scars too', London : W.H. Allen,
1973.
ISBN 0-349-13740-4 Pbk : £0.60

(B74-11737)

AKDW/HHW/E(P) — Blues. Melly, George. Biographies
Melly, George
Owning-up / [by] George Melly ; illustrated by Trog. —
Harmondsworth : Penguin, 1974. — 251p : ill ; 18cm.
Originally published: London: Weidenfeld and Nicolson, 1965.
ISBN 0-14-002936-2 Pbk : £0.35

(B74-07434)

AKDW/HK/E(P) — Presley, Elvis. Biographies
Hopkins, Jerry
Elvis / [by] Jerry Hopkins. — London : Abacus, 1974. — 3-365p,
[16]p of plates : ill, ports ; 20cm.
Originally published: New York: Simon and Schuster, 1971; London: Open
Gate Books, 1972. — List of gramophone records: p.345-361. — List of
films: p.362-363.
ISBN 0-349-11717-9 Pbk : £1.00

(B74-04795)

AKDW/K/G(YD/XFZ155) — Ballads. England, 1780-1934
Palmer, Roy
Poverty knock : a picture of industrial life in the nineteenth
century through songs, ballads and contemporary accounts /
selected and edited by Roy Palmer. — London : Cambridge
University Press, 1974. — 64p : ill, music ; 28cm. — (The
resources of music ; 9)
Bibl. — List of gramophone records: p.62. — Index.
ISBN 0-521-20443-7 Sd : £0.80(non-net)
Also classified at 784.6'8'33120942

(B74-30366)

**AKE/TWDW(YD/XDZS14) — With lute. Songs, etc. Collections.
England, 1597-1610**
The **Turpyn** book of lute songs : King's College, Cambridge, Rowe
MS 2 / made in facsimile by Leslie Hewitt ; with an introduction
by Richard Rastall. — Leeds (5 Albert Grove, Leeds 6) : Boethius
Press, 1973. — [56]p : music ; 33cm. — (Early music in
facsimile ; 2)
' "The Turpyn book of lute songs" takes its name from the signatures of
Francis Turpyn which are found in the book. He was apparently an early
owner of the book, perhaps even the first ...' - Introduction.
ISBN 0-904263-00-2 : £8.70

(B74-03504)

AKGH/E(P) — MacEwan, Sydney. Biographies
MacEwan, Sydney
On the high C's : (a light-hearted journey): an autobiography / by
Sydney MacEwan. — Glasgow : J. Burns, 1973. — 326p,[15]p of
plates : ill, ports ; 20cm.
ISBN 0-900243-38-4 : £1.60

(B74-03194)

AL — MUSICAL LITERATURE. INSTRUMENTAL MUSIC
AL(XE151) — Instrumental music, 1600-1750
Edwards, Owain
Baroque instrumental music / prepared by Owain Edwards for the
Course Team. — Milton Keynes : Open University Press. —
(Arts, a third level course: the development of instruments and
their music; units 4-6) (A304;4-6)
1 : People, instruments and the continuo. — 1974. — 128p : ill, music,
ports ; 30cm.
ISBN 0-335-00852-6 Pbk : £2.20

(B74-08077)

2 : Suite, sonata and concerto. — 1974. — 157p : ill, music, ports ; 30cm.
ISBN 0-335-00853-4 Pbk : Unpriced

(B74-08078)

AL/B(XD351) — Instruments, 1500-1850
Clemenicic, René
Old musical instruments / [by] René Clemenicic ; [translated from
the German MS. by David Hermges]. — London : Octopus
Books, 1973. — 96p : ill(some col), facsims, ports ; 25cm.
This translation originally published: London: Weidenfeld and Nicolson,
1968.
ISBN 0-7064-0057-7 : £0.99

(B74-07433)

AL/B(XD401) — Instruments, 1500-1900
Paganelli, Sergio
Musical instruments from the Renaissance to the 19th century /
[by] Sergio Paganelli ; [translated from the Italian by Anthony
Rhodes]. — London [etc.] : Hamlyn, 1970 [i.e. 1974]. — 157p :
col ill ; 19cm. — (Cameo)
This translation originally published: 1970. — Translation of: 'Gli Strumenti
musicale nell'arte'. Milano : Fabbri, 1967.
ISBN 0-600-31853-2 Pbk : £0.50

(B74-20189)

AL/BC — Instrument making
Southworth, Mary
How to make musical sounds / [by] Mary Southworth. —
London : Studio Vista, 1973. — 68p : ill(some col) ; 22cm. —
([How-to series])
Index.
ISBN 0-289-70405-7 : £1.25

(B74-05792)

AM — MUSICAL LITERATURE. ORCHESTRAL MUSIC
Blackwood, Alan, *b.1932*
A trip to the concert / [created and edited by Desmond
Marwood; written by Alan Blackwood; illustrated by Philip
Corke]. — [London] ([36 Park St., W1Y 4DE]) : Nelson Young
World, 1973. — [29]p : chiefly col ill, music, col ports ; 18x23cm.
— (A Young World tripper book)
ISBN 0-7238-0946-1 : £0.45

(B74-13709)

AMM/E(QB/X) — London Symphony Orchestra. History
Pearton, Maurice
The LSO at 70 : a history of the orchestra / by Maurice Pearton.
— London : Gollancz, 1974. — 240p,[16]p of plates : ill, ports ;
23cm.
Bibl.: p.232-233. — Index.
ISBN 0-575-01763-5 : £3.50

(B74-24906)

AMME(X) — Symphonies. History
Middleton, Richard
The rise of the symphony / prepared by Richard Middleton for
the Course Team. — Milton Keynes : Open University Press. —
(Arts, a third level course: the development of instruments and
their music; units 15-16) (A304; 15-16)
2. — 1974. — 104p : ill, facsims, music, ports ; 30cm.
Bibl.: p.102-103.
ISBN 0-335-00859-3 Pbk : £1.70

(B74-18934)

AMT — MUSICAL LITERATURE. JAZZ
Collier, Graham, *b.1937*
Inside jazz / [by] Graham Collier. — London : Quartet Books,
1973. — 144p : ill, music, ports ; 23cm.
ISBN 0-7043-2028-2 : £2.75
ISBN 0 7043 3022 9 Pbk: £1.50

(B74-00162)

AMT(M) — Musicians
Carr, Ian, *b.1933*
Music outside : contemporary jazz in Britain / [by] Ian Carr. — London : Latimer New Dimensions, 1973. — xi,179p,[32]p of plates : ports ; 23cm.
Bibl.: p.174. — List of gramophone records: p.149-173. — Index.
ISBN 0-901539-25-2 : £3.00
(B74-01930)

AMT(M/XMK41) — Jazz musicians, 1910-1950
McCarthy, Albert
The dance band era : the dancing decades from ragtime to swing, 1910-1950 / [by] Albert McCarthy. — London [etc.] : Spring Books, 1974. — 176p : ill, map, music, ports ; 31cm.
Originally published: Philadelphia : Chilton ; London : Studio Vista, 1971. — Bibl.: p.173. — List of records p.171-173. — Index.
ISBN 0-600-32907-0 : £1.95
(B74-30607)

AMT(M/XN54) — Musicians, 1920-1973
Feather, Leonard
From Satchmo to Miles / [by] Leonard Feather. — London : Quartet Books, 1974. — 258p : ports ; 23cm.
Originally published: New York : Stein and Day, 1972.
ISBN 0-7043-2055-x : £2.95
ISBN 0-7043-3053-9 Pbk : £1.50
(B74-21539)

AMT(P) — Beiderbecke, Bix. Biographies
Sudhalter, Richard M
Bix - man & legend / by Richard M. Sudhalter & Philip R. Evans, with William Dean-Myatt. — London : Quartet Books, 1974. — 512p : ill, facsims, music, ports ; 22cm.
List of gramophone records: p.405-472. — Index.
ISBN 0-7043-2070-3 : £4.95
ISBN 0-7043-1188-7 Pbk : £1.95
(B74-27251)

AMT(P) — Condon, Eddie. Biographies
Condon, Eddie
The Eddie Condon scrapbook of jazz / by Eddie Condon and Hank O'Neal. — London : Hale, 1974. — [288]p : of ill, facsims, music, ports ; 26cm.
Ill. on lining papers. — Originally published: New York : St Martin's Press, 1973.
ISBN 0-7091-4476-8 : £4.80
(B74-13108)

AMT(P) — Ellington, Duke. Biographies
Ellington, Duke
Music is my mistress / by Edward Kennedy Ellington. — London [etc.] : W.H. Allen, 1974. — iii-xv,523p : ill, music, ports ; 27cm.
Originally published: Garden City, N.Y. : Doubleday, 1973. — Bibl.: p.523.
ISBN 0-491-01720-0 : £5.50
(B74-20925)

AMT(P) — Foster, 'Pops'. Biographies
Foster, Pops
Pops Foster - the autobiography of a New Orleans jazzman / as told to Tom Stoddard ; introduction by Bertram Turetzky ; interchapters by Ross Russell; discography by Brian Rust. — Berkeley [etc.] ; London : University of California Press, 1973. — xxii,208p,[42]p of plates : facsim, ports ; 23cm.
Originally published: 1971. — Bibl.: p.199. — List of records: p.180-197. — Index.
ISBN 0-520-02355-2 Pbk : £1.65
(B74-03506)

AMT(P) — Morton, Jelly Roll. Biographies
Lomax, Alan
Mister Jelly Roll : the fortunes of Jelly Roll Morton, New Orleans Creole and 'inventor of jazz' / by Alan Lomax ; drawings by David Stone Martin. — 2nd ed. — Berkeley [etc.] ; London : University of California Press, 1973. — xvii,318p : ill, facsims, map, music, port ; 21cm. — (The Lomax books of American folk song)
Previous ed.: New York : Duell, Sloan and Pearce, 1950; London : Cassell, 1952.
ISBN 0-520-02402-8 : £5.20
ISBN 0-520-02237-8 Pbk: £1.75
(B74-14971)

AMT(P) — Parker, Charlie. Biographies
Reisner, Robert George
Bird - the legend of Charlie Parker / by Robert George Reisner. — London : Quartet Books, [1974]. — 256p : ill, ports ; 26cm.
Originally published: New York : Citadel Press, 1962 ; London : MacGibbon and Kee, 1963. — List of gramophone records : p.241-256.
ISBN 0-7043-2063-0 : £3.95
ISBN 0-7043-1166-6 Pbk : £1.75
(B74-27252)

AMT(X) — Jazz. History
Postgate, John
A plain man's guide to jazz / [by] John Postgate. — London (61 Berners St., W1P 3AE) : Hanover Books Ltd, 1973. — [7],146p ; 21cm.
Bibl.: p.136. — Index.
ISBN 0-900994-05-3 : £1.50
(B74-13710)

AMT(XMT56) — History, 1918-1973
McCarthy, Albert
Big band jazz / [by] Albert McCarthy. — London : Barrie and Jenkins, 1974. — 368p : ill, ports ; 31cm.
Bibl. and list of gramophone records: p.356-360. — Index.
ISBN 0-214-66894-0 : £5.00
(B74-17388)

AP — MUSICAL LITERATURE. INDIVIDUAL INSTRUMENTS & INSTRUMENTAL GROUPS
APV/BT — Electronic instruments. Maintenance
Wels, Byron Gerald
How to repair musical instrument amplifiers / [by] Byron Wels ; with a specially written chapter for the guidance of the English reader by W. Oliver. — Slough (Yeovil Rd, Slough, Bucks. SL1 4JH) : Foulsham-Tab Ltd, 1973. — viii,3-288p(8fold) : ill ; 22cm.
Also published: Blue Ridge Summit: G/L Tab Books, 1973. — Index.
ISBN 0-7042-0050-3 Pbk : £1.50
(B74-05794)

APW — MUSICAL LITERATURE. KEYBOARD INSTRUMENTS
APW(B) — Periodicals
The **English** Harpsichord Magazine, and early keyboard instrument review. — Chesham Bois (Rose Cottage, Bois La., Chesham Bois, Amersham, Bucks. HP6 6BP) : Edgar Hunt.
Continues 'The Harpsichord Magazine'.
Vol.1, no.2- ; Apr. 1974-. — 1974-. — ill, port ; 25cm.
Twice yearly. — 32p. in 1st issue.
Sd : £0.55
(B74-12390)

The **Harpsichord** Magazine, and early keyboard instrument review. — Chesham Bois (Rose Cottage, Bois La., Chesham Bois, Amersham, Bucks. HP6 6BP) : Edgar Hunt.
Vol.1, no.1; Oct. 1973. — 1973. — ill, port ; 25cm.
Twice yearly. — 33p. in 1st issue. — Continued by 'The English Harpsichord Magazine'.
Sd : £0.50
(B74-12391)

APW/BC(XCS401/C) — Instrument makers, 1440-1840. Encyclopaedias
Boalch, Donald Howard
Makers of the harpsichord and clavichord, 1440-1840 / [by] Donald H. Boalch. — 2nd ed. — Oxford : Clarendon Press, 1974. — xxi,225p,[12]p of plates : ill, facsims, geneal tables ; 29cm.
Previous ed.: London : G. Ronald, 1956. — Bibl.: p.211-221. — Index.
ISBN 0-19-816123-9 : £9.75
(B74-21541)

AQ — Piano
Hutcheson, Ernest
The literature of the piano : a guide for amateur and student / [by] Ernest Hutcheson. — 3rd ed., revised. — London : Hutchinson, 1974. — xvi,435,xxxiv p : music ; 24cm.
Previous ed./revised by Rudolph Ganz. 1969. — Bibl.: p.431-435. — Index.
ISBN 0-09-119120-3 : £4.75
(B74-17389)

AQ(W/YDL) — Piano. Concerts. Scotland
Piano Panel
The concert piano in Scotland : a report to the Scottish Arts Council / [the Piano Panel]. — [Edinburgh] ([19 Charlotte Sq., Edinburgh EH2 4DF]) : [Scottish Arts Council], 1972. — [1],36p : map ; 30cm.
Chairman of the Panel: John S. Boyle.
ISBN 0-902989-13-8 Sd : £0.25
(B74-09233)

AQ/B(X) — Piano. Instruments. History
Closson, Ernest
History of the piano / [by] Ernest Closson ; translated [from the French] by Delano Ames. — 2nd ed. / edited and revised by Robin Golding. — London : Elek, 1974. — 154p : ill, music ; 23cm.
Previous ed. of this translation: 1974. — Translation of: 'Histoire du piano'. Bruxelles [Brussels] : Editions universitaires, 1944. — Bibl.: p.141-148. — Index.
ISBN 0-236-17685-4 : £3.50
(B74-09232)

AQ/B/E(XA1849) — Piano. Instruments. Performance. To 1849
Ratcliffe, Ronald V
From classical to romantic keyboard music / prepared by Ronald V. Ratcliffe, [J. Barrie Jones, Gerald Hendrie] for the Course Team. — Milton Keynes : Open University Press, 1974. — 186p : ill(some col), music, ports ; 30cm. — (Arts, a third level course : the development of instruments and their music ; units 20-22) (A304 ; 20-22)
ISBN 0-335-00864-x Pbk : Unpriced

(B74-23499)

AQ/E(VC) — Piano. Teaching
Enoch, Yvonne
Group piano-teaching / [by] Yvonne Enoch. — London [etc.] : Oxford University Press, 1974. — viii,113p : music ; 20cm.
Bibl.: p.111-113.
ISBN 0-19-318421-4 : £2.30

(B74-15524)

McLain, Margaret Starr
Class piano / [by] Margaret Starr McLain. — Bloomington ; London : Indiana University Press, 1974. — xix,284p : music ; 28cm.
Originally published: Boston, Mass. : Allyn and Bacon, 1969. — Index.
ISBN 0-253-31357-0 Sp : £2.80

(B74-22162)

AQ/ED(P) — Moore, Gerald. Biographies
Moore, Gerald, *b.1899*
Am I too loud? : memoirs of an accompanist / [by] Gerald Moore. — Harmondsworth : Penguin, 1974. — 286p,8p of plates : ports ; 18cm.
Originally published: London : Hamilton, 1962. — Index.
ISBN 0-14-002480-8 Pbk : £0.60

(B74-21540)

AR(YC/VP/Q) — Organists. Great Britain. Royal College of Organists
Royal College of Organists
Year book / Royal College of Organists. — London (Kensington Gore, SW7 2QS) : The College.
1973-1974. — [1973]. — [1],vi,168p : ill, port ; 21cm.
Cover title.
ISBN 0-902462-04-0 Pbk : £0.75

(B74-14972)

AR/B(X) — Organ. Instruments. History
Sumner, William Leslie
The organ : its evolution, principles of construction and use / by William Leslie Sumner. — 4th ed. revised and enlarged. — London : Macdonald and Co., 1973. — 603p,[41]p of plates : ill, music, ports ; 23cm.
Previous ed.: 1962. — Bibl.: p.579-592. — Index.
ISBN 0-356-04162-x : £5.00

(B74-01931)

AR/B(XE151) — Organ. Instruments 1600-1750
Hendrie, Gerald
The Baroque organ (containing an introduction to units 1-2); [and, Bach organ music] / prepared by Gerald Hendrie for the Course Team. — Milton Keynes : Open University Press, 1974. — 121p : ill, map, music ; 30cm. — (Arts, a third level course: the development of instruments and their music; units 1 and 2) (A304; 1-2)
'Bach organ music scores' ([2],22p.: of music) available as unit 3. — Bibl.: p.82 and 84. — List of gramophone records: p.84-86.
ISBN 0-335-00850-x Pbk : £2.00
Also classified at 786.5'092'4

(B74-07435)

AR/B(YDHNLB) — Organs. Lichfield. Lichfield Cathedral
Greening, Richard
The organs of Lichfield Cathedral / by Richard Greening. — Lichfield (c/o 28 Walsall Rd, Lichfield, Staffs. WS13 8AB) : Dean and Chapter of Lichfield, 1974. — [1],20p : ill ; 26cm.
ISBN 0-9503008-1-0 Sd : £0.45

(B74-13712)

AR/BC(YD/P) — Instrument makers. England. Harrison and Harrison
Elvin, Laurence
The Harrison story : Harrison and Harrison, organ builders, Durham / by Laurence Elvin ; foreword by Sir Ernest Bullock. — Lincoln (10 Almond Ave., Swanpool, Lincoln) : The author, 1973. — [3],292p,[62]p of plates : ill, facsims, ports ; 23cm.
Limited ed. of 1000 copies. — Bibl.: p.273-278. — Index.
ISBN 0-9500049-2-8 : £5.95

(B74-15898)

AR/BC(YD/P) — Instrument makers. England. Renn, Samuel
Sayer, Michael
Samuel Renn : English organ builder / [by] Michael Sayer. — London [etc.] : Phillimore, 1974. — [9],133p,fold leaf : ill, facsims, geneal table, ports ; 26cm.
Index.
ISBN 0-85033-078-5 : £5.50

(B74-18936)

AR/E(YDEUW) — St Georges Chapel. Windsor. Organists
Fellowes, Edmund Horace
Organists and Masters of the Choristers of St George's Chapel in Windsor Castle / by Edmund H. Fellowes. — London (S.P.C.K. House, Northumberland Ave., W.C.2) : Society for the Promotion of Christian Knowledge for the Dean and Canons of St George's Chapel in Windsor Castle, [1974]. — xv,108p,[7] leaves of plate : facsims, ports ; 23cm. — (Historical monographs relating to St George's Chapel, Windsor Castle)
Originally published: 1939. — 'This volume includes a supplement (pp.105-8) for the years 1939-1973'.
Unpriced

(B74-23496)

ARPV/BT — Electronic organs. Maintenance
Applebaum, Max H
Servicing electronic organs / [by] Max H. Applebaum & Donald A. John ; with a specially written chapter for the guidance of the English reader by W. Oliver. — Slough : Foulsham-Tab, 1974. — vii,3-160,[12]p(12 fold) : ill ; 28cm.
Originally published: Blue Ridge Summit : Tab Books, 1969. — Index.
ISBN 0-7042-0108-9 Pbk : £1.80

(B74-27249)

ARW — MUSICAL LITERATURE. STRING INSTRUMENTS
ARX/BT — Bowed string instruments. Maintenance
Burgan, Arthur
Basic string repairs : a guide for string-class teachers / [by] Arthur Burgan. — London [etc.] : Oxford University Press, 1974. — vii,59p,[9]p of plates : ill ; 19cm.
ISBN 0-19-318509-1 : £1.75

(B74-09234)

ARXNS(X) — Bowed string instruments. Quartets. History
Olleson, Philip
The rise of the string quartet / prepared by Philip Olleson for the Course Team. — Milton Keynes : Open University Press, 1974. — 48p : facsims, music ; 30cm. — (Arts, a third level course : the development of instruments and their music; unit 18) (A304; 18)
ISBN 0-335-00862-3 Pbk : Unpriced

(B74-18935)

AS/BC — Violin. Instrument making
Heron-Allen, Edward
Violin-making as it was and is : being a historical, theoretical and practical treatise on the science and art of violin-making for the use of violin makers and players, amateur and professional / by Ed. Heron-Allen. — 2nd ed. — London : Ward Lock, [1973]. — xxii,366p,[5]leaves(3 fold) : ill, port ; 23cm.
Facsimile reprint of: 2nd ed., 1885. — Bibl.: p.329-343. — Index.
ISBN 0-7063-1045-4 : £4.50

(B74-02416)

AS/E/CS — Violin. Performance. Psychology
Havas, Kato
Stage fright : its causes and cures, with special reference to violin playing / by Kato Havas. — London : Bosworth, 1973. — iii-xv, 136p : ill, music, ports ; 22cm.
ISBN 0-900180-69-2 : £2.50

(B74-12392)

ASQ/E(P) — Tertis, Lionel. Biographies
Tertis, Lionel
My viola and I : a complete autobiography, with, Beauty of tone in string playing, and other essays / [by] Lionel Tertis. — London : Elek, 1974. — xv,184p,[8]p of plates : ill, facsim, plan, ports ; 23cm.
List of works for viola: p.171-174. — List of gramophone records: p.175-180. — Index.
ISBN 0-236-31040-2 : £4.00

(B74-23500)

ASR/E — Cello. Performance
Stanfield, Milly Bernardine
The intermediate cellist / [by] Milly B. Stanfield. — London : Oxford University Press, 1973. — xvii,142p : music ; 21cm.
Index.
ISBN 0-19-318508-3 : £2.00

(B74-03505)

ASS/E/CY — Double bass. Technique
Turetzky, Bertram
The contemporary contrabass / [by] Bertram Turetzky. — Berkeley [etc.] ; London : University of California Press, 1974. — xiii,114p : ill, music ; 28cm. — (The new instrumentation ; 1)
Gramophone record (2s., 7in., 33 1/3rpm) in pocket. — Bibl.: p.110-114.
ISBN 0-520-02291-2 Sp : £4.40

(B74-28317)

AT — MUSICAL LITERATURE. PLUCKED STRING INSTRUMENTS
ATR/BT — Fretted plucked string instruments. Maintenance
Sloane, Irving

Guitar repair : a manual of repair for guitars and fretted instruments / [by] Irving Sloane. — London [etc.] : Nelson, 1974. — 95p : ill ; 29cm. Originally published: New York : Dutton, 1973. — Index. ISBN 0-17-149062-2 : £2.50

(B74-28318)

ATS(X) — Guitar. History
Turnbull, Harvey

The guitar : from the Renaissance to the present day / [by] Harvey Turnbull. — London : Batsford, 1974. — vii,168p,[32]p of plates : ill, facsims, music, ports ; 23cm. Bibl.: p.146-157. — Index. ISBN 0-7134-2784-1 : £4.00

(B74-14312)

ATS/E/CY — Guitar playing. Technique
Bobri, Vladimir

The Segovia technique / by Vladimir Bobri. — New York : Macmillan ; London : Collier Macmillan, 1972. — [9],94p : ill, ports ; 31cm. Bibl.: p.83-87. — Index. ISBN 0-02-511990-7 : £5,45

(B74-13713)

AU — MUSICAL LITERATURE. WIND INSTRUMENTS
AV/E(VK) — Woodwind instruments. Secondary schools
Tomlin, Peter

Woodwind for schools / [by] Peter Tomlin. — Leicester : Dryad Press, 1973. — [2],70p : ill ; 25cm. Bibl.: p.70. ISBN 0-85219-089-1 : £2.25

(B74-14973)

AVR/E/CY — Flute. Technique
Howell, Thomas

The avant-garde flute : a handbook for composers and flutists / [by] Thomas Howell. — Berkeley [etc.] ; London : University of California Press, 1974. — ix,290p : chiefly music, ill ; 28cm. — (The new instrumentation ; 2) Record in pocket. ISBN 0-520-02305-6 Sp : £5.50

(B74-21542)

AWM(QB/YDGJ) — Brass bands. Yorkshire
Cooper, Thomas Leonard

Brass bands of Yorkshire / by T.L. Cooper. — Clapham, Yorkshire : Dalesman, 1974. — 166p : ill, facsims, music ; 22cm. Bibl.: p.164. ISBN 0-85206-195-1 Pbk : £1.60

(B74-09231)

AX — MUSICAL LITERATURE. PERCUSSION INSTRUMENTS
AXS/B — Bells. Instruments
Cockett, Mary

Bells in our lives / [by] Mary Cockett ; drawings by Janet Duchesne. — Newton Abbot : David and Charles, 1973. — 80p : ill ; 22cm. ISBN 0-7153-6229-1 : £1.60

(B74-01380)

AXSQ — Handbells
Bedford, Philip

An introduction to English handbell tune ringing / by Philip Bedford. — Chelmsford (22 Tavistock Rd, Springfield Green, Chelmsford, Essex CM1 53L) : Handbell Ringers of Great Britain, 1974. — 54p : ill, music ; 23cm. ISBN 0-904289-00-1 : £1.50

(B74-25501)

AXSR — Church bells
Camp, John

Bell ringing : chimes, carillons, handbells - the world of the bell and the ringer / [by] John Camp. — Newton Abbot : David and Charles, 1974. — 160p : ill, music, ports ; 23cm. Bibl.: p.152-153. — Index. ISBN 0-7153-6088-4 : £2.95

(B74-05793)

AXSR/B(YDEU) — Church bells. Berkshire
Sharpe, Frederick

The church bells of Berkshire : their inscriptions and founders, arranged alphabetically by parishes ... / [by] Frederick Sharpe. — 2nd ed. ; with a foreword by the Bishop of Oxford. — Bath : Kingsmead Reprints, 1970 [i.e. 1971]. — viii,404p,[64]p of plates : ill ; 22cm. 'The eighteen articles serialised in volumes 43 (1939) to 57 (1959) of the "Berkshire Archaeological Journal" and as a supplement to volume 61, with an appendix bringing the original survey up to date'. ISBN 0-901571-46-6 : £4.00

(B74-05271)

AXSR/E(YDCH) — Change-ringing. Churchbells. Surrey
Jennings, Trevor Stanley

A short history of Surrey bells and ringing customs / [by] Trevor S. Jennings. — Kingston-upon-Thames ('Marchants', 53 Latchmere La., Kingston-upon-Thames, Surrey KT2 5SF) : The author, [1974]. — [1],20p ; 30cm. Index. ISBN 0-9500076-3-3 Sd : £1.00

(B74-18432)

B — INDIVIDUAL COMPOSERS
BBJ — Beethoven, Ludwig van
Scott, Marion Margareta

Beethoven / by Marion M. Scott. — Revised [ed.] / revised by Sir Jack Westrup. — London : Dent, 1974. — ix,339p,[8]p of plates : ill, facsims, music, ports ; 20cm. — (The master musicians series) Previous ed.: 1934. — Bibl.: p.318-327. — Index. ISBN 0-460-03149-x : £2.95 ISBN 0-460-02140-0 Pbk : £1.50

(B74-22161)

BBJ(D) — Beethoven, Ludwig van. Essays
Tyson, Alan

Beethoven : studies / edited by Alan Tyson. — London : Oxford University Press, 1974. — xiv,246p : facsims, music ; 24cm. Index. ISBN 0-19-315312-2 : £4.50

(B74-11734)

BBLN(N) — Berlin, Irving. Biographies
Freedland, Michael

Irving Berlin / [by] Michael Freedland. — London [etc.] : W.H. Allen, 1974. — ix,307p,[17]p of plates : ill, ports ; 23cm. Index. ISBN 0-491-01112-1 : £3.50

(B74-05268)

BBTAN — Brahms, Johannes. Chamber music
Keys, Ivor

Brahms chamber music / [by] Ivor Keys. — London : British Broadcasting Corporation, 1974. — 68p : music ; 20cm. — (British Broadcasting Corporation. Music guides) Index. ISBN 0-563-10168-7 Pbk : £0.45

(B74-14311)

BBTNAME — Brian, Havergal. Symphonies
MacDonald, Malcolm, *b.1948*

The symphonies of Havergal Brian / [by] Malcolm MacDonald. — London ([25 Thurloe St., S.W.7]) : Kahn and Averill. In 2 vols. Vol.1 : Symphonies 1-12. — 1974. — 207p : music ; 23cm. ISBN 0-900707-28-3 : £3.50

(B74-14310)

BBU(TC) — Britten, Benjamin. Bibliographies of scores
Boosey and Hawkes Limited

Benjamin Britten - a complete catalogue of his published works / Boosey and Hawkes and Faber Music. — [New and revised ed.]. — London : Boosey and Hawkes : Faber Music, 1973. — 52p : music, port ; 26cm. Previous ed.: 1963. — Index. ISBN 0-85162-022-1 : £2.00

(B74-03157)

BBUADX — Britten, Benjamin. Secular cantatas
Britten, Benjamin

Children's crusade = Kinderkreuzzug. Op.82 : a ballad for children's voices and orchestra / music by Benjamin Britten; words by Bertolt Brecht; [translated from the German by Hans Keller]; illustrations by Sidney Nolan. — London : Faber Music : Faber, [1974]. — [54]p,[12]p of plates : 12 col ill, music ; 40cm. Limited ed. of 1007 copies, 300 numbered and signed by composer and artist, 7 hors commerce. — Parallel German text and English translation of poem. ISBN 0-571-10370-7 : £15.00 ISBN 0-571-10369-3 Signed and numbered ed. : £50.00

(B74-21537)

BCBG — Cage, John
Kostelanetz, Richard

John Cage / edited by Richard Kostelanetz. — London : Allen Lane, 1974. — xvii,237p,[32]p of plates : ill, facsims, music, port ; 22cm. — (Documentary monographs in modern art) (Pelican books) Originally published: New York: Praeger; London : Allen Lane, 1970. — Bibl.: p.218-230. — Index. — Includes selections from Cage's own writings. ISBN 0-7139-0762-2 Pbk : £2.00

(B74-11048)

BCE — Chopin, Frédéric
Hedley, Arthur
Chopin / by Arthur Hedley. — Revised ed. / revised by Maurice
J.E. Brown. — London : Dent, 1974. — viii,214p,[8]p of plates :
ill, facsims, music, ports ; 20cm. — (The master musicians series)
Previous ed.: 1963. — List of works: p.187-196. — Bibl.: p.202-204. —
Index.
ISBN 0-460-03154-6 : £2.50
ISBN 0-460-02152-4 Pbk: £1.25

(B74-13109)

BCQRACPP — Crocker, John. Robinson Crusoe. Librettos
Crocker, John, *b.1925*
Robinson Crusoe : a pantomime / by John Crocker ; lyrics and
music by Eric Gilder. — London : Evans Plays, 1972. — [7],
111p ; 23cm.
Eight men, 4 women, 10 chorus.
ISBN 0-237-74975-0 Pbk : £0.50

(B74-12388)

BCRAC — Crosse, Gordon. The story of Vasco. Librettos
Crosse, Gordon, *b.1937*
The story of Vasco : opera in three acts / music by Gordon
Crosse ; libretto based on an English version by Ted Hughes of
the play 'L'Histoire de Vasco' by Georges Schehadé. — London :
Oxford University Press, Music Department, 1974. — viii,46p ;
19cm.
'I [Gordon Crosse] asked Ted Hughes if he would undertake a very free
translation of the play, from which I could then make a libretto' - notes.
ISBN 0-19-335702-x Sd : £0.70

(B74-09228)

BDR(B) — Donizetti, Gaetano. Periodicals
Donizetti Society
The Journal of the Donizetti Society. — London (The Secretary,
56 Harbut Rd, SW11 2RB) : The Society.
Issue no.1-. — 1974. — ill, facsims, music, ports ; 23cm.
Annual. — 152p. in 1st issue.
ISBN 0-9503333-0-1 Pbk : £2.50

(B74-13107)

BDX(N) — Dvořák, Antonín. Biographies
Robertson, Alec
Dvořák / by Alec Robertson. — Revised ed. — London : Dent,
1974. — ix,234p,[8]p of plates : ill, facsims, music, ports ; 20cm.
— (The master musicians series)
Revised ed. originally published: 1964. — List of works: p.206-217. — Bibl.:
p.225-226. — Index.
ISBN 0-460-03116-3 : £3.00
ISBN 0-460-02157-5 Pbk (Aldine paperbacks) : £1.50

(B74-27797)

BGH(N) — Gershwin, George. Biographies
Jablonski, Edward
The Gershwin years / by Edward Jablonski and Lawrence D.
Stewart ; with an introduction by Carl van Vechten. — London :
Robson Books, 1974. — 416p : ill, facsims, ports ; 27cm.
Also published: Garden City, N.Y. : Doubleday, 1974. — List of works:
p.339-358. — List of gramophone records: p.361-387. — Index.
ISBN 0-903895-19-6 : £6.95

(B74-27798)

Kimball, Robert
The Gershwins / [by] Robert Kimball and Alfred Simon ;
designed by Bea Feitler. — London : Cape, 1974. — iii-xliii,292p,
[8]p of plates : ill(some col), facsims, music, ports(some col) ;
31cm.
Originally published: New York : Atheneum, 1973. — Bibl.: p.291-292. —
List of gramophone records: p.281-285. — List of piano roll recordings:
p.286-290.
ISBN 0-224-01014-x : £9.50

(B74-24209)

Schwartz, Charles
Gershwin : his life and music / by Charles Schwartz. — London :
Abelard-Schuman, 1974. — [14],428p : ill, facsims, music, ports ;
26cm.
Originally published: in the United States, 1973. — List of works: p.335-349.
— List of films: p.351-352. — List of gramophone records: p.353-365. —
Bibl.: p.367-393. — Index.
ISBN 0-200-72129-1 : £4.90

(B74-20923)

BGL(N) — Glinka, Mikhail Ivanovich. Biographies
Brown, David, *b.1929*
Mikhail Glinka : a biographical and critical study / [by] David
Brown. — London [etc.] : Oxford University Press, 1974. — viii,
340p,[1],vi leaves of plates : music, ports ; 23cm.
Bibl.: p.316-320. — List of music: p.321-332. — Index.
ISBN 0-19-315311-4 : £7.00

(B74-03503)

BGT — Grieg, Edvard
Horton, John
Grieg / by John Horton. — London : Dent, 1974. — xv,255p,[8]p
of plates : ill, facsims, music, ports ; 20cm. — (The master
musicians series)
List of works: p.212-233. — Bibl.: p.240-244. — Index.
ISBN 0-460-03135-x : £2.95

(B74-13104)

BGTAM/JMBN — Grieg, Edvard. Peer Gynt. Stories
Suzuki, Yoshiharu
E.H. Grieg's 'Peer Gynt' / illustrated by Yoshiharu Suzuki ;
adapted by Makoto Oishi ; translated by Ann Brannen. —
London : F. Warne, 1974. — [30]p : chiefly col ill ; 25x27cm. —
(Fantasia pictorial, stories from famous music)
Sheet of music ([1]p.) as insert. — These illustrations originally published:
with Japanese text, Tokyo : Gakken, 1971.
ISBN 0-7232-1784-x : £1.75

(B74-26152)

BHBD(N) — Hadley, Patrick. Biographies
Todds, Walter
Patrick Hadley : a memoir / [by] Walter Todds ; with a catalogue
of works compiled by Christopher Palmer, and a discography by
Eric Hughes. — London (10e Prior Bolton St., N.1) : Triad Press,
1974. — [4],22p : music ; 23cm.
Limited ed. of 175 numbered copies. — List of records: p.17-18. — List of
works: p.19-21.
ISBN 0-902070-10-x Sd : £1.75

(B74-11050)

BHC(WJ) — Handel, George Frideric. Exhibitions
Fitzwilliam Museum
Handel and the Fitzwilliam : a collection of essays and a
catalogue of an exhibition of Handeliana in the Fitzwilliam
Museum in May and June 1974 on the occasion of three concerts
of the music of Handel and some of his contemporaries. —
Cambridge (Trumpington St., Cambridge) : Fitzwilliam Museum,
1974. — 45p,[4]p of plates : ports ; 25cm.
ISBN 0-904454-00-2 Sd : £0.75

(B74-16446)

BHCADD — Handel, George Frideric. Oratorios
Handel, George Frideric
[Messiah]. Handel's conducting score of 'Messiah' : reproduced in
facsimile from the manuscript in the library of St Michael's
College, Tenbury Wells / introduction by Watkins Shaw. —
London : Scolar Press for the Royal Musical Association, 1974. —
[7]p,82,140 leaves : of music ; 26x32cm.
Published for the Association on the occasion of its centenary. — Leaves
printed on both sides.
ISBN 0-85967-158-5 : £37.50

(B74-24210)

BHEARXNS — Haydn, Joseph. String quartets
Barrett-Ayres, Reginald
Joseph Haydn and the string quartet / [by] Reginald
Barrett-Ayres. — London : Barrie and Jenkins, 1974. — xiii,
417p : ill, music ; 26cm.
Bibl.: p.388-403. — Index.
ISBN 0-214-66803-7 : £11.00

(B74-25500)

BHNDAC — Hoddinott, Alun. The beach of Falesá. Librettos
Jones, Glyn, *b.1905*
The beach of Falesá : opera in three acts / libretto by Glyn
Jones ; based on a short story by R.L. Stevenson, music by Alun
Hoddinott. — London : Oxford University Press, Music
Department, 1974. — vii,40p ; 19cm.
ISBN 0-19-336833-1 Sd : £0.70

(B74-09229)

BHP(N) — Holst, Gustav. Biographies
Holst, Gustav
Gustav Holst - letters to W.G. Whittaker / edited by Michael
Short ; with an introduction by Imogen Holst. — [Glasgow] ([The
University, Glasgow G12 8QG]) : University of Glasgow Press,
1974. — xv,138p,[6]p of plates,leaf of plate : ill, facsims, ports ;
23cm.
Index.
ISBN 0-85261-106-4 : £4.00
Also classified at 780'.7

(B74-26028)

Holst, Imogen
Holst / [by] Imogen Holst. — London : Faber, 1974. — 96p,[12]p
of plates : ill, facsims, map, music, ports ; 26cm. — (The great
composers)
Bibl.: p.91. — List of works: p.92-93. — Index.
ISBN 0-571-09967-x : £2.30

(B74-06502)

BHP(TD) — Holst, Gustav. Thematic catalogues
Holst, Imogen
A thematic catalogue of Gustav Holst's music / [by] Imogen Holst. — London (38 Russell Sq., WC1B 5DA) : Faber Music Ltd : G. and I. Holst Ltd, 1974. — xxviii,285p,[8]p of plates : facsim, music ; 26cm.
Index.
ISBN 0-571-10004-x : £15.00

(B74-21167)

BIV(N) — Ives, Charles. Biographies
Ives, Charles
Memos / [by] Charles E. Ives; edited by John Kirkpatrick. — London : Calder and Boyars, 1973. — 355p,[12]p of plates : facsims, music, ports ; 24cm.
Originally published: New York: Norton, 1972. — Index.
ISBN 0-7145-0953-1 : £5.00

(B74-01379)

BKDBAM/HMBN — Kabalevesky, Dmitry. The comedians. Stories
Watanabe, Saburo
D.B. Kabalevsky's 'Joey the clown' ('The comedians') / illustrated by Saburo Watanabe ; adapted by Keisuke Tsutsui ; translated by Ann King Herring. — London : F. Warne, 1974. — [27]p : chiefly col ill ; 25x27cm. — (Fantasia pictorial, stories from famous music)
Sheet of music ([2]p.) as insert. — These illustrations originally published: with Japanese text, Tokyo : Gakken, 1970.
ISBN 0-7232-1783-1 : £1.75

(B74-26153)

BLBP(N) — Lambert, Constant. Biographies
Shead, Richard
Constant Lambert / [by] Richard Shead ; with a memoir by Anthony Powell. — London (c/o Lutterworth Press, Luke House, Farnham Rd, Guildford, Surrey) : Simon Publications, 1973. — 208p,11p of plates : ill, music, ports ; 22cm.
List of works: p.175-186. — List of records: p.187-192. — Bibl.: p.193-196. — Index.
ISBN 0-903620-01-4 : £2.95

(B74-05266)

BMBDACM — MacDermot, Galt. Hair
Davis, Lorrie
Letting down my hair / by Lorrie Davis with Rachel Gallagher. — London : Elek, 1974. — 279p,[8]p of plates ; 23cm.
Originally published: New York : Arthur Fields Books, 1973.
ISBN 0-236-31072-0 : £3.50

(B74-28314)

BME(N) — Mahler, Gustav. Biographies
Kennedy, Michael, *b.1926*
Mahler / by Michael Kennedy. — London : Dent, 1974. — xii, 196p,[8]p of plates : ill, music, ports ; 20cm. — (The master musicians series)
Bibl.: p.187-189. — List of works: p.172-180. — Index.
ISBN 0-460-03141-4 : £2.75

(B74-16725)

La Grange, Henry-Louis de
Mahler / [by] Henry-Louis de La Grange. — London : Gollancz.
In 2 vols.
Vol.1. — 1974. — xxv,987p,[39]p of plates : ill, facsims, music, ports ; 24cm.
Originally published: Garden City, N.Y. : Doubleday, 1973. — Bibl.: p.954-964. — Index.
ISBN 0-575-01672-8 : £7.50

(B74-11049)

Werfel, Alma Mahler
Gustav Mahler : memories and letters / by Alma Mahler; edited by Donald Mitchell; translated [from the German] by Basil Creighton. — 3rd ed. ; further enlarged with a new appendix and chronology by Knud Martner and Donald Mitchell. — London : J. Murray, 1973. — xlii,393p,[16]p of plates : ill, facsims, music, ports ; 25cm.
Previous ed. of this translation: 1968. — Translation of: 'Gustav Mahler: Erinnerungen und Briefe'. Amsterdam: Albert de Lange, 1940. — Index.
ISBN 0-7195-2944-1 : £5.00
ISBN 0 7195 2950 6 Pbk: £2.50

(B74-00161)

BMJ(N) — Mendelssohn, Felix. Biographies
Blunt, Wilfrid
On wings of song : a biography of Felix Mendelssohn / [by] Wilfrid Blunt. — London : Hamilton, 1974. — 288p : ill(some col), facsims, music, ports(some col) ; 26cm.
Bibl.: p.279-281. — Index.
ISBN 0-241-02455-2 : £5.50

(B74-14969)

BMLE — Moeran, Ernest John
Wild, Stephen
E.J. Moeran / [by] Stephen Wild ; introduction by Peers Coetmore with a comprehensive discography compiled by Lewis Foreman. — London (10e Prior Bolton St., N.1) : Triad Press, 1974. — [1],36p : music, ports ; 26cm.
Limited ed. of 200 numbered copies. — Bibl.: p.22. — Discography: p.24-35.
ISBN 0-902070-09-6 Sd : £1.50

(B74-08075)

BMU — Musorgsky, Modest
Calvocoressi, Michael Dimitri
Mussorgsky / by M.D. Calvocoressi. — Revised ed. / completed and revised by Gerald Abraham. — London : Dent, 1974. — viii, 216p,[8]p of plates : ill, music, ports ; 20cm. — (The master musicians series)
Revised ed. originally published: 1946. — List of works: p.201-204. — Bibl.: p.209-210. — Index.
ISBN 0-460-03152-x : £2.75

(B74-13105)

BOFGACN — O'Gorman, Denis. The wild rover. Librettos
O'Gorman, Denis
The wild rover : the story of the Prodigal Son: a musical play for children / texts and songs Denis O'Gorman; accompaniment Jim Brand. — Nottingham : Grail Publications, 1974. — iv,37p : music, plan, port ; 25cm.
ISBN 0-901829-22-6 Sd : £0.50

(B74-11053)

BPU(N) — Puccini, Giacomo. Biographies
Jackson, Stanley, *b.1910*
Monsieur Butterfly : the story of Puccini / [by] Stanley Jackson. — London [etc.] : W.H. Allen, 1974. — x,267p,[24]p of plates : ill, facsim, music, ports ; 23cm.
Bibl.: p.263-264. — Index.
ISBN 0-491-01162-8 : £3.50

(B74-05267)

BRC(N) — Rachmaninoff, Sergei. Biographies
McCabe, John
Rachmaninov / [by] John McCabe. — Sevenoaks : Novello, 1974. — 32p ; 19cm. — (Novello short biographies)
ISBN 0-85360-059-7 Sd : £0.20

(B74-25491)

BRCAM — Rachmaninoff, Sergei. Orchestral music
Piggott, Patrick
Rachmaninov orchestral music / [by] Patrick Piggott. — London : British Broadcasting Corporation, 1974. — 61p : music ; 20cm. — (British Broadcasting Corporation. Music guides)
Index.
ISBN 0-563-12468-7 Pbk : £0.45

(B74-14309)

BREAQ — Ravel, Maurice. Piano
Midwinter, Eric
Preschool priorities / editor Eric Midwinter. — London : Ward Lock, 1974. — [5],54p ; 22cm.
ISBN 0-7062-3383-2 Sd : £0.85

(B74-12162)

BSET — Schoenberg, Arnold
Adorno, Theodor Wiesengrund
Philosophy of modern music / [by] Theodor W. Adorno ; translated [from the German] by Anne G. Mitchell and Wesley V. Bloomster. — London : Sheed and Ward, 1973. — xviii,220p ; 23cm.
This translation originally published: New York: Seabury Press, 1973. — Translation of: 'Philosophie der neuen Musik'. Tübingen: Mohr, 1949.
ISBN 0-7220-7339-9 : £4.50
Also classified at BSV

(B74-09866)

BSET(N) — Schoenberg, Arnold. Biographies
Schoenberg, Arnold
Letters [of] Arnold Schoenberg / selected and edited by Erwin Stein; translated from the original German by Eithne Wilkins and Ernst Kaiser. — London : Faber, 1974. — 309p,[3] leaves of plates : facsim, ports ; 22cm.
This translation originally published: 1964. — Translation of: 'Arnold Schoenberg, ausgewählte Briefe'. Mainz: B. Schott's Söhne, 1958. — Index.
ISBN 0-571-10514-9 Pbk : £2.95

(B74-04793)

BSET(T) — Schoenberg, Arnold. Bibliographies
Lambeth Libraries
Arnold Schoenberg, 1874 to 1951 - books, records and scores / [Lambeth Libraries]. — [London] ([Central Library, Brixton Oval, S.W.2]) : Lambeth Libraries, 1974. — [14]p : 1 ill ; 21cm.
ISBN 0-9501893-6-7 Sd : Free

(B74-25103)

BSF — Schubert, Franz
  Gal, Hans
    Franz Schubert and the essence of melody / [by] Hans Gal ; [translated from the German by the author]. — London : Gollancz, 1974. — 205p : music ; 23cm.
    Translation of: 'Franz Schubert; oder, Die Melodie'. Frankfurt am Main: S. Fischer, 1970. — Bibl.: p.195. — Index.
    ISBN 0-575-01559-4 : £3.50

                                      (B74-04794)

BSFAKDW — Schubert, Franz. Songs, etc
  Capell, Richard
    Schubert's songs / [by] Richard Capell. — 3rd ed. ; with a preface by Martin Cooper. — London : Duckworth, 1973. — xii,292p,[2]p of plates : music, port ; 23cm.
    Third ed. also published: London: Pan Books, 1973. — Previous ed.: New York: Macmillan; London: Duckworth, 1957. — Index.
    ISBN 0-7156-0735-9 : £4.95

                                        (B74-05269)

BSK(TC) — Sousa, John Philip. Bibliographies of scores
  Bierley, Paul E
    John Philip Sousa - a descriptive catalog of his work / [by] Paul E. Bierley. — Urbana [etc.] ; London : University of Illinois Press, 1973. — [14],177p,[8]p of plates : ill, music, ports ; 27cm.
    Bibl.: p.170-171.
    ISBN 0-252-00297-0 : £4.75

                                        (B74-11345)

BSNK — Stockhausen, Karlheinz
  Cott, Jonathan
    Stockhausen : conversations with the composer / [by] Jonathan Cott. — London : Pan Books, 1974. — 235p,[8]p of plates : ill, facsims, music, ports ; 20cm. — (Picador)
    Originally published: New York : Simon and Schuster, 1973 ; London : Robson Books, 1974. — List of works: p.229-230. — List of gramophone records: p.231-235.
    ISBN 0-330-24165-6 Pbk : £0.95

                                        (B74-27248)

  Cott, Jonathan
    Stockhausen : conversations with the composer / [by] Jonathan Cott. — London (28 Poland St., W1V 3DB) : Robson Books Ltd, 1974. — 252p : ill, facsims, music, ports ; 24cm.
    Originally published: New York : Simon and Schuster, 1973. — List of works: p.247-248. — List of gramophone records: p.249-252.
    ISBN 0-903895-12-9 : £3.50

                                        (B74-10399)

BSV — Stravinsky, Igor
  Adorno, Theodor Wiesengrund
    Philosophy of modern music / [by] Theodor W. Adorno ; translated [from the German] by Anne G. Mitchell and Wesley V. Bloomster. — London : Sheed and Ward, 1973. — xviii,220p ; 23cm.
    This translation originally published: New York: Seabury Press, 1973. — Translation of: 'Philosophie der neuen Musik'. Tübingen: Mohr, 1949.
    ISBN 0-7220-7339-9 : £4.50
    Primary classification BSET

                                        (B74-09866)

BTDAM/HMBN — Tchaikovsky, Peter. Swan lake. Stories
  Hatsuyama, Shigeru
    P.I. Tchaikovsky's 'Swan Lake' / illustrated by Shigeru Hatsuyama ; adapted by Eriko Kishida ; translated by Ann King Herring. — London : F. Warne, 1974. — [27]p : chiefly col ill ; 25x27cm. — (Fantasia pictorial, stories from famous music)
    Sheet of music ([2]p.) as insert. — These illustrations originally published: with Japanese text, Tokyo : Gakken, 1970.
    ISBN 0-7232-1759-9 : £1.75

                                        (B74-26150)

BTDAM/HMBN — Tchaikovsky, Peter. The nutcracker. Stories
  Hori, Fumiko
    P.I. Tchaikovsky's 'The nutcracker' / based on Tchaikovsky's ballet after the story by E.T.A. Hoffmann ; illustrated by Fumiko Hori ; adapted by Magoichi Kushida ; translated by Ann King Herring. — London : F. Warne, 1974. — [30]p : chiefly col ill ; 25x27cm. — (Fantasia pictorial, stories from famous music)
    Sheet of music ([2]p.) as insert. — These illustrations originally published: with Japanese text, Tokyo : Gakken, 1971.
    ISBN 0-7232-1760-2 : £1.75

                                        (B74-26151)

BTE — Telemann, Georg Philipp
  Petzoldt, Richard
    Georg Philipp Telemann / by Richard Petzoldt ; [translated from the German] by Horace Fitzpatrick. — London : E. Benn, 1974. — xv,255p : ill, facsims, music, port ; 22cm.
    Translation of: 'Georg Philipp Telemann - Leben und Werk'. Leipzig : VEB Deutscher Verlag für Musik, 1967. — Bibl.: p.223-242. — Index.
    ISBN 0-510-35905-1 : £3.25

                                        (B74-26608)

BVE(N) — Verdi, Giuseppe. Biographies
  Hussey, Dyneley
    Verdi / by Dyneley Hussey. — [Revised ed.]. — London : Dent, 1973 [i.e. 1974]. — xiii,365p,[8]p of plates : ill, music, ports ; 20cm. — (The master musicians series)
    Previous ed.: 1968. — Bibl.: p.354-355. — List of works: p.345-346. — Index.
    ISBN 0-460-03151-1 : £2.50
    ISBN 0-460-02144-3 Pbk: £1.25

                                        (B74-17892)

BVE(N) — Verdi, Guiseppe. Biographies
  Wechsberg, Joseph
    Verdi / [by] Joseph Wechsberg. — London : Weidenfeld and Nicolson, 1974. — 255p : ill(some col), facsims, music, ports(some col) ; 26cm.
    Ill. on lining papers. — Index.
    ISBN 0-297-76818-2 : £4.50

                                        (B74-22804)

BWC(N) — Wagner, Richard. Biographies
  Jacobs, Robert Louis
    Wagner / by Robert L. Jacobs. — [Revised ed.]. — London : Dent, 1974. — x,278p,[8]p of plates : ill, facsim, music, ports ; 20cm. — (The master musicians series)
    Previous ed.: 1965. — Bibl.: p.232-239. — Index.
    ISBN 0-460-03153-8 : £2.75
    ISBN 0-460-02150-8 Pbk : £1.25

                                        (B74-25494)

BWCAC — Wagner, Richard. Der Ring des Nibelungen
  Donington, Robert
    Wagner's 'Ring' and its symbols : the music and the myth / [by] Robert Donington. — 3rd ed. — London : Faber, 1974. — 3-342p : music ; 23cm.
    Previous ed.: 1969. — Bibl.: p.316-328. — Index.
    ISBN 0-571-04825-0 : £3.95
    ISBN 0-571-04818-8 Pbk: £1.40

                                        (B74-09867)

BWJ — Walton, Sir William
  Howes, Frank
    The music of William Walton / [by] Frank Howes. — 2nd ed. — London : Oxford University Press, 1974 [i.e.1973]. — xvi,248,[8] p : ill, music, ports ; 23cm.
    Previous ed. 1965. — Index.
    ISBN 0-19-315431-5 : £3.00

                                        (B74-00528)

BWKH(TC) — Warlock, Peter. Bibliographies of scores
  Tomlinson, Fred
    A Peter Warlock handbook / compiled by Fred Tomlinson. — London (10e Prior Bolton St., N.1) : Triad Press.
    In 2 vols.
    Vol.1. — 1974. — 54p : 1 ill ; 30cm.
    Limited ed. of 300 numbered copies.
    ISBN 0-902070-11-8 Pbk : £2.75

                                        (B74-21168)

BWNRB — Wilbye, John
  Brown, David, *b.1929*
    Wilbye / [by] David Brown. — London [etc.] : Oxford University Press, 1974. — 55p : music ; 22cm. — (Oxford studies of composers ; 11)
    Bibl.: p.54. — List of works: p.54-55.
    ISBN 0-19-315220-7 Pbk : £1.65

                                        (B74-13708)

BWPDACN — Wood, David. Flibberty and the penguin. Librettos
  Wood, David, *b.1944*
    Flibberty and the penguin : a musical play / by David Wood. — London [etc.] : French, 1974. — [5],68p : plans ; 22cm. — (French's acting edition)
    Fifteen characters.
    ISBN 0-573-05033-3 Pbk : £0.50

                                        (B74-22805)

BWPDACN — Wood, David. Hijack over Hygenia. Librettos
  Wood, David, *b.1944*
    Hijack over Hygenia : a musical play for children / [by] David Wood. — London [etc.] : French, 1974. — [5],54p : plans ; 22cm. — (French's acting edition)
    Twentyfour characters.
    ISBN 0-573-05034-1 Pbk : £0.75

                                        (B74-28315)

BZ — LITERATURE ON NON-EUROPEAN MUSIC
BZF — India
  Menon, Raghava Raghava
    Discovering Indian music / [by] Raghava R. Menon. — Tunbridge Wells : Abacus Press, 1973. — xii,88p,[12]p of plates : ill ; 21cm.
    Originally published: Bombay: Somaiya Publications, 1973. — Bibl.: p.86-87.
    ISBN 0-85626-033-9 : £2.40

                                        (B74-02979)

BZHAC — China. Opera. Librettos
Hung, Josephine Huang
Classical Chinese plays / by Josephine Huang Hung. — 2nd ed. — London : Vision Press, 1972. — [1],xiii,277p,[10] leaves of plates : ill(some col) ; 22cm.
Second ed. originally published: Taipei : Mei Ya Publications, 1971. — Bibl.: p.274-275.
ISBN 0-85478-302-4 : £3.80
(B74-13707)

BZHPAL — Japan. Instrumental music
Adriaansz, Willem
The Kumiuta and Danmono traditions of Japanese koto music / by Willem Adriaansz. — Berkeley [etc.] ; London : University of California Press, 1973. — xii,493p : music ; 29cm.
Bibl.: p.478-482. — Index.
ISBN 0-520-01785-4 : £9.50
(B74-14313)

BZNR — South Africa. Venda tribe
Blacking, John
How musical is man? / [by] John Blacking. — Seattle ; London : University of Washington Press, 1973. — xiii,116p,[12]p of plates : ill, music ; 23cm. — (The John Danz lectures)
Tape recording of Venda music also available.
ISBN 0-295-95218-0 : £3.25
(B74-30188)

C/AC — GENERAL MUSICIANSHIP
Morrish, Donald James
Basic goals in music / British edition consultant, D.L. Morrish ; original Canadian edition by Lloyd H. Slind, Frank Churchley ; consultant, Lloyd Bradshaw. — London : McGraw-Hill.
Book 3. — 1974. — x,134p ; 8vo.
ISBN 0-07-094432-6 : Unpriced
(B74-50862)
Book 4. — 1974. — [10],134p ; 8vo.
ISBN 0-07-094433-4 : Unpriced
(B74-50863)
Book 5. — 1974. — [10],150p ; 8vo.
ISBN 0-07-094434-2 : Unpriced
(B74-50864)

C/AY — GENERAL COLLECTIONS
The **great** ones. — New York ; London : Wise.
1 : Great film music. — 1973. — 96p ; 4to. — £1.50
Also classified at C/JR/AY
(B74-50000)
2 : Seventeen exciting singer songwriters. — 1973. — 112p ; 4to. — £1.50
Also classified at C/JR/AY
(B74-50001)
3 : Great groups. — 1973. — 125p ; 4to. — £1.50
Also classified at KDW/GB/AY
(B74-50002)
4 : Nineteen famous singers and their songs & 17 more songs. — 1973. — 96p ; 4to. — £1.50
Also classified at KDW/GB/AY
(B74-50003)

C/CY — COLLECTIONS, EXERCISES, ETC. , ILLUSTRATING TECHNIQUES OF PERFORMANCE
C/JR/AY — Films. Collections
The **great** ones. — New York ; London : Wise.
1 : Great film music. — 1973. — 96p ; 4to. — £1.50
Primary classification C/AY
(B74-50000)
2 : Seventeen exciting singer songwriters. — 1973. — 112p ; 4to. — £1.50
Primary classification C/AY
(B74-50001)

CB — VOCAL MUSIC
CB/AY — Collections
Mossman, Sheila
Lyra songbook : hymns and songs / arranged SSA by Sheila Mossman. — Hamburg ; London : Rahter.
Volume 1. — 1974. — 28p ; 4to. —
Unpriced
(B74-50004)
Volume 2. — 1974. — 29p ; 4to. —
Unpriced
(B74-50005)

CB/DR/AZ — Psalms. Collected works of individual composers
Liszt, Franz
[Works, psalms. Collections]. Six psalms (1864-81) / [by] Franz Liszt. — Farnborough, Hants. : Gregg, 1971. — 236p ; fol.
Facsimile reprints of the original editions published: Leipzig : Kahnt, 1864, 1869, 1871, 1881.
ISBN 0-576-28230-8 : £6.60
(B74-50865)

CB/LD — Church music
Tallis, Thomas
[Works, church music. Selections]. English sacred music / by Thomas Tallis ; transcribed and edited by Leonard Ellinwood with revisions by Paul Doe. — London : Stainer and Bell. — (Early English Church Music)
1 : Anthems. — 1974. — xviii,133p ; 8vo.
Unpriced
(B74-50329)
2 : Service music. — 1974. — xvi,212p ; 8vo.
Unpriced
(B74-50330)

CC — OPERA. VOCAL SCORES
Delius, Frederick
[Koanga. Vocal score]. Koanga : opera in three acts with prologue and epilogue / by Frederick Delius ; vocal score by Eric Fenby ; revised libretto by Douglas Craig and Andrew Page. — London : Boosey and Hawkes, 1974. — ix,166p ; 8vo.
Unpriced
(B74-50866)

Donizetti, Gaetano
[Caterina Cornaro. Vocal score]. Caterina Cornaro / by Gaetano Donizetti ; [with foreword by John S. Allitt]. — London : Egret House : (Under the auspices of the Donizetti Society), 1974. — 8, 198p ; obl.4to.
A facsimile reprint of the edition published Milan, Ricordi, circa 1845.
Unpriced
(B74-50867)

Donizetti, Gaetano
[Lucrezia Borgia. Vocal score]. Lucrezia Borgia / by Gaetano Donizetti ; Italian libretto by Felice Romani after Victor Hugo's play; published under the auspices of the Donizetti Society. — London (93 Chancery La., W.C.2) : Egret House, 1973. — [16], 241p ; 8vo.
Facsimile reprint of: the edition published Milan: Ricordi, ca 1870.
Unpriced
(B74-50868)

Donizetti, Gaetano
[Maria Stuarda. Vocal score]. Maria Stuarda / by Gaetano Donizetti ; [libretto by Giuseppe Bardari, altered by Salatino]: ; published under the auspices of the Donizetti Society. — London (93 Chancery La., W.C.2) : Egret House, 1973. — [12],279p ; 8vo.
Also known as Buondelmonte. — Facsimile reprint of: the edition published Paris: Gerard, ca 1855.
Unpriced
(B74-50869)

Johnson, Tom
The four note opera : an opera in one act for soprano, contralto, tenor, baritone and bass with piano accompaniment / words and music by Tom Johnson. — New York ; London : Associated Music, 1973. — vi,128p ; 8vo.
Unpriced
(B74-50331)

Maconchy, Elizabeth
[The birds. Vocal score]. The birds : extravaganza in one act after Aristophanes / [by] Elizabeth Maconchy. — London : Boosey and Hawkes, 1974. — 71p ; fol.
Duration 40 min.
£2.75
(B74-50870)

Rorem, Ned
[Fables]. Fables : five very short operas / by Ned Rorem ; poems by Jean de la Fontaine, translation by Marianne Moore. — New York ; [London] : Boosey and Hawkes, 1974. — 40p ; 4to.
£3.25
(B74-50871)

Rorem, Ned
[Three sisters who are not sisters. *Vocal score*]. Three sisters who are not sisters : an opera / music by Ned Rorem ; melodrama by Gertrude Stein. — New York ; [London] : Boosey and Hawkes, 1974. — 68p ; 4to.
£4.25
(B74-50872)

CF — OPERETTAS. VOCAL SCORES
Offenbach, Jacques

[La Périchole. Vocal score]. La Périchole : operetta in three acts: music / by Jacques Offenbach ; adapted and arranged by Ronald Hanmer; original libretto by H. Meilhac and L. Halévy; new libretto by John Grinsey & Phil Park. — London : Weinberger, 1974. — 242p ; 4to.
Unpriced

(B74-50332)

CM — MUSICAL PLAYS. VOCAL SCORES
Ornadel, Cyril

[Treasure island. Vocal score]. Treasure island : a musical adventure / by Cyril Ornadel ; book by Bernard Miles and Josephine Wilson; lyrics by Hal Shaper. — London : Sparta Florida Music : Aviva Music, 1973. — 48p ; 4to.
£0.99

(B74-50006)

CN/L — Children's religious musical plays. Vocal scores
Arch, Gwyn

That's the Spirit : musical play / music by Gwyn Arch ; words by Pat Rooke. — London : British and Continental, 1974. — 41p ; 8vo.
Unpriced

(B74-50333)

CQC — OPERA. FULL SCORES
Maconchy, Elizabeth

The birds : extravaganza in one act after Aristophanes / [by] Elizabeth Maconchy. — London : Boosey and Hawkes, 1974. — 4to.
Duration 40 min.
Unpriced

(B74-50873)

CQM — MUSICAL PLAYS. FULL SCORES
CQN — Children's musical plays. Full scores
Lipkin, Malcolm

The white crane : [for voices, descant, recorders, percussion and piano, violins and guitar ad lib] / music by Malcolm Lipkin; words by M.K. Richardson. — London : Chester, 1974. — 4to & 8vo.
Score (20p.) & 6 parts. — With separate leaf bearing a narrator's part inserted. — Duration 20 min.
Unpriced

(B74-50334)

DE — RELIGIOUS CANTATAS WITH KEYBOARD ACCOMPANIMENT
Patterson, Paul

Gloria : for choir, SATB and piano, with two players, one at the keyboard and the other manipulating the strings / [by] Paul Patterson. — London : Weinberger, 1974. — 30p ; 4to.
Unpriced

(B74-50874)

Williamson, Malcolm

Canticle of fire : for chorus (SATB) and organ / [by] Malcolm Williamson ; words from the New Testament and 13th cent. hymn, tr. [by] J.M. Neale; organ score. — London : Weinberger, 1973. — [2],29p ; 4to.
Unpriced

(B74-50875)

DE/LL — Easter
Effinger, Cecil

A cantata for Easter : four part chorus of mixed voices with organ accompaniment / by Cecil Effinger; text adapted from the Scriptures. — New York ; London : Schirmer, 1974. — 48p ; 8vo.
Unpriced

(B74-50876)

DFF — ROMAN LITURGY
DG — Ordinary of the Mass
Gelineau, Joseph

Festival mass for unison (or mixed) choir congregation and organ / by Joseph Gelineau. — London : Boosey and Hawkes, 1974. — 4to & 8vo.
Score & people's part.
Unpriced
Primary classification JDG

(B74-50438)

Haydn, Joseph

[Mass, no.1, in B flat major, 'Heiligmesse'. Vocal score]. Missa Sancti Bernardi de Offida, 'Heiligmesse' : for four-part chorus of mixed voices / by Joseph Haydn ; edited with piano or organ accompaniment by H.C. Robbins Landon. — New York ; London : Schirmer, 1972. — 98p ; 8vo.
Unpriced

(B74-50007)

Haydn, Joseph

[Mass, no.8, in B flat major, 'Sancti Joannis de Deo'. Vocal score]. Missa brevis Sancti Joannis de Deo, 'Small organ mass' : for four-part chorus of mixed voices / by Joseph Haydn ; edited with piano or organ accompaniment by H.C. Robbins Landon. — New York ; London : Schirmer, 1972. — 43p ; 8vo.
Called missa brevis from the popular custom of telescoping the text of the Gloria and Credo so that at times four different texts are sung simultaneously.
Unpriced

(B74-50008)

Haydn, Joseph

[Mass, no.15, in C major, 'Mariazellermesse'. Vocal score]. Missa Cellensis in C, 'Mariazellermesse' : for four-part chorus of mixed voices / by Joseph Haydn ; edited with piano or organ accompaniment by H.C. Robbins Landon. — New York ; London : Schirmer, 1972. — 98p ; 8vo.
Unpriced

(B74-50009)

Huber, Klaus

[Kleine deutsche Messe (1969). *Vocal score*]. Kleine deutsche Messe = Missa brevissima (1969) : für Chor und Orgel (Gemeinde und Schlagzeug ad libitum) oder für Chor a cappella (Schlagzeug ad libitum) oder Originalfassung, für Chor, Orgel, Streichtrio und Harfe (Gemeinde und Schlagzeng ad libitum) / von Klaus Huber. — Cassel ; London : Bärenreiter, 1973. — 27p ; 8vo.
£1.80
Also classified at DGK

(B74-50335)

Krol, Bernhard

Esslinger Sankt Pauls-Messe nach Texten aus den Briefen des Apostels Paulus : für vierstimmigen gemischten Chor, Gemeinde, Orgel und (ad libitum) Rhythmusgruppe, Orgel (oder Klavier) / von Bernhard Krol. — Hamburg ; London : Simrock, 1974. — 15p ; 4to.
Unpriced
Also classified at DGK

(B74-50336)

Mozart, Wolfgang Amadeus

[Mass in C major. K.337. Vocal score]. Missa for Archibishop Colloredo, (Mass in C) : for four-part chorus of mixed voices / by Wolfgang Amadeus Mozart ; edited with piano or organ accompaniment by H.C. Robbins Landon. — New York ; London : Schirmer, 1973. — 68p ; 8vo.
Unpriced

(B74-50337)

Schubert, Franz

[Mass in G major. D.167. Vocal score]. Mass in G [D.167] / by Franz Schubert ; organ score by Norris L. Stephens. — New York ; London : Schirmer, 1973. — 49p ; obl fol.
Unpriced

(B74-50338)

DGC — Ordinary of the Mass. Gloria
Vivaldi, Antonio

[Gloria: arr]. Gloria : for four-part chorus of mixed voices, two solo sopranos and solo alto / [by] Antonio Vivaldi ; edited and with keyboard reduction and foreword by William Herrmann. — New York ; London : Schirmer, 1973. — viii,73p ; 8vo.
£0.95

(B74-50339)

DGE — Ordinary of the Mass. Sanctus
Monteverdi, Claudio

[Selva morale e spirituale. Messa a 4 da capella. Sanctus. Vocal score]. Holy holy holy = Sanctus / [by] Claudio Monteverdi ; edited for four-part chorus of mixed voices with piano accompaniment; edited and realization by Walter Ehret; English text by W.E. — New York ; London : Schirmer, 1974. — 8p ; 8vo.
Unpriced

(B74-50877)

DGF — Ordinary of the Mass. Agnus Dei
Monteverdi, Claudio

[Selva morale e spirituale. Messa a 4 da capella. Agnus Dei. Vocal score]. Lamb of God = Agnus dei / [by] Claudio Monteverdi ; edited for four-part chorus of mixed voices with piano accompaniment; edited and realization by Walter Ehret; English text by W.E. — New York ; London : Schirmer, 1974. — 7p ; 8vo.
Unpriced

(B74-50878)

DGK — Proper of the Mass
Huber, Klaus
[Kleine deutsche Messe (1969). *Vocal score*]. Kleine deutsche Messe = Missa brevissima (1969) : für Chor und Orgel (Gemeinde und Schlagzeug ad libitum) oder für Chor a cappella (Schlagzeug ad libitum) oder Originalfassung, für Chor, Orgel, Streichtrio und Harfe (Gemeinde und Schlagzeug ad libitum) / von Klaus Huber. — Cassel ; London : Bärenreiter, 1973. — 27p ; 8vo.
£1.80
Primary classification DG

(B74-50335)

Krol, Bernhard
Esslinger Sankt Pauls-Messe nach Texten aus den Briefen des Apostels Paulus : für vierstimmigen gemischten Chor, Gemeinde, Orgel und (ad libitum) Rhythmusgruppe, Orgel (oder Klavier) / von Bernhard Krol. — Hamburg ; London : Simrock, 1974. — 15p ; 4to.
Unpriced
Primary classification DG

(B74-50336)

DGKADD/LL — Victimae paschali
Byrd, William
[Gradulia, lib 2. Victimae paschali]. Victimae paschali = Unto Christ the victim : motet for five voices, SSATB [unacc] / [by] William Byrd ; edited by R.R. Terry ; revised by John Morehen. — London : Oxford University Press, 1974. — 15p ; 8vo.
ISBN 0-19-352010-9 : £0.30

(B74-50879)

DGKAV — Requiem mass
Donizetti, Gaetano
[Requiem. Vocal score]. Messa di requiem / composed in memory of Vincenzo Bellini ; by Gaetano Donizetti ; [with foreword by John S. Allitt]. — London : Egret House : (Under the auspices of the Donizetti Society), 1974. — 8,152p ; 4to.
A facsimile reprint of the edition published Milan, Lucca, 1870. The requiem was unfinished.
Unpriced

(B74-50880)

DGKHB — Divine Office. Matins. Te Deum
Dvořák, Antonin
[Te Deum. Op.103. Vocal score]. Te Deum. Op.103 : for full chorus of mixed voices with soprano and bass soli accompaniment / by Antonin Dvořák. — New York ; London : Schirmer, 1974. — 50p ; 8vo.
Unpriced

(B74-50881)

DGKJ/LF — Divine Office. Vespers. Christmas
Aston, Peter
Hodie Christus natus est = On this day, Christ the Lord is born : anthem for SATB and organ / by Peter Aston; words from the Vespers for Christmas Day ; English words by Peter Aston. — Sevenoaks : Novello, 1974. — 8p ; 8vo.
Unpriced
Primary classification DH/LF

DGM — ANGLICAN LITURGY
Royal School of Church Music
Festival service books / Royal School of Church Music. — Croydon : Royal School of Church Music.
7 : The journey: a meditation / with words and music devised by J.W. Poole. — 1974. — 64p ; 8vo. —
Unpriced

(B74-50340)

DGMM/KDD — Preces and Responses. Weddings
Guest, Donald
The wedding responses : SATB unacc / by Douglas Guest. — London : Oxford University Press, 1974. — [2]p ; 8vo.
Composed for the marriage of H.R.H. the Princess Anne.
ISBN 0-19-351649-7 : £0.06

(B74-50341)

DGNS — Morning Prayer. Benedictus
Stoker, Richard
[Benedictus. Vocal score]. Benedictus : for SATB and organ, or for SATB, organ and orchestra / by Richard Stoker. — London : Ashdown, 1974. — 8p ; 8vo.
Unpriced

(B74-50882)

DGPP — Evening prayer. Canticles
Weelkes, Thomas
[First evening service]. Magnificat and Nunc dimittis : SSAATB / by Thomas Weelkes ; reconstructed and edited by David Brown. — London : Oxford University Press, 1974. — 13p ; 8vo.
ISBN 0-19-351646-2 : £0.30

(B74-50342)

DGS — Communion
Mathias, William
Missa brevis. Op.64 : for mixed voices and organ / [by] William Mathias. — London : Oxford University Press, 1974. — 38p ; 8vo.
ISBN 0-19-351647-0 : Unpriced

(B74-50883)

DGT — LITURGIES OF DENOMINATIONS OTHER THAN ROMAN & ANGLICAN
DGU — Jewish liturgy
Aleynu l'shabench : a new Friday evening service, cantor solo with mixed chorus, SATB and organ, commissioned by the Anshe Emet Synagogue, Chicago, Illinois, on the occasion of the hundredth jubilee year (1873-1973). — Carlstadt : Ethnic Music ; [London] : [Phoenix].
[1] : Adon olam / by Maurice Goldman. — 1974. — 14p ; 8vo.
Unpriced

(B74-50884)

[2] : Ahavat olam / by Herbert Fromm. — 1974. — 8p ; 8vo.
Unpriced

(B74-50885)

[3] : Hashkivenu / by Sholom Secunda. — 1974. — 11p ; 8vo.
Unpriced

(B74-50886)

[4] : Kiddush l'shabat / by Sholom Kalib. — 1974. — 12p ; 8vo.
Unpriced

(B74-50887)

[5] : Ma toru / by Samuel Adler. — 1974. — 7p ; 8vo.
Unpriced

(B74-50888)

[6] : May the words / by Lazar Weiner. — 1974. — 4p ; 8vo.
Unpriced

(B74-50889)

[7] : Psalm 150 / by Heinrich Schalit. — 1974. — 7p ; 8vo.
Unpriced

(B74-50890)

[8] : Rozo d'shabos / by Charles Davidson. — 1974. — 6p ; 8vo.
Unpriced

(B74-50891)

[9] : Shiru ladonai shir chadash / by Frederick Picket. — 1974. — 9p ; 8vo.
Unpriced

(B74-50892)

[10] : Veshomru / by Lazar Weiner. — 1974. — 6p ; 8vo.
Unpriced

(B74-50893)

DH — MOTETS, ANTHEMS, HYMNS, ETC.
Amner, John
[Sacred hymns. My Lord is hence removed. *Vocal score*]. My Lord is hence removed : SSATTB [with tenor solo and viol accompaniment] / by John Amner ; edited by Anthony Greening. — London : Oxford University Press, 1974. — 5p ; 8vo.
ISBN 0-19-350326-3 : Unpriced

(B74-50343)

Artman, Ruth
God is alive : for SATB chorus and piano / words and music by Ruth Artman. — New York : Warner ; [London] : [Blossom], 1974. — 16p ; 8vo.
Unpriced

(B74-50344)

Bach, Johann Sebastian
[Jesu, meine Freude. S.227. Vocal score]. Jesu, priceless treasure : motet for two sopranos, alto, tenor and bass / by Johann Sebastian Bach ; edited with piano accompaniment by Robert Hufstader. — New York ; London : Schirmer, 1972. — 56p ; 8vo.
Unpriced

(B74-50010)

Beck, John Ness
Exhortation : for mixed chorus and piano / by John Ness Beck. — New York : Galaxy ; [London] : [Galliard], 1971. — 13p ; 8vo.
Unpriced

(B74-50894)

Bernhard, Christoph
[Geistlicher Harmonien, erster Teil. *Wie der Hirsch schreiet*]. As the deer cries for flowing water : for four-part chorus of mixed voices with organ accompaniment / by Christoph Bernhard ; edited by David Streetman. — Wendover : Roberton, 1973. — 23p ; 8vo.
Duration 7 min.
£0.26

(B74-50011)

Chapple, Brian
Hallelujahs : for two choirs and organ / [by] Brian Chapple. — London : Chester : Hansen, 1974. — 53p ; 4to.
Duration 10 min.
Unpriced

(B74-50895)

Davis, Katherine Kennicott
The shot heard round the world : for SATB chorus, organ and optional B flat trumpets / by Katherine Kennicott Davies ; text Ralph Waldo Emerson. — New York : Warner ; [London] : [Blossom], 1974. — 11p ; 8vo.
The parts for 1st and 2nd B flat trumpet are printed on pages 10 and 11.
Unpriced

(B74-50345)

Drayton, Paul
My soul, there is a country : SATB / music by Paul Drayton; words by Henry Vaughan. — London : Oxford University Press, 1974. — 8p ; 8vo.
ISBN 0-19-350348-4 : £0.12

(B74-50896)

Handel, George Frideric
[Rinaldo. Lascia ch'io panga: arr]. Evening hymn / music by G.F. Handel ; adapted SATB by Lionel Lethbridge; words by Lionel Lethbridge. — London : Oxford University Press, 1973. — 4p ; 8vo.
ISBN 0-19-351119-3 : Unpriced

(B74-50012)

Herbst, Johannes
[Fürwahr, Er trug uns're Krankheit: arr]. Surely he has borne our sorrows = Fürwahr, Er trug uns're Krankheit : [S.A.T.B. with accompaniment] / [by] Johannes Herbst ; edited and arranged by Karl Kroeger; German text from Isaiah 53:4-5, English version by K.K. — Moramus ed. — [New York] ; [London] : Boosey and Hawkes, 1974. — 11p ; 8vo.
Unpriced

(B74-50346)

Herbst, Johannes
[Höret alle die ihr von Hause: arr]. Listen all who enter these portals = Höret alle die ihr von Hause : [S.A.T.B. with accompaniment] / [by] Johannes Herbst ; edited and arranged by Karl Kroeger; German text from Isaiah 57:15, Lamentations 4:22 and J.E. Schmidt, English version by K.K. — Moramus. ed. — [New York] ; [London] : Boosey and Hawkes, 1974. — 15p ; 8vo.
Unpriced

(B74-50347)

Hughes, Edward
Out of the depths, based on Psalm 129 (130) : (SATB) / by Edward Hughes ; arr., W.L. Reed; words by Peter Westmore. — London : Campbell, Connelly, 1974. — 7p ; 8vo.
Unpriced

(B74-50348)

Joubert, John
Behold the tabernacle of God. Op.70 : anthem for SATB, with divisions and organ / [by] John Joubert ; words from the Sarum antiphon for the dedication of a church. — Sevenoaks : Novello, 1974. — 10p ; 8vo.
£0.16

(B74-50897)

Mathias, William
Alleluya psallat = Sing alleluya. Op. 58 : SATB / by William Mathias ; anonymous 13th century words; English version by John Morehen. — London : Oxford University Press, 1974. — 12p ; 8vo.
ISBN 0-19-350339-5 : £0.15

(B74-50013)

Mechem, Kirke
The children of David. Op.37 : five modern psalms, for mixed chorus and organ / by Kirke Mechem. — New York ; [London] : Boosey and Hawkes.
1 : Psalm / words by Carol Dinklage. — 1974. — 4,22p ; 8vo.
Unpriced

(B74-50898)

2 : Joy / words by Robinson Jeffers. — 1974. — 11p ; 8vo.
Unpriced

(B74-50899)

3 : The song of David / words by Christopher Smart. — 1974. — 24p ; 8vo.
Unpriced

(B74-50900)

4 : Man of my own people / words by Florence Kiper Frank. — 1974. — 12p ; 8vo.
Unpriced

(B74-50901)

5 : Pied beauty / words by Gerard Manley Hopkins. — 1974. — 2,16p ; 8vo.
Unpriced

(B74-50902)

Newbury, Kent A
Praise to the Lord : hymn-anthem for four-part chorus of mixed voices with organ or piano accompaniment, melody 'Lobe den Herrn' from Stralsund Gesangbuch / arranged by Kent A. Newbury; words adapted from Psalms 103 and 150 by Joachim Neander; English translation by Catherine Winkworth. — New York ; London : Schirmer, 1972. — 7p ; 8vo.
Unpriced

(B74-50014)

Peter, Johann Friedrich
[Lobe den Herrn meine Seele: arr]. Praise the Lord, O my soul = Lobe den Herrn meine Seele : [S.A.T.B. with accompaniment] / [by] Johann Friedrich Peter ; edited and arranged by Karl Kroeger; German text from Psalm 103:2-4, English version by K.K. — Moramus ed. — [New York] ; [London] : Boosey and Hawkes, 1974. — 11p ; 8vo.
Unpriced

(B74-50349)

Rorem, Ned
Three motets : SATB and organ / by Ned Rorem on poems of Gerard Manley Hopkins. — [New York] ; [London] : Boosey and Hawkes, 1974. — 27p ; 8vo.
Unpriced

(B74-50350)

Routley, Erik
Three antiphonal canticles : for SATB and congregation (or two groups of singers) and organ / composed and arranged by Erik Routley. — Sevenoaks : Novello, 1974. — 8p ; 8vo.
£0.10

(B74-50015)

Wills, Arthur
Prayer : anthem for SATB and organ / music by Arthur Wills, words by George Herbert. — Sevenoaks : Novello, 1974. — 8p ; 8vo.
£0.12

(B74-50903)

DH/LF — Christmas
Aston, Peter
Hodie Christus natus est = On this day, Christ the Lord is born : anthem for SATB and organ / by Peter Aston; words from the Vespers for Christmas Day ; English words by Peter Aston. — Sevenoaks : Novello, 1974. — 8p ; 8vo.
Unpriced
Also classified at DGKJ/LF

(B74-50904)

Forcucci, Samuel L
[Child of wonder. Alleluia and chorale]. Alleluia and chorale : SATB with piano, four-hands / by Samuel L. Forcucci ; words by Christina Rossetti. — New York ; London : Schirmer, 1970. — 11p ; 8vo.
Unpriced

(B74-50016)

Schütz, Heinrich
[Hodie Christus natus est. S.W.V.456. *Vocal score].* Hodie Christus natus est = On this day Christ the Lord is born : motet for six-part chorus of mixed voices / by Heinrich Schutz ; edited, with piano accompaniment, by Maynard Klein, English text by M.K.. — New York ; London : Schirmer, 1973. — 20p ; 8vo.
Unpriced

(B74-50351)

DH/LFM — New Year
Ferguson, Edwin Earle
We pause beside this door : anthem for the New Year, for four-part chorus of mixed voices with organ accompaniment / by Edwin Earle Ferguson ; words by January Lucy Larcom. — Wendover : Roberton, 1966. — 7p ; 8vo.
£0.10

(B74-50017)

DH/LL — Easter
Rose, Michael
Easter day : anthem for female or boys' voices and organ / by Michael Rose ; words by Christopher Smart. — Sevenoaks : Novello, 1974. — 12p ; 8vo.
£0.14

(B74-50018)

DJ — MOTETS
Carissimi, Giacomo
Nisi Dominus. Psalm 127 : motet for SSATB and organ continuo / attributed to Giacomo Carissimi; edited by Janet Beat. — Sevenoaks : Novello, 1974. — 16p ; 8vo.
£0.20
Primary classification DR

DK — ANTHEMS
Palmer, Peggy Spencer
[This is the day which the Lord hath made: arr]. This is the day which the Lord hath made : festival anthem / [by] Peggy Spencer Palmer ; arr. for SATB with organ, [text from] Psalm 118. — London : Cramer, 1974. — 16p ; 8vo.
£0.15

(B74-50905)

Stoker, Richard
[Proverbs. Vocal score]. Proverbs : for SATB and organ / by Richard Stoker. — London : Ashdown, 1974. — 8p ; 8vo.
£0.15

(B74-50906)

DM — HYMNS

Davis, Katherine Kennicott
Amazing grace / adapted from the early American hymn tune for accompanied mixed chorus SATB by Katherine K. Davis ; words by John Newton. — New York : Galaxy ; London : Galliard, 1974. — 8vo.
Unpriced
(B74-50907)

Whalum, Wendell
Amazin' grace : old negro hymn tune / arranged for four-part chorus of mixed voices with organ accompaniment by Wendell Whalum, words by John Newton. — Wendover : Roberton, 1974. — 11p ; 8vo.
£0.13
(B74-50019)

DM/AY — Collections

Maxwell-Timmins, Donald
Morning has broken : hymns to play and sing / selected and edited by Donald Maxwell-Timmins, edition [with] full accompaniments, simplified accompaniments and instrumental arrangements. — Huddersfield : Schofield and Sims, 1974. — 8vo.
Piano edition (121p.) & melody edition.
ISBN 0-7217-2524-4 : Unpriced
(B74-50352)

Pulkingham, Betty
Sound of living waters : songs of revival / compiled by Betty Pulkingham and Jeanne Harper. — London : Hodder and Stoughton, 1974. — 256p ; 8vo.
ISBN 0-340-18893-6 : Unpriced
(B74-50908)

Routley, Erik
Hymns for celebration : a supplement for use at Holy Communion today / selected and edited by Erik Routley and John Wilson. — Croydon : Royal School of Church Music, 1974. — 8vo.
Full ed. (62p.) & melody ed. (46p.).
ISBN 0-85402-055-1 : Unpriced
(B74-50353)

Spiritual songs, with music. — Bradford : The Horton Trust, 1973. — 18p ; 8vo.
Unpriced
(B74-50020)

Spiritual songs with music. — Bradford (1 Sherbourne Rd., Great Horton, Bradford) : Horton Trust, 1974. — 91p ; 8vo.
Unpriced
(B74-50909)

DM/AYDK — Collections. Wales

Battye, Ken
Welsh flavour : a selection of Welsh hymn tunes set to English words / compiled by Ken Battye. — Burton in Lonsdale : Ken Battye.
Vol.7. — 1974. — 27p ; 8vo. —
Unpriced
(B74-50354)

DP — CAROLS

DP/LF — Christmas

Rutter, John
Jesu child : SATB / words and music by John Rutter. — London : Oxford University Press, 1974. — 12p ; 8vo.
ISBN 0-19-343045-2 : £0.20
(B74-50910)

Two Christmas carols : SATB and organ or piano. — Croydon : Royal School of Church Music, 1973. — 7p ; 8vo.
Contents: 1: Gabriel to Mary came; medieval melody - 2: Sweet Jesu, King of bliss, by Derek Melville.
£0.20
(B74-50911)

DP/LL — Easter

Drayton, Paul
Now glad of heart be every one : Easter carol, for SATB and organ / by Paul Drayton ; words German 16th century, translated by A.H. Fox-Strangeways. — Sevenoaks : Novello, 1974. — 8p ; 8vo.
£0.10
(B74-50021)

Ives, Charles
Easter carol : solo quartet, SATB and organ / by Charles Ives ; edited and with notes by John Kirkpatrick. — New York ; London : Associated Music, 1974. — 20p ; 8vo.
Unpriced
(B74-50355)

DR — PSALMS

Allanbrook, Douglas
Psalm 131 : SATB and organ / by Douglas Allanbrook. — New York ; [London] : Boosey and Hawkes, 1971. — 11p ; 8vo.
Unpriced
(B74-50912)

Brian, Havergal
[Psalm 23. Vocal score]. Psalm 23 : tenor solo, chorus (SATB) and orchestra / by Havergal Brian ; edited by Graham Hatton. — Chelmsford : Musica Viva, 1974. — 28p ; 4to.
Duration 18 min.
£1.20
(B74-50022)

Carissimi, Giacomo
Nisi Dominus. Psalm 127 : motet for SSATB and organ continuo / attributed to Giacomo Carissimi; edited by Janet Beat. — Sevenoaks : Novello, 1974. — 16p ; 8vo.
£0.20
Also classified at DJ
(B74-50913)

Jackson, Francis
Sing a new song to the Lord. Op.36, no.4 : anthem for soprano solo, SATB with divisions and organ / by Francis Jackson; Psalm 98. — Sevenoaks : Novello, 1974. — 14p ; 8vo.
Unpriced
(B74-50356)

Saunders, Neil
Benedic anima mea. Psalm 104 : for mixed voice choir, soprano and tenor soli and organ / by Neil Saunders. — Wendover : Roberton, 1974. — 27p ; 8vo.
With an errata slip inserted.
£0.32
(B74-50914)

Tomblings, Philip
Behold now praise the Lord : anthem for SATB / by Philip Tomblings; Psalm 134. — Hoddesdon : St Gregory Publications, 1973. — 4p ; 8vo.
£0.15
(B74-50915)

DS/LDB — Litanies. Roman Catholic Church

Haydn, Michael
[Litaniae de S.S. Nomine Jesu]. Litany in B flat (In nomine Jesu) for four-part chorus of mixed voices, soprano, alto, tenor and bass soli / [by] Michael Haydn ; edited, with piano accompaniment, by Alison I. Maitland. — New York ; London : Schirmer, 1974. — iii,72p ; 8vo.
Unpriced
(B74-50916)

DW — SONGS, ETC.

Artman, Ruth
Well, what do you know? : SATB with piano accompaniment and optional violins, string bass and guitar / words and music by Ruth Artman. — New York : Warner ; [London] : [Blossom], 1971. — 4to.
Score & part - The parts for 1st and 3rd violins in score and for 2nd violin are printed in the verso of the part for guitar and/or string bass.
Unpriced
(B74-50917)

Atkinson, Condit
The house by the side of the road : mixed chorus and piano with optional percussion and string bass / by Condit Atkinson. — New York : Galaxy ; London : Galliard, 1972. — 8p ; 8vo.
Unpriced
(B74-50918)

Brahms, Johannes
Zigeunerlieder = Gypsy songs. Op.103 : for four-part chorus of mixed voices with soprano and tenor solos and piano accompaniment / [by] Johannes Brahms ; text by Hugo Conrat; edited and with English texts by Maynard Klein. — New York ; London : Schirmer, 1973. — 30p ; 4to.
Unpriced
(B74-50357)

Brejean, Philippe
[Quand la chance est là]. This old world = Quand la chance est là : for SATB chorus accompanied / by Philippe Brejean ; arranged by Jacques Rizzo; original French lyric by Patrick Loubie; English lyric by Carl Sigman. — New York ; [London] : Chappell, 1974. — 11p ; 8vo.
Unpriced
(B74-50358)

Habash, John Mitri
Adam's apple : SATB / composed and arranged by John Mitri Habash and Arnold Freed. — New York ; [London] : Robbins, 1971. — 13p ; 8vo.
Unpriced
(B74-50919)

Habash, John Mitri
The sea of life : SATB / composed and arranged by John Mitri
Habash and Arnold Freed. — New York ; [London] : Robbins,
1971. — 8p ; 8vo.
Unpriced
(B74-50920)

Habash, John Mitri
Silent spring : SATB / composed and arranged by John Mitri
Habash and Arnold Freed. — New York ; [London] : Robbins,
1971. — 10p ; 8vo.
Unpriced
(B74-50921)

Habash, John Mitri
Smokey smokestack : SATB / composed and arranged by John
Mitri Habash and Arnold Freed. — New York ; [London] :
Robbins, 1971. — 11p ; 4to.
Unpriced
(B74-50922)

Habash, John Mitri
To you, my love : four part SATB / words and music by J.M.
Habash, based on a theme of Beethoven from Symphony no.3. —
New York ; [London] : Robbins, 1971. — 7p ; 8vo.
Unpriced
(B74-50923)

Hague, Albert
[We're all in this together : arr]. We're all in this together : for
mixed chorus (SATB) / words and music by Albert Hague ;
arranged by Chuck Cassey. — New York ; [London] : Chappell,
1971. — 8p ; 8vo.
Unpriced
(B74-50924)

Martini, Giovanni
[Plaisir d'amour: arr]. Plaisir d'amour / by Giovanni Martini ;
arranged, SATB, by Richard Cumming. — New York ; London :
Boosey and Hawkes, 1971. — 8p ; 8vo.
Unpriced
(B74-50359)

Menten, Dale
[America sings: arr]. America sings / words and music by Dale
Menten, arranged for mixed chorus, SATB, by Jacques C. Rizzo.
— New York : Unichappell ; London : Chappell, 1971. — 8p ;
8vo.
Unpriced
(B74-50360)

Merrill, Marlin
Let it be forgotten : for mixed chorus (SSAATB) or treble chorus
(SSAA) and piano / by Marlin Merrill ; poems by Sara Teasdale.
— New York ; London : Oxford University Press, 1972. — 6p ;
4to.
Unpriced
Also classified at FDW
(B74-50361)

Millet, Kadish
Stained glass windows (and simple wood benches) / by Kadish
Millet ; arranged for mixed chorus (SATB) by Jacques C. Rizzo ;
words by Kadish Millet. — New York ; [London] : Chappell,
1971. — 6p ; 8vo.
Unpriced
(B74-50925)

Muczynsky, Robert
Synonyms for life. Op. 33 : for four-part chorus of mixed voices
with piano accompaniment / by Robert Muczynski ; text adapted
from Roget's Thesaurus. — New York ; London : Schirmer, 1973.
— 15p ; 8vo.
Unpriced
(B74-50023)

Peet, Richard
Stand up for America! : for mixed chorus, SATB / words and
music by Richard Peet and Samuel Loboda. — New York ;
London : Chappell, 1971. — 8p ; 8vo.
Unpriced
(B74-50362)

Platts, Kenneth
[Musick's empire. Op.9. Vocal score]. Musick's empire. Opus 9 :
for SATB, piano and optional strings / music by Kenneth Platts ;
words by Andrew Marvell. — London : Ashdown, 1974. — 11p ;
8vo.
£0.15
(B74-50926)

Previn, André
[Good companions. Slippin' around the corner]. Slippin' around
the corner / [song] ; music by André Previn; lyrics by Johnny
Mercer. — London : Chappell, 1974. — 5p ; 4to.
Unpriced
(B74-50363)

Previn, André
[Good companions. Stage struck]. Stage struck : [song] / music by
André Previn; lyrics by Johnny Mercer. — London : Chappell,
1974. — 6p ; 4to.
Unpriced
(B74-50364)

Purcell, Henry
[The mock marriage. Man is for the woman made: arr]. Man is
for the woman made / by Henry Purcell ; arranged, SATB, by
Richard Cumming. — New York ; London : Boosey and Hawkes,
1971. — 10p ; 8vo.
Unpriced
(B74-50365)

Young, Douglas
[Sir Patrick Spens. Vocal score]. Sir Patrick Spens : chorus and
orchestra, SATB / by Douglas Young ; words: traditional border
ballad. — London : Faber Music, 1973. — 25p ; 4to.
Unpriced
(B74-50024)

DW/AY — Collections
Sargent, Brian
Minstrels : medieval music to sing and play / selected and edited
by Brian Sargent. — London : Cambridge University Press, 1974.
— 47p : ill ; 8vo.
ISBN 0-521-20166-7 : Unpriced
(B74-50367)

Sargent, Brian
Troubadours : medieval music to sing and play / selected and
edited by Brian Sargent. — London : Cambridge University Press,
1974. — 40p ; 8vo.
ISBN 0-521-20471-2 : Unpriced
(B74-50368)

Tischler, Hans
A medieval motet book : a collection of 13th century motets in
various vocal and instrumental combinations / compiled and
edited by Hans Tischler. — New York ; London : Associated
Music, 1973. — vi,134p ; 8vo.
Unpriced
(B74-50366)

DW/G/AYSXC — Folk songs. Collections. Eastern Canada
Churchill, John
Three songs from eastern Canada : for mixed voices [S.A.T.B.]
and piano / arranged with English words by John Churchill. —
South Croydon : Lengnick.
1 : Les trois canes (Cheticamp, N.S.). — 1973. — 8p ; 8vo. —
£0.12
(B74-50025)
2 : Ave maris stella (Acadian 17th cent.). — 1973. — 5p ; 8vo. —
£0.12
(B74-50026)
3 : I'se the b'y (Newfoundland). — 1973. — 8p ; 8vo. —
£0.12
(B74-50027)

DW/LC — Spirituals
Hudson, Hazel
Behold that star ... Rise up, shepherd an' foller! : a quodlibet /
arranged, from negro spirituals, for treble and alto or tenor and
bass or treble and bass with optional parts for descant recorders
and percussion by Hazel Hudson. — London : Ashdown, 1974. —
8p ; 8vo.
£0.12
Primary classification FDW/LC

DW/LF — Christmas
Rocherolle, Eugenie R
Christmas child : for unison, SA or SAB chorus and piano /
words and music by Eugenie R. Rocherolle. — New York :
Warner ; London : Blossom, 1974. — 15p ; 8vo.
Unpriced
Primary classification JDW/LF
(B74-50448)

DW/X — Canons
Gersch, Paul J
The awakening : canon for equal voices / music by Paul J.
Gersch; words by Ruth Goldthorpe. — Sydney ; [London] :
Chappell, 1974. — [4]p ; 8vo.
Unpriced
(B74-50369)

DX — SECULAR CANTATAS
Creston, Paul
[Calamus. Op.104. Vocal score]. Calamus. Op.104 : mixed chorus
of brass-percussion ensemble or piano : music by Paul Creston /
text by Walt Whitman. — New York ; London : Schirmer, 1974.
— 28p ; 8vo.
Unpriced
(B74-50927)

Fraser, Shena
Full fathom five : for SAB chorus, soprano and tenor soloists and
piano / by Shena Fraser. — London : Thames, 1974. — 39p ; 4to.
£0.75

(B74-50928)

Hedges, Anthony
[To music. *Vocal score*]. To music : for tenor solo, SATB and
orchestra / by Anthony Hedges. — London : Chappell, 1974. —
44p ; 4to.
Unpriced

(B74-50370)

Hindemith, Paul
[Lehrstuch (1929). Vocal score]. Lehrstuck (1929) / [by] Paul
Hindemith ; text Bertold Brecht ; translated by Geoffrey Skelton.
— Mainz ; London : Schott, 1974. — 52p ; 8vo.
English version of the edition published Mainz, Schott, 1929.
£4.35

(B74-50929)

Mahler, Gustav
[Das klagende Lied, no.1. Waldmärchen. Vocal score].
Waldmärchen = A forest legend (Das klagende Lied: 1) / [by]
Gustav Mahler ; text Gustav Mahler; English translation by Basil
Swift; piano reduction by Herbert Haufrecht. — New York ;
[Croydon] : Belwin-Mills, 1973. — viii,56p ; 8vo.
Unpriced

(B74-50371)

Washburn, Robert
[Ode to freedom. Vocal score]. Ode to freedom : mixed chorus,
SATB accompanied by band and/or orchestra / [by] Robert
Washburn. — New York ; London : Oxford University Press,
1974. — 12p ; 8vo.
Unpriced

(B74-50930)

**E — CHORAL WORKS WITH ACCOMPANIMENT OTHER
THAN KEYBOARD**
ELDE — With instruments. Religious cantatas
Blarr, Oskar Gottlieb
Oekumenische Beatmesse : Liebe ist nicht nur ein Wort /
herausgegeben von Oskar Gottlieb Blarr, Uwe Seidel und Diethard
Zils mit Liedern (Klavier und Chorsätzen) und Texten zum
Thema. — Regensburg : Bosse ; [London] : [Bärenreiter], 1973. —
33p ; 4to.
£1.60

(B74-50372)

EMDD — With orchestra. Oratorios
Liszt, Franz
[Works, selections]. Die Legende von der heiligen Elisabeth :
Oratorium / von F. Liszt ; [with], Die heilige Cäcilia : Legende
gedichtet von Madame Emilie de Giradin, für ein
Mezzo-Sopran-Stimme mit Chor (ad libitum) und Orchester oder
Pianoforte, (Harmonium und Harfe) Begleitung / componirt von
F. Liszt. — Farnborough, Hants. : Gregg, 1971. — 380p ; 4to.
Study score of Die heilige Elisabeth. The version with piano, harmonium
and harp of Die heilige Cäcilia - Facsimile reprints of the editions published:
Leipzig : Kahnt, 1869, 1876.
ISBN 0-576-28231-6 : £8.40

(B74-50931)

EMDE — With orchestra. Religious cantatas
Bach, Johann Sebastian
Siehe zu dass deine Gottesfurcht nicht Heuchelei sei : Kantate 179
(auf den 11 Sonntag nach Trinitis) / von Johann Sebastian Bach ;
nach dem Autograph herausgegeben und mit Vorwort versehen
von Hans Grischkat, English translation by Henry S. Drinker. —
London : Eulenburg, 1970. — x,29p ; 8vo.
Miniature score.
£1.00

(B74-50028)

Liszt, Franz
Christus : Oratorium nach Texten aus der heligen Schrift und der
katholischen Liturgie : Soli, Chor, Orgel und grosses Orchester /
componirt von Franz Liszt. — Farnborough, Hants. : Gregg,
1971. — 6,332p ; 4to.
Study score. — Facsimile reprint of the edition published: Leipzig : Kahnt,
1872.
ISBN 0-576-28232-4 : £7.80

(B74-50932)

EMDGKADD/LK — With orchestra. Stabat mater
Bononcini, Antonio
Stabat mater : for SATB soli and chorus, string orchestra and
organ continuo / by Antonio Bononcini ; edited from Bologna
Civico museo bibliografico musicale MS. DD 187 by Peter Smith.
— Sevenoaks : Novello, 1974. — 84p ; 8vo.
£1.25

(B74-50373)

EMDGKHB — With orchestra. Divine Office. Matins. Te Deum
Berlioz, Hector
Te Deum / [von] Hector Berlioz ; vorgelegt von Denis McCaldin.
— Wiesbaden : Breitkopf and Härtel ; Cassel ; London :
Bärenreiter, 1972. — 160p ; fol.
Separate edition based on 'Hector Berlioz, New edition of the complete
works', vol.10.
£13.20

(B74-50374)

EMDP/LF — With orchestra. Carols. Christmas
Rutter, John
Shepherd's pipe carol : for mixed voices and small orchestra / by
John Rutter. — London : Oxford University Press, 1973. — 20p ;
4to.
Score (20p.) & 11 parts.
ISBN 0-19-344803-3 : £1.00

(B74-50029)

EMDX -- With orchestra. Secular cantatas
Horovitz, Joseph
[Horrortorio. Vocal score]. Horrortorio : a choral extravaganza for
SATB soli & chorus and orchestra / words by Alistair Sampson;
music by Joseph Horovitz. — Sevenoaks : Novello, 1974. — 43p ;
8vo.
£0.65

(B74-50375)

Lambert, Constant
The Rio Grande / by Constant Lambert ; the poem by Sacheverell
Sitwell. — London : Oxford University Press, 1974. — [1],51p ;
8vo.
Miniature score. — A reissue of the original publication of 1930.
ISBN 0-19-337303-3 : £1.30

(B74-50376)

Lang, Istvan
In memoriam N.N : cantata / by Istvan Lang ; to poems by Janos
Pilinszky. — London : Boosey and Hawkes, 1973. — 68p ; 8vo.
Duration 26-27 min.
£2.50

(B74-50030)

Orff, Carl
De temporum fine comoedia = Das Spiel vom Ende der Zeiten
Vigilia / [von] Carl Orff ; Interlinearversion von Werner Thomas ;
Übersetzung der griechischen Texte von Wolfgang Schadewaldt.
— Mainz ; London : Schott, 1974. — 192p ; 8vo.
Study score.
Unpriced

(B74-50933)

Rands, Bernard
Metalepsis Z : [cantata for mezzo-soprano solo, SATB and
orchestral accompaniment] / by Bernard Rands ; words by John
Wain. — London : Universal, 1974. — iv,28p ; obl 4to.
Unpriced

(B74-50377)

Tredici, David del
Pop-pourri : for soprano, rock group, chorus (SATB) and
orchestra / by Dick Tredici. — New York ; [London] : Boosey
and Hawkes, 1974. — 116p ; 8vo.
Unpriced

(B74-50934)

ENVXUDG — With trombones & strings. Ordinary of the Mass
Machaut, Guillaume de
La Messe de Nostre Dame : SATB, strings and two trombones /
by Guillaume de Machaut ; edited by Denis Stevens. — London :
Oxford University Press, 1973. — 32p ; 8vo.
ISBN 0-19-337395-5 : £0.75

(B74-50031)

ENXDD — With strings and keyboard. Oratorios
Carissimi, Giacome
[Jephte. Vocal score]. Jephte (Jephthah) : oratorio for SATB soli,
SSSATB chorus, optional strings without violas, and organ
continuo / revised and edited by Janet Beat. — Sevenoaks :
Novello, 1974. — 33p ; 8vo.
£0.55

(B74-50378)

ENYHXPNPDK — With brass & percussion septet. Anthems
Webb, Evelyn
Sing aloud unto God our strength : SATB chorus with three
trumpets, three trombones and timpani / by Evelyn Webb ; verses
selected from the Psalms and Isaiah. — London : Schott, 1973. —
obl. 4to.
Score (17p.) & chorus part.
£2.00

(B74-50032)

ENYLDE — With keyboard & percussion. Religious cantatas
Sansom, Clive A
Cantate rag : for S.A.T.B., piano and percussion / [by] Clive A.
Sansom. — London : Paterson, 1974. — 13p ; 8vo.
Duration 2 1/2 min.
Unpriced

(B74-50935)

ENYLDH — With percussion & keyboard. Motets, Anthems, Hymns, etc
Bernstein, Leonard
[Mass. *Gloria tibi: arr*]. Gloria tibi : for two-part chorus of treble
voices with tenor solo and piano and bongo accompaniment / by
Leonard Bernstein, text from the liturgy of the Roman mass. —
New York ; London : Amberson : Schirmer, 1973. — 8p ; 8vo.
Unpriced

(B74-50033)

ENYLDP/LF — With keyboard & percussion. Carols. Christmas
Stent, Keith
Two carols for the Caribbean / arranged for SATB piano and
percussion by Keith Stent. — Sevenoaks : Novello, 1974. — 12p ;
8vo.
Contents: 1: Angels from de realms of glory (traditional French melody) - 2:
Lulay thou liddle tiny chile (traditional English melody).
£0.24

(B74-50936)

ESSDE — With double bass. Religious cantatas
Dickinson, Peter
Winter afternoons : cantata for six solo voices and double bass /
music by Peter Dickinson ; words by Emily Dickinson. —
Sevenoaks : Novello, 1974. — 18p ; 8vo.
Duration 12 min.
£0.50

(B74-50937)

ESSPLRSDW — With double bass & accordion. Songs, etc
Boyd, Jack
Must I now = Muss i denn : German folk song / arranged for
SATB chorus with accordion and string bass or piano by Jack
Boyd. — New York : Warner ; [London] : [Blossom], 1974. —
12p ; 8vo.
Unpriced

(B74-50379)

ETQNSRDE — With three harps & organ. Religious cantatas
Panufnik, Andrzej
Universal prayer : for 4 solo voices, 3 harps, organ and mixed
chorus / by Andrzej Panufnik ; words by Alexander Pope. —
London : Boosey and Hawkes, 1973. — 63p ; 4to.
£4.50

(B74-50034)

ETSDE — With guitar. Religious cantatas
Surinach, Carlos
Via crucis : a cycle of fifteen saetas, for four-part chorus of mixed
voices and Spanish guitar / by Carlos Surinach ; guitar part edited
by Vladimir Bobri, text vignettes from the Bible (King James
version). — New York ; London : Associated Music, 1973. —
55p ; 4to.
Unpriced

(B74-50380)

ETSDP/LF — With guitar. Carols. Christmas
Dinham, Kenneth J
Three kings came to Bethlehem Town : solo, unison or two-part
(or mixed voices), [with accompaniment for guitar or piano ad
lib] / words and music by K.J. Dinham. — York : Banks, 1974.
— 3p ; 8vo.
Unpriced
Primary classification KE/TSDP/LF

ETWDU — With lute. Madrigals
Brown, Howard Mayer
Mon mary m'a diffamée : chanson, S.T.T. / edited by Howard
Mayer Brown; arrangement for lute (in A) by F. Spinacino. —
London : Oxford University Press, 1973. — 5p ; 8vo.
ISBN 0-19-341203-9 : Unpriced

(B74-50035)

EUMDM — With wind band. Hymns
Vaughan Williams, Ralph
The Old Hundreth Psalm tune ('All people that on earth do
dwell') / accompaniment by R. Vaughan Williams; [melody
attributed to L. Bourgeois] : anthem for unison or mixed (SATB)
choir accompanied by organ with band and/or orchestra ; band
arrangement by Robert Washburn. — New York ; [London] :
Oxford University Press, 1974. — 4to.
Score (12p.) & 59 parts.
Unpriced

(B74-50381)

EVRPLRDH — With flute & organ. Motets, Anthems, Hymns, etc
Geisler, Johann Christian
[Die Frucht des Geistes ist Liebe]. The fruit of the spirit is love =
Die Frucht des Geistes ist Liebe : SATB chorus, flute and organ /
[by] Johann Christian Geisler ; edited and arranged by Karl
Kroeger; German text from Galatians 5:22, English text adapted
by K.K. — Moramus ed. — [New York] ; [London] : Boosey and
Hawkes, 1974. — 15p ; 8vo.
The flute part is printed on p.14-15.
Unpriced

(B74-50382)

EVVPLVWDX — With clarinet & bassoon. Secular cantatas
Einem, Gottfried von
Die träumenden Knaben, Op.41 : Cantata für vierstimmigen
gemischten Chor, Klarinette und Fagott / von Gottfried von
Einem ; Worte von Oskar Kokoschka. — London : Boosey and
Hawkes, 1974. — 31p ; 8vo.
Unpriced

(B74-50383)

EWMDM/AY — With brass band. Hymns. Collections
Rutter, John
Two hymns of praise : with introductory fanfares / arranged for
mixed choir and brass ensemble with timpani, percussion ad lib,
and organ (or orchestra) by John Rutter. — London : Oxford
University Press.
Score (17p.) & voice part - Duration 5 1/2 min.
1 : Now thank we all our God / melody by J. Cruger. — 1974. — 8vo.
ISBN 0-19-367376-2 : £1.00

(B74-50938)

Rutter, John
Two hymns of praise : with introductory fanfares / arranged for
mixed choir and brass ensemble with timpani percussion ad lib.
and organ (or orchestra) by John Rutter. — London : Oxford
University Press.
Score (14p.) & voice part - Duration 6 min.
2 : All creatures of our God and king : melody from Geistliche
Kirchengesang (Köln 1623). — 1974. — 8vo.
ISBN 0-19-367359-2 : £1.10

(B74-50939)

EWNQDE — With brass sextet. Religious cantatas
Payne, Anthony
Phoenix mass : for mixed chorus, 3 trumpets and 3 trombones /
by Anthony Payne. — London : Chester : Hansen, 1974. — 54p ;
8vo.
'The use of three languages stems from the original liturgical function. As it
now stands, the work is a concert mass' - Composer's note. — Duration 20
min.
Unpriced

(B74-50940)

**EWNRDGNT — With brass quintet. Anglican liturgy. Morning
Prayer. Jubilate**
Saunders, Neil
Jubilate Deo : for 5-part chorus of mixed voices, [S.S.A.T.B.],
soprano and baritone soli and brass ensemble / by Neil Saunders.
— Wendover : Roberton, 1974. — 16p ; 8vo.
£0.20

(B74-50941)

EWNSDK — With brass quartet. Anthems
Tamblyn, William
You are Peter : [brass accompaniment, 3 trumpets and
trombone] / by William Tamblyn. — London : Boosey and
Hawkes, 1974. — 4pt ; 4to.
£0.40

(B74-50384)

EXXDW/X — With woodblock. Canons
Beethoven, Ludwig van
[Ta, ta, ta. G.205]. To Maelzel : for 4-part chorus of mixed voices
unaccompanied or with wood-block / [by] Ludwig van
Beethoven ; edited by Alfred Davis. — Wendover : Roberton,
1972. — 6p ; 8vo.
£0.12
Primary classification EZDW/X

(B74-50412)

EZ — UNACCOMPANIED CHORAL WORKS
EZDE — Religious cantatas
Joubert, John
Four stations on the road to freedom, Opus 73 : for SSAATTBB
soli or chorus (unaccompanied) / by John Joubert ; words by
Dietrich Bonhoeffer; translated by Frank Clarke. — Sevenoaks :
Novello, 1974. — 18p ; 8vo.
Duration 8 min.
Unpriced
Primary classification JNEZAYDE

(B74-50456)

Mews, Douglas
Ghosts, fire, water : for alto solo and unaccompanied mixed voices / by Douglas Mews ; words by James Kirkup. — London : Oxford University Press, 1974. — 12p ; 8vo.
Duration 10 min.
ISBN 0-19-343670-1 : £0.30

(B74-50036)

Wetzler, Robert
Trilogy of praise : for four-part chorus of mixed voices a cappella / by Robert Wetzler ; words by Herbert Brokering. — New York ; London : Schirmer, 1973. — 20p ; 8vo.
Unpriced

(B74-50037)

EZDG — Ordinary of the Mass
Rorem, Ned
Missa brevis : for mixed chorus unaccompanied / [by] Ned Rorem. — New York ; [London] : Boosey and Hawkes, 1974. — 25p ; 8vo.
Unpriced

(B74-50385)

EZDGKADD/LK — Stabat mater
Palestrina, Giovanni Pierluigi da
Stabat mater dolorosa : for eight voices / [by] G.P. da Palestrina ; edited and arranged for modern use by Henry Washington. — London : Chester, 1974. — 36p ; 8vo.
Duration 25 min.
Unpriced

(B74-50942)

EZDGKAF — Proper of the Mass. Offertory
Byrd, William
[Gradualia, lib.1. Sacerdotes Domini]. Sacerdotes Domini = Then did priests make offering : SATB / by William Byrd ; edited by R.R. Terry. — Revised ed. / by John Morehen. — London : Oxford University Press, 1973. — 3p ; 8vo.
ISBN 0-19-352008-7 : Unpriced

(B74-50038)

EZDH — Motets, Anthems, Hymns, etc
Allen, Peter
[Feed us now, O Son of God: arr]. Feed us now, O Son of God / by Peter Allen ; arranged for accompanied mixed chorus by Warren Swenson. — New York : Galaxy ; London : Galliard, 1974. — 9p ; 8vo.
Unpriced

(B74-50386)

Binkerd, Gordon
Eternitie : SSATB / by Gordon Binkerd ; poem by Robert Herrick. — New York ; [London] : Boosey and Hawkes, 1971. — 20p ; 8vo.
Unpriced

(B74-50943)

Eldridge, Guy
Hymn to God the Father : anthem for 4-part chorus of mixed voices SATB, unaccompanied / music by Guy Eldridge, words by John Donne. — Wendover : Roberton, 1974. — 8p ; 8vo.
£0.12

(B74-50387)

Hovhaness, Alan
Four motets. Op.268 : SATB a cappella / by Alan Hovhaness. — New York ; London : Associated Music.
1 : Blessed is the man that trusteth in the Lord; text from Jeremiah 17. — 1973. — 10p ; 8vo. —
£0.20

(B74-50388)
2 : Help, Lord, for the godly man ceaseth; text from Psalm 12. — 1973. — 7p ; 8vo. —
£0.15

(B74-50389)
3 : Lord, who shall abide in thy tabernacle? Text from Psalm 15. — 1973. — 12p ; 8vo. —
£0.20

(B74-50390)
4 : The fool hath said in his heart; text from Psalm 14. — 1973. — 8p ; 8vo. —
£0.15

(B74-50391)

Mendelssohn, Felix
[Deutsche Liturgie. Heilig]. Heilig = Holy holy holy : for double chorus of mixed voices a cappella / [by] Felix Mendelssohn ; edited by Maynard Klein, English text by M.K. — New York ; London : Schirmer, 1974. — 12p ; 8vo.
Unpriced

(B74-50944)

O'Neal, Barry
Lord have mercy : for four-part chorus of mixed voices a cappella / by Barry O'Neal. — New York ; London : Associated Music, 1973. — 6p ; 8vo.
Unpriced

(B74-50039)

Petrich, Roger
O wondrous type! : anthem for the Feast of the Transfiguration, SATB choir unaccompanied / [by] Roger Petrich ; text: Latin hymn, XV cent., translated by Neale. — New York ; [London] : Oxford University Press, 1974. — 6p ; 8vo.
Unpriced

(B74-50945)

Rubbra, Edmund
Blessed be he. Op. 147 : SATB / by Edmund Rubbra ; words by Georgina Cook. — Croydon : Lengnick, 1974. — 8p ; 8vo.
£0.12

(B74-50040)

Schutz, Heinrich
[Geistliche Chormusik. Verleih uns Frieden genadiglich]. Verleih uns Frieden genadiglich = Lord grant us peace : for five-part chorus of mixed voices a cappella / [by] Heinrich Schutz ; edited by Maynard Klein ; English text by M.K. — New York ; London : Schirmer, 1974. — 8p ; 8vo.
Unpriced

(B74-50946)

Walton, *Sir* William
Cantico del sole : for unaccompanied mixed voices / [by] William Walton ; [Italian words by] S. Francesco d'Assisi. — London : Oxford University Press, 1974. — 15p ; 8vo.
Duration 7 1/2 min.
ISBN 0-19-338490-6 : £0.50

(B74-50947)

EZDH/AYE — Motets, Anthems, Hymns, etc. Collections. Germany
Ameln, Konrad
Biblische Motetten : für das Kirchenjahr / herausgegeben von Konrad Ameln und Harald Kümmerling. — Cassel ; London : Bärenreiter.
Band 2 : Darstellung des Herrn bis Trinitas. — 1973. — 129p ; 8vo.
Unpriced

(B74-50392)

EZDH/LF — Motets, Anthems, Hymns, etc. Christmas
Le Fleming, Christopher
[3 Motets for Christmas. I sing of a maiden]. I sing of a maiden / music by Christopher le Fleming, words anon. — Wendover : Roberton, 1974. — 7p ; 8vo.
Unpriced

(B74-50948)

Le Fleming, Christopher
[Three motets for Christmas, nos.2,3]. Two motets for Christmas : SSATBB unaccompanied / by Christopher le Fleming. — Wendover : Roberton, 1974. — 12p ; 8vo.
Duration 3 min. — Contents: 1: The changing night (Grace Armitage) - 2: Cradle song (Arthur Fforde).
£0.16

(B74-50393)

O'Neal, Barry
Nativitie : SATB a cappella / by Barry O'Neal ; poem by John Donne. — New York ; London : Associated Music, 1973. — 12p ; 8vo.
Unpriced

(B74-50041)

EZDJ — Motets
Benjamin, Thomas
Adoramus te = We adore thee : SATB a cappella / by Thomas Benjamin. — New York ; London : Associated Music, 1973. — 9p ; 8vo.
Unpriced

(B74-50042)

Berkeley, Lennox
Three Latin motets : for five voices / [by] Lennox Berkeley. — London : Chester, 1974. — 24p ; 8vo.
Contents: 1: Eripe me, Domine - 2: Veni sponsa Christi - 3: Regina coeli laetare.
Unpriced

(B74-50394)

Byrd, William
[Liber primus sacrarum cantionum. Vigilate]. Vigilate = Be ye watchful : motet for five voices S.A.T.Ba.B. / by William Byrd ; edited by A. Ramsbotham, revised edition by John Morehen. — London : Oxford University Press, 1974. — 15p ; 8vo.
ISBN 0-19-352056-7 : £0.20

(B74-50395)

Croce, Giovanni
Exaudi Deus = Oh hear me Lord God : general motet, for four-part chorus of mixed voices a cappella / by Giovanni Croce ; edited by Maynard Klein, text from Psalm 143, English text by M.K. — New York ; London : Schirmer, 1973. — 4p ; 8vo.
Unpriced

(B74-50043)

Hassler, Hans Leo
[Cantiones sacrae. Verbum caro factum est]. Verbum caro factum
est = And the Word became flesh : motet for six-part chorus of
mixed voices a cappella / [by] Hans Leo Hassler ; edited by
Maynard Klein, adaptation of Scripture from John 1 by M.K. —
New York ; London : Schirmer, 1974. — 8p ; 8vo.
Unpriced

(B74-50949)

Josquin Des Prés
Tu solus, qui facis mirabilia : for four-part chorus of mixed voices
a cappella / by Josquin Desprez ; edited by George Hunter. —
New York ; London : Associated Music, 1973. — 12p ; 8vo.
Unpriced

(B74-50396)

Lasso, Orlando di
[Sacrae cantiones quatuor vocum. Jubilate Deo]. Jubilate Deo =
Sing to God : motet for four-part chorus of mixed voices a
cappella / by Orlando di Lasso ; edited by Maynard Klein, Psalm
100, English text by M.K. — New York ; London : Schirmer,
1973. — 8p ; 8vo.
Unpriced

(B74-50044)

Okeghem, Jean
Salve regina : for four-part chorus of mixed voices a cappella / by
Johannes Okeghem ; edited by George Hunter. — New York ;
London : Associated Music, 1973. — 28p ; 8vo.
Unpriced

(B74-50397)

Palestrina, Giovanni Pierluigi da
Alma redemptoris mater = Loving Mother of our Saviour : motet
for four-part chorus of mixed voices a cappella / [by] Giovanni
Pierluigi da Palestrina ; edited by Maynard Klein, English text by
M.K. — New York ; London : Schirmer, 1974. — 7p ; 8vo.
Unpriced

(B74-50950)

Perti, Giacomo Antonio
Adoramus te = We adore thee : motet for four-part chorus of
mixed voices a cappella / by Jacopo Perti; edited by Maynard
Klein, English text by M.K. — New York ; London : Schirmer,
1974. — 4p ; 8vo.
Unpriced

(B74-50951)

Scarlatti, Alessandro
[Exultate Deo]. Sing aloud with gladness = Exultate Deo : SATB
a cappella / [by] Alessandro Scarlatti ; transcribed with English
text by Robert McDowall ; text from Ps.81. — Croydon : Royal
School of Church Music, 1973. — 11p ; 8vo.
£0.32

(B74-50952)

Schütz, Heinrich
[Cantiones sacrae. In te Domine, speravi]. In te Domine, speravi
= Lord in thee do I put my trust : motet for four-part chorus of
mixed voices a cappella / by Heinrich Schutz ; edited by Maynard
Klein, text [from] Psalm 31. — New York ; London : Schirmer,
1973. — 11p ; 8vo.
Unpriced

(B74-50398)

Schütz, Heinrich
[Cantiones sacrae. Quoniam ad te clamabo, Domine]. Quoniam ad
te clamabo, Domine = Now behold to thee I cry, O Lord : motet
for four-part chorus of mixed voices a cappella / by Heinrich
Schutz ; edited by Maynard Klein; text from Psalm 5, English text
by M.K. — New York ; London : Chappell, 1973. — 8p ; 8vo.
Unpriced

(B74-50399)

Victoria, Tomàs Luis de
[Motecta. Ne timeas, Maria]. In venisti enim gratiam = You have
been acclaimed the chosen one. The Annunciation : for four-part
chorus of mixed voices a cappella / by Tomàs Luis de Victoria ;
edited by Maynard Klein, text from Luke 1; English text by M.K.
— New York ; London : Schirmer, 1973. — 8p ; 8vo.
Unpriced

(B74-50400)

Wesley, Samuel
[Works, motets. Selections]. Two motets / [by] Samuel Wesley ;
edited by John Marsh. — Sevenoaks : Novello, 1974. — 10p ;
8vo.
Contents: 1: Tu es sacerdos, for SATB unaccompanied - 2: Constitues eos
principes, for SATB unaccompanied.
£0.16

(B74-50401)

EZDJ/LF — Motets. Christmas
Handl, Jacob
[Tomus primis operis musici. *Hodie Christus natus est]*. Hodie
Christus natus est = Christ was born today : song, for full chorus
of mixed voices a cappella / by Jacob Handl ; voices edited by
Jerry Weseley Harris. — Wendover : Roberton, 1973. — 8p ; 8vo.
£0.10

(B74-50045)

Victoria, Tomàs Luis de
[Motecta. Quem vidistis pastores?]. Quem vidistis, pastores =
Whom did you see, kind shepherds? : Motet for Christmas time,
for six-part chorus of mixed voices a cappella / [by] Tomàs Luis
de Victoria ; edited by Maynard Klein, English text by M.K. —
London ; London : Chappell, 1973. — 8p ; 8vo.
Unpriced

(B74-50402)

EZDJ/LFP — Motets. Epiphany
Handl, Jacob
[Tomus primus operis musici. Omnes de Saba venient]. Omnes de
Saba venient : motet for Epiphany, SATTB unacc. / [by] Jacob
Handl ; edited by Andrew Parker. — London : Oxford University
Press, 1974. — 4p ; 8vo.
ISBN 0-19-350342-5 : £0.08

(B74-50403)

EZDJ/LG — Motets. Lent
Ingegneri, Marco Antonio
[Responsoria hebdomadae sanctae. Caligaverunt oculi mei].
Caligaverunt oculi mei = My eyes are blinded by my weeping :
Lenten motet for four-part chorus of mixed voices a cappella / by
Marco Antonio Ingegneri ; edited by Maynard Klein, English text
by M.K. — New York ; London : Schirmer, 1973. — 7p ; 8vo.
Unpriced
Primary classification FEZDGKH/LHL

(B74-50073)

EZDJ/LK — Motets. Good Friday
Victoria, Tomás Luis de
[Motecta. Vere languores nostres]. Vere languores nostres = Truly
our Saviour suffered : motet for four-part chorus of mixed voices a
cappella / [by] Tomás Luis de Victoria ; edited by Maynard
Klein, English text by M.K. — New York ; London : Schirmer,
1974. — 8p ; 8vo.
Unpriced

(B74-50953)

EZDJ/LM — Motets. Ascension
Marenzio, Luca
[Motectorum quarternis vocibus liber primus. O rex gloriae]. O
rex gloriae : motet for Ascension Day, SATB unacc. / [by] Luca
Marenzio ; edited by Andrew Parker. — London : Oxford
University Press, 1974. — 4p ; 8vo.
ISBN 0-19-350343-3 : £0.08

(B74-50404)

EZDK — Anthems
Amner, John
O Lord, of whom I do depend : the humble suit of a sinner,
SATB / by John Amner ; edited by Anthony J. Greening. —
Croydon : Royal School of Church Music, 1973. — 4p ; 8vo.
Unpriced

(B74-50046)

Chorbajian, John
When David heard that his son was slain : for full chorus of
mixed voices a cappella / [by] John Chorbajian; text from II
Samuel 18. — New York ; London : Schirmer, 1974. — 8p ; 8vo.
Unpriced

(B74-50954)

Tomkins, Thomas
Musica Deo sacra III / by Thomas Tomkins ; transcribed and
edited by Bernard Rose. — London : Stainer and Bell for the
British Academy, 1973. — xiii,273p ; 8vo.
Unpriced

(B74-50047)

Weelkes, Thomas
O Lord arise : anthem for seven voices, S.S.A.A.T.B.B. / by
Thomas Weelkes ; edited by Edmund H. Fellowes ; revised edition
by Roger Brag, [text from] Psalm 132 and Te Deum. — London :
Oxford University Press, 1974. — 10p ; 8vo.
ISBN 0-19-352126-1 : £0.20

(B74-50955)

Whitcomb, Robert
Great is the Lord : SATB a cappella / [by] Robert Whitcomb ;
words from Psalm 48. — New York ; London : Associated Music,
1974. — 11p ; 8vo.
Unpriced

(B74-50956)

EZDK/LM — Anthems. Ascension
Newbury, Kent A
Send forth thy spirit, O Lord : Ascension or general anthem, for
four-part chorus of mixed voices a cappella (or optional piano) /
[by] Kent A. Newbury. — New York ; London : Schirmer, 1974.
— 8p ; 8vo.
Unpriced

(B74-50957)

EZDP — Carols
Kechley, Gerald
Pleasure it is : for unaccompanied mixed chorus / by Gerald
Kechley ; based on the melody 'Es muss die ganze Christenschar'
by Burkard Waldis ; words by William Cornish. — New York :
Galaxy ; London : Galliard, 1971. — 8p ; 8vo.
Unpriced

(B74-50958)

EZDP/AYDKLM — Carols. Collections. Celtic
Gomer, Llywelyn
Four Celtic Christmas carols : for four-part chorus of mixed
voices (a cappella) / arranged by Llywelyn Gomer. — New
York ; London : Schirmer, 1973. — 17p ; 8vo.
Unpriced

(B74-50048)

EZDP/LEZ — Carols. Advent
Hilty, Everett Jay
O come, O come Emmanuel = Veni Emmanuel : Advent anthem
for unison or 2-part mixed chorus and organ / arranged by
Everett Jay Hilty; words, Latin, translated by Neale, final verse
from Henry Sloan Coffin. — New York ; London : Oxford
University Press, 1971. — 4p ; 8vo.
Unpriced
Primary classification JDP/LEZ

(B74-50444)

EZDP/LF — Carols. Christmas
Bent, Margaret
Two songs for Christmas / edited by Margaret Bent; texts edited
by John Stevens. — London : Oxford University Press, 1974. —
8p ; 8vo.
Text of no.2 in Latin. — Contents: 1: Glad and blithe: AT - 2: Gaude terra
tenebrom: A.T.T..
ISBN 0-19-341208-x : Unpriced

(B74-50405)

Brahms, Johannes
[Songs of Ophelia, nos. 3, 4]. Christmas cradle song / music by
Johannes Brahms; arranged for soprano solo and SATBB
unaccompanied by Stephen Wilkinson, fresh words by Richard
Rowlands and Coelius Sedulius. — Sevenoaks : Novello, 1974. —
8p ; 8vo.
Unpriced

(B74-50959)

Butterworth, Neil
Christmas day : SATB unacc. / by Neil Butterworth ; words by
Andrew Young. — York : Banks, 1974. — 4p ; 8vo.
Unpriced

(B74-50960)

Carter, Andrew
Down in yon forest : English traditional carol, SSAATBB unacc /
arr Andrew Carter. — York : Banks, 1974. — 5p ; 8vo.
Unpriced

(B74-50961)

Dinham, Kenneth J
O my lord : negro spiritual / arr. SATB (unacc.) [by] K.J.
Dinham ; Christmas words by K.J. Dinham ; alternative [and
original] words for other seasons. — York : Banks, 1974. — 6p ;
8vo.
Unpriced
Also classified at EZDW/LC

(B74-50962)

Glarum, Leonard Stanley
The bells do ring : based on a French tune for four-part chorus of
mixed voices with optional handbells / arranged by L. Stanley
Glarum ; words by Steuart Wilson. — New York ; London :
Schirmer, 1974. — 8p ; 8vo.
Unpriced

(B74-50963)

McCabe, John
Upon the high midnight : three nativity carols for SATB soli and
chorus (unaccompanied) / [by] John McCabe. — Sevenoaks :
Novello, 1974. — 26p ; 8vo.
Unpriced

(B74-50964)

Owen, David
Welcome Yule : SATB unacc. / by David Owen ; words anon. —
London : Oxford University Press, 1973. — 4p ; 8vo.
The sixteen-year old composer of this carol was awarded a prize in The
Bach Choir 1973 Carol Competition.
ISBN 0-19-343044-4 : Unpriced

(B74-50049)

Parkinson, John Alfred
Why this haste, O shepherd, say : old French noël / arranged
SSATB unacc. by John A. Parkinson; English words by J.A.P. —
London : Oxford University Press, 1974. — 3p ; 8vo.
ISBN 0-19-343047-9 : £0.08

(B74-50965)

Payne, Mary Monroe
In Bethlehem, that fair city : Christmas carol for mixed chorus
unaccompanied / by Mary Payne; words 15th century. — New
York ; London : Oxford University Press, 1971. — 4p ; 8vo.
Unpriced

(B74-50406)

Popplewell, Richard
There is no rose : solo voice and SSAATTBB unacc / [by]
Richard Popplewell ; [words] anon. — York : Banks, 1974. —
3p ; 8vo.
Unpriced

(B74-50966)

Shaw, Martin
[I sing of a Maiden : arr]. I sing of a Maiden / by Martin Shaw ;
arranged SATB unaccompanied by Milburn Price, 15th century
English words. — New York ; [London] : Oxford University
Press, 1970. — 4p ; 8vo.
Unpriced

(B74-50967)

Stevens, Gillian
This endris night : SATB unacc. / [by] Gillian Stevens ; [words]
anon. — York : Banks, 1974. — 2p ; 8vo.
Unpriced

(B74-50968)

Whitter, Mark
A carol for Mary : SATB unacc. / by Mark Whitter ; words
anon. — London : Oxford University Press, 1973. — 2p ; 8vo.
The nine-year old composer of this carol was awarded a prize in the Bach
Choir 1973 Carol Competition.
ISBN 0-19-343043-6 : £0.05

(B74-50050)

EZDP/LF/AY — Carols. Christmas. Collections
Carter, Andrew
Two traditional carols : SATB unacc. / arranged by Andrew
Carter. — York : Banks, 1974. — 4p ; 8vo.
Contents: Benidicamus Domino - The holly and the ivy.
Unpriced

(B74-50969)

EZDP/LF/AYH — Carols. Christmas. Collections. France
Ratcliffe, Desmond
Eight for Christmas : French carols with English words /
harmonized for SATB by Desmond Ratcliffe. — Sevenoaks :
Novello, 1974. — 8p ; 8vo.
Unpriced

(B74-50970)

EZDR — Psalms
Schütz, Heinrich
[Cantiones sacrae. Deus misereatur nostri]. Deus misereatur nostri
= God be merciful unto us : for four-part chorus of mixed voices
a cappella / by Heinrich Schutz ; edited by Maynard Klein, text:
Psalm 67, English text by M.K. — New York ; London :
Schirmer, 1973. — 8p ; 8vo.
Unpriced

(B74-50407)

Waters, James
Psalm 31 : for four-part chorus of mixed voices a cappella / [by]
James Waters. — New York ; London : Schirmer, 1974. — 11p ;
8vo.
Unpriced

(B74-50971)

Wyner, Yehudi
Psalm 143 : full chorus of mixed voices a cappella, SAATTB / by
Yehudi Wyner. — New York ; London : Associated Music, 1973.
— 20p ; 8vo.
Unpriced

(B74-50051)

EZDR/LL — Psalms. Easter
Kameke, Ernst Ulrich von
Osterpsalm für gemischten Chor / von Ernst-Ulrich von Kameke.
— Cassel ; [London] : Bärenreiter, 1973. — 8p ; 8vo.
£0.75

(B74-50408)

EZDU — Madrigals

Lasso, Orlando di
[Libro de villanelle. *S'io fusse ciaul*]. S'io fusse ciaul = Were I a tiny bird : canzonetta, for four-part chorus of mixed voices a cappella / by Orlando di Lasso ; edited by Maynard Klein, English text by M.K. — New York ; London : Schirmer, 1972. — 7p ; 8vo.
Unpriced

(B74-50052)

Lasso, Orlando di
[Libro de villanelle. *Tutto lo di mi dici 'Canta'*]. Tutto lo di mi dici 'Canta' = Day after day they all say 'Sing' : canzonetta, for four-part chorus of mixed voices a cappella / by Orlandi di Lasso ; edited by Maynard Klein, English text by M.K. — New York ; London : Schirmer, 1972. — 8p ; 8vo.
Unpriced

(B74-50053)

Lasso, Orlando di
[Newe teutsche Lieder mit vier Stimmen. *Ich waiss mir en Meidlein*]. Ich waiss mir Meidlein = I know a fair maiden : madrigal, for four-part chorus of mixed voices a cappella / by Orlando di Lasso ; edited by Maynard Klein, English text by M.K. — New York ; London : Schirmer, 1972. — 6p ; 8vo.
Unpriced

(B74-50054)

Manchicourt, Pierre de
Nine chansons : for four voices or instruments / [by] Pierre de Manchicourt ; edited by Bernard Thomas. — London : London Pro musica, 1974. — 20p ; 4to.
Unpriced
Also classified at LNS

(B74-50972)

Vasquez, Juan
[Recopilacion de sonetos y villancicos. *En la fuente del rosel*]. En la fuente del rosel = 'Neath the rosebush in the stream : for four-part chorus of mixed voices a cappella / by Juan Vasquez ; edited by Marlin Merrill, English translation by M.M. — Wendover : Roberton, 1968. — 7p ; 8vo.
£0.10

(B74-50055)

EZDU/AYH — Madrigals. Collections. France

Thomas, Bernard
Twelve chansons (c.1530) : for four instruments or voices / edited by Bernard Thomas. — London : Pro Musica, 1973. — 16p ; 4to.
Unpriced
Primary classification LNS

(B74-50124)

EZDW — Songs, etc

Allcock, Stephen
Three almanack verses : SATB / by Stephen Allcock ; verses by Samuel Danforth I. — New York ; [London] : Boosey and Hawkes, 1971. — 15p ; 8vo.
Unpriced

(B74-50973)

Bailey, Leon
A shanty sequence : for 4-part chorus of mixed voices unaccompanied / arranged by Leon Bailey. — Wendover : Roberton, 1973. — 23p ; 8vo.
Staff & tonic sol-fa notation.
£0.26

(B74-50056)

Binkerd, Gordon
The lamb : SATB / by Gordon Binkerd ; poem by William Blake. — New York ; [London] : Boosey and Hawkes, 1971. — 8p ; 8vo.
Unpriced

(B74-50974)

Blacher, Boris
Vokalisen für Kammerchor / von Boris Blacher. — London : Boosey and Hawkes, 1974. — 24p ; 8vo.
Duration 12 min. — Nos 2 and 4 are for female and male voices respectively.
£0.30

(B74-50057)

Calder, Robert
Pity me not : SATB a cappella / by Robert Calder ; words by Edna St. Vincent Millay. — New York ; London : Associated Music, 1973. — 7p ; 8vo.
Unpriced

(B74-50058)

Chorbajian, John
Dark house : for full chorus of mixed voices a cappella / [by] John Chorbajian ; words by Alfred, Lord Tennyson (from 'In memoriam A.H.H.'). — New York ; London : Schirmer, 1974. — 8p ; 8vo.
Unpriced

(B74-50975)

Chorbajian, John
The silver swan : for full chorus of mixed voices a cappella / [by] John Chorbajian; words anonymous (Elizabethan). — New York ; London : Schirmer, 1974. — 4p ; 8vo.
Unpriced

(B74-50976)

Corigliano, John
A black November turkey : for four-part chorus of mixed voices with soprano and alto solos a cappella / by John Corigliano ; words by Richard Wilbur. — New York ; London : Schirmer, 1974. — 12p ; 8vo.
Unpriced

(B74-50059)

Corigliano, John
L'Invitation au voyage : for four-part chorus of mixed voices with soprano, alto, tenor, and bass solos a cappella / [by] John Corigliano ; words by Charles Baudelaire, translation Richard Wilbur. — New York ; London : Schirmer, 1974. — 11p ; 8vo.
Unpriced

(B74-50977)

Gay, John
[Beggar's opera. Selections: arr]. Four songs from the Beggar's Opera / by John Gay ; arranged for unaccompanied mixed chorus by Gregor Medinger. — New York ; [London] : Oxford University Press, 1971. — 8p ; 8vo.
Unpriced

(B74-50978)

Hopkins, Ewart
Metyelitsa : SATB unaccompanied Russian folk song / arranged by Ewart Hopkins; translation by Geoffrey Brace. — Aylesbury : Roberton, 1974. — 4p ; 8vo.
Duration 2 1/2 min. — Staff & tonic sol-fa notation.
£0.07

(B74-50410)

Kent, Richard
Here's Jupiter : SATB a capella (or improvised rock accompaniment ad lib.) / by Richard Kent ; lyric by Burt Shepherd. — New York : Warner ; [London] : [Blossom], 1971. — 12p ; 8vo.
Unpriced

(B74-50979)

Peuerl, Paul
[Weltspiegel. *O Musika du edle Kunst*]. O Musica, thou noble art : for five-part chorus of mixed voices a cappella / by Paul Peuerl ; edited by Leonard Van Camp, English text by L.V.C. — Wendover : Roberton, 1973. — 7p ; 8vo.
£0.10

(B74-50060)

Rose, Gregory
Animals etcetera : unaccompanied voices, 4-part / words and music by Gregory Rose. — London : Boosey and Hawkes, 1973. — 3p ; 8vo.
£0.05

(B74-50061)

Rutter, John
Five childhood lyrics : for unaccompanied mixed voices / by John Rutter. — London : Oxford University Press, 1974. — 28p ; 8vo.
ISBN 0-19-343716-3 : £0.80

(B74-50980)

Stoker, Richard
The glory of the dove : for S.A., T.B., or SATB (unaccompanied) / words and music by Richard Stoker. — London : Ashdown, 1974. — 8p ; 8vo.
Unpriced
Also classified at FEZDW; GEZDW

(B74-50409)

Stoker, Richard
A supplication : for SAB unaccompanied / by Richard Stoker ; words by Sir Thomas Wyatt. — London : Ashdown, 1974. — 8p ; 8vo.
£0.12

(B74-50062)

Sutcliffe, James H
Love will find out the way : English folk song / arranged for four-part chorus of mixed voices a cappella by James H. Sutcliffe. — Wendover : Roberton, 1966. — 7p ; 8vo.
£0.10

(B74-50063)

Woolf, Gregory
A time's passing : SATB a cappella / by Gregory Woolf ; words by John Dryden. — New York ; London : Associated Music, 1973. — 8p ; 8vo.
Unpriced

(B74-50064)

Yannatos, James
Three settings of E.E. Cummings / by James Yannatos. — New York ; London : Associated Music.
Nos 1 and 2 classified at GEZDW and FEZDW respectively.
3 : In just- : SSATB a cappella. — 1972. — 5p ; 8vo.
Unpriced

(B74-50065)

EZDW/AY — Songs, etc. Collections
Hughes, Donald Jefferson
Loth to depart : eleven songs for mixed voices / edited by Donald J. Hughes. — London : Oxford University Press, 1974. — 36p ; 8vo.
ISBN 0-19-330492-9 : £0.35

(B74-50411)

EZDW/LC — Spirituals
Dinham, Kenneth J
O my lord : negro spiritual / arr. SATB (unacc.) [by] K.J. Dinham ; Christmas words by K.J. Dinham ; alternative [and original] words for other seasons. — York : Banks, 1974. — 6p ; 8vo.
Unpriced
Primary classification EZDP/LF

EZDW/X — Canons
Beethoven, Ludwig van
[Ta, ta, ta. G.205]. To Maelzel : for 4-part chorus of mixed voices unaccompanied or with wood-block / [by] Ludwig van Beethoven ; edited by Alfred Davis. — Wendover : Roberton, 1972. — 6p ; 8vo.
£0.12
Also classified at EXXDW/X

(B74-50412)

EZDX — Secular cantatas
Washburn, Robert
Spring cantata : SATB / [by] Robert Washburn. — New York ; [London] : Boosey and Hawkes.
I : The succession of the four sweet months / words adapted from Robert Herrick. — 1974. — 8p ; 8vo.
Unpriced

(B74-50981)

II : April / words adapted from John Greenleaf Whittier. — 1974. — 8p ; 8vo.
Unpriced

(B74-50982)

III : May / words adapted from Richard Edwardes. — 1974. — 12p ; 8vo.
Unpriced

(B74-50983)

IV : Lazy June / words by Robert Washburn. — 1974. — 8p ; 8vo. —
Unpriced

(B74-50984)

V : July / words adapted from Thomas Dekker. — 1974. — 12p ; 8vo.
Unpriced

(B74-50985)

F — FEMALE VOICES, CHILDREN'S VOICES
FDE — Religious cantatas
Pert, Morris
[Missa festiva. Vocal score]. Missa festiva : for two-part choir, (upper voices), and orchestra / by Morris Pert. — London : Oxford University Press, 1973. — 24p ; 8vo.
Duration 19 min. — Not a mass as such; English and Latin words from various sources.
ISBN 0-19-337830-2 : £0.60

(B74-50066)

FDG — Ordinary of the Mass
Maria of the Cross, *Sister*
Mass for peace : for choir in two parts and organ / [by] Sister Maria of the Cross. — New York ; [London] : Oxford University Press, 1974. — 7p ; 8vo.
Unpriced

(B74-50986)

FDGPP — Anglican liturgy. Evening Prayer
Sumsion, Herbert
Magnificat and Nunc dimittis in D : for boys' voices / by Herbert Sumsion. — Croydon : Royal School of Church Music, 1972. — 12p ; 8vo.
Unpriced

(B74-50067)

FDH — Motets, Anthems, Hymns, etc
Vivaldi, Antonio
[Magnificat. Esurientes implevit. Vocal score]. He hath filled the hungry = Esurientes implevit : for two-part chorus of treble voices, [s.A.] / by Antonio Vivaldi ; edited [with piano accompaniment] by Jerry Weseley Harris ; English text by J.W.H. — Wendover : Roberton, 1974. — 7p ; 8vo.
£0.12

(B74-50987)

FDH/AY — Motets, Anthems, Hymns, etc. Collections
Ledger, Philip
Anthems for choirs. — London : Oxford University Press.
Vol.1 is edited by Francis Jackson.
2 : Twenty-four anthems for sopranos & altos (unison and two-part) / edited by Philip Ledger. — 1973. — 4,108p ; 8vo.
ISBN 0-19-353240-9 : Unpriced

(B74-50068)

3 : Twenty-four anthems for sopranos & altos (three or more parts) / edited by Philip Ledger. — 1973. — 9,100p ; 8vo.
ISBN 0-19-353242-5 : Unpriced

(B74-50069)

FDH/LF — Motets, Anthems, Hymns, etc. Christmas
Schütz, Heinrich
Heute ist Christus der Herr geboren = Jesus our Lord on this day was born : motet for Christmas, for three-part chorus of women's voices with continuo (or piano) accompaniment / by Heinrich Schutz ; edited by Maynard Klein, English text by M.K. — New York ; London : Schirmer, 1973. — 15p ; 8vo.
Unpriced

(B74-50413)

FDP/LF — Carols. Christmas
Blake, Leonard
[Carol of the sun. *Vocal score*]. Carol of the sun : for two-part or unison chorus / by Leonard Blake ; words by William Austin. — Wendover : Roberton, 1974. — 6p ; 8vo.
Staff & tonic sol-fa notation.
£0.10
Also classified at JDP/LF

(B74-50414)

Schubart, Christian Friedrich David
The shepherds' carol : old German Weihnachtslied / melody by C.F.D. Schubart : arranged, S.S.A. by Brian Trant ; [words] translated by Brian Trant. — York : Banks, 1974. — 4p ; 8vo.
Attributed to Schubart in this publication. In fact, the words only from C.F.D. Schubart's 'Musikalische Rhapsodien'.
Unpriced

(B74-50988)

Wilcock, Anthea
Christus natus est : [unison with descant] / words and music by Anthea Wilcock. — London : Chappell, 1974. — 4p ; 4to.
Unpriced

(B74-50989)

FDP/LF/AYK — Carols. Christmas. Collections. Spain
Hudson, Hazel
The shepherds : a Spanish Christmas carol sequence for voices with optional parts for guitar, tuned and untuned percussion and piano / by Hazel Hudson ; arranged from traditional Spanish folk tunes with English words by Hazel Hudson. — London : Ashdown, 1974. — 32p ; 8vo.
The pianoforte part is optional but preferable.
£0.40

(B74-50415)

FDW — Songs, etc
Brown, Christopher
Strawberry fair : two-part / English folk-song arranged by Christopher Brown. — London : Oxford University Press, 1974. — 4p ; 8vo.
ISBN 0-19-341509-7 : £0.08

(B74-50990)

Clements, John
Come, dark-eyed sleep : S.S.C. and pianoforte / music by John Clements; words by Michael Field. — London : Ashdown, 1974. — 5p ; 8vo.
Duration 2 1/4 min.
£0.10

(B74-50416)

Dexter, Harry
The crawdad song : based on a folksong from the Kentucky Mountains / arranged for two-part singing by Harry Dexter. — London : Ashdown, 1974. — 7p ; 8vo.
£0.12

(B74-50417)

Dexter, Harry
The peanut song : an adaptation of a popular American folksong / arranged for two-part singing by Harry Dexter. — London : Ashdown, 1974. — 7p ; 8vo.
Duration 2 min.
£0.12

(B74-50418)

Habash, John Mitri
Adam's apple : SSA / composed and arranged by John Mitri Habash and Arnold Freed. — New York ; [London] : Robbins, 1971. — 9p ; 8vo.
Unpriced

(B74-50991)

Habash, John Mitri
The sea of life : SSA / composed and arranged by John Mitri
Habash and Arnold Freed. — New York ; [London] : Robbins,
1971. — 8p ; 8vo.
Unpriced

(B74-50992)

Habash, John Mitri
Silent spring : SSA / composed and arranged by John Mitri
Habash and Arnold Freed. — New York ; [London] : Robbins,
1971. — 8p ; 8vo.
Unpriced

(B74-50993)

Habash, John Mitri
Smokey smokestack : SSA / composed and arranged by John
Mitri Habash and Arnold Freedman. — New York ; [London] :
Robbins, 1971. — 8p ; 8vo.
Unpriced

(B74-50994)

Hogben, Dorothy
The four sisters : part-song for SSA and piano / by Dorothy
Hogben. — London : Oxford University Press, 1974. — 10p ; 8vo.
Unpriced

(B74-50419)

Hudson, Hazel
Mary Ann - Jamaica farewell : a quodlibet for two-part singing
with piano accompaniment and optional parts for percussion [with
or without] descant recorder / arranged from West Indian folk
songs by Hazel Hudson. — London : Ashdown, 1973. — 11p ;
8vo.
Duration 2 min.
£0.10

(B74-50070)

Josephs, Wilfred
Happitaphs. Op.81 : 12 happy epitaphs for children's or adult
voices and piano / by Wilfred Josephs. — London : Boosey and
Hawkes, 1973. — 13p ; 8vo.
£0.30

(B74-50071)

Merrill, Marlin
Let it be forgotten : for mixed chorus (SSAATB) or treble chorus
(SSAA) and piano / by Marlin Merrill ; poems by Sara Teasdale.
— New York ; London : Oxford University Press, 1972. — 6p ;
4to.
Unpriced
Primary classification DW

(B74-50361)

Nelson, Havelock
The king's daughter : SA and piano / by Havelock Nelson ; words
by John O' the North. — [South Croydon] : Lengnick, 1974. —
6p ;
£0.12

(B74-50420)

Plumstead, Mary
Slowly : three-part women's voices and piano / by Mary
Plumstaed ; words by James Reeves. — London : Boosey and
Hawkes, 1974. — 4p ; 8vo.
Unpriced

(B74-50421)

Rossini, Gioachino Antonio
Duets for two cats : for 2-part chorus of female voices or SA duet
with piano / by Gioachino Rossini; edited by Alfred Davis. —
Wendover : Roberton, 1972. — 7p ; 8vo.
Ascribed to Rossini in this publication. Probably the work of Robert Lucas
Pearsall, composed under the pseudonym of G. Berthold.
£0.12
Also classified at JNFEDW

(B74-50422)

Willson, Meredith
[The music man. Goodnight, my someone. *Vocal score: arr*].
Goodnight, my someone / [by] Meredith Willson ; arranged for
women's chorus (SSA) with piano by Gerald Myrow. — Boston ;
London : Frank Music, 1974. — 8vo.
Unpriced

(B74-50995)

FDW/G/AY — Folk songs. Collections
Cammin, Heinz
Lied über die Grenze : Folklore fremder Länder für drei gleiche
Stimmen mit Begleitung / bearbeitet von Heinz Cammin. —
Mainz ; London : Schott.
Heft II. — 1974. — 32p ; 8vo. —
£2.61

(B74-50996)

FDW/LC — Spirituals
Dexter, Harry
Joshua fought the battle of Jericho : negro spiritual / arranged for
two-part singing with piano accompaniment by Harry Dexter. —
London : Ashdown, 1974. — 10p ; 8vo.
Unpriced

(B74-50423)

Dexter, Harry
Listen to the lambs : negro spiritual / arranged for two-part
singing by Harry Dexter. — London : Ashdown, 1974. — 6p ;
8vo.
£0.12

(B74-50072)

Hudson, Hazel
Behold that star ... Rise up, shepherd an' foller! : a quodlibet /
arranged, from negro spirituals, for treble and alto or tenor and
bass or treble and bass with optional parts for descant recorders
and percussion by Hazel Hudson. — London : Ashdown, 1974. —
8p ; 8vo.
£0.12
Also classified at GDW/LC; DW/LC

(B74-50997)

FDW/LF — Songs. Christmas
Rocherolle, Eugenie R
Christmas child : for unison, SA or SAB chorus and piano /
words and music by Eugenie R. Rocherolle. — New York :
Warner ; London : Blossom, 1974. — 15p ; 8vo.
Unpriced
Primary classification JDW/LF

(B74-50448)

FDX — Secular cantatas
Panufnik, Andrzej
Thames pageant : a cantata for young players and singers / music
by Andrzej Panufnik; words by Camilla Jessel. — London :
Boosey and Hawkes, 1974. — 162p ; 4to.
Includes a piano reduction printed beneath the full score.
£1.50
Primary classification FE/MDX

(B74-50424)

Withams, Eric L
The horse of wood : a pop-style cantata / music and text by Eric
L. Withams. — London : Universal, 1974. — 8vo.
Score (48p.) & part.
Unpriced

(B74-50998)

FE/MDX — With orchestra. Secular cantatas
Panufnik, Andrzej
Thames pageant : a cantata for young players and singers / music
by Andrzej Panufnik; words by Camilla Jessel. — London :
Boosey and Hawkes, 1974. — 162p ; 4to.
Includes a piano reduction printed beneath the full score.
£1.50
Also classified at FDX

(B74-50424)

FE/NYJNRDW — With strings & percussion quintet. Songs, etc
Cole, Bruce
Autumn cicada : ko-uta on four Japanese texts, [for] SSA, harp
and 4 handbells / [by] Bruce Cole ; translation by Geoffrey
Bownas and Anthony Thwaite. — London : Boosey and Hawkes,
1974. — 8p ; 8vo.
£0.10

(B74-50427)

FE/TQDPDE/LF — With harp. Carol cantatas. Christmas
Rutter, John
Dancing day : a cycle of traditional Christmas carols / arranged
for S.S.A. voices and harp (or piano) by John Rutter. — London :
Oxford University Press, 1974. — 46p ; 8vo.
Duration 22 min.
ISBN 0-19-338065-x : £1.50

(B74-50999)

FE/TQPLTSDH — With harp & guitar. Motets, Anthems, Hymns,
etc
Argento, Dominick
Tria carmina paschalia : for women's voices (SSA) harp and guitar
(or harpsichord / by Dominick Argento. — New York ;
[London] : Boosey and Hawkes, 1971. — 30p ; 8vo.
Unpriced

(B74-51000)

FE/TSDP/LF — With guitar. Carols. Christmas
Dinham, Kenneth J
Three kings came to Bethlehem Town : solo, unison or two-part
(or mixed voices), [with accompaniment for guitar or piano ad
lib] / words and music by K.J. Dinham. — York : Banks, 1974.
— 3p ; 8vo.
Unpriced
Primary classification KE/TSDP/LF

FE/VRPLXTQSDX — With flute & marimba. Secular cantatas
Nystedt, Knut
Suoni. Op.62 : for flute, marimba and full chorus of women's voices / by Knut Nystedt. — New York ; London : Associated Music, 1972. — 16p ; 8vo.
Unpriced

(B74-50425)

FE/XNDW/XC — With percussion ensemble. Rounds
Sound in the round. — London : National Federation of Women's Institutes, 1974. — 17p ; obl. 4to.
ISBN 0-900556-42-0 : £0.15

(B74-50426)

FE/XXDW/X — With woodblock. Canons
Beethoven, Ludwig van
[Ta, ta, ta. K.-H 162]. To Maelzel : for 4-part chorus of female voices unaccompanied or with wood-block / by Ludwig van Beethoven ; edited by Alfred Davis. — Wendover : Roberton, 1972. — 6p ; 8vo.
£0.10
Primary classification FEZDW/X

(B74-50432)

FEZDGKH/LHL — Unaccompanied voices. Roman liturgy. Divine Office. Tenebrae
Ingegneri, Marco Antonio
[Responsoria hebdomadae sanctae. Caligaverunt oculi mei]. Caligaverunt oculi mei = My eyes are blinded by my weeping : Lenten motet for four-part chorus of mixed voices a cappella / by Marco Antonio Ingegneri ; edited by Maynard Klein, English text by M.K. — New York ; London : Schirmer, 1973. — 7p ; 8vo.
Unpriced
Also classified at EZDJ/LG

(B74-50073)

Victoria, Tomas Luis de
[Officium hebdomadie sanctae. Tenebrae factae sunt]. Tenebrae factae sunt = Darkness was o'er the earth : Passion motet for four-part chorus of women's voices a cappella / by Tomas Luis de Victoria ; edited by Maynard Klein, English text by M.K.. — New York ; London : Chappell, 1974. — 8p ; 8vo.
Unpriced

(B74-50428)

FEZDGPQ — Unaccompanied female voices, children's voices. Anglican liturgy. Evening Prayers. Magnificat
Russell, Carlton T
Magnificat : for three-part chorus of women's voices a cappella / [by] Carlton T. Russell. — New York ; London : Schirmer, 1974. — 8p ; 8vo.
Unpriced

(B74-51001)

FEZDH — Motets, Anthems, Hymns, etc
Nelson, Havelock
Come down, O love divine : anthem for SSA (unaccompanied) suitable for Whitsun or general use / by Havelock Nelson ; words by Bianco da Siena, translated by R.F. Littledale. — Sevenoaks : Elkin, 1973. — 4p ; 8vo.
£0.07

(B74-50074)

FEZDJ/LF — Unaccompanied female voices, children's voices. Motets. Christmas
Hannahs, Roger C
Two Christmas motets : SSA a cappella / [by] Roger C. Hannahs. — New York ; London : Associated Music.
1 : When all the world - introit in Christmas-tide. — 1974. — 8p ; 8vo. — Unpriced

(B74-51002)

Hannahs, Roger C
Two Christmas motets : SSA a cappella / [by] Roger C. Hannahs. — New York ; London : Associated Music.
2 : A hallowed day - alleluia for Christmas Day. — 1974. — 8p ; 8vo. — Unpriced

(B74-51003)

FEZDP/LF — Unaccompanied female voices, children's voices. Carols. Christmas
Shirley, Nancy
Infant holy : Polish carol / arranged for four-part chorus of treble voices (SSAA) a cappella by Nancy Shirley. — Wendover : Roberton, 1968. — 4p ; 8vo.
£0.07

(B74-50075)

FEZDW — Unaccompanied voices. Songs, etc
Binkerd, Gordon
Hope is the thing with feathers : SSAA / by Gordon Binkerd ; poem by Emily Dickinson. — New York ; [London] : Boosey and Hawkes, 1971. — 16p ; 8vo.
Unpriced

(B74-51004)

Binkerd, Gordon
Infant joy : SSAA / by Gordon Binkerd ; poem by William Blake. — New York ; [London] : Boosey and Hawkes, 1971. — 12p ; 8vo.
Unpriced

(B74-51005)

Blyton, Carey
Ladies only. Op.58 : five songs for SSA unaccompanied / by Carey Blyton. — Sevenoaks : Novello, 1974. — 8vo.
Unpriced

(B74-51006)

Kennedy, John Brodbin
Lala and la : SSA / by John Brodbin Kennedy ; poem by John Garrigue. — New York ; [London] : Boosey and Hawkes, 1971. — 8p ; 8vo.
Unpriced

(B74-51007)

Kennedy, John Brodbin
Two reflections : SSA unaccompanied / by John Brodbin Kennedy ; poem by Samuel Menashe. — New York ; [London] : Boosey and Hawkes, 1971. — 7p ; 8vo.
Contents: 1. Lament - 2. Brigand heart.
Unpriced

(B74-51008)

Stoker, Richard
The glory of the dove : for S.A., T.B., or SATB (unaccompanied) / words and music by Richard Stoker. — London : Ashdown, 1974. — 8p ; 8vo.
Unpriced
Primary classification EZDW

(B74-50409)

Trant, Brian
The riddle song : a folk-song from Kentucky, SSA (S.solo) unacc. / arranged by Brian Trant. — London : Oxford University Press, 1974. — 4p ; 8vo.
ISBN 0-19-342595-5 : Unpriced

(B74-50429)

Walker, Robert
Three early English lyrics : for SSAA unaccompanied chorus / by Robert Walker. — London : Weinberger, 1974. — 7p ; 8vo.
Contents: 1: How long this night is/ anon: early 13th century - 2: Fowles in the frith/ anon: late 13th century - 3: Nowe welcome somer/Geoffrey Chaucer.
£0.15

(B74-50430)

Whitecotton, Shirley
Two idylls : for unaccompanied women's chorus, (SSA) / by Shirley Whitecotton. — New York : Galaxy ; London : Galliard, 1974. — 4p ; 8vo.
Contents: 1: The skylark/ (Christina Rossetti) - 2: A pressed flower/ (James Russell Lowell).
Unpriced

(B74-50431)

Yannatos, James
Three settings of E.E. Cummings / by James Yannatos. — New York ; London : Associated Music.
Nos 1 and 3 classified at GEZDW and EZDW respectively.
2 : The rose: SSAA a capella. — 1972. — 5p ; 8vo.
Unpriced

(B74-50076)

FEZDW/LC — Unaccompanied voices. Spirituals
Lees, Heath
Deep river : spiritual for full female voice choir unaccompanied, [S.S.A.] / arranged by Heath Lees. — Wendover : Roberton, 1974. — 4p ; 8vo.
Staff and tonic sol-fa notation.
£0.08

(B74-51009)

FEZDW/X — Unaccompanied voices. Canons
Beethoven, Ludwig van
[Ta, ta, ta. K.-H 162]. To Maelzel : for 4-part chorus of female voices unaccompanied or with wood-block / by Ludwig van Beethoven ; edited by Alfred Davis. — Wendover : Roberton, 1972. — 6p ; 8vo.
£0.10
Also classified at FE/XXDW/X

(B74-50432)

FHYE/XMDX — Speaking chorus with percussion band. Secular cantatas
Russell-Smith, Geoffry
A box of toys and entertainment for speech and percussion / by Geoffry Russell-Smith ; words by Mollie Russell-Smith. — Sevenoaks : Novello, 1973. — 8vo.
Score (30p.) & 4 parts. — Duration 25 min.
£1.02

(B74-50077)

FLDGNQD — Treble voices. Anglican liturgy. Morning Prayer. Deus misereatur
Naylor, Bernard
Deus misereatur : two-part trebles / by Bernard Naylor. — Toronto : Oxford University Press ; Wendover : Roberton, 1971. — 6p ; 8vo.
£0.10

(B74-50078)

FLDP/LF — Treble voices. Carols. Christmas
Benger, Richard
Two Christmas carols : unison or two-part / [by] Richard Benger. — York : Banks, 1974. — 8p ; 8vo.
Contents: 1: Puer nobis - 2: Lute-book lullaby (Ballet).
Unpriced
Primary classification JFLDP/LF

Smith, Peter Melville
Joy to the world : treble voices / [by] Peter Melville Smith ; words from Joshua Sylvester 'Christmas carols and ballads'. — York : Banks, 1974. — 4p ; 8vo.
Unpriced

(B74-51010)

Walters, Edmund
Babe of Bethlehem : a carol for treble voices (with audience or additional choral participation) / words and music by Peter Kennerley. — London : Boosey and Hawkes, 1974. — 8vo.
£0.10

(B74-51011)

Walters, Edmund
Little camel boy : a carol for treble voices with audience (or choral) participation / music by Edmund Walters ; words by Peter Kennerley. — London : Boosey and Hawkes, 1974. — 10p ; 8vo.
£0.15

(B74-51012)

FLDX — Treble voices. Secular cantatas
Pehkonen, Elis
Fafnir and the knights, and other settings of poems by Stevie Smith : for treble voices and piano duet / by Elis Pehkonen. — South Croydon : Lengnick, 1974. — 4to.
Vocal score (51p.) & choral part. — Duration 21 min.
£2.00

(B74-50079)

FLEZDP/LF — Unaccompanied treble voices. Carols. Christmas
Davye, John J
A Child is born to us : a Christmas choral cycle for full chorus of treble voices a cappella / by John J Davye. — New York ; London : Associated Music, 1973. — 24p ; 8vo.
Unpriced

(B74-50433)

G — MALE VOICES
GDH — Motets, Anthems, Hymns, etc
Wilson, Robert Barclay
[Mors janua vitae. Vocal score]. Mors janua vitae : for male-voice choir (TTBB) and piano or organ or strings / by Robert Barclay Wilson ; the poem by Dyland Thomas. — London : Cramer, 1974. — 8p ; 8vo.
£0.12

(B74-51013)

GDW/LC — Spirituals
Hudson, Hazel
Behold that star ... Rise up, shepherd an' foller! : a quodlibet / arranged, from negro spirituals, for treble and alto or tenor and bass or treble and bass with optional parts for descant recorders and percussion by Hazel Hudson. — London : Ashdown, 1974. — 8p ; 8vo.
£0.12
Primary classification FDW/LC

GEZDGB — Unaccompanied voices. Ordinary of the Mass. Kyrie
Stapert, Calvin R
Kyrie and Gloria for the Saturday Lady Mass : two-part (male voices) / anonymous (c 1265-1275) ; edited by Calvin R. Stapert. — London : Oxford University Press, 1974. — 10p ; 8vo.
ISBN 0-19-341217-9 : £0.20
Also classified at GEZDGC

(B74-51014)

GEZDGC — Unaccompanied voices. Ordinary of the Mass. Gloria
Power, Leonel
Gloria : TTTBB / by Leonel Power ; edited by Margaret Bent. — London : Oxford University Press, 1974. — 8p ; 8vo.
ISBN 0-19-341209-8 : Unpriced

(B74-50080)

Stapert, Calvin R
Kyrie and Gloria for the Saturday Lady Mass : two-part (male voices) / anonymous (c 1265-1275) ; edited by Calvin R. Stapert. — London : Oxford University Press, 1974. — 10p ; 8vo.
ISBN 0-19-341217-9 : £0.20
Primary classification GEZDGB

GEZDH — Unaccompanied voices. Motets, Anthems, Hymns, etc
Bernstein, Leonard
[Mass. Almighty Father: arr]. Almighty Father : chorale / by Leonard Bernstein ; arranged for four-part chorus of men's voices a cappella by Daryl Millard ; words by Stephen Schwartz and Leonard Bernstein. — New York ; London : Amberson : Schirmer, 1973. — 3p ; 8vo.
Unpriced

(B74-50434)

GEZDK — Unaccompanied voices. Anthems
Leighton, Kenneth
Three psalms. Op.54 : for T.T. Bar. B.B., unaccompanied, [by] Kenneth Leighton. — Sevenoaks : Novello, 1974. — 38p ; 8vo.
Contents: 1: Like as the hart - 2: The Lord is my shepherd - 3: O sing unto the Lord a new song.
£0.44

(B74-50435)

GEZDP/LF/AY — Unaccompanied voices. Carols. Christmas. Collections
Brown, Frank Edwin
Cramer's carols : for male voice choir / arranged by Frank E. Brown. — London : Cramer, 1974. — 19p ; 8vo.
Unpriced

(B74-51015)

GEZDW — Unaccompanied voices. Songs, etc
Bantock, *Sir* Granville
The fighting Téméraire : TTBB / music by Granville Bantock ; poem by Henry Newbolt. — Wendover : Roberton, 1973. — 12p ; 8vo.
Staff and tonic sol-fa edition. Originally published London, Joseph Williams, 1923.
£0.16

(B74-51016)

Nelson, Havelock
The maid of Bunclody : traditional Irish song / arranged for 4-part chorus of unaccompanied male voices by Havelock Nelson. — Aylesbury : Roberton, 1974. — 8p ; 8vo.
Duration 2 1/2 min.
£0.10

(B74-50437)

Nelson, Ron
Meditation on the syllable Om : for men's voices / by Ron Nelson ; text by James Scherill. — New York ; London : Boosey and Hawkes, 1971. — 8p ; 8vo.
Unpriced

(B74-50436)

Stoker, Richard
The glory of the dove : for S.A., T.B., or SATB (unaccompanied) / words and music by Richard Stoker. — London : Ashdown, 1974. — 8p ; 8vo.
Unpriced
Primary classification EZDW

(B74-50409)

Yannatos, James
Three settings of E.E. Cummings / by James Yannatos. — New York ; London : Associated Music.
Nos 2 and 3 classified at FEZDW and EZDW respectively.
1 : Buffalo Bill's: TTBB a cappella. — 1972. — 5p ; 8vo.
Unpriced

(B74-50081)

GEZDW/LC — Unaccompanied voices. Spirituals
Russell, Wilbur F
Michael, row the boat ashore : Georgia sea island chant for four-part chorus of men's voices a cappella / arranged by Wilbur F. Russell. — Wendover : Roberton, 1970. — 4p ; 8vo.
£0.07

(B74-50082)

J — VOICES IN UNISON
JDG — Ordinary of the Mass
Gelineau, Joseph
Festival mass for unison (or mixed) choir congregation and
organ / by Joseph Gelineau. — London : Boosey and Hawkes,
1974. — 4to & 8vo.
Score & people's part.
Unpriced
Also classified at DG

(B74-50438)

JDGB — Roman liturgy. Ordinary of the Mass. Kyrie
Senator, Ronald
Kyrie in D minor and Gloria in A major : unison / by Ronald
Senator. — South Croydon : Lengnick, 1974. — 6p ; 8vo.
£0.12
Also classified at JDGC

(B74-50439)

JDGC — Roman liturgy. Ordinary of the Mass. Gloria
Senator, Ronald
Kyrie in D minor and Gloria in A major : unison / by Ronald
Senator. — South Croydon : Lengnick, 1974. — 6p ; 8vo.
£0.12
Primary classification JDGB

(B74-50439)

JDGS — Anglican liturgy. Communion
Sharp, Ian
St Katherine's Communion service, (series 3) : for congregational
use, unaccompanied or with keyboard accompaniment / [by] Ian
Sharp. — London : Stainer and Bell, 1974. — 8vo.
Score (10p.) & congregational part.
Unpriced

(B74-50440)

Walker, Robert
Communion service in E, series 3 : for congregational use / [by]
Robert Walker. — Sevenoaks : Novello, 1974. — 10p ; 8vo.
The international text is shown as an alternative.
£0.16

(B74-50441)

JDH — Motets, Anthems, Hymns, etc
Lindeman, Ludvig Matthias
[Melodien til Landstads Salmebog. Kirken den er et]. Built on the
rock : anthem for unison choir or solo voice and organ / by
Ludvig Matthias Lindeman ; arranged by Everett Jay Hilty ;
words by N.F.S. Grundtvig ; translated by Carl Doving. — New
York ; [London] : Oxford University Press, 1971. — 4p ; 8vo.
Unpriced

(B74-51017)

Pratt, George
Four anthems : [unison] / [by] George Pratt. — Croydon : Royal
School of Church Music, 1973. — 16p ; 8vo.
Contents: 1: O sing unto the Lord a new song - 2: By the waters of
Babylon - 3: The earth is the Lord's - 4: O praise the Lord of heaven.
£0.32

(B74-51018)

JDK — Anthems
Eldridge, Guy
The shield of faith : anthem for unison voices with
accompaniment for organ or piano / [by] Guy Eldridge ; words
from the Epistle to the Ephesians VI. — London : Cramer, 1974.
— 4p ; 8vo.
£0.09

(B74-51019)

JDM — Hymns
Beaumont, Geoffrey
Hymn tunes : a collection of ten setting of well-loved hymns / by
Geoffrey Beaumont. — London : Weinberger, 1974. — 16p ; 8vo.
£0.50

(B74-50083)

Hodson, Keith
The world belongs to Jesus : nine contemporary songs of
worship / [music] by Keith Hodson and [words] by Eric A.
Thorn. — Heywood : the Baptist Church, Rochdale Rd,
Heywood, Lancs. OL10 1LG : Wigwam Publications for
Songcrafts, 1974. — [19]p ; 4to.
Individual songs also available in leaflet form, (melody line and words only).
ISBN 0-904434-00-1 : Unpriced

(B74-50442)

Hunter, Ian
Hosanna to the living Lord : unison / [by] Ian Hunter ; words by
Bishop Heber. — London : Thames, 1974. — 3p ; 8vo.
Unpriced

(B74-51020)

Mills, Betty Lou
Jesus is alive today : unison hymn / by Betty Lou Mills ; arr.
Tony Mettrick. — St Austell (32a Fore St., St Austell, Cornwell) :
Good News Crusade, 1974. — 2p ; 8vo.
£0.20

(B74-50443)

Turner, Roy
Glory choruses / composed by Roy Turner. — Newark (112a
Beacon Hill Rd, Newark) : Henri's Evangelical Revival
Association.
No.3; arranged by Walter Eden and Norman Wicker. — 1974. — 33p ; 8vo.
Unpriced

(B74-51021)

JDM/AY — Hymns. Collections
Hodson, Keith
The wigwam tune book : 20 exciting modern tunes to your
favourite hymns / by Keith Hodson. — Heywood : Wigwam
Publications, 1973. — 22p ; 4to.
Unpriced

(B74-50084)

JDP — Carols
Carter, Sydney
Green print for song / by Sydney Carter ; with illuminations by
Robert Reid. — London : Galliard, Stainer and Bell, 1974. —
94p ; 8vo.
ISBN 0-85249-284-7 : Unpriced

(B74-51022)

JDP/LEZ — Carols. Advent
Hilty, Everett Jay
O come, O come Emmanuel = Veni Emmanuel : Advent anthem
for unison or 2-part mixed chorus and organ / arranged by
Everett Jay Hilty; words, Latin, translated by Neale, final verse
from Henry Sloan Coffin. — New York ; London : Oxford
University Press, 1971. — 4p ; 8vo.
Unpriced
Also classified at EZDP/LEZ

(B74-50444)

JDP/LF — Carols. Christmas
Blake, Leonard
[Carol of the sun. *Vocal score*]. Carol of the sun : for two-part or
unison chorus / by Leonard Blake ; words by William Austin. —
Wendover : Roberton, 1974. — 6p ; 8vo.
Staff & tonic sol-fa notation.
£0.10
Primary classification FDP/LF

(B74-50414)

Hughes-Jones, Llifon
Balulalow : unison voices (or solo) and piano (or organ) / [by]
Llifon Hughes-Jones ; words by James, John and Robert
Wedderburn. — London : Thames, 1974. — 8vo.
Unpriced
Also classified at KDP/LF

(B74-51023)

JDP/LF/AY — Carols. Christmas. Collections
Hitchcock, Gordon
Let joybells ring / compiled and with words by Gordon
Hitchcock ; arranged by Ian Copley. — Newton Abbott : David
and Charles, 1974. — 96p ; 8vo.
Some recorder or percussion parts have been added to many of the carols
which are all optional.
ISBN 0-7153-6712-9 : £2.95

(B74-51024)

JDR — Psalms
Chappell, Herbert
Psalms for today / [unison by] Herbert Chappell. — London :
Chappell, 1974. — 43p ; 8vo.
Unpriced

(B74-50445)

Wills, Arthur
Singing joyfully, God's power proclaim : unison voices and piano
or organ / by Arthur Wills ; a modern paraphrase of Psalms 127
and 128 by William Barnett. — London : Boosey and Hawkes,
1974. — 3p ; 8vo.
Unpriced

(B74-50446)

JDW — Songs, etc
Grundman, Clare
[Zoo illogical. *Vocal score*]. Zoo illogical : for solo voice, or voices
in unison or octaves with piano / [by] Clare Grundman. — New
York ; [London] : Boosey and Hawkes, 1974. — 12p ; 8vo.
Unpriced
Also classified at KDW

(B74-50447)

Nelson, Havelock

The girl with the buckles on her shoes : Irish traditional melody, unison song with piano / arr. Havelock Nelson, words by Sydney Bell. — Wendover : Roberton, 1974. — 4p ; 8vo.
£0.07

(B74-50085)

Sturman, Paul

Seasons : unison / by Paul Sturman. — London : Ashdown, 1974. — 8vo.
Vocal score (17p.) & melody edition. — Duration 6 min. — Contents: 1: Spring (Sir J. Davies) - 2: Summer (Rossetti) - 3: Autumn (Sylvester) - 4: Winter (anon).
£0.40

(B74-50086)

JDW/LF — Songs. Christmas
Rocherolle, Eugenie R

Christmas child : for unison, SA or SAB chorus and piano / words and music by Eugenie R. Rocherolle. — New York : Warner ; London : Blossom, 1974. — 15p ; 8vo.
Unpriced
Also classified at FDW/LF; DW/LF

(B74-50448)

JDX — Secular cantatas
Foster, Anthony

Jonah and the whale : an entertainment for junior choirs and audience with piano and optional instruments / by Anthony Foster ; words by Trevor Harvey. — London : Oxford University Press, 1974. — 4to.
Score (13p.) & 6 parts. — Duration 11 min.
ISBN 0-19-336120-5 : £1.59

(B74-50449)

JE/NYFSRDW — With descant recorder, keyboard and percussion. Songs, etc
Lord, David

Nonsongs : six songs about nothing in particular for voices, descant recorders, pitched and unpitched percussion and piano / music, David Lord, text, Michael Dennis Browne. — London : Universal, 1974. — 26p ; obl 8vo.
Unpriced

(B74-51025)

JE/NYHNMDE — With wind & percussion nonet. Songs, etc
Grundman, Clare

Zoo illogical : for solo voice, or voices in unison or octaves, with instrumental ensemble [woodwind, brass & percussion], (optional piano) / [by] Clare Grundman. — New York ; [London] : Boosey and Hawkes, 1974. — 8vo.
Score (40p.) & 9 parts. — Contents: 1: The mongoose 2: The anteater - 3: The Llama - 4: The giraffe - 5: The hippo.
Unpriced
Also classified at KE/NYHNMDW

(B74-50450)

JE/TSDM/AY — With guitar. Hymns. Collections
Pulkingham, Betty Carr

Songs of fellowship / arranged and compiled by Betty Carr Pulkingham and Oressa Wise; assisted by Mimi Armstrong ... [and others]. — London : The Fishermen Inc., by arrangement with the Fountanin Trust, 1972. — [7],86p ; 8vo.
Unpriced

(B74-50087)

Smith, Peter

Jesus folk : a new collection of folk songs / edited by Peter Smith. — London : Galliard : Stainer and Bell, 1974. — 32p ; 8vo.
ISBN 0-85249-304-5 : Unpriced

(B74-51026)

JE/TSDP/LF — With guitar. Carols. Christmas
Dinham, Kenneth J

Three kings came to Bethlehem Town : solo, unison or two-part (or mixed voices), [with accompaniment for guitar or piano ad lib] / words and music by K.J. Dinham. — York : Banks, 1974. — 3p ; 8vo.
Unpriced
Primary classification KE/TSDP/LF

JE/TSDW — With guitar, Songs, etc
Donald, Mike

Travelling the northern road / [mostly by] Mike Donald. — London : EFDS, 1974. — 40p ; 8vo.
Unpriced

(B74-51027)

JE/TSDW/AY — With guitar. Songs, etc. Collections
Festival folk : songs in folk song style. — London : EFDS, 1974. — 60p ; 8vo.
Unpriced

(B74-51028)

Whyton, Wally

Guitar song book / [by] Wally Whyton. — London : Durham Music.
Book 1. — 1974. — 1,45p ; 8vo. —
£1.25

(B74-51029)

JE/TSDW/AYD — With guitar. Folk songs. Collections. England
Palmer, Roy

Love is pleasing : songs of courtship and marriage / selected and edited by Roy Palmer. — London : Cambridge University Press, 1974. — 80p ; obl.8vo.
ISBN 0-521-20445-3 : £0.50

(B74-51030)

JEZDTDM — Unaccompanied voices. Gregorian chant
Jubilate Deo : simple Gregorian chants for the faithful to learn as recommended in the Second Vatican Council's Constitution on the Sacred Liturgy. — London : Catholic Truth Society, 1974. — 54p ; 8vo.
Unpriced

(B74-51031)

JEZDW/G/AYD — Unaccompanied voices. Folk songs. England
Karpeles, Maud

Cecil Sharp's collection of English folk songs / edited by Maud Karpeles. — London : Oxford University Press, 1974. — 2v. (xxxvi,751,66)p ; 8vo.
ISBN 0-19-313125-0 : £44 for set

(B74-51032)

JEZDW/G/AYDK — Unaccompanied voices. Folk songs. Collections. Wales
Saer, D Roy

Canenon llafar gwlad = Songs from oral tradition / selected and edited with notes by D. Roy Saer, music transcriptions made for the Museum by Phyllis Kenney, Meredydd Evans and D. Roy Saer. — Cardiff : National Museum of Wales, Welsh Folk Museum.
Vol.1. — 1974. — 72p ; 8vo.
ISBN 0-85485-026-0 : Unpriced

(B74-51033)

JEZDW/G/AYPE — Unaccompanied voices. Folk songs. Collections. Greece
Frye, Ellen

The marble threshing floor : a collection of Greek folksongs / by Ellen Frye. — Austin ; London : University of Texas Press for the American Folklore Society, 1973. — xvi,327p,[8]p of plates : ill, map, ports ; 4to.
ISBN 0-292-75005-6 : £5.85

(B74-50451)

JEZDW/G/AYSX — Unaccompanied voices. Folk songs. Collections. Canada
Fowke, Edith

The Penguin book of Canadian folk songs / selected and edited by Edith Fowke; music consultant Keith MacMillan. — Harmondsworth : Penguin, 1973. — 224p ; 8vo.
ISBN 0-14-070842-1 : £0.75

(B74-50452)

JEZDW/G/AYT — Unaccompanied voices. Folk songs. Collections. United States
Erdei, Peter

150 American folk songs to sing, read and play / selected and edited by Peter Erdei and the staff of the Kodaly Musical Training Institute, collected principally by Katalin Komlos. — New York ; London : Boosey and Hawkes, 1974. — xiv,117p ; 8vo.
£3.75

(B74-50088)

JEZDW/GNF/AY — Cowboy songs. Collections
Ohrlin, Glenn

The hell-bound train : a cowboy songbook / by Glenn Ohrlin ; with a biblio-discography by Harlan Daniel. — Urbana ; London : University of Illinois Press, 1973. — xix,29p ; 8vo.
Bibl. and list of records: p.241-281. — Index.
ISBN 0-252-00190-7 : £4.30

(B74-50453)

JFDE — Female voices, Children's voices. Religious cantatas
Parry, William Howard

St Jerome and the lion : a legend for voices, piano and optional recorders and percussion / by W.H. Parry ; poem (abridged) by Rumer Godden. — London : Keith Prowse Music, 1974. — 4to.
Conductor & 7 parts. — Duration 20 min.
£0.75

(B74-50089)

JFDH/LL — Female voices, Children's voices, Motets, Anthems, Hymns, etc. Easter

Ager, Laurence
The rising again : a calypso for voices and piano / by Laurence Ager ; words by Kenneth Allen. — London : Ashdown, 1974. — 7p ; 8vo.
Duration 3 min.
£0.12

(B74-50090)

JFDW — Female voices, Children's voices. Songs, etc

Davies, Laurence Hector
The Cavern : [unison song] / arr. by Laurence H. Davies; words by Laurence H. Davies. — London : Ashdown, 1973. — 3p ; 8vo.
Arranged from the traditional tune 'A piper came to our town'. — Duration 2 min.
£0.05

(B74-50091)

JFDW/AY — Female voices, Children's voices. Songs. Collections

Girl guide song book : unison voices. — London : Girl Guides Association.
Book 1. — 1974. — 36p ; 8vo. —
Unpriced

(B74-51034)

Book 2. — 1974. — 36p ; 8vo. —
Unpriced

(B74-51035)

JFDW/G/AY — Female voices, Children's voices. Folk songs. Collections

Coombes, Douglas
Songs for 'Singing Together' : fifty songs from around the world taken from the BBC's music programme Singing Together / compiled and arranged by Douglas Coombes. — London : British Broadcasting Corporation, 1974. — 91p ; 4to.
Teacher's book. — Originally published: 1973.
ISBN 0-563-13189-6 : £1.25

(B74-51036)

Raven, Jon
Turpin hero : 30 folk songs for voices and guitar / compiled by Jon Raven. — London : Oxford University Press, 1974. — 69p ; 8vo.
ISBN 0-19-330626-3 : £1.60

(B74-51037)

JFDW/GK/AYD — Female voices, Children's voices. Nursery rhymes. Collections. England

Crane, Walter
The baby's opera : a book of old rhymes with new dresses / by Walter Crane ; the music by the earliest masters. — London : Pan, 1974. — 56p ; 8vo.
Originally published: London : Routledge, 1877.
ISBN 0-330-24088-9 : £0.60

(B74-51038)

JFDW/GS/AYULD — Female voices, Children's voices. Games. Collections. Jamaica

Lewin, Olive
Brown gal in de ring : 12 Jamaican folk-songs / collected and arranged for schools by Olive Lewin. — London : Oxford University Press, 1974. — 16p ; obl. 8vo.
ISBN 0-19-330544-5 : £0.40

(B74-51039)

JFE/NYJDW/G/AYDK — Female voices, Children's voices with strings & percussion. Folk songs. Collections. Wales

Lewis, Esme
Ten Welsh folk-songs for juniors / arranged for unison voices with easy instrumental accompaniment by Esme Lewis; English translations by Ifor Rees. — Cardiff : University of Wales Press, 1973. — 17p ; 4to.
Also published in Welsh as 'Deg o ganenon gwerin i blant'.
£0.50

(B74-50092)

JFE/XMDW — Female voices, Children's voices with percussion band. Songs, etc

Kelly, Bryan
Half a fortnight : seven songs for group music making / by Bryan Kelly ; words by John Fuller. — Sevenoaks : Novello, 1973. — 4to.
Score (46p.) & 4 parts. — Duration 21 min. — This work may be performed without permission.
£1.60

(B74-50093)

JFEZDW/G/AYDLZL — Unaccompanied female voices, children's voices. Folk songs. Collections. Isle of Lewis

Mackenzie, Anne
Amhrain Anna Sheumais / compiled by Anne Mackenzie. — Point (Isle of Lewis) : Ann Mackenzie, 1973. — 26p ; 8vo.
Staff & tonic sol-fa notation.
Unpriced

(B74-50094)

JFEZDW/PP/AY — Unaccompanied female voices, children's voices. Songs, etc. Pentatonic music. Collections

Kersey, Robert E
Just five : a collection of pentatonic songs / compiled by Robert E. Kersey. — Croydon : Belwin-Mills. — (Junior ensemble series)
Book 1. — 1972. — 40p ; 8vo. —
£0.40

(B74-50454)

Book 2. — 1972. — 40p ; 8vo. —
£0.40

(B74-50455)

JFLDP/LF — Treble voices. Carols. Christmas

Benger, Richard
Two Christmas carols : unison or two-part / [by] Richard Benger. — York : Banks, 1974. — 8p ; 8vo.
Contents: 1: Puer nobis - 2: Lute-book lullaby (Ballet).
Unpriced
Also classified at FLDP/LF

(B74-51040)

Walters, Edmund
Ding-dong-doh : a carol for unison treble voices (with optional second and third parts) / words and music by Edmund Walters. — London : Boosey and Hawkes, 1974. — 5p ; 8vo.
£0.10

(B74-51041)

JFLE/NYLDW — Treble voices with keyboard & percussion. Songs, etc

Platts, Kenneth
Three bird songs : for treble voices, piano and percussion / by Kenneth Platts. — London : Ashdown, 1974. — 11p ; 4to.
£0.30

(B74-51042)

JN — SINGLE VOICES IN COMBINATION

JNBDH — Vocal quintets. Motets, Anthems, Hymns, etc

Scheidt, Samuel
[Geistliche Concerten, Tl.2. Dialogus]. Kommt her ihr Gesegneten meines Vaters = Come ye blessed ones of my Father : dialogue for five voices (SATTB) and continuo / [by] Samuel Scheidt ; edited by Paul Steinitz. — Sevenoaks : Novello, 1974. — 16p ; 8vo.
£1.00

(B74-51043)

JNEZAYDE — Vocal octets. Religious cantatas

Joubert, John
Four stations on the road to freedom, Opus 73 : for SSAATTBB soli or chorus (unaccompanied) / by John Joubert ; words by Dietrich Bonhoeffer; translated by Frank Clarke. — Sevenoaks : Novello, 1974. — 18p ; 8vo.
Duration 8 min.
Unpriced
Also classified at EZDE

(B74-50456)

JNFEDW — Female voice, Child's voice duets. Songs, etc

Rossini, Gioachino Antonio
Duets for two cats : for 2-part chorus of female voices or SA duet with piano / by Gioachino Rossini; edited by Alfred Davis. — Wendover : Roberton, 1972. — 7p ; 8vo.
Ascribed to Rossini in this publication. Probably the work of Robert Lucas Pearsall, composed under the pseudonym of G. Berthold.
£0.12
Primary classification FDW

(B74-50422)

JNGEZAZDX — Unaccompanied male sextets. Secular cantatas

Penderecki, Krzysztof
Ecloga VIII (Vergili 'Bucolica') : for 6 male voices (1972) / by Krzysztof Penderecki. — Mainz ; London : Schott, 1974. — 29p ; 4to.
Study score.
£2.40

(B74-50095)

K — VOCAL SOLOS

K/EG/AL — Sight reading. Examinations

London College of Music
Examination in pianoforte playing and singing sight reading tests as set throughout 1973. Grades I-VIII and diplomas. — London : Ashdown, 1973. — 15p ; 4to.
£0.35
Primary classification Q/EG/AL

(B74-50159)

KDH — MOTETS, ANTHEMS, HYMNS, ETC. SOLOS
Wyner, Yehudi
Psalms and early songs / by Yehudi Wyner. — New York ;
London : Associated Music, 1973. — 12p ; 4to.
Contents: Psalm 119 - Psalm 66 - When you are old (Yeats) - Exeunt
(Richard Wilbur).
Unpriced
Also classified at KDW

(B74-50097)

KDP — CAROLS. SOLOS
KDP/LF — Christmas
Hughes-Jones, Llifon
Balulalow : unison voices (or solo) and piano (or organ) / [by]
Llifon Hughes-Jones ; words by James, John and Robert
Wedderburn. — London : Thames, 1974. — 8vo.
Unpriced
Primary classification JDP/LF

KDTF — LORD'S PRAYER. SOLOS
Fanshawe, David
[African Sanctus: arr]. The Lord's Prayer / by David Fanshawe.
— London : Chappell, 1974. — 4p ; 4to.
Unpriced

(B74-51044)

KDW — SONGS, ETC. SOLOS
Adler, Samuel
Two songs for three years / music by Samuel Adler. — [New
York] ; [London] : Boosey and Hawkes, 1974. — 14p ; 4to.
Contents: 1: My daughter the cypress (Ruth Whitman) - 2: Song to be sung
by the father of infant female children (Ogden Nashe).
Unpriced

(B74-51045)

Binkerd, Gordon
And I am old to know : song / by Gordon Binkerd ; poem by
Pauline Hanson. — New York ; [London] : Boosey and Hawkes,
1971. — 10p ; 4to.
Unpriced

(B74-51046)

Campion, Thomas
[Works, songs. Selections]. Selected songs of Thomas Campion /
selected and prefaced by W.H. Auden; introduction by John
Hollander. — Boston : David Godine ; London : Bodley Head,
1972. — 164p ; 4to.
ISBN 0-370-10306-8 : £6.00

(B74-50457)

Churchill, Sarah
Songs / words and music by Sarah Churchill. — London : Sparta
Florida : Chappell, 1974. — 19p ; 4to.
Unpriced

(B74-50458)

Duke, John
When I was one and twenty : for voice and piano / by John
Duke ; poem by A.E. Housman. — New York ; London :
Schirmer, 1972. — 5p ; 4to.
Unpriced

(B74-50098)

Fennimore, Joseph
Berlitz: introduction to French : for voice and piano / [by] Joseph
Fennimore. — New York ; London : Schirmer, 1974. — 30p ;
8vo.
Unpriced

(B74-51047)

Grundman, Clare
[Zoo illogical. *Vocal score*]. Zoo illogical : for solo voice, or voices
in unison or octaves with piano / [by] Clare Grundman. — New
York ; [London] : Boosey and Hawkes, 1974. — 12p ; 8vo.
Unpriced
Primary classification JDW

(B74-50447)

Holst, Gustav
[The planets. Jupiter. *Selections: arr*]. Joybringer : [song] based on
'Jupiter' by Gustav Holst / arranged by Manfred Mann. —
London : Feldman, 1973. — 4p ; 4to.
£0.25

(B74-50459)

Holst, Gustav
Softly and gently. Op.4, no.3 : for voice and piano / music by
Gustav Holst ; German words by Heinrich Heine ; translated by
Gustav Holst. — London : Bosworth, 1974. — 3p ; 4to.
Unpriced

(B74-51048)

Joplin, Scott
The entertainer / by Scott Joplin ; words by John Brimhall. —
New York : California Music ; London : Chappell, 1974. — 4p ;
4to.
Unpriced

(B74-50460)

Kander, John
[70 girls 70 : Selections]. 70 girls 70 / by John Kander ; lyrics by
Fred Ebb. — New York ; [London] : Valando, 1971. — 36p ; 4to.
Unpriced

(B74-51049)

Mathias, William
A vision of time and eternity. Op.61 : song / [by] William
Mathias ; words by Henry Vaughan. — London : Oxford
University Press, 1974. — 16p ; 4to.
ISBN 0-19-345570-6 : £1.10

(B74-50461)

Newman, Anthony
Barricades (after Couperin) : for voice, guitar and keyboard /
music by Anthony Newman ; words by Mary Jane Newman. —
New York ; London : Schirmer, 1974. — 12p ; 4to.
A freely written melodic line is superimposed on the constantly changing
harmonic base of Couperin's 'Les Barricades mystérieuses', not a note of
which has been altered.
Unpriced
Primary classification KE/TSPDW

Novello, Ivor
[Works, songs. Selections]. Ivor Novello song album. — London :
Chappell, 1974. — 68p ; 4to.
Unpriced

(B74-51050)

Porter, Cole
Songs from Cole : an entertainment / based on the words and
music of Cole Porter. — London : Chappell, 1974. — 129p ; 4to.
Unpriced

(B74-51051)

Previn, André
[The good companions. Good companions: arr]. Good
companions : song / music by André Previn, [arranged] for voice
and piano; lyrics by Johnny Mercer. — London : Chappell, 1974.
— 4p ; 4to.
Unpriced

(B74-50462)

Previn, André
[The good companions. *Selections: arr*]. The good companions /
music by Andre Previn ; the musical of the novel by J.B.
Priestley, vocal lyrics by Johnny Mercer. — London : Chappell,
1974. — 49p ; 4to.
Unpriced

(B74-51052)

Previn, André
[The good companions. Ta luv: arr]. Ta luv : song / music by
André Previn, [arranged] for voice and piano; lyrics by Johnny
Mercer. — London : Chappell, 1974. — 3p ; 4to.
Unpriced

(B74-50463)

Previn, André
[The good companions. The dance of life: arr]. The dance of life :
song / music by André Previn [arranged] for voice and piano;
lyrics by Johnny Mercer. — London : Chappell, 1974. — 4p ; 4to.
Unpriced

(B74-50464)

Previn, André
[The good companions. The pleasure of your company: arr]. The
pleasure of your company : song / music by André Previn,
[arranged for voice and piano]; lyrics by Johnny Mercer. —
London : Chappell, 1974. — 3p ; 4to.
Unpriced

(B74-50465)

Rorem, Ned
The serpent / music by Ned Rorem ; words by Theodore
Roethke. — New York ; [London] : Boosey and Hawkes, 1974. —
6p ; 4to.
Unpriced

(B74-51053)

Schäfer, Karl-Heinz
Rise eagle rise / musique [par] Karl-Heinz Schafer sur un théme
de Verdi ; paroles de David Inayat. — Paris : Maneges, Chappell ;
London : Chappell, 1974. — 3p ; 4to.
Unpriced

(B74-50466)

Stephens, Hugh
Humming bird : waltz song / words and music by Hugh Stephens;
arranged by Donald Henshilwood. — St Ives, [Cornwall] :
Hambly Music, 1972. — 4p ; 4to.
£0.20

(B74-50467)

Sullivan, *Sir* **Arthur Seymour**
[Works, operettas. Selections: arr]. The best of Gilbert and
Sullivan : [songs from operettas arranged with piano
accompaniment]. — London : Chappell, 1974. — 88p ; 4to.
Unpriced

(B74-50468)

Tredici, David Del
Four songs on poems of James Joyce : for voice and piano / by
David Del Tredici. — [New York] ; [London] : Boosey and
Hawkes, 1974. — 30p ; 4to.
£2.25

(B74-50469)

Warlock, Peter
Candlelight : a cycle of nursery jingles / by Peter Warlock ;
introduction by Fred Tomlinson with facsimile illustrations from
'Nurse Lovechild's Legacy'. — London : Thames Music, 1974. —
19p ; 8vo.
Originally published London, Stainer and Bell, 1924. A facsimile of this
edition with additional material.
Unpriced

(B74-51054)

Wyner, Yehudi
Psalms and early songs / by Yehudi Wyner. — New York ;
London : Associated Music, 1973. — 12p ; 4to.
Contents: Psalm 119 - Psalm 66 - When you are old (Yeats) - Exeunt
(Richard Wilbur).
Unpriced
Primary classification KDH

(B74-50097)

KDW/AY — Collections
Formby, George
George Formby complete / edited by Andrew Bailey and Peter
Foss with contributions by Alan Randall; special articles by John
Walley. — New York ; London : Wise, 1973. — 237p ; 4to.
Unpriced

(B74-50099)

This is show business : songs. — London : Chappell.
Vol.1. — 1974. — 2,63p ; 4to. —
Unpriced

(B74-50470)

Vol.2. — 1974. — 65p ; 4to. —
Unpriced

(B74-50471)

Vol.3. — 1974. — 62p ; 4to. —
Unpriced

(B74-51055)

Vol.4. — 1974. — 62p ; 4to. —
Unpriced

(B74-51056)

KDW/AYVD — Collections. Israel
Jerusalem city of gold : songs of modern and ancient Israel / arr.
by Heskel Brisman, and others. — New York ; London :
Chappell, 1971. — 32p ; 4to.
Unpriced

(B74-50472)

KDW/AZ — Collected works of individual composers
Bernstein, Leonard
[Works, songs. Collections]. Collected songs / [by] Leonard
Bernstein. — New York ; London : Amberson : Schirmer, 1973.
— 106p ; 4to.
Unpriced

(B74-50473)

Rachmaninoff, Sergei
[Songs. Collections]. Songs with piano accompaniment / by Sergei
Rachmaninov. — London : Boosey and Hawkes.
Volume 1. — 1974. — 127p ; fol.
£4.00

(B74-50100)

Volume 2. — 1974. — 141p ; fol.
£4.00

(B74-50101)

KDW/G/AYD — Folk songs. Collections. England
Broadwood, Lucy Etheldred
English traditional songs and carols / collected and edited with
annotations and pianoforte accompaniments by Lucy E.
Broadwood. — Totowa : Rowman and Littlefield ; East Ardsley :
EP Publishing, 1974. — xii,125p ; 4to.
Facsimile reprint of the original edition published, London: Boosey, 1908.
ISBN 0-7158-1025-1 : Unpriced

(B74-50474)

KDW/GB/AY — Popular songs. Collections
The Gatsby era greats : [songs with] photographs from the film
'The great Gatsby'. — [London] : Chappell, 1974. — 47p ; 4to.
Unpriced

(B74-50475)

The great ones. — New York ; London : Wise.
3 : Great groups. — 1973. — 125p ; 4to. —
£1.50
Primary classification C/AY

(B74-50002)

4 : Nineteen famous singers and their songs & 17 more songs. — 1973. —
96p ; 4to. —
£1.50
Primary classification C/AY

(B74-50003)

Great songs of the 60's. — New York ; London : Wise, 1973. —
320p ; 4to.
Unpriced

(B74-50102)

The Pop generation : to-day's singers and their songs for to-day's
people. — London : EMI, 1974. — 160p ; 4to.
Unpriced

(B74-51057)

They don't write songs like these any more : 50 songs from the
golden age of song writing. — London : Wise.
1. — 1972. — 147p ; 4to. —
£1.50

(B74-50103)

2. — 1972. — 147p ; 4to. —
£1.50

(B74-50104)

3. — 1972. — 147p ; 4to. —
£1.50

(B74-50105)

4. — 1972. — 147p ; 4to. —
£1.50

(B74-50106)

5. — 1972. — 138p ; 4to. —
£1.50

(B74-50107)

KDW/GB/AY(XH564) — Popular songs. Collections, 1837-1901
Turner, Michael R
The parlour song book : a casquet of vocal gems / the music
edited by Antony Miall ; edited and introduced by Michael
Turner. — London : Pan Books, 1974. — x,374p ; 8vo.
ISBN 0-330-24113-3 : £1.75

(B74-51058)

KDW/JR — Films
Cole, Tony
Take me high : song album / words and music by Tony Cole. —
London : Coronado Music, 1974. — 32p ; 4to.
From the film.
£0.75

(B74-50108)

The great Gatsby : the songs of the twenties from the film of the
seventies. — London : EMI Music, 1974. — 43p ; 4to.
Unpriced

(B74-50476)

KDW/K/G/AYDJJ — Ballads. Collections. Northumberland
Stokoe, John
Songs and ballads of northern England / collected and edited by
John Stokoe. — [1st ed., reprinted]. — Newcastle upon Tyne :
Graham, 1974. — [10],198p ; 4to.
Facsimile reprint of 1st ed.: Newcastle upon Tyne: Scott, 1893.
ISBN 0-85983-040-3 : £5.00

(B74-50109)

KDX — SECULAR CANTATAS. SOLOS
Corigliano, John
[Poem in October. Vocal score]. Poem in October : for voice and
orchestra / by John Corigliano ; poem by Dylan Thomas;
reduction for voice and piano by the composer. — New York ;
London : Schirmer, 1974. — 27p ; 8vo.
Unpriced

(B74-51059)

**KE — VOCAL SOLOS WITH ACCOMPANIMENT OTHER
THAN KEYBOARD**
**KE/LNTDW/AYH (XCTQ26) — With instrumental trio. Songs, etc.
Collections. France, 1475-1500**
Wilkin, Nigel
Three French songs from the late 14th century : for voice and 2
or 3 instruments / edited by Nigel Wilkins. — Lustleigh : Antico,
1974. — 4to.
Score (8p.) & 4 parts. — Contents: 1: Alarme alarme/ by Grimace - 2: Soit
tart, tempre, main ou soir/ anon - 3: Quiconques vent d'amours joir/ anon.
Unpriced
Also classified at LN/AYH (XCTQ26)

(B74-50477)

KE/MDW — With orchestra. Songs, etc
Mahler, Gustav
Kindertotenlieder : für eine Singstimme und Orchester auf
Gedichte von Friedrich Rückert / [von] Gustav Mahler ; nach
den Quellen herausgegeben von Eberhardt Klemm. — Leipzig ;
[London] : Peters, 1973. — viii,74p ; 8vo.
Miniature score - Duration 24 min.
Unpriced

(B74-51060)

KE/NYHNMDW — With wind & percussion nonet. Songs, etc
Grundman, Clare
Zoo illogical : for solo voice, or voices in unison or octaves, with
instrumental ensemble [woodwind, brass & percussion], (optional
piano) / [by] Clare Grundman. — New York ; [London] : Boosey
and Hawkes, 1974. — 8vo.
Score (40p.) & 9 parts. — Contents: 1: The mongoose 2: The anteater - 3:
The Llama - 4: The giraffe - 5: The hippo.
Unpriced
Primary classification JE/NYHNMDE

(B74-50450)

KE/SRPDW — With cello & piano. Songs, etc
Rorem, Ned
Last poems of Wallace Stevens : for voice, cello and piano / by
Ned Rorem. — New York ; London : Boosey and Hawkes, 1974.
— 4to.
Score (35p.) & part.
£3.00

(B74-50478)

KE/TQDW/G/AYDK — With harp. Folk songs. Collections. Wales
Rose, Michael
Seven Welsh folk songs : voice and harp / arranged by Michael
Rose. — Abergavenny : Adlais, 1973. — 32p ; 8vo.
Unpriced

(B74-51061)

KE/TSDP/LF — With guitar. Carols. Christmas
Dinham, Kenneth J
Three kings came to Bethlehem Town : solo, unison or two-part
(or mixed voices), [with accompaniment for guitar or piano ad
lib] / words and music by K.J. Dinham. — York : Banks, 1974.
— 3p ; 8vo.
Unpriced
Also classified at JE/TSDP/LF; FE/TSDP/LF; ETSDP/LF

(B74-51062)

KE/TSDW — With guitar. Songs, etc
Carter, Elliott
Tell me where is fancy bred : for voice and guitar / by Elliott
Carter ; guitar part edited by Stanley Silverman, words by William
Shakespeare. — New York ; London : Associated Music, 1972. —
4p ; 4to.
Unpriced

(B74-50110)

Garrett, John M
Jim's yolk songs / words and music by John M. Garrett. —
London : English Folk Dance and Song Society, 1974. — 28p ;
8vo.
ISBN 0-85418-103-2 : £0.45

(B74-50479)

Newman, Anthony
Barricades (after Couperin) : for voice, guitar and keyboard /
music by Anthony Newman ; words by Mary Jane Newman. —
New York ; London : Schirmer, 1974. — 12p ; 4to.
A freely written melodic line is superimposed on the constantly changing
harmonic base of Couperin's 'Les Barricades mystérieuses', not a note of
which has been altered.
Unpriced
Primary classification KE/TSPDW

Surinach, Carlos
Prayers : for voice and guitar / by Carlos Surinach ; text by
Michel Quoist. — New York ; London : Associated Music
Publishers, 1973. — 8p ; 4to.
£0.70

(B74-50480)

**KE/TSDW/G/AYDF — With guitar. Folk songs. Collections. West
Country**
Baring-Gould, Sabine
Folk songs of the West Country / collected by Sabine
Baring-Gould; annotated from the MSS at Plymouth Library and
with additional material by Gordon Hitchcock. — Newton
Abbot : David and Charles, 1974. — 112p ; 4to.
ISBN 0-7153-6419-7 : £3.25

(B74-50111)

**KE/TSDW/GM/AYC — With guitar. Working songs. Collections.
Great Britain**
Dallas, Karl
One hundred songs of toil : with guitar chords / compiled and
edited by Karl Dallas. — London : Wolfe, 1974. — 255p ; 8vo.
ISBN 0-7234-0525-5 : £1.75

(B74-50112)

KE/TSDW/JM — With guitar. Songs, etc. Incidental music
Walton, *Sir* William
[Christopher Columbus. Beatriz's song: arr]. Beatriz's song /
music by William Walton ; adapted for voice and guitar by Hector
Quine, words by Louis MacNeice. — London : Oxford University
Press, 1974. — 4p ; 4to.
From the radio play.
ISBN 0-19-345866-7 : £0.35

(B74-50481)

**KE/TSDW/K/G/AYD(XFYK145) — With guitar. Ballads.
Collections. England, 1170-1914**
Palmer, Roy
A touch of the times : songs of social change, 1770 to 1914 /
illustrated with old photographs ; edited by Roy Palmer. —
Harmondsworth : Penguin, 1974. — 352p ; 8vo.
ISBN 0-14-081182-6 : £0.80

(B74-51063)

KE/TSNDW/AY — With guitar ensemble. Songs, etc. Collections
Ashlund, Ulf Goran
Play together : for voice and guitar / songs compiled and
arranged by Ulf Goran Ashlund, in association with Yorkshire
Television. — London : Oxford University Press, 1974. — 16p ;
obl 4to.
ISBN 0-19-322212-4 : £0.65

(B74-50482)

KE/TSPDW — With guitar & piano. Songs, etc
Newman, Anthony
Barricades (after Couperin) : for voice, guitar and keyboard /
music by Anthony Newman ; words by Mary Jane Newman. —
New York ; London : Schirmer, 1974. — 12p ; 4to.
A freely written melodic line is superimposed on the constantly changing
harmonic base of Couperin's 'Les Barricades mystérieuses', not a note of
which has been altered.
Unpriced
Also classified at KDW; KE/TSDW

(B74-51064)

**KE/TWTTDW/AY — With Appalachian dulcimer. Songs, etc.
Collections**
Hellman, Neal
Life is like a mountain dulcimer : songs / compiled by Neal
Hellman and Sally Holden. — New York : Ludlow Music ;
[London] : [Essex Music], 1974. — 52p ; 4to.
With gramophone record.
Unpriced

(B74-51065)

KEZ — UNACCOMPANIED VOCAL SOLOS
**KEZDW/G/AYD — Unaccompanied voices. Folk songs. Collections.
England**
Purslow, Frank
The foggy dew : more English folk songs from the Hammond
Gardiner Mss / selected and edited by Frank Purslow. —
London : E.F.D.S., 1974. — iv,127p ; 8vo.
£0.90

(B74-50113)

KF — FEMALE VOICE, CHILD'S VOICE
KFLDH — Soprano voice. Motets, Anthems, Hymns, etc
Laderman, Ezra
From the psalms : for soprano and piano / by Ezra Laderman. —
New York ; London : Oxford University Press, 1971. — 23p ; 4to.
Unpriced

(B74-50483)

KFLDW/AY — Soprano voice. Songs, etc. Collections
Women speaking : six songs for sopranos. — London : Thames,
1974. — 28p ; 4to.
Contents: Song for a girl (Dryden), by Donald Swann - Entreat me not to
leave thee (Ruth 1), by Peter Naylor - When I am dead (Rossetti), by James
Butt - The bakery (Hyan), by Betty Roe - The exile, by Thomas Pitfield -
Small-town Gladys (Campbell), by William Blezard.
Unpriced

(B74-51066)

KFLE/MDX — Soprano voice with orchestra. Secular cantatas
Tippett, *Sir* Michael
Symphony no.3 / music and text by Michael Tippett. — London :
Schott, 1974. — 216p ; 8vo.
Duration 55 min.
Unpriced

(B74-50114)

**KFLE/NUPNQDW — Soprano voice. With woodwind, strings &
keyboard sextet. Songs, etc**
Shifrin, Seymour
Satires of circumstance (1969) : [song cycle], soprano, flute
(piccola), clarinet, violin, violoncello, double bass and piano / [by]
Seymour Shifrin ; poems by Thomas Hardy. — New York ;
London : Peters, 1971. — 54p ; 4to.
Duration 6 1/2 min.
Unpriced

(B74-51067)

KFLE/NYHRDX — Soprano voice with flute & percussion. Secular cantatas
Boucourechliev, André
Grodek d'apres Georg Trakl (1963, revision 1969) : for soprano voice, flute and percussion / [by] André Boucourechliev. — London : Universal, 1974. — 13p ; obl. fol.
Unpriced

(B74-51068)

KFLE/RXNSDX — Soprano voice with string quartet. Secular cantatas
Tredici, David del
I hear an army : for soprano and string quartet / by David del Tredici ; text XXXVI from 'Chamber music' by James Joyce. — New York ; [London] : Boosey and Hawkes, 1974. — 8vo.
Study score (35p.) & 4 parts.
£2.00

(B74-51069)

KFLE/VVPDW — Soprano voice with clarinet & piano. Songs, etc
Rorem, Ned
Ariel : five poems of Sylvia Plath, for soprano clarinet and piano / by Ned Rorem. — New York ; London : Boosey and Hawkes, 1974. — 4to.
Score (31p.) & part.
£3.00

(B74-50115)

KFLE/WSPLRDE — Soprano voice with trumpet & organ. Religious cantatas
Einem, Gottfried von
Geistliche Sonate : für Sopran, Trompete und Orgel. Op.38 / [von] Gottfried von Einem ; registrierung von Irmgard Knitl ; [words from the Bible] ; English words adapted from the Scriptures by Martin Hall. — London : Boosey and Hawkes, 1974. — obl.4to & 4to.
Score (28p.) & part.
Unpriced

(B74-51070)

KFT — HIGH VOICE
KFTDW/AY — Songs, etc. Collections
Liddell, Claire
The kindling fire : twelve Burns songs, arranged for high voice using the airs to which Burns set his verses / piano accompaniments and notes by Claire Liddell. — Wendover : Roberton, 1974. — 31p ; 4to.
£1.00

(B74-51072)

KFTE/TSDW — With guitar. Songs, etc
Argento, Dominick
Letters from composers : for high voice and guitar / by Dominick Argento. — New York ; [London] : Boosey and Hawkes, 1971. — 31p ; 4to.
Unpriced

(B74-51073)

KFTE/VVDW — With clarinet. Songs, etc
Argento, Dominick
To be sung upon the water : barcarolles and nocturnes for high voice, piano and clarinet (also bass clarinet) / by Dominick Argento ; poems by William Wordsworth. — New York ; [London] : Boosey and Hawkes, 1974. — 4to.
Score (46p.) & part. — Only one player is required for the two clarinets.
Unpriced

(B74-50484)

KFV — MIDDLE VOICE
KFVDW — Songs, etc
Berthomieu, Marc
Jardins de Paris : pour voix moyenne / par Marc Berthomieu ; poèmes de Daniel Schmitt. — Paris ; [London] : Chappell, 1974. — 26p ; fol.
Unpriced

(B74-50485)

Carter, Elliot
Voyage : for medium voice and piano / by Elliot Carter ; poem by Hart Crane. — New York ; London : Associated Music Publishers, 1973. — 7p ; 4to.
£0.40

(B74-50486)

Einem, Gottfried von
[Rosa mystica. Op.40. Vocal score]. Rosa mystica. Op.40 : acht Gesänge für mittlere Singstimme / von Gottfried von Einem ; Worte von H.C. Artmann. — London : Boosey and Hawkes, 1974. — 36p ; 4to.
£2.50

(B74-50116)

Hamilton, Alasdair
The plumes of time : 4 songs for medium voice and piano / by Alasdair Hamilton ; words by Lewis Spence. — Wendover : Roberton, 1973. — 11p ; 4to.
£0.50

(B74-50117)

Rorem, Ned
War scenes : for medium-low voice and piano / by Ned Rorem ; text by Walt Whitman. — New York ; [London] : Boosey and Hawkes, 1971. — 24p ; 4to.
Unpriced

(B74-51074)

Rubbra, Edmund
Nocturne, Op.54 : song for medium voice and piano / by Edmund Rubbra ; words by Aleman; translated from the Greek by H.T. Wade-Gery. — South Croydon : Lengnick, 1974. — 3p ; 4to.
£0.30

(B74-50487)

KFVE/MDW — With orchestra. Songs, etc
Einem, Gottfried von
Rosa mystica. Op. 40 : acht Gesänge für mittlere Singstimme und Orchester / von Gottfried von Einem ; Worte von H.C. Artmann. — London : Boosey and Hawkes, 1974. — 47p ; 8vo.
Miniature score.
Unpriced

(B74-50118)

KFVE/TSDW — With guitar. Songs, etc
Gammie, Ian
Five 17th century songs / arranged for medium voice and guitar (optional part for gamba or cello) by Ian Gammie. — London : Thames, 1974. — 8p ; 8vo.
Unpriced

(B74-51075)

KFX — LOW VOICE
KFXDW — Songs, etc
Hovhaness, Alan
Four songs, Opus 238 and Four songs, Opus 242 : low voice and piano / by Alan Hovhaness. — New York ; London : Peters, 1974. — 46p ; 4to.
Words of Opus 238 in Armenian Van dialect and English.
£6.00

(B74-51076)

KFXE/VRPDE — With flute & piano. Religious cantatas
Reitter, Hermann
Prediger Salomo 12, 1-9 : Solokantate für tiefe Singstimme, Flöte und Klavier (oder Orgel) / [von] Herman Reutter. — Mainz ; London : Schott, 1974. — 4to.
Score (11p.) & 2 parts.
£2.32

(B74-50488)

KG — MALE VOICE
KGE/SPDX — With violin & piano. Secular cantatas
Henze, Hans Werner
[Concerto for violin, no.2. Vocal score]. 2nd violin concerto for solo violin, tape, voices and 33 instrumentalists / by Hans Werner Henze, using the poem 'Hommage à Godel' by Hans Magnus Enzenberger; translated by Desmond Clayton and Hans Magnus Enzenberger, piano score by Henning Brauel. — Mainz ; London : Schott, 1974. — 4to.
Score (82p.) & part. — Duration 29 min.
£7.20

(B74-50119)

KGNDW — Baritone voice. Songs, etc
Alwyn, William
Mirages : a song cycle for baritone and piano / words and music by William Alwyn. — South Croydon : Lengnick, 1974. — 32p ; 4to.
£1.25

(B74-50489)

Hohensee, Wolfgang
Drei Lieder : für Bariton und Klavier / [von] Wolfgang Hohensee ; nach Worten von Rabindranath Tagore. — Leipzig ; [London] : Peters, 1973. — 12p ; 8vo.
Unpriced

(B74-51077)

KGXDW — Bass voice. Songs, etc
Travis, Roy
Songs and epilogues : for bass voice and piano / by Roy Travis ;
words by Sappho ; translated by William Ellery Leonard and
others. — New York ; [London] : Oxford University Press, 1971.
— 17p ; 4to.
Unpriced

(B74-51078)

KHYE/M — Speaker with orchestra
Roxburgh, Edwin
How pleasant to know Mr. Lear : for narrator and orchestra / by
Edwin Roxburgh. — London : United Music, 1972. — 126p ; 4to.
Unpriced

(B74-50120)

KHYE/QRP — Speaker with harpsichord
Kagel, Mauricio
Recitativarie : für singende Cembalistin, 1971/72 / [von] Mauricio
Kagel. — London : Universal, 1973. — 11p ; 4to.
The harpsichordist speaks to his own accompaniment.
Unpriced

(B74-51079)

KHYE/SPM — Speaker with violin
Ridout, Alan
Ferdinand : for speaker and solo violin / by Alan Ridout ; words
by Munro Leaf. — London : Chappell, 1974. — 12p ; 4to.
Unpriced

(B74-51080)

LH — DANCES
LH/H/AY — Dances for dancing. Collections
Matthews, Nibs
Callers' choice : a selection of recently composed dances /
prepared for publication by Nibs and Jean Matthews. — London :
English Folk Dance and Song Society.
Book 1. — 1973. — 16p ; 8vo.
ISBN 0-85418-035-4 : Unpriced

(B74-50121)

LN — ENSEMBLES
LN/AYH (XCTQ26) — Collections. France, 1475-1500
Wilkin, Nigel
Three French songs from the late 14th century : for voice and 2
or 3 instruments / edited by Nigel Wilkins. — Lustleigh : Antico,
1974. — 4to.
Score (8p.) & 4 parts. — Contents: 1: Alarme alarme/ by Grimace - 2: Soit
tart, tempre, main ou soir/ anon - 3: Quiconques vent d'amours joir/ anon.
Unpriced
Primary classification KE/LNTDW/AYH (XCTQ26)

(B74-50477)

LN/L — Ensembles. Religious music
Reynolds, Gordon
Praise with instruments / by Gordon Reynolds. — Sevenoaks :
Novello.
Volume 1. — 1974. — 52p ; 8vo. —
£0.75

(B74-50122)

LNRH — Quintets. Dances
Demantius, Johann Christoph
[77 newe ausserlesne liebliche zierliche Polnischer und Teutscher
Art Tantze. Selections]. Fifteen German and Polish dances, 1601 :
for five instruments / [by] Johann Christoph Demantius ; edited by
Bernard Thomas. — London : London Pro Musica, 1974. —
4to.
Score (16p.) & 7 parts - With a continuo part and an optional decorated top
part.
Unpriced

(B74-51081)

LNS — Quartets
Manchicourt, Pierre de
Nine chansons : for four voices or instruments / [by] Pierre de
Manchicourt ; edited by Bernard Thomas. — London : London
Pro musica, 1974. — 20p ; 4to.
Unpriced
Primary classification EZDU

Thomas, Bernard
Four pieces of the late fifteenth century : for four instruments
ATTB / edited by Bernard Thomas. — London : Pro Musica,
1973. — 4to.
Score (12p.) & 4 parts. — Contents: 1: La Spagna - 2: La Spagna - 3: Ma
bouche rit, by Pierre de la Rue - 4: La Guercia.
Unpriced

(B74-50123)

Thomas, Bernard
Twelve chansons (c.1530) : for four instruments or voices / edited
by Bernard Thomas. — London : Pro Musica, 1973. — 16p ; 4to.
Unpriced
Also classified at EZDU/AYH

(B74-50124)

LNS — Quartets. Score reading
Wilkinson, Philip George
100 score-reading exercises / by Philip G. Wilkinson. —
Sevenoaks : Novello, 1974. — 79p ; obl.4to.
£1.50
Primary classification LNT

LNSH — Quartets. Dances
Bendusi, Francesco
Opera nova de balli, 1553 : for four instruments / [by] Francesco
Bendusi ; edited by Bernard Thomas. — London : London Pro
Musica, 1974. — 24p ; 4to.
Unpriced

(B74-51082)

LNT — Trios
Ruffo, Vincenzo
[Capricci in musica a tre voci, nos. 4, 10, 1]. Three pieces for
three instruments / by Vincenzo Ruffo ; edited by Bernard
Thomas. — London : Pro Musica, 1973. — 4to.
Score (8p.) & 3 parts. — Contents: 1: La Brava - 2: Martin minoit son
portiau au marche - 3: La sol fa re mi.
Unpriced

(B74-50125)

LNT — Trios. Score reading
Wilkinson, Philip George
100 score-reading exercises / by Philip G. Wilkinson. —
Sevenoaks : Novello, 1974. — 79p ; obl.4to.
£1.50
Also classified at LNS

(B74-51083)

LNTQ/AY — Two instruments & piano. Collections
Máriássy, István
Chamber music for beginners : for two melodic instruments and
bass, with continuo / edited by Máriássy István. — London :
Boosey and Hawkes ; Budapest : Editio Musica, 1973. — 4to.
Score (19p.) & part.
£1.25

(B74-51084)

LNU — Duets
Guami, Francesco
[Ricercari a due voci, nos. 1-3, 6-10, 16-23]. Ten ricercari, 1588 :
for two instruments, A.T. / by Francesco Guami ; edited by
Bernard Thomas. — London : Pro Musica, 1973. — 16p ; 4to.
Unpriced

(B74-50126)

Guami, Francesco
[Ricercari for two instruments. *Selections*]. Seven ricercari, 1588 :
for two instruments, S.A. / [by] Francesco Guami Luchese ;
edited by Bernard Thomas. — London : London Pro Musica,
1974. — 15p ; 4to.
Unpriced

(B74-51085)

LNUH/G/AY — Duets. Folk dances. Collections
Wood, Barbara
Join the band : a selection of folk dance tunes for beginners, with
second parts / compiled by Barbara Wood. — London : English
Folk Dance and Song Society, 1974. — 52p ; obl. 4to.
ISBN 0-85418-079-6 : Unpriced

(B74-50490)

**LP — WORKS FOR UNSPECIFIED INSTRUMENT WITH
PIANO**
LPH/AYD(XEJ10) — Dances. Collections. England, 1609-1618
Walls, Peter
Twenty-one masque dances of the early seventeenth century for
one instrument and continuo / [edited by] Peter Walls [and]
Bernard Thomas. — London : London Pro musica, 1974. — 4to.
Score (24p.) & part - From British Museum Add. Ms.10444.
Unpriced

(B74-51086)

LPJ — Miscellaneous works
Kagel, Mauricio
Unguis incarnatus est : für Klavier und ... / von Mauricio Kagel.
— London : Universal, 1973. — 7p ; 4to.
Unpriced

(B74-50127)

LPM/AYDM — Collections. Ireland
Bulmer, Dave
Music from Ireland / compiled by D. Bulmer, N. Sharpley. —
South Shields (154 Bamburgh Ave, South Shields) : Dave Bulmer.
Vol.1. — 1974. — 26p ; 4to.
Unpriced

(B74-51087)

LPMJ — Miscellaneous works
Kagel, Mauricio
General Bass : für kontinuierliche Instrumentalklange / von Mauricio Kagel. — London : Universal, 1973. — 4p ; 4to.
This composition may be performed on any instrument which is capable of producing sounds in the prescribed range.
Unpriced

(B74-50128)

M — ORCHESTRAL MUSIC
M/AF — Exercises
Erdmann, Veit
Exercises and pieces for orchestra groups / by Veit Erdmann. — Mainz ; London : Schott, 1973. — 11p ; 4to.
£1.20

(B74-50129)

ME — SYMPHONIES
Stoker, Richard
Little symphony / by Richard Stoker. — London : Boosey and Hawkes, 1973. — 4to.
Score (15p.) & parts.
£3.30

(B74-50130)

MH — DANCES
Liadov, Anatoly
[Eight Russian folksongs. Op.58, nos. 6-8: arr]. Russian folksongs. Set 2 / [by] Anatole Liadov ; arranged by David Stone. — London : Boosey and Hawkes, 1974. — 4to.
Score (24p.), Piano conductor (8p.) & 23 parts.
£4.50

(B74-51088)

MJ — MISCELLANEOUS WORKS
Platts, Kenneth
Prelude and scherzo for small orchestra. Op.7 / by Kenneth Platts. — London : Keith Prowse, 1973. — 12p ; 4to.
£0.50

(B74-50131)

MK — ARRANGEMENTS
Haydn, Joseph
[Quartet for strings, no.17, in B flat major. Op.3, no.5. Serenade: arr]. Serenade / by Joseph Haydn ; arranged for woodwind, brass and percussion by Stuart Johnson. — London : Oxford University Press, 1974. — 4to.
Score (15p.) & 19 parts. — Attributed in this publication to Haydn; probably by Romanus Hofstetter.
ISBN 0-19-364179-8 : Unpriced

(B74-51089)

Liadov, Anatoly
[Eight Russian folksongs. Op. 58, nos. 1, 2, 4: arr]. Russian folksongs, set 1 / [by] Anatole Liadov; arranged for school orchestra by David Stone. — London : Boosey and Hawkes, 1974. — 4to.
Score (23p.), Piano conductor (8p.) & 23 parts.
Score £1.50, Piano conductor £0.50, Set £2.50

(B74-51090)

Tchaikovsky, Peter
['1812' overture: arr]. '1812' overture : for school orchestra / by P. Tchaikovsky ; arranged by Anthony Carter. — London : Bosworth, 1974. — fol.
Score (35p.) with additional score with 'ad lib' parts starting at letter U.
£2.10

(B74-50491)

MK/AHR — Arrangements. Minuets
Bach, Johann Sebastian
[Brandenburg concerto, no.1, in F major. S.1046. Menuetto: arr]. Menuetto / by J.S. Bach ; arranged for orchestra by Philip Gordon. — New York : Warner ; London : Blossom, 1974. — 4to.
Score (12p.), condensed score (4p.) & 34 parts.
Unpriced

(B74-50492)

MK/JM — Arrangements. Incidental music
Bizet, Georges
[L'Arlesienne, 1st suite. Carillon: arr]. Carillon / [by] Georges Bizet ; arranged for school orchestra by David Stone. — London : Boosey and Hawkes, 1974. — 4to.
Score (27p.), Piano conductor (8p.) & 24 parts.
Score £1.50, Piano conductor £0.50, Set £2.50

(B74-51091)

MM — WORKS FOR SYMPHONY ORCHESTRA
MM/HM — Ballet music
Kay, Hershey
The clowns : a ballet / by Hershey Kay ; choreography by Gerald Arpino. — New York ; [London] : Boosey and Hawkes, 1971. — 81p ; 4to.
Unpriced

(B74-51092)

MM/JM — Incidental music
Mendelssohn, Felix
[A midsummer night's dream. Op 61. Selections]. Five orchestral pieces, Op.61 / [by] Felix Mendelssohn-Bartholdy ; foreword by Roger Fiske. — London : Eulenburg, 1974. — 80p ; 8vo.
Miniature score.
Unpriced

(B74-51093)

MM/JR — Films
Copland, Aaron
Our town : music from the film score / by Aaron Copland. — London : Boosey and Hawkes, 1967. — 4to.
Score (24p.) & 26 parts.
£6.75

(B74-51094)

MM/T — Variations
Russell, Leslie
Blaydon races : variations for orchestra / [by] Leslie Russell. — London : Boosey and Hawkes, 1974. — 4to.
Score (31p.) & 26 parts.
£10.50

(B74-51095)

MM/Y/JR — Fugues. Films
Thomson, Virgil
[Louisiana story. *Boy fights alligator*]. Boy fights alligator : fugue, for orchestra / by Virgil Thomson. — New York ; London : Schirmer, 1972. — 24p ; 4to.
Duration 4 min.
Unpriced

(B74-50132)

MME — Symphonies
Alwyn, William
Symphony no.5, 'Hydriotaphia' / by William Alwyn. — South Croydon : Lengnick, 1973. — 60p ; 4to.
Facsimile of the composer's autograph. — Commissioned by the Arts Council of Great Britain for the Norfolk and Norwich Triennial Festival of 1973.
£4.00

(B74-50133)

Anis, Fulaihan
Symphony no.2 / by Anis Fulaihan. — New York ; [London] : Boosey and Hawkes, 1971. — 121p ; 4to.
Unpriced

(B74-51096)

Arnold, Malcolm
Symphony no.6. Op.95 / [by] Malcolm Arnold. — London : Faber Music, 1974. — 126p ; 8vo.
Duration 26 min.
Unpriced

(B74-50493)

Berlioz, Hector
Symphonie fantastique / von Hector Berlioz ; vorgelegt von Nicholas Temperley. — Wiesbaden : Breitkopf and Härtel ; Cassel ; London : Bärenreiter, 1973. — 164p ; fol.
Separate edition based on 'Hector Berlioz, New edition of the complete works', vol.16.
£13.20

(B74-50494)

Bizet, Georges
[Symphony in C major]. Symphony, C major / by Georges Bizet ; edited from the sources by Hans-Hubert Schonzeler ; foreword by Felix Aprahamian. — London : Eulenburg, 1973. — xi,114p ; 8vo.
Miniature score.
Unpriced

(B74-51097)

Hovhaness, Alan
[Symphony no.1. Op.17, no.2 (Exile)]. Exile symphony, (Symphony no.1). Op.17, no.2 / [by] Alan Hovhaness. — New York ; London : Peters, 1972. — 92p ; 4to.
£7.50

(B74-51098)

Simpson, Robert
Symphony no.3 / by Robert Simpson. — South Croydon : Lengnick, 1974. — 118p ; 4to.
£6.50

(B74-50134)

Simpson, Robert
Symphony no.3 (1962) / by Robert Simpson. — Revised ed. — South Croydon : Lengnick, 1974. — 118p ; 4to.
Unpriced

(B74-50495)

Skriabin, Aleksandr Nikolaevich
Symphony no.2 in C minor. Op. 29 / by Alexander Scriabin ;
foreword by Faubion Bowers. — London : Eulenburg, 1973. —
viii,248p ; 8vo.
Miniature score.
Unpriced

(B74-50135)

MMF — Concertos
Carter, Elliott
Concerto for orchestra / by Elliott Carter. — New York ;
London : Associated Music, 1972. — viii,189p ; fol.
Duration 23 min.
Unpriced

(B74-50136)

Laderman, Ezra
Concerto for orchestra / [by] Ezra Laderman. — New York ;
[London] : Oxford University Press, 1974. — 78p ; 4to.
Duration 22 min.
ISBN 0-19-385533-x : Unpriced

(B74-50496)

Menotti, Gian Carlo
Triplo concerto a tre / by Gian Carlo Menotti. — New York ;
London : Schirmer, 1972. — 80p ; 8vo.
Duration 20 min.
Unpriced

(B74-50137)

Williamson, Malcolm
Concerto grosso / by Malcolm Williamson. — London :
Weinberger, 1974. — 65p ; 8vo.
Miniature score. — Duration 11 min.
Unpriced

(B74-50497)

MMF/W — Concertos. Rondos
Diemer, Emma Lou
Rondo concertante : for orchestra / by Emma Lou Diemer. —
New York ; [London] : Boosey and Hawkes, 1971. — 4to.
Score & 33 parts.
Unpriced

(B74-51099)

MMG — Suites
Burkhard, Willy
Die schwarze Spinne, Op.80a : Suite für Orchester / von Willy
Burkhard. — Cassel ; London : Bärenreiter, 1973. — 99p ; 4to.
Facsimile of the composer's autograph. — Duration 20 min.
£3.25

(B74-50498)

McCabe, John
[The lion, the witch and the wardrobe. Selections]. Suite, The lion,
the witch and the wardrobe : for orchestra / by John McCabe. —
Sevenoaks : Novello, 1974. — 100p ; 4to.
£3.50

(B74-50499)

MMG/HM — Ballet suites
Carter, Elliott
Pocohontas : orchestral suite from the ballet / by Elliott Carter.
— New York ; London : Associated Music, 1969. — iv,79p ; 4to.
Duration 20 min.
Unpriced

(B74-50138)

MMH — Dances
Mathias, William
Celtic dances. Opus 60 : for orchestra / by William Mathias. —
London : Oxford University Press, 1974. — 88p ; 4to.
ISBN 0-19-365572-1 : £3.50

(B74-51100)

Washburn, Robert
Prologue and dance : for orchestra / by Robert Washburn. —
New York ; London : Oxford University Press, 1974. — 32p ; 4to.
Duration 7 min.
Unpriced

(B74-50500)

MMJ — Miscellaneous works
Barber, Samuel
Fadograph of a western scene : for orchestra. Op.44 / by Samuel
Barber. — New York ; London : Schirmer, 1972. — 26p ; 4to.
Duration 6 1/2 min.
Unpriced

(B74-50139)

Berio, Luciano
Chemins IIb-c / by Luciano Berio. — London : Universal, 1973.
— 66p ; 4to.
The bass clarinet solo is optional; when omitted the work is called Chemins
IIb, when played, Chemins IIc.
Unpriced

(B74-50501)

Berlioz, Hector
Waverley. Op.1 : overture / by Hector Berlioz ; foreword by
Roger Fiske. — London : Eulenberg, 1974. — vii,59p ; 8vo.
Miniature score.
Unpriced

(B74-50502)

Birtwistle, Harrison
An imaginary landscape : orchestra / by Harrison Birtwistle. —
London : Universal, 1974. — 85p ; 8vo.
Duration 17 min.
Unpriced

(B74-50140)

Chavez, Carlos
Discovery = Descubrimiento : for orchestra / by Carlos Chavez.
— New York ; London : Schirmer, 1973. — 43p ; 8vo.
Study score.
£2.35

(B74-50503)

Copland, Aaron
[Music for radio (1937)]. Prairie journal : [for orchestra] / [by]
Aaron Copland. — London : Boosey and Hawkes, 1967. — 4to.
Score (59p.) & 31 parts.
£15.00

(B74-51101)

Dodgson, Stephen
Zigeunerlieder = Gypsy songs. Op.103 : for four-part chorus of
mixed voices with soprano and tenor solos and piano
accompaniment / [by] Johannes Brahms ; text by Hugo Conrat;
edited and with English texts by Maynard Klein. — London :
Chappell, 1974. — 29p ; 4to.
Unpriced

(B74-50504)

Franck, César
Le Chasseur maudit / by César Franck ; edited by André
Coeuroy ; foreword by Roger Fiske. — London : Eulenburg, 1973.
— x,116p ; 8vo.
Miniature score.
Unpriced

(B74-50505)

Herrmann, Bernard
Portrait of Hitch : a musical portrait of Alfred Hitchcock, for
orchestra / [by] Bernard Herrmann. — Sevenoaks : Novello, 1974.
— 80p ; 4to.
Duration 8 min.
Unpriced

(B74-51102)

Johnson, Hunter
Past the evening sun : orchestra / by Hunter Johnson. — New
York : Galaxy ; London : Galliard, 1971. — 23p ; 4to.
Unpriced

(B74-50506)

Muczynski, Robert
Charade. Op.28 : for orchestra / by Robert Muczynski. — New
York ; London : Schirmer, 1974. — 4to.
Score (43p.) & 30 parts. — Various parts are in duplicate.
Unpriced

(B74-51103)

Rachmaninoff, Sergei
The isle of the dead. Op. 29 : symphonic poem / by Sergei
Rachmaninoff. — London : Boosey and Hawkes, 1974. — 71p ;
8vo.
Miniature score.
£1.25

(B74-50141)

Saint-Saëns, Camille
Le Carnival des animaux : grande fantasie zoologique / [by]
Camille Saint-Saëns ; edited by Max Pommer. — Leipzig ;
[London] : Peters, 1973. — x,68p ; 8vo.
Miniature score - Duration 24 min.
Unpriced

(B74-51104)

Sculthorpe, Peter
Sun music IV : for orchestra / by Peter Sculthorpe. — London :
Faber Music, 1973. — 24p ; 4to.
Duration 9 min.
Unpriced

(B74-50142)

Smetana, Bedřich
[My country. Vltava]. My fatherland = Ma vlast : a cycle of
symphonic poems / by Bedřich Smetana ; revised by Vilem
Zemanek. — London : Eulenburg.
Miniature score.
No.2 : Vltava / foreword by John Clapham. — 1972. — vi,104p ; 8vo.
Unpriced

(B74-50507)

Strauss, Richard
[Till Eulenspiegel. Op.28]. Till Eulenspiegels Lustige Streiche :
nach alter Schelmenweise in Rondeauforme / by Richard Strauss
; foreword by Norman Del Mar. — London : Eulenburg, 1974. —
xiii,100p ; 8vo.
Miniature score.
Unpriced

(B74-51105)

MMK — Arrangements
Strauss, Johann, *b.1825*
[Der Zigeunerbaron. Selections: arr]. The gypsy baron suite / by
Johann Strauss ; arranged for orchestra by Hans Schwieger. —
New York ; London : Boosey and Hawkes, 1973. — 4to.
Score (116p.) & 28 parts.
£15.00

(B74-50143)

MMK/DW — Arrangements. Songs, etc
Villa-Lobos, Heitor
Bachianas brasileiras, no.5. Aria (Cantilena) / [by] Heitor
Villa-Lobos ; arranged for orchestra by John Krance. — New
York ; London : Associated Music, 1971. — 27p ; 4to.
Unpriced

(B74-50508)

MP — WORKS FOR SOLO INSTRUMENT (S) & ORCHESTRA
MPQ — Piano & orchestra
Lazarof, Henri
Textures : for piano and 5 instrumental groups / by Henri
Lazarof. — New York ; London : Associated Music, 1972. — iv,
52p ; 8vo.
Duration 23 1/2 min.
Unpriced

(B74-50144)

MPQF — Concertos
Mozart, Wolfgang Amadeus
[Concerto for piano, no.25, in C major. K.503]. Piano concerto, C
major. K.503 / [by] Wolfgang Amadeus Mozart ; foreword by
Denis Matthews. — London : Eulenburg, 1974. — xiii,98p ; 8vo.
Miniature score.
Unpriced

(B74-51106)

MPQNU — Two pianos & orchestra
Halffter, Cristóbal
Procesional : para dos pianos solistas y orquesta / [de] Cristóbal
Halffter. — London : Universal, 1974. — 33p ; fol.
Unpriced

(B74-51107)

MPRF — Organ & orchestra. Concertos
Halffter, Cristóbal
Pinturas negras : concierto para organo y orquesta (1972) / [de]
Cristóbal Halffter. — London : Universal, 1974. — 34p ; fol.
Unpriced

(B74-51108)

Handel, George Frideric
[Concertos for organ. Op.7]. Organ concertos. Op.7 / by George
Frideric Handel ; edited with a foreword by Peter Williams. —
London : Eulenburg.
No.1 : B flat major. — 1974. — xx,41p ; 8vo.
Miniature score.
£0.80

(B74-50509)

No.2 : A major. — 1974. — xvi,20p ; 8vo.
Miniature score.
£0.80

(B74-50510)

No.3 : B flat major. — 1974. — xvi,27p ; 8vo.
Miniature score.
£0.80

(B74-50511)

No.4 : D minor. — 1974. — xvi,19p ; 8vo.
Miniature score.
£0.80

(B74-50512)

No.5 : G minor. — 1974. — xvi,16p ; 8vo.
Miniature score.
£0.80

(B74-50513)

No.6 : B flat major. — 1974. — xvi,14p ; 8vo.
Miniature score.
£0.80

(B74-50514)

MPSF — Violin & orchestra. Concertos
Telemann, Georg Philipp
[Concerto for violin in E minor]. Konzert, E-moll, für Violine,
zwei Oboen, Streicher und Basso continuo, (Fagott ad libitum) /
[von] Georg Philipp Telemann ; herausgegeben von Hans Rudolf
Jung ; Continuo-Aussetzung von Johannes Gerdes. — Leipzig ;
[London] : Peters, 1973. — 24p ; 4to.
Unpriced

(B74-51109)

MPSQF — Viola & orchestra. Suites
Burkhard, Willy
[Concerto for viola and orchestra]. Konzert für Viola und
Orchester / von Willy Burkhard. — Cassel ; Basel ; [London] :
Bärenreiter, 1973. — 69p ; 4to.
A facsimile of the composer's autograph. — Duration 20 min.
£2.55

(B74-50515)

MPTQF — Harp & orchestra. Concertos
Ginastera, Alberto
[Concerto for harp. Op.25]. Harp concerto. Op.25 / by Alberto
Ginastera. — London : Boosey and Hawkes, 1974. — 111p ; 4to.
Duration 23 min.
£7.50

(B74-51110)

MPUNSE — Wind quartet & orchestra. Symphonies
Pleyel, Ignaz
[Sinfonia concertante for flute, oboe, horn, bassoon, no.5, in F
major: arr]. Symphonie concertante no.5 in F major : for flute,
oboe (clarinet), horn, bassoon and orchestra / by Ignaz Pleyel ;
edited by David Lasocki, piano reduction by R.P. Block. —
London : Musica rara, 1973. — 4to.
Score (45p.) & 5 parts.
Unpriced

(B74-50516)

MPVR — Flute & orchestra
Dorati, Antal
Night music : for solo flute and small orchestra / [by] Antal
Dorati. — London : Chester : Hansen, 1974. — 54p ; 8vo.
Duration 27 min.
Unpriced

(B74-51111)

MPVTPLSRE — Cello, oboe & orchestra. Symphonies
Bach, Johann Christian
[Sinfonia concertante for cello & oboe in F major]. Sinfonia
concertante in F major / by J.C. Bach ; edited by Frank Dawes.
— London : Eulenburg, 1973. — 8pt ; 4to.
£2.60

(B74-50146)

Bach, Johann Christian
Sinfonia concertante, F major for oboe, violoncello and orchestra /
by Johann Christian Bach ; edited with a foreword by Frank
Dawes. — London : Eulenburg, 1973. — vi,32p ; 8vo.
Miniature score.
Unpriced

(B74-50145)

MPVVF — Clarinet & orchestra. Concertos
Mozart, Wolfgang Amadeus
[Concerto for clarinet in A major. K.622]. Concerto, A major, for
clarinet and orchestra. K.622 / by Wolfgang Amadeus Mozart ;
edited by Rudolf Gerber ; foreword by Alan Hacker. — London :
Eulenburg, 1971. — viii,68p ; 8vo.
Miniature score.
£0.85

(B74-51112)

MPWTF — Horn & orchestra. Concertos
Musgrave, Thea
[Concerto for horn]. Horn concerto / by Thea Musgrave. —
London : Chester, 1974. — 88p ; 8vo.
Duration 21 min.
Unpriced

(B74-50517)

MR — WORKS FOR CHAMBER ORCHESTRA
MRE — Symphonies
Bach, Johann Christian
[Symphony in G minor. Opus 6, no.6]. Symphony, G minor. Op.
6, no.6 / by Johann Christian Bach ; edited with a foreword by
Richard Platt. — London : Eulenburg, 1974. — viii,29p ; 8vo.
Miniature score.
£0.80

(B74-50147)

Erskine, Thomas, *Earl of Kelly*
[Periodical overture, no.17, in E flat major]. Symphony in E flat
major, Periodical overture 17 : for flutes, clarinets/oboes, bassoon,
horns, strings and continuo / by Thomas Erskine, Earl of Kelly ;
edited by David Johnson. — London : Oxford University Press,
1974. — 4to.
Score (31p.) & 16 parts.
ISBN 0-19-365170-x : £2.75

(B74-50518)

Wesley, Samuel
[Symphony no.5 in A major]. Symphony 5 in A major : for horns and strings / by Samuel Wesley. — London : Oxford University Press, 1974. — 4to.
Score (34p.) & 7 parts.
ISBN 0-19-368650-3 : Score £3.50, parts unpriced

(B74-50519)

MRF — Concertos
Ligeti, György
Chamber concerto for 13 instrumentalists / [by] György Ligeti. — Mainz ; London : Schott, 1974. — 106p ; 4to.
Study score.
£8.12

(B74-51113)

MRG — Suites
Handel, George Frideric
Water music / by George Frideric Handel ; edited and with a foreword by Roger Fiske. — London : Eulenburg, 1973. — xvi, 88p ; 8vo.
Miniature score.
£0.70

(B74-50148)

MRJ — Miscellaneous works
Greene, Maurice
Overture no.5 in D major / by Maurice Greene ; edited by Richard Platt. — London : Eulenburg, 1973. — 7pt ; 4to.
£1.50

(B74-50149)

Greene, Maurice
Overture no.6 in E flat major / by Maurice Greene ; edited by Richard Platt. — London : Eulenburg, 1973. — 7pt ; 4to.
£1.50

(B74-50150)

Holloway, Robin
Evening with angels : nine movements for chamber ensemble, woodwind, brass and strings / by Robin Holloway. — London : Oxford University Press, 1974. — 209p ; 8vo.
ISBN 0-19-357238-9 : £5.00

(B74-51114)

Horovitz, Joseph
Horizon overture : [for chamber orchestra] / by Joseph Horovitz. — Sevenoaks : Novello, 1974. — 27p ; 8vo.
Unpriced

(B74-50520)

Lazarof, Henri
Espaces : for chamber ensemble / by Henri Lazarof. — New York ; London : Associated Music, 1972. — 38p ; 8vo.
Unpriced

(B74-50151)

Morthenson, Jan W
Labor : meta-music for chamber orchestra / [by] Jan W. Morthenson. — London : Universal, 1974. — 35p ; 4to.
Unpriced

(B74-51115)

NU — WIND, STRINGS & KEYBOARD
NUNME — Nonets. Sonatas
Höffner, Anton
[Sonata for two trumpets, bassoon, string quintet & basso continuo in C major]. Sonata à 8 in C for 2 trumpets, bassoon, strings and continuo / [by] Anton Höffner ; [edited by] Robert Paul Block. — London : Musica rara, 1972. — 4to.
Score (14p.) & 12 parts.
Unpriced

(B74-50521)

NUNRE — Quintets. Sonatas
Schmelzer, Johann Heinrich
[Sonata for trumpet, violin, trombone, bassoon & basso continuo in G major, 'La Carioletta']. Sonata in G, 'La Carioletta' : for cornetto (trumpet), violin, trombone, bassoon and basso continuo / [by] J.H. Schmelzer ; [edited] Robert Minter. — London : Musica rara, 1974. — 4to.
Score (12p.) & 5 parts.
Unpriced

(B74-50522)

NUNSE — Quartets. Sonatas
Schmelzer, Johann Heinrich
[Sonata for violin, trombone, bassoon & basso continuo in A minor]. Sonata à 3 : for violin, trombone, bassoon & basso continuo / [by] J.H. Schmelzer ; [edited] Robert Minter. — London : Musica rara, 1974. — 4to.
Score (12p.) & 4 parts.
Unpriced

(B74-50523)

NUNTK/LE — Arrangements. Sonatas
Höffner, Anton
[Sonata for two trumpets, bassoon, string quintet & basso continuo in C major]. Sonata à 8 in C for 2 trumpets, bassoon, strings and continuo / [by] Anton Höffner ; trumpet, bassoon and piano reduction [edited by] Robert Paul Block. — London : Musica rara, 1972. — 4to.
Score (11p.) & 5 parts.
Unpriced

(B74-50524)

NUPNRF — Woodwind, string & keyboard quintets. Concertos
Vivaldi, Antonio
[Concerto for treble recorder, oboe, violin, bassoon and basso continuo in G major. P.105]. Concerto in G major : for treble recorder (flute), oboe, violin, bassoon and basso continuo. P.105 / [by] Antonio Vivaldi ; ed. David Lasocki, realization of basso continuo by R.P. Block. — London : Musica rara, 1973. — 4to.
Score (23p.) & 5 parts.
Unpriced

(B74-50525)

Vivaldi, Antonio
[Concerto for treble recorder, oboe, violin, bassoon & basso continuo in G minor. P.403]. Concerto in G minor : for treble recorder (flute), oboe, violin, bassoon and basso continuo. P.403 / [by] Antonio Vivaldi ; ed. David Lasocki, realization of basso continuo by R.P. Block. — London : Musica rara, 1973. — 4to.
Score (16p.) & 6 parts.
Unpriced

(B74-50526)

NURNT — Flute, strings & keyboard. Trios
Luening, Otto
Trio for flute, violin and piano (cello or bassoon ad lib.) / [by] Otto Luening. — New York : Highgate Press : Galaxy ; London : Galliard, 1974. — 4to.
Score (22p.) & 3 parts.
Unpriced

(B74-51116)

NUTNQF — Oboe, strings & keyboard sextets. Concertos
Albinoni, Tommaso
[Concerto for oboe, string quartet & basso continuo in C major. Op.9, no.5]. Concerto à 5 for oboe strings and continuo. Op.9, no.5 / [by] Tommaso Albinoni ; [edited by] Franz Giegling. — London : Musica rara, 1973. — 4to.
Score (32p.) & 6 parts.
Unpriced

(B74-50527)

NUTNRF — Oboe, strings & keyboard quintets. Concertos
Pepusch, Johann Christoph
[Concerto for woodwind & string quartet & basso continuo in B flat major. Op.8, no.3]. Concerto in B flat for 2 oboes or violins, 2 violins or oboes and basso continuo. Opus 8, no.3 / [by] Johann Christoph Pepusch ; ed. David Lasocki, realization of basso continuo by R.P. Block. — London : Musica rara, 1974. — 4to.
Score (14p.) & 5 parts - 'Although the title page of the Roger edition (circa 1717) of the Opus 8 set indicates that the concertos are for 2 treble recorders, 2 flutes or oboes or violins, and basso continuo, only numbers 1 and 4-6 can be thus played' - Editor's note.
Unpriced

(B74-50528)

Telemann, Georg Philipp
[Concerto for oboe, strings & basso continuo in C minor]. Concerto a 5 für Oboe, Streicher und Basso continuo C-moll / [von] Georg Philipp Telemann ; zum ersten Mal herausgegeben von Kurt Janetzky ; Generalbassaussetzung von Walter Heinz Bernstein. — Frankfurt : Litolff ; London : Peters, 1974. — 14p ; 4to.
£2.80

(B74-51117)

NUTNTE — Oboe, strings & keyboard trios. Suites
Telemann, Georg Philipp
[Sonata for oboe, violin & basso continuo in G major]. Sonata in G major for oboe, violin and basso continuo / by Georg Philipp Telemann ; first printed edition, edited by Klaus Hofmann. — Cassel ; London : Bärenreiter, 1973. — 4to.
Score (12p.) & 3 parts.
£1.80

(B74-50529)

NUTNTK/LF — Oboe, strings & keyboard trios. Arrangements. Concertos
Vivaldi, Antonio
[Concerto for oboe, violin & string orchestra in C minor, 'Lund': arr]. Concerto in C minor for oboe, violin and strings (Lund) / [by] Antonio Vivaldi ; ed. David Lasocki, piano reduction [and] realization of basso continuo by R.P. Block. — London : Musica rara, 1973. — 4to.
Score (15p.) & 2 parts.
Unpriced

(B74-50530)

NUVNT — Clarinet, strings & keyboard. Trios
Eberl, Anton
[Trio for clarinet, cello & piano in E flat major, Op.36]. Grand trio for piano, clarinet and violoncello. Op.36 / [by] Anton Eberl ; edited by H. Voxman. — London : Musica rara, 1973. — 4to.
Score (44p.) & 2 parts.
£2.85

(B74-50531)

NUVNT — Oboe, strings & keyboard. Trios
Berger, Wilhelm
[Trio for clarinet, cello and piano in G minor. Opus 94]. Trio in G minor for clarinet, cello and piano. Opus 94 / [by] Wilhelm Berger. — London : Musica rara, 1974. — 4to.
Score (55p.) & part.
Unpriced

(B74-50532)

NUXSNQE — Trumpet, strings & keyboard sextets. Sonatas
Grossi, Andrea
[Sonata for trumpet, string quartet & basso continuo in D major. Op.3, no.11]. Sonata a 5. Op.3, no.11 : for trumpet and strings / [by] Andrea Grossi ; ed. R.F. Block. — London : Musica rara, 1973. — 4to.
Score (18p.) & 9 parts.
Unpriced

(B74-50533)

Grossi, Andrea
[Sonata for trumpet, string quartet & basso continuo in D major. Op.3, no.12]. Sonata à 5. Op.3, no.12 : for trumpet and strings / [by] Andrea Grossi ; ed. R.P. Block. — London : Musica rara, 1973. — 4to.
Score (17p.) & 9 parts.
Unpriced

(B74-50534)

NUXSNRE — Trumpet, strings & keyboard quintets. Sonatas
Brückner, H
[Sonata for two trumpets, two violins & basso continuo]. Sonata for 2 cornetti (trumpets), 2 violins and basso continuo / [by] H. Brückner ; [edited by] Robert Minter. — London : Musica rara, 1974. — 4to.
Score (6p.) & 5 parts.
Unpriced

(B74-50537)

Torelli, Giuseppe
[Sonata for trumpet, string trio & basso continuo in D major. G.1]. Sonata for trumpet, strings and continuo in D. G. I / [by] Giuseppe Torelli ; edited and arranged by E.H. Tarr. — London : Musica rara, 1973. — 4to.
Score (19p.) & 9 parts.
Unpriced

(B74-50536)

Torelli, Giuseppe
[Sonata for trumpet, string trio & basso continuo in D major. G.2]. Sonata for trumpet, strings and continuo in D. G.2 / [by] Giuseppe Torelli ; edited and arranged by E.H. Tarr. — London : Musica rara, 1973. — 4to.
Score (12p.) & 9 parts.
Unpriced

(B74-50535)

NUXTNS/T — Horn, strings & keyboard quartets. Variations
Einem, Gottfried von
Reifliches Divertimento. Op. 35a : Variationen über Thema aus dem 3. Bild der Oper 'Der Besuch der alten dame' / für Violine, Bratsche, Horn und Klavier ; von Gottfried von Einem. — London : Boosey and Hawkes, 1974. — 4to.
Score (8p.) & 3 parts.
£1.50

(B74-50152)

NV — WIND & STRINGS
NVNN/T — Octets. Variations
Laderman, Ezra
Theme, variations and finale : for four winds and four strings / by Ezra Laderman. — New York ; [London] : Oxford University Press, 1974. — 4to.
Score (19p.) & 8 parts. — Duration 15 min.
Unpriced

(B74-50538)

NVNRE — Quintets. Sonatas
Thomson, Virgil
[Sonata da chiesa for wind & string quintet (Revised version)]. Sonata da chiesa (Revised version) : for clarinet in E flat, trumpet in C, viola, horn in F and trombone / [by] Virgil Thomson. — New York ; London : Boosey and Hawkes, 1974. — 4to.
Score (19p.) & 5 parts. — Contents: 1: Chorale - 2: Tango - 3: Fugue.
Unpriced

(B74-50539)

NVNS — Quartets
Boatwright, Howard
Serenade : for two strings and two winds / by Howard Boatwright. — New York ; [London] : Oxford University Press, 1974. — 26p ; 4to.
Duration 17 min.
ISBN 0-19-385008-7 : Unpriced

(B74-50540)

NVPNT — Woodwind & strings. Trios
Wiseman, Charles
Trio for 2 flutes & cello or bassoon in D major / by Carlo Wiseman; edited by John Leach. — Wendover : Roberton, 1974. — 4to.
Score (8p.) & part.
£0.50
Also classified at VNT

(B74-50541)

NVRNR — Flute & strings. Quintets
Kuhlau, Friedrich
[Quintet for flute & strings in A major. Op.51, no.3]. Quintet in A for flute and strings. Op.51, no.3 / [by] Frederic Kuhlau; ed. R.P. Block. — London : Musica rara, 1974. — 4to.
Score (52p.) & 5 parts.
Unpriced

(B74-50542)

NVTNS — Oboe & strings. Quartets
Vanhal, Jan
[Quartets for oboe & strings, nos.1,2]. Quartet for oboe (flute), violin, viola and cello. Op.7, nos.1 and 2 / [by] Jan Wanhal; [edited by] Denis Mulgan. — London : Musica rara, 1973. — 4pt ; 4to.
Unpriced

(B74-50543)

NVVG — Clarinets & strings. Suites
Slack, Roy
Too many clarinets : mini-suite for clarinets and strings / by Roy Slack. — London : Keith Prowse, 1973. — 4to.
Conductor & 10 parts.
£0.65

(B74-50153)

NVVNR — Clarinet & strings. Quintets
Coleridge-Taylor, Samuel
Quintet for clarinet and strings / [by] S. Coleridge-Taylor. — London : Musica rara, 1974. — 5pt ; 4to.
Unpriced

(B74-50544)

Lefanu, Nicola
Quintet for clarinet and string quartet / by Nicola Lefanu. — Sevenoaks : Novello, 1973. — 55p ; 4to.
£1.50

(B74-50154)

NWNRE — Wind & keyboard quintets. Sonatas
Carcasio, Giuseppe
[Sonata for two trumpets, two oboes & basso continuo, no.1, in D major]. Sonata for 2 trumpets, 2 oboes, ad lib and organ-basso continuo, no.1 / del Sigr. Giuseppe Carcasio ; transcribed and edited by Barry Cooper. — London : Musica rara, 1973. — 4to.
Score (15p.) & 6 parts. — The oboe parts are ad. lib.
Unpriced

(B74-50545)

NWNTE — Oboe & keyboard trios. Sonatas
Telemann, Georg Philipp
[Essercizii musici, trio 12. Sonata for instruments in E flat major]. Sonata Es-Dur, für Oboe, obligates Cembalo und Basso continuo / [von] Georg Philipp Telemann ; herausgegeben von Hugo Ruf. — Mainz ; London : Schott, 1974. — 4to.
Score (19p.) & 3 parts.
£2.61

(B74-51118)

NWPNRF — Woodwind & keyboard quintets. Concertos
Pepusch, Johann Christoph
[Concerto for woodwind quartet & basso continuo in G major. Op.8, no.2]. Concerto in G for 2 flutes, 2 oboes, violins and basso continuo. Op.8, no.2 / [by] Johann Christoph Pepusch ; ed. David Lasocki, realization of basso continuo by R.P. Block. — London : Musica rara, 1974. — 4to.
Score (10p.) & 5 parts. — 'Although the title page of the Roger edition (circa 1717) of the Opus 8 set indicates that the concertos are for 2 treble recorders, 2 flutes or oboes or violins, and basso continuo, only numbers 1 and 4-6 can be thus played' - Editor's note.
Unpriced

(B74-50546)

Pepusch, Johann Christoph
[Concertos for woodwind quartet & basso continuo. Op.8, nos. 1, 4-6]. 4 concerti for 2 treble recorders, 2 flutes, tenor recorders, oboes, violins & basso continuo. Op.8, nos. 1,4,5,6 / [by] Johann Christoph Pepusch ; ed. David Lasocki, realization of basso continuo by R.P. Block. — London : Musica rara.
Score (12p.) & 5 parts.
Opus 8, no.5 in C major. — 1974. — 4to.
Unpriced

(B74-50550)

Pepusch, Johann Christoph
[Concertos for woodwind quartet & basso continuo. Op.8, nos. 1, 4-6]. 4 concerti for 2 treble recorders, 2 flutes, tenor recorders, oboes, violins & basso continuo. Op.8, nos. 1, 4, 5, 6 / [by] Johann Christoph Pepusch ; ed. David Lasocki, realization of basso continuo by R.P. Block. — London : Musica rara.
Score (11p.) & 5 parts.
Opus 8, no.6 : in F major. — 1974. — 4to.
Unpriced

(B74-50548)

Opus 8, no.4 in F major. — 1974. — 4to.
Unpriced

(B74-50549)

Pepusch, Johann Christoph
[Concertos for woodwind quartet & basso continuo. Op.8, nos. 1, 4-6]. 4 concerti for 2 treble recorders, 2 flutes, tenor recorders, oboes, violins & basso continuo. Op.8, nos. 1,4,5,6 / [by] Johann Christoph Pepusch ; ed. David Lasocki, realization of basso continuo by R.P. Block. — London : Musica rara.
Score (19p.) & 5 parts.
Opus 8, no.1 : in B flat major. — 1974. — 4to.
Unpriced

(B74-50547)

NX — STRINGS & KEYBOARD
NXNRE — Quintets. Sonatas
Cazzati, Mauritio
[Sonata for strings & basso continuo in G minor. Op.35, 'La Sampiera']. Sonata 'La Sampiera' : for strings and continuo / by Mauritio Cazzati ; edited by Peter Smith. — London : Schott, 1974. — 4to.
Score (11p.) & 4 parts.
£1.50

(B74-50155)

NXNS — Quartets
Piston, Walter
Quartet for violin, viola, cello and piano / by Walter Piston. — New York ; London : Associated Music, 1974. — 4to.
Score (28p.) & 3 parts.
Unpriced

(B74-51119)

NXNT — Trios
Piston, Walter
Trio for violin, cello and piano / by Walter Piston. — New York ; London : Associated Music, 1974. — 4to.
Score (26p.) & 2 parts.
Unpriced

(B74-51120)

Standford, Patric
Trio for violin, cello & piano / by Patric Standford. — Sevenoaks : Novello, 1973. — 4to.
Duration 25 min. — Score (34p.) & 2 parts.
£1.50

(B74-50156)

Weingarden, Louis
Things heard and seen in summer : for piano, violin and cello / by Louis Weingarden. — New York ; [London] : Oxford University Press, 1974. — 17p ; 4to.
Unpriced

(B74-50551)

NYH — WIND & PERCUSSION
NYHNPHX — Septets. Jazz
Levitt, Rod
Woodmen of the world : jazz fantasy on a rock theme for woodwind quintet (with finger cymbals and tambourine) / [by] Rod Levitt. — New York ; London : Associated Music, 1973. — 4to.
Duration 6 min.
Unpriced

(B74-50552)

NYL — KEYBOARD & PERCUSSION
NYLNN — Octets
Creston, Paul
Ceremonial. Op.103 : for percussion ensemble and piano / by Paul Creston. — New York ; London : Schirmer, 1973. — 32p ; 4to.
Duration 4 1/2 min.
Unpriced

(B74-50553)

PWP — KEYBOARD SOLOS
PWP/AYH — Collections. France
Solymos, Peter
French piano music : for the young musician / edited by Peter Solymos. — London : Boosey and Hawkes, 1973. — 53p ; 4to. £1.00

(B74-50157)

PWP/Y — Fugues
Bach, Johann Sebastian
[Das wohltemperirte Clavier, Tl.1. Prelude and fugue, no.5. S.850]. Praeludium V und Fuga V : Klavier (Cembalo) / von Johann Sebastian Bach ; herausgegeben von Edith Picht-Axenfeld. — Mainz ; London : Schott, 1973. — 11p ; 4to. £0.60

(B74-50554)

Bach, Johann Sebastian
[Das wohltemperirte Clavier, Tl.1. Prelude and fugue, no.6. S.851]. Praeludium VI und Fuga VI : Klavier (Cembalo) / von Johann Sebastian Bach ; herausgegeben von Edith Picht-Axenfeld. — Mainz ; London : Schott, 1973. — 11p ; 4to. £0.60

(B74-50555)

Bach, Johann Sebastian
[Das wohltemperirte Clavier, Tl.1. Prelude and fugue, no.16. S.861]. Praeludium XVI und Fuga XVI : Klavier (Cembalo) / von Johann Sebastian Bach ; herausgegeben von Edith Picht-Axenfeld. — Mainz ; London : Schott, 1973. — 11p ; 4to. £0.60

(B74-50556)

Bach, Johann Sebastian
[Das wohltemperirte Clavier, Tl.2. Prelude and fugue, no.2. S.871]. Praeludium II and Fuga II : Klavier (Cembalo) / von Johann Sebastian Bach ; herausgegeben von Edith Picht-Axenfeld. — Mainz ; London : Schott, 1973. — 11p ; 4to. £0.60

(B74-50557)

PWPJ — Miscellaneous works
Arne, Thomas Augustine
[Concerto for keyboard, no.1, in C major. Allegro]. Keyboard allegro / [by] T.A. Arne ; edited by Christopher Hogwood. — London : Oxford University Press, 1974. — 4p ; 4to.
ISBN 0-19-372151-1 : £0.50

(B74-51121)

Crees, Kathleen
Jonathan and the magic clavichord : a children's story with music / by Kathleen Crees. — London : Autocylus, 1974. — 35p ; 8vo.
Unpriced

(B74-50158)

PWPK/AY(XF101) — Arrangements. Collections, 1700-1800
Zeraschi, Helmut
Drehorgelstücklein aus dem 18. Jahrhundert in Originalen, zubereitet für Flötlein sowie für Klavier oder andere Tasteninstrumente / herausgegeben von Helmut Zeraschi. — Leipzig ; [London] : Peters, 1973. — 28p ; obl. 8vo.
Unpriced

(B74-51122)

Q — PIANO
Q/AC — Tutors
Holzweissig, Erika
Klavierschule für den Elementarunterricht / [von] Erika und Christa Holzweissig. — Leipzig ; [London] : Peters, 1973. — 186p ; 4to.
Mit beiheft kleiner Lehrgang für Liedspiel und Improvisation.
Unpriced

(B74-51123)

Zayde, Jascha
Let's play piano / by Jasha Zayde. — New York : Experience Music ; [London] : Chappell, 1974. — 79p ; 4to.
Unpriced

(B74-51124)

Q/AF — Exercises
Adler, Samuel
Gradus : 40 studies for piano : by Samuel Adler. — New York ; [London] : Oxford University Press.
Book 1. — 1971. — 11p ; 4to. —
Unpriced

(B74-51125)

Adler, Samuel
Gradus : 40 studies for piano / by Samuel Adler. — New York ; [London] : Oxford University Press.
Book 2. — 1971. — 23p ; 4to. —
Unpriced

(B74-51126)

Applebaum, Stan
Sound world : a collection of new keyboard experiences for the intermediate pianist and the advanced beginner / by Stan Applebaum. — New York ; London : Schroeder and Gunther, 1974. — 23p ; 4to.
Unpriced
(B74-51127)

Liszt, Franz
[Technische Studien. *Selections].* The Liszt studies : essential selections from the technical studies for the piano, including the first English edition of the legendary Liszt Pedagogue, a lesson-diary of the master as teacher as kept by Mme August Boisser, 1831-2 / selections, editions and English translation by Elyse Mach; 'Reminiscences' (Memoirs by Liszt's great-granddaughter) by Mme Blandine Ollivier de Prevaux. — New York ; London : Associated Music, 1973. — xxvi,85p ; 4to.
Unpriced
(B74-50558)

Palmieri, Robert
Twenty piano exercises / by Robert Palmieri. — New York ; London : Oxford University Press, 1971. — 21p ; 4to.
Unpriced
(B74-50559)

Wendt, Wolfgang
Studies for the piano / edited by Wolfgang Wendt. — Leipzig ; [London] : Peters.
Book 2 : Portato, legato and staccato in combinations, introduction to other kinds of touch. — 1973. — 56p ; 4to. —
Unpriced
(B74-51128)

Q/AL — Examinations
Associated Board of the Royal Schools of Music
Pianoforte examinations, 1975. — London : Associated Board of the Royal Schools of Music.
Grade 1 : Lists A and B (primary). — 1974. — 11p ; 4to. — £0.35
(B74-51129)
Grade 2 : Lists A and B (elementary). — 1974. — 13p ; 4to. — £0.35
(B74-51130)
Grade 3 : Lists A and B (transitional). — 1974. — 12p ; 4to. — £0.35
(B74-51131)
Grade 4 : Lists A and B (lower). — 1974. — 20p ; 4to. — £0.35
(B74-51132)
Grade 5 : List A (higher). — 1974. — 11p ; 4to. — £0.35
(B74-51133)
Grade 5 : List B (higher). — 1974. — 13p ; 4to. — £0.35
(B74-51134)
Grade 6 : List A (intermediate). — 1974. — 13p ; 4to. — £0.35
(B74-51135)
Grade 6 : List B (intermediate). — 1974. — 17p ; 4to. — £0.35
(B74-51136)
Grade 7 : List A (advanced). — 1974. — 20p ; 4to. — £0.35
(B74-51137)
Grade 7 : List B (advanced). — 1974. — 20p ; 4to. — £0.35
(B74-51138)

Q/EG/AL — Sight reading. Examinations
London College of Music
Examination in pianoforte playing and singing sight reading tests as set throughout 1973. Grades I-VIII and diplomas. — London : Ashdown, 1973. — 15p ; 4to.
£0.35
Also classified at K/EG/AL
(B74-50159)

Q/ELM/AF — Fingering. Exercises
Symons, Mary
Fingers and thumbs : a project of preliminary exercises at the pianoforte / devised by Mary Symons. — London (60 Muswell Rd, N.10) : C.W. Daniel, 1974. — 136p ; 4to.
ISBN 0-85207-112-4 : Unpriced
(B74-50560)

QNTZN — TWO PIANOS, 8 HANDS
QNTZNK — Arrangements
Handel, George Frideric
[Water music. Selections: arr]. Three pieces / by George Frideric Handel ; arranged for two pianos, eight hands, by Virginia Speiden Carper. — New York ; London : Schirmer, 1972. — 2pt ; 4to.
Contents: Allegro in F - Minuet in D - Minuet in F.
Unpriced
(B74-50160)

QNU — TWO PIANOS, 4 HANDS
Lazarof, Henri
Intonazione : for two piano / by Henri Lazarof. — New York ; London : Associated Music, 1972. — 16p ; fol.
£12.00
(B74-50561)

QNUH — Dances
McCabe, John
Basse danse : for two pianos / by John McCabe. — Sevenoaks : Novello, 1974. — 40p ; 4to.
Price accounts for two copies.
£5.00
(B74-50161)

QNUHG — Dance suites
Haufrecht, Herbert
Square set : for two pianos / by Herbert Haufrecht. — New York ; London : Associated Music, 1972. — 31p ; 4to.
Two copies. — Contents: 1: Reel - II: Clog dance - III: Jig Time.
Unpriced
(B74-50162)

QNUK — Arrangements
Beethoven, Ludwig van
[Selections : arr]. Adagio for a musical clock and Rondo a capriccio 'Rage over the lost groschen' / by Ludwig van Beethoven ; arranged for piano and orchestra by Donald Waxman : two-piano score. — New York : Galaxy ; London : Galliard, 1971. — 34p ; 4to.
Unpriced
(B74-51139)

Gottschalk, Louis Moreau
[L'Union. Op. 48: arr]. L'Union. [Op.48] : paraphrase de concert sur les airs nationaux / [by] Louis Moreau Gottschalk ; arranged for piano and orchestra by Samuel Adler, edited by Eugene List, [two piano score]. — New York ; London : Schirmer, 1972. — 27p ; 4to.
£1.40
(B74-50562)

QNUK/LF — Arrangements. Concertos
Bernstein, Seymour
[Concerto for piano, 'For our time': arr]. Concerto ('For our time') / by Seymour Bernstein: two-piano score. — New York ; London : Schroeder and Gunther, 1973. — 31p ; 4to.
Two copies.
Unpriced
(B74-50163)

Martinu, Bohuslav
[Concerto for piano, no.4, 'Incantation': arr]. Incantation : 4th piano concerto / by Bohuslav Martinu ; piano reduction by Karel Solc. — Prague : Supraphon ; Cassel ; London : Bärenreiter, 1972. — 55p ; 4to.
£3.60
(B74-50563)

Rorem, Ned
[Concerto in six movements for piano and orchestra: arr]. Concerto in six movements for piano and orchestra / [by] Ned Rorem : piano reduction. — New York ; [London] : Boosey and Hawkes, 1974. — 76p ; 4to.
£5.00
(B74-51140)

Schedrin, Rodion
[Concerto for piano, no.2(1966)]. Konzert Nr.2 für Klavier und Orchester (1966) / [von] Rodion Stschedrin ; Ausgabe fur zwei Klaviere vom Komponisten. — Leipzig ; [London] : Peters, 1973. — 58p ; 4to.
Unpriced
(B74-51141)

QNUK/Y — Arrangements. Fugues
Mozart, Wolfgang Amadeus
[Adagio and fugue for string quartet in C minor. K.546: arr]. Adagio and fugue in C minor. K.546 and 426 / by Wolfgang Amadeus Mozart ; [adagio] arranged for two pianos, four hands by Paul Badura-Skoda [with Mozart's own transcription of the fugue]. — New York ; London : Schirmer, 1973. — 18p ; 4to.
Two copies. Included is a foreword by Paul Badura-Skoda.
Unpriced
(B74-50564)

QNV — ONE PIANO, 4 HANDS
Helyer, Marjorie
Eight duets : [for piano] / by Marjorie Helyer. — London : Ashdown, 1974. — 15p ; 4to.
Unpriced
(B74-50565)

Sugár, Rezso
Hungarian children's songs : for piano duet / by Rezso Sugár. — London : Boosey and Hawkes, 1973. — 35p ; 4to.
£0.85

(B74-50566)

QNV/AY — Collections
Goebels, Franzpeter
For two to play : early English duets for keyboard, four hands, or for organ (two players, two manuals) / edited by Franzpeter Goebels. — Cassel : Nagel ; London : Bärenreiter, 1973. — 13p ; 4to.
Contents: A fancy/ (Thomas Tomkins) - A verse/ (Nicholas Carlston).
£1.45

(B74-50567)

QNVK/DW/AY — Arrangements. Songs, etc. Collections
Kasschau, Howard
Three singing duets / arranged for piano, four-hands, by Howard Kasschau. — New York ; London : Schirmer, 1972. — 11p ; 4to.
Contents: Down Mobile - Singin' Johnny - Ja, ja, ja!.
Unpriced

(B74-50164)

QNVK/DW/GK/AY — Arrangements. Nursery rhymes. Collections
Kasschau, Howard
[Seventeen duets on nursery tunes]. 17 duets on nursery tunes / arranged for piano four hands by Howard Kasschau. — New York ; London : Schirmer, 1972. — 21p ; 4to.
£0.50

(B74-50165)

QP — PIANO SOLOS
QP/AY — Collections
Grant, Lawrence
More classic to contemporary piano music in its original form / selected and compiled by Lawrence Grant. — Carlstadt : Ashley ; London : Phoenix, 1973. — 160p ; 4to.
Contents: Works by Bach, Bartok, Bertini, Corelli, Couperin, Czerny, Franck, Kabalevsky, Kullak, Mozart, Pachelbel, Purcell, Rebikoff, Rameau, Scarlatti, Shostakovich, Telemann, Turk.
Unpriced

(B74-50568)

Lake, Ian
Classics for the young pianist / [compiled and edited by] Ian Lake. — London : Chappell, 1974. — 32p ; 4to.
Unpriced

(B74-51142)

Szávai, Magda
Music for piano (intermediate) / edited by Magda Szavai, Lili Veszpremi. — London : Boosey and Hawkes, 1973. — 55p ; 4to.
£1.00

(B74-50166)

QP/AYM — Collections. Russia
Aldridge, Maisie
Easy Russian piano music / compiled by Maisie Aldridge. — London : Oxford University Press.
Book 1 / arrangements by Boris Evseyevich Milich. — 1974. — 9p ; 4to.
ISBN 0-19-372131-7 : £0.50

(B74-50569)

Book 2 / arrangements by Boris Evseyevich Milich. — 1974. — 12p ; 4to.
ISBN 0-19-372132-5 : £0.60

(B74-50570)

Roisman, Leonid
Piano pieces by Soviet composers for children / edited by Leonid Roisman. — Leipzig ; [London] : Peters.
Vol.3. — 1973. — 78p ; 4to. —
Unpriced

(B74-51143)

QP/AZ — Collected works of individual composers
Liszt, Franz
[Works, piano. Selections]. Piano works / by Franz Liszt. — Cassel ; London : Bärenreiter.
Vol.4 : Hungarian rhapsodies II, nos 10-19 / edited by Zoltan Gárdonyi and István Szelényi. — 1973. — xvi,151p ; 4to.
£2.90

(B74-50571)

QPE — Sonatas
Hoddinott, Alun
[Sonata for piano, no.6. Op.78, no.3]. Sonata no.6. Opus 78, no.3 / by Alun Hoddinott. — London : Oxford University Press, 1974. — 15p ; 4to.
Duration 10 min.
ISBN 0-19-372840-0 : £1.25

(B74-50572)

Mozart, Wolfgang Amadeus
[Sonata for piano no.13 in B flat major. K.333]. Sonata in B flat, K. 333 / by Mozart; edited by Stanley Sadie, fingering and notes on performance by Denis Matthews. — London : Associated Board of the Royal Schools of Music, 1974. — 25p ; 4to.
Unpriced

(B74-50167)

Mozart, Wolfgang Amadeus
[Sonata for piano, no.15, in C major. K.545]. Sonata in C, K.545 / [by] Mozart ; edited by Stanley Sadie ; fingering and notes on performance by Denis Matthews. — London : Associated Board of the Royal Schools of Music, 1974. — 16p ; 4to.
£0.35

(B74-51144)

Stoker, Richard
[Sonata for piano, no.1. Opus 26]. Piano sonata, no.1. Opus 26 / by Richard Stoker. — London : Peters, 1973. — 11p ; 4to.
Duration 12 min.
Unpriced

(B74-50573)

QPE/AY — Sonatas. Collections
Beethoven, Ludwig van
[Sonatas for piano. Selections]. Sonatinen und leichte Sonaten fur Klavier / von L. van Beethoven ; nach den Quellen herausgegeben von Peter Hauschild ; Fingersatzbezeichnung von Gerhard Erber. — Leipzig ; [London] : Peters, 1974. — 87p ; 4to.
Unpriced

(B74-51145)

QPEM — Sonatinas
Camilleri, Charles
Sonatina classica : [piano] / by Charles Camilleri. — Wendover : Roberton, 1974. — 9p ; 4to.
£0.50

(B74-51146)

Camilleri, Charles
[Sonatina for piano, no.1]. Sonatine number one : [piano] / by Charles Camilleri. — Wendover : Roberton, 1974. — 16p ; 4to.
£0.60

(B74-51147)

Guarnieri, Mozart Camargo
[Sonatina for piano, no.4]. Sonatina no.4 for piano / by M. Camargo Guarnieri. — New York ; London : Associated Music, 1973. — 19p ; 4to.
Unpriced

(B74-50574)

Guarnieri, Mozart Camargo
[Sonatina for piano, no.6]. Sonatina no.6 for piano / by M. Camargo Guarnieri. — New York ; London : Associated Music, 1973. — 19p ; 4to.
Unpriced

(B74-50575)

QPG — Suites
Bennett, *Sir* William Sterndale
Suite de pièces. Op.24 / [by] Sterndale Bennett; transcribed and edited by Geoffrey Bush. — London : Stainer and Bell, 1972. — 4to.
Unpriced

(B74-50576)

Bernstein, Seymour
Birds 2 : a second suite of nine impressionistic studies for piano solo / by Seymour Bernstein. — New York ; London : Schroeder and Gunther, 1973. — 17p ; 4to.
Unpriced

(B74-50577)

Blezard, William
Hours of the day : a suite of six piano pieces for young people with supplementary exercises / [by] William Blezard. — Surbiton (167 Ewell Rd, Surbiton, Surrey) : Camera Music, 1974. — 12p ; 4to.
Unpriced

(B74-51148)

Brydson, John Callis
Fantasy : suite of five pieces for pianoforte / by John C. Brydson. — London : Freeman, 1973. — 12p ; 4to.
£0.35

(B74-50168)

Jacques, Michael
Five piece suite : for piano / by Michael Jacques. — Wendover : Roberton, 1974. — 12p ; 4to.
£0.40

(B74-51149)

Jong, Conrad de
Little suite : for piano / by Conrad de Jong. — New York ;
London : Schroeder and Gunther, 1972. — 7p ; 4to.
Unpriced

(B74-50169)

Pick, Karl-Heinz
Kleine Marchensuite : für Klavier / [von] Karl-Heinz Pick. —
Leipzig ; [London] : Peters, 1973. — 19p ; 4to.
Unpriced

(B74-51150)

Wilson, Robert Barclay
A miniature suite for piano / by Robert Barclay Wilson. —
London : Freeman, 1974. — 8p ; 4to.
Unpriced

(B74-50170)

QPH/H/AYDL — Dances for dancing. Collections. Scotland
Rankine, Andrew
Two Scottish country dances / composed and arranged for piano
by Andrew Rankine; dances devised by Christopher Blair. —
Newcastle (42 Whinfell Rd, Darras Hall, Ponteland, Newcastle) :
Royal Scottish Country Dance Society (Newcastle and District
Branch), 1967. — [5]p ; 4to.
£0.125

(B74-50578)

QPHJP — Czardas
Liszt, Franz
[Csardas. Selections]. Two csardas for piano / by Franz Liszt ;
edited by Joseph Prostakoff. — New York ; London : Schirmer,
1968. — 34p ; 4to.
Contents: Csardas obstiné - Csardas macabre.
Unpriced

(B74-50171)

QPHP — Jigs
Bullard, Alan
Air and gigue for clavichord (or piano) / by Alan Bullard. —
London : Oxford University Press, 1974. — 6p ; 4to.
ISBN 0-19-372394-8 : Unpriced
Primary classification QTPHP

QPHX — Jazz
Previn, André
The invisible drummer : five preludes for piano / [by] Andre
Previn. — New York ; [London] : Boosey and Hawkes, 1974. —
29p ; 4to.
£1.50

(B74-51151)

QPHXJ — Ragtime
Joplin, Scott
[The entertainer: arr]. The entertainer : piano solo / by Scott
Joplin ; arranged by Frank Naylor. — London : Bosworth, 1974.
— 3p ; 4to.
Unpriced

(B74-51152)

Joplin, Scott
The entertainer : a ragtime two step, for piano / by Scott Joplin.
— London : Chappell, 1974. — 5p ; 4to.
Unpriced

(B74-50172)

Joplin, Scott
The entertainer : a rag time two step / by Scott Joplin ; edited by
Alexander Shealy. — Carlstadt : Lewis Music ; [London] :
[Ashley Fields], 1972. — 5p ; 4to.
Unpriced

(B74-51153)

Joplin, Scott
[The entertainer: arr]. The entertainer / by Scott Joplin ; modified
piano edition with words by Bob Gumer. — Carlstadt : Lewis
Music ; [London] : [Ashley-Fields], 1974. — 5p ; 4to.
Unpriced

(B74-51154)

Joplin, Scott
[The entertainer: arr]. The entertainer : piano solo / by Scott
Joplin ; arranged and adapted by Gunther Schuller. — Croydon :
Belwin-Mills, 1974. — 5p ; 4to.
£0.30

(B74-50579)

Joplin, Scott
[The entertainer: arr]. The entertainer : a ragtime two step :
composed by Scott Joplin / easy piano solo, arranged by
Lawrence Grant. — Carlstadt : Lewis Music ; London : Ashley
Fields, 1974. — 4p ; 4to.
Unpriced

(B74-51155)

Joplin, Scott
[The entertainer: arr]. The entertainer : ragtime two step / by
Scott Joplin ; modified piano edition, arranged by Alexander
Shealy. — Carlstadt : Lewis Music ; [London] : [Ashley Fields],
1974. — 5p ; 4to.
Unpriced

(B74-51156)

Joplin, Scott
[The entertainer: arr]. The entertainer : ragtime two step / by
Scott Joplin ; simplified edition arranged by Alexander Shealy. —
Carlstadt : Lewis Music ; [London] : [Ashley Fields], 1972. —
5p ; 4to.
Unpriced

(B74-51157)

Joplin, Scott
Gladiolus rag / by Scott Joplin. — London : Chappell, 1974. —
5p ; 4to.
Unpriced

(B74-51158)

Joplin, Scott
Piano rags / by Scott Joplin. — London : Chappell, 1974. —
48p ; 4to.
Unpriced

(B74-50173)

Joplin, Scott
Piano rags / by Scott Joplin. — Sevenoaks : Novello, 1974. —
32p ; 4to.
£0.55

(B74-50580)

Joplin, Scott
Pine apple rag : piano / by Scott Joplin. — London : Chappell,
1974. — 5p ; 4to.
Unpriced

(B74-50581)

Joplin, Scott
[Selections: arr]. Scott Joplin : the king of ragtime writers: easy
piano / arranged by Lawrence Grant. — Carlstadt : Lewis
Music ; [London] : [Ashley-Fields], 1974. — 32p ; 4to.
Unpriced

(B74-51159)

Joplin, Scott
Solace : a Mexican serenade, for piano / by Scott Joplin. —
London : Chappell, 1974. — 5p ; 4to.
Unpriced

(B74-50582)

QPJ — Miscellaneous works
Allanbrook, Douglas
Twelve preludes for all seasons : piano solo / by Douglas
Allanbrook. — New York ; [London] : Boosey and Hawkes, 1974.
— 25p ; 4to.
£2.50

(B74-51160)

Alt, Hansi
Five summer Sundays : for the piano / [by] Hansi Alt. — New
York ; [London] : Oxford University Press, 1974. — 11p ; 4to.
Unpriced

(B74-51161)

Applebaum, Stanley
Folk music, Bach style : 21 two-part inventions / by Stanley
Applebaum ; based on international folk melodies. — New York ;
London : Schroeder and Gunther, 1972. — 24p ; 4to.
£0.50

(B74-50174)

Ashburnham, George
Summer rhapsody : [for piano] / by George Ashburnham. — New
Malden : Ashburnham School of Music, 1974. — 11p ; 4to.
Unpriced

(B74-51162)

Bach, Johann Sebastian
[Capriccio sopra la lontanza del suo fratello dilettissimo. S.992].
Capriccio / by Johann Sebastian Bach ; edited for the piano by
David Goldberger. — New York ; London : Schirmer, 1973. —
13p ; 4to.
Unpriced

(B74-50583)

Barham, John
Five piano solos / by John Barham. — London : Acuff-Rose,
1974. — 22p ; 4to.
Contents: 1: Nat Bhairav - 2: Brindavani Tilang - 3: Marwa - 4:
Mishra-Kalavati - 5: Nat Bhairav.
£1.00

(B74-50175)

Beethoven, Ludwig van
Bagatelles. Opus 119 : [piano solo] / by Beethoven ; [edited by]
Hermann Keller. — London : Peters, [1974]. — 15p ; 4to.
Unpriced
(B74-50584)

Brown, Rosemary
The Rosemary Brown piano album : 7 pieces inspired by
Beethoven, Schubert, Chopin, Schumann, Brahms and Liszt / by
Rosemary Brown. — Sevenoaks : Paxton, 1974. — 32p ; 4to.
£0.60
(B74-50585)

Camilleri, Charles
Due canti : two songs for piano solo / by Charles Camilleri. —
Wendover : Roberton, 1974. — 8p ; 4to.
Contents: Cantilena - Arabesque.
£0.40
(B74-51163)

Camilleri, Charles
Etudes : [piano] / [by] Charles Camilleri. — Wendover :
Roberton.
Book 1. — 1974. — 49p ; 4to. —
£0.75
(B74-51164)

Book 2. — 1974. — 16p ; 4to. —
£0.75
(B74-51165)

Book 3. — 1974. — 11p ; 4to. —
£0.55
(B74-51166)

Camilleri, Charles
Hemda : for piano solo / by Charles Camilleri. — Sevenoaks :
Fairfield, Distributed by Novello, 1973. — 4p ; 4to.
Duration 6 min.
£0.40
(B74-50176)

Camilleri, Charles
Mantra : for piano solo / by Charles Camilleri. — Sevenoaks :
Fairfield, Distributed by Novello, 1973. — 23p ; 4to.
Duration 12 min.
£1.00
(B74-50177)

Camilleri, Charles
Three African sketches : [piano] / by Charles Camilleri. —
Wendover : Roberton, 1974. — 8p ; 4to.
Contents: Invocation and dance - Ulumbundu - Lament for an African
drummer.
£0.40
(B74-51167)

Camilleri, Charles
Times of day : five Southern impressions, [piano] / by Charles
Camilleri. — Wendover : Roberton, 1974. — 16p ; 4to.
£0.60
(B74-51168)

Cines, Eugene
Abbreviations : piano solo / by Eugene Cines. — New York ;
London : Boosey and Hawkes, 1974. — 7p ; 4to.
Unpriced
(B74-50586)

Copland, Aaron
In evening air : piano solo / [by] Aaron Copland. — New York ;
[London] : Boosey and Hawkes, 1974. — 4p ; 4to.
£0.40
(B74-51169)

Crumb, George
Makrokosmos / [by] George Crumb. — New York ; London :
Peters.
Duration 33 min.
Volume 1 : [for] amplified piano. — 1974. — 19p ; obl.fol.
£6.00
(B74-51170)

Crump, Peter
Unum ex illorum sabbatorum : [piano] / [by] Peter Crump. —
London : Thames, 1974. — fol.
Unpriced
(B74-51171)

Debussy, Claude
[Works, piano. Selections].
World's favourite best known Debussy piano music / compiled by
Alexander Shealy. — Carlstadt : Ashley ; London : Phoenix, 1973.
— 159p ; 4to.
Unpriced
(B74-50587)

Fauré, Gabriel
[Works, piano. Selections].
Gabriel Fauré - his greater piano solos / compiled by Alexander
Shealy. — Carlstadt : Copa ; [London] : [Phoenix], 1973. —
191p ; 4to.
Unpriced
(B74-50588)

Gershwin, George
[Selections]. George Gershwin - for piano. — New York ;
London : Chappell, 1974. — 11p ; 4to.
Unpriced
(B74-50589)

Gottschalk, Louis Moreau
[Works, piano. Selections]. Piano music of Louis Moreau
Gottschalk : 26 complete pieces from original editions / selected
and introduced by Richard Jackson. — New York : Dover ;
London : Constable, 1973. — xvi,301p ; 4to.
ISBN 0-486-21683-7 : £3.36
(B74-50590)

Harvey, Jonathan
Round the star and back : for piano and a small number of other
instruments capable of reasonable blend / [by] Jonathan Harvey.
— Sevenoaks : Novello, 1974. — [3] leaves in folder(4)p ; fol.
£1.50
(B74-50591)

Herschel, Yossel Ben
Hebraic rhapsody, no.2 : [piano] / [by] Yossel Ben Herschel. —
Stamford (Conn.) : Pandian Press ; [London] : [Galliard], 1974. —
12p ; 4to.
Unpriced
(B74-51172)

Johnson, Robert Sherlaw
Asterogenesis : [piano] / [by] Robert Sherlaw Johnson. —
London : Oxford University Press, 1974. — 19p ; 4to.
ISBN 0-19-372990-3 : £2.20
(B74-51173)

Kirkby-Mason, Barbara
For children : piano solos. — London : Keith Prowse Music.
Book 1. — 1974. — 12p ; 4to.
Unpriced
(B74-51174)

Book 2. — 1974. — 11p ; 4to.
Unpriced
(B74-51175)

Last, Joan
Black and white : eight tunes for young pianists / by Joan Last.
— London : Oxford University Press, 1973. — 8p ; 4to.
ISBN 0-19-373104-5 : £0.45
(B74-50178)

Last, Joan
The day's play / [by] Joan Last. — Manchester ; London :
Forsyth, 1974. — 11p ; 4to.
Unpriced
(B74-51176)

Last, Joan
Notes and notions : eight short pieces for piano / by Joan Last.
— London : Oxford University Press, 1974. — 8p ; 4to.
ISBN 0-19-373135-5 : £0.45
(B74-50179)

Liszt, Franz
[Works, piano. Selections]. Miniatures for piano / by Franz Liszt ;
selected and edited by Joseph Prostakoff. — New York ; London :
Schirmer, 1968. — 21p ; 4to.
Unpriced
(B74-50180)

Lombardi, Nilson
Cantilena no.1 : piano / de Nilson Lombardi. — Rio de Janeiro :
Arthur Napoleão ; [London] : [Essex Music], 1974. — 4p ; 4to.
Unpriced
(B74-51177)

Miguez, Leopoldo
Bluetes, 1, a serie / [de] Leopoldo Miguez. — Rio de Janeiro :
Arthur Napoleão ; [London] : [Essex Music].
Album no.1. Op.31 (de 1 a 10) : piano. — 1974. — 13p ; 4to. —
Unpriced
(B74-51178)

Pope, Roger Hugh
Impressions : piano solos / by Roger Hugh Pope. — London (196
Grays Inn Rd WC IX 8EW) : Warren and Phillips, 1974. — 4to.
Unpriced
(B74-51179)

Price, Beryl
On the go : six sketches for piano / by Beryl Price. — London : Oxford University Press, 1973. — 7p ; 4to.
ISBN 0-19-373534-2 : £0.40

(B74-50181)

Reimann, Aribert
Spektren für Klavier (1967) / von Aribert Reimann. — Mainz ; London : Ars Viva, 1971. — 19p ; 4to.
£1.92

(B74-50182)

Shaw, Francis
Four little pieces : for piano / by Francis Shaw. — London : Ashdown, 1974. — 7p ; 4to.
Contents: Funny face - Serious song - Ostinato - Allegro.
Unpriced

(B74-50183)

Skempton, Howard
Piano pieces / by Howard Skempton. — London : Faber Music, 1974. — 12p ; obl 8vo.
Unpriced

(B74-50184)

Skriabin, Aleksandr Nikolaevich
[Studies for piano. Op.8]. 12 studies for piano. Op.8 / by Alexander Skrjabin. — Leipzig ; [London] : Peters, 1973. — 47p ; 4to.
Unpriced

(B74-51180)

Sugár, Rezső
Hungarian children's songs : for piano / by Rezső Sugár. — London : Boosey and Hawkes, 1973. — 33p ; 4to.
£0.85

(B74-50185)

Taylor, Colin
[Three fables]. 3 fables : piano solo / by Colin Taylor. — Revised ed. — London : Boosey and Hawkes, 1973. — 8p ; 4to.
£0.45

(B74-50186)

Tcherepnin, Alexander
Canzona for piano. Op.28 / by Alexander Tcherepnin. — New ed. / revised and edited by the composer. — Hamburg ; London : Simrock, 1974. — 5p ; 4to.
Unpriced

(B74-50187)

Tcherepnin, Alexander
[Toccata for piano, no.2. Op.20]. Toccata no.2 for piano. Op.20 / by Alexander Tcherepnin. — New ed. / revised and edited by the composer. — Hamburg ; London : Simrock, 1974. — 16p ; 4to.
Unpriced

(B74-50188)

Thomson, Virgil
Edges : a portrait of Robert Indiana for piano / by Virgil Thomson. — New York ; London : Schirmer, 1973. — 5p ; 4to.
Unpriced

(B74-50592)

Weingarden, Louis
Triptych : three pieces for piano / [by] Louis Weingarden. — New York ; [London] : Boosey and Hawkes, 1974. — 28p ; 4to.
£2.25

(B74-51181)

Wilson, Robert Barclay
Caprice : piano solo / by Robert Barclay Wilson. — South Croydon : Lengnick, 1974. — 4p ; 4to.
£0.18

(B74-50189)

Wilson, Robert Barclay
Three contrasts : [piano] / [by] Robert Barclay Wilson. — London : Cramer, 1974. — 4p ; 4to.
Contents: 1: Follow-my-leader - 2: Merry-go-round - 3: Waltz.
£0.15

(B74-51182)

Wyner, Yehudi
Three short fantasias : for piano / by Yehudi Wyner. — New York ; London : Associated Music, 1973. — 11p ; 4to.
Unpriced

(B74-50593)

QPK — Arrangements
Beethoven, Ludwig van
[Concerto for piano, no.1, in C major. Op.15. Allegro con brio: arr]. Theme from piano concerto no.1 / by Ludwig van Beethoven ; arranged for piano by R. Enstone. — London : Leonard, Gould and Bolttler, 1974. — 7p ; 4to.
Unpriced

(B74-50594)

Cruft, Adrian
Elegy for horn and strings / [by] Adrian Cruft, with piano reduction for piano solo. — Sevenoaks : Novello, 1974. — 28p ; 4to.
£2.50
Primary classification RXMPWT

Haydn, Joseph
[Works, selections: arr].
Haydn / selected and edited for piano by Henry Duke. — London : Freeman, 1974. — 28p ; 4to.
Unpriced

(B74-51183)

Mendelssohn, Felix
[Selections: arr]. Mendelssohn's greatest hits; arranged for all organ. — London : Chappell, 1974. — 56p ; 4to.
Unpriced

(B74-50190)

Mozart, Wolfgang Amadeus
[Concerto for piano, no.21, in C major. K.467. Andante: arr]. Theme from Elvira Madigan / arranged for piano solo from the music of W.A. Mozart. — London : Chappell, 1974. — 4p ; 4to.
Unpriced

(B74-50595)

QPK/AAY — Arrangements. Collections
Grant, Lawrence
World's favorite preludes : offertories and postludes for the piano / compiled and edited by Lawrence Grant. — Carlstadt : Ashley ; London : Phoenix.
Vol.1. — 1972. — 128p ; 4to. —
Unpriced

(B74-50596)

Vol.2. — 1973. — 128p ; 4to. —
Unpriced

(B74-50597)

Keith, Alan
The world of your 100 best tunes requested by listeners to the popular BBC radio series devised and presented by Alan Keith, easy-to-play piano album, piano arrangements by James Burt. — London : Chappell.
Vol.4. — 1974. — 66p ; 4to.
Unpriced

(B74-50598)

Keith, Alan
The world of your 100 best tunes requested by listeners to the popular BBC radio series / devised and presented by Alan Keith; easy-to-play piano album, piano arrangements by James Burt. — London : Chappell.
Vol.1. — 1972. — 40p : port ; 4to.
£0.50

(B74-50599)

Vol.2. — 1972. — 46p ; 4to.
£0.50

(B74-50600)

Vol.3. — 1972. — 52p ; 4to.
£0.95

(B74-50601)

QPK/AGM/AY — Arrangements. Marches. Collections
Medway, Carol
Twelve famous marches / arranged for piano solo by Carol Medway. — London : Cramer, 1974. — 20p ; 4to.
£0.36

(B74-51184)

QPK/AH — Arrangements. Dances
Bailey, Andrew
The Strauss family / editor Andrew Bailey, arrangements Cyril Ornadel. — London : Wise ; London : [Distributed by] Music Sales Ltd, 1973. — 96p ; 4to.
£1.50

(B74-50602)

QPK/AHW/JR — Arrangements. Waltzes. Films
Bennett, Richard Rodney
[Murder on the Orient Express. Waltz theme: arr]. Waltz theme / by Richard Rodney Bennett ; arranged for piano solo. — London : EMI, 1974. — 4p ; 4to.
£0.25

(B74-51185)

QPK/AHW/JS — Arrangements. Waltzes. Television
Josephs, Wilfred
Lady Glencora's waltz : from 'The Pallisers' BBC television series / composed by Wilfred Josephs. — London : Weinberger, 1974. — 4p ; 4to.
£0.25

(B74-50191)

QPK/DW — Arrangements. Songs, etc
Wakeman, Rick
Journey to the centre of the earth: arr]. Journey to the centre of the earth / words and music, Rick Wakeman, transcribed for piano by Jeff Muston. — London : Rondor : Music Sales, 1974. — 40p ; 4to.
Contents: The journey - Recollection - The battle - The forest.
Unpriced

(B74-50603)

QPK/DW/JR/AY — Arrangements. Film songs. Collections
Premiere film music : piano - vocal. — London : Chappell.
Vol.1. — 1974. — 60p ; 4to. —
Unpriced

(B74-50192)

Vol.2. — 1974. — 60p ; 4to. —
Unpriced

(B74-50193)

QPK/HM — Arrangements. Ballet
Stravinsky, Igor
[Firebird. Selections: arr]. L'Oiseau de feu = Der Feuervogel / par Igor Stravinsky ; transcription pour piano solo par Soulima Stravinsky. — Mainz ; London : Schott, 1973. — 19p ; 4to.
Contents: Scherzo - Berceuse - Danse infernale.
£1.44

(B74-50194)

QPK/JR — Arrangements. Films
Bennett, Richard Rodney
[Murder on the Orient Express. Theme: arr]. Murder on the Orient Express : theme / by Richard Rodney Bennett ; arranged for piano solo. — London : EMI, 1974. — 3p ; 4to.
£0.25

(B74-51186)

Devor, Don
[From the mixed-up files of Mrs. Basil E. Frankweiler. Claudia theme: arr]. Claudia theme / music by Don Devor, from the motion picture, arranged for piano. — New York ; London : Edwin H. Morris, 1973. — 3p ; 4to.
Unpriced

(B74-50604)

QPK/JS — Arrangements. Television
Narholz, Gerhard
[Ricochet: arr]. Ricochet. Fasten seat belts : original theme music, [arranged for piano] from the BBC Radio Two series / by Gerhard Narholz. — London : Berry Music, 1974. — 4p ; 4to.
Unpriced

(B74-51187)

QPK/JS/AY — Arrangements. Television. Collections
Simpson, Dudley
Great TV themes : piano arrangements / by Dudley Simpson, and others. — London : Affiliated Music, 1974. — 48p ; 4to.
£0.75

(B74-50195)

QPK/KDD/AY — Arrangements. Weddings. Collections
Grant, Lawrence
World's favorite wedding music for piano / arranged and compiled by Lawrence Grant. — Carlstadt : Ashley ; London : Phoenix, 1973. — 128p ; 4to.
Unpriced

(B74-50605)

QRP — HARPSICHORD SOLOS
QRPJ — Miscellaneous works
Dodgson, Stephen
Six inventions for harpsichord / by Stephen Dodgson. — London : Chappell.
Three sets of six inventions, comprising eighteen pieces in all.
Set 1. — 1974. — 25p ; 4to.
Unpriced

(B74-50606)

Set 2. — 1974. — 25p ; 4to.
Unpriced

(B74-50607)

Set 3. — 1974. — 26p ; 4to.
Unpriced

(B74-50608)

Lazarof, Henri
Three pieces for harpsichord / by Henri Lazarof. — New York ; London : Associated Music, 1972. — 7p ; fol.
£3.50

(B74-50609)

QTP — CLAVICHORD SOLOS
QTPG — Suites
Dodgson, Stephen
[Suite for clavichord, no.1, in C]. Suite no.1 in C for clavichord / by Stephen Dodgson. — London : Chappell, 1974. — 16p ; 4to.
Unpriced

(B74-50610)

Dodgson, Stephen
[Suite for clavichord, no.2, in E flat]. Suite no.2 in E flat / by Stephen Dodgson. — London : Chappell, 1974. — 15p ; 4to.
Unpriced

(B74-50611)

QTPHP — Jigs
Bullard, Alan
Air and gigue for clavichord (or piano) / by Alan Bullard. — London : Oxford University Press, 1974. — 6p ; 4to.
ISBN 0-19-372394-8 : Unpriced
Also classified at QPHP

(B74-51188)

R — ORGAN
R/AY — Collections
Marr, Peter
Three organists of St. Dionis Backchurch, London / edited by Peter Marr. — London : Hinrichsen, 1973. — 27p ; obl 4to.
Contents: Fugue in A major, by Philip Hart - Introduction for the diapasons, Voluntary in E minor, Fugue in F minor, by Charles Burney - Voluntary in B minor, by John Bennett.
Unpriced

(B74-50612)

Modern organ music. — London : Oxford University Press.
Contents: Gigue de Pan, by Douglas Mews. — Trope on 'Canite tuba', by Robert Sherlaw Johnson. — Scherzo, by James Brown. — Sarum fanfare, by Alun Hoddinott. Op.37, no.3 - Tableau, by Sebastian Forbes.
Book 3 : Five pieces by contemporary composers. — 1974. — 24p ; 8vo.
ISBN 0-19-375143-7 : £0.95

(B74-50196)

R/AZ — Collected works of individual composers
Hart, Philip
[Works, organ. Collections]. Organ works / by Philip Hart ; edited by Frank Dawes. — London : Hinrichsen, 1973. — 23p ; obl 4to.
Unpriced

(B74-50613)

R/KDD — Weddings
Hamilton, Alasdair
Epithalamios : choruses for organ / by Alasdair Hamilton. — Wendover : Roberton, 1973. — 8p ; 4to.
£0.30

(B74-50197)

R/Y — Fugues
Busoni, Ferruccio Benvenuto
[Works, organ. Selections]. Praeludium, Basso ostinato. Op.7, and Doppelfuge zum Choral. Op.76 / by Ferruccio Busoni. — London : Cranz, 1973. — 12p ; 4to.
£0.60

(B74-50614)

Handel, George Frideric
[Fugue for organ in E major]. Fugue in E major / by George Frideric Handel ; edited by H. Diack Johnstone. — Sevenoaks : Novello, 1974. — 3p ; 4to.
Unpriced

(B74-50615)

Marshall, Philip
Fantasy and fugue on 'Edward Cuthbert Bairstow' : for organ / by Philip Marshall. — London : Ashdown, 1974. — 14p ; 4to.
Written in the composer's hand.
£0.40

(B74-50616)

RDFF — Roman Catholic liturgical music
Corrette, Michel
[Premier livre d'orgue. *Selections*]. Magnificat du 3e et 4e ton : [for organ / by] Michel Corrette ; edited by Edward Higginbottom. — Sevenoaks : Novello, 1974. — 12p ; 4to.
Unpriced

(B74-50617)

RE — Sonatas
Jackson, Francis
Sonata giocosa per la renascita di una cattedrale. Opus 42 : [organ] / [by] Francis Jackson. — London : Oxford University Press, 1974. — 24p ; 4to.
£1.80

(B74-51189)

RG — Suites
Popplewell, Richard
Suite for organ / by Richard Popplewell. — London : Oxford University Press, 1974. — 16p ; 4to.
Duration 10 min. — Contents: I: March - II: Intermezzo - III: Fugue.
ISBN 0-19-375658-7 : £1.10

(B74-50618)

RHP — Jigs
Mews, Donald
Gigue de Pan : organ with optional drums / [by] Donald Mews. — London : Oxford University Press, 1974. — 4to.
ISBN 0-19-375565-3 : £0.60
(B74-51190)

RHT — Passacaglias
Thomson, Virgil
Passacaglia for organ / [by] Virgil Thomson. — New York ; London : Schirmer, 1974. — 4to.
Unpriced
(B74-51191)

RJ — Miscellaneous works
Bamert, Matthias
Organism : for organ solo / [by] Matthias Bamert. — New York ; London : Schirmer, 1974. — 36p ; obl 4to.
Unpriced
(B74-51192)

Cruft, Adrian
Meditation on the Passion chorale. Op.72 : for organ / by Adrian Cruft. — London : Chappell, 1974. — 4p ; 4to.
Unpriced
(B74-50198)

Fricker, Peter Racine
Intrada : for organ. Op.64 / by Peter Racine Fricker. — London : Faber Music, 1973. — 13p ; 4to.
Duration 5 1/2 min.
Unpriced
(B74-50199)

Henriksen, Josef
Forty nine trio preludes for organ based on Sarum plainsong hymn melodies / by Josef Henriksen. — Hoddesdon : St Gregory, 1970. — 44p ; fol.
£1.65
(B74-50200)

Jongen, Joseph
Petit prelude. Aria : organ / by Joseph Jongen ; edited by John Scott Whiteley. — London : Oxford University Press, 1974. — 4p ; 4to.
ISBN 0-19-375495-9 : £0.35
(B74-50619)

Károlyi, Pál
Triphtongas 1 : for organ / by Pál Károlyi. — London : Boosey and Hawkes, 1973. — 12p ; obl.fol.
£0.75
(B74-50201)

Korn, Peter Jona
Gloria. Opus 49 : rhapsodische Fantasie für Orgel / [von] Peter Jona Korn. — Frankfurt : Litolff ; London : Peters, 1974. — 30p ; obl 4to.
£4.20
(B74-51193)

Laxton, Alwyn
Elegy and Le Motif : organ / by Alwyn Laxton. — Sevenoaks : Paxton, 1973. — 8p ; 4to.
£0.35
(B74-50202)

Newman, Anthony
Bhajeb : for organ / [by] Anthony Newman. — New York ; London : Schirmer, 1974. — 22p ; obl.4to.
The full title Bhajebochstiannanas is an anagram on the name Johann Sebastian Bach.
Unpriced
(B74-51194)

Organ music for today. — London : Chappell.
Contents: Ceremonies/ by Anthony Hedges - Passacaglia/ by Alan Ridout - Three interludes/ by John Hall - Toccata/ by John Hall.
Vol.1. — 1974. — 25p ; 4to.
Unpriced
(B74-50620)

Ridout, Alan
2 organ pieces / by Alan Ridout. — London : Chappell, 1974. — 4to.
Contents: Processions - Resurrection dances.
Unpriced
(B74-51195)

Slonimsky, Sergei
Chromatic poem : for organ (1969) / [by] Sergej Slonimski. — Leipzig ; [London] : Peters, 1974. — 17p ; obl.4to.
Unpriced
(B74-51196)

Speth, Johann
Ars magna consoni et dissoni : for organ / by Johann Speth ; edited by Traugott Fedtke. — Cassel ; London : Bärenreiter, 1974. — 68p ; obl 4to.
Contents: 10 toccatas, 8 Magnificats, 3 Partitas.
£3.80
(B74-50621)

Thiman, Eric Harding
[Works, organ. Selections]. A collection of organ music / by Eric H. Thiman. — Sevenoaks : Novello, 1974. — 40p ; 4to.
£1.50
(B74-50622)

Turvey, A W
Epilogue to evensong : organ solo / by A.W. Turvey. — London : Cramer, 1974. — 4p ; 4to.
Unpriced
(B74-50623)

Turvey, A W
Meditation on a folk tune : organ solo / [by] A.W. Turvey. — London : Cramer, 1974. — 4p ; 4to.
Unpriced
(B74-51197)

Walmisley, Thomas Attwood
[Works, organ. Selections]. Selected organ works / by Thomas Attwood Walmisley ; edited by A.G. Mathew and Gordon Phillips. — London : Peters, 1973. — 28p ; obl 4to.
Unpriced
(B74-50624)

Waters, Charles Frederick
Impromptu for the organ / by Charles F. Waters. — London : Cramer, 1973. — 4p ; 4to.
£0.24
(B74-50203)

Williamson, Malcolm
Little carols of the saints : for organ / by Malcolm Williamson. — London : Weinberger, 1974. — 28p ; obl 4to.
Unpriced
(B74-50625)

Wills, Arthur
Trio sonata : organ / by Arthur Wills. — London : Boosey and Hawkes, 1974. — 16p ; fol.
£1.00
(B74-50204)

RK — Arrangements
Arne, Thomas Augustine
[Sonata for harpsichord, no.3, in G. *Allegro*]. Allegro / by Thomas Augustine Arne ; arranged for organ by Arthur J. Gibson. — London : Cramer, 1973. — 4p ; 4to.
Unpriced
(B74-50205)

Binkerd, Gordon
[Concert set for piano : arr]. Concert set for organ / [by] Gordon Binkerd ; transcribed by Rudy Shackelford from the version for piano. — New York ; [London] : Boosey and Hawkes, 1974. — 19p ; 4to.
Contents: 1: Witch doctor - 2: Legend - 3: Etude - 4: Mice.
£3.75
(B74-51198)

Johannesen, Grant
[Improvisation on a Mormon hymn: arr]. Improvisation on a Mormon hymn: Come, come ye saints / by Grant Johannesen ; arranged for organ by Alexander Schreiner. — New York ; London : Oxford University Press, 1971. — 32p ; 4to.
Unpriced
(B74-50626)

RK/AAY — Arrangements. Collections
Dearnley, Christopher
Ceremonial music for organ / arranged by Christopher Dearnley. — London : Oxford University Press.
Book 1, by David Willcocks was entered under his name.
Book 2. — 1974. — 15p ; 4to.
ISBN 0-19-375345-6 : £0.50
(B74-50627)

Dexter, Harry
The first year organist : eleven famous melodies for all organs / arranged by Harry Dexter. — London : Ashdown, 1974. — 33p ; 4to.
£0.80
(B74-51199)

Grant, Lawrence
World's favorite contemporary music for all organs / compiled
and edited by Lawrence Grant. — Carlstadt (N.J.) : Ashley ;
[London] : [Phoenix], 1971. — 128p ; 4to.
Unpriced

(B74-51200)

RK/AHXJ — Arrangements. Ragtime
Joplin, Scott
[The entertainer: arr]. The entertainer : a ragtime two step :
composed by Scott Joplin / easy piano solo, arranged by
Lawrence Grant. — Carlstadt : Lewis Music ; [London] :
[Ashley-Fields], 1974. — 6p ; 4to.
Unpriced

(B74-51201)

RK/DH — Arrangements. Motets, Anthems, Hymns, etc
Bach, Johann Sebastian
[Also hat Gott die Welt geliebt. S.68. Mein glaubiges Herz: arr].
'Air', My heart ever faithful / by J.S. Bach ; arranged for the
organ by Patrick Williams. — London : Cramer, 1973. — 8p ;
4to.
£0.21

(B74-51202)

RK/DW — Arrangements. Songs, etc
Humperdinck, Engelbert
[Hänsel und Gretel. *Abends will ich schlafen gehen: arr*]. Angel
scene / by Humperdinck; arranged for organ by Francis G.
Walker. — London : Cramer, 1973. — 7p ; 4to.
Unpriced

(B74-50206)

RK/JM — Arrangements. Incidental music
Purcell, Henry
[King Arthur. *Selections: arr*]. Music from 'King Arthur' / by
Henry Purcell ; arranged and edited by Desmond Ratcliffe. —
Sevenoaks : Paxton, 1974. — 12p ; 4to.
£0.40

(B74-50628)

RK/KDD — Arrangements. Weddings
Purcell, Henry
[The married beau. *Selections: arr*]. Wedding march / [by] Henry
Purcell ; arranged for organ by J. Stanley Shirtcliff. — Sevenoaks :
Paxton, 1974. — 3p ; 4to.
£0.35

(B74-51203)

RK/LF — Arrangements. Concertos
Stanley, John
[Concerto for keyboard & string orchestra. Op.10, no.6: arr].
Concerto in C major / [by] John Stanley ; edited for organ by
Peter le Huray. — London : Oxford University Press, 1974. —
16p ; 4to.
Duration 10 min.
ISBN 0-19-367705-9 : £0.90

(B74-51204)

RPV — ELECTRIC ORGANS
RPVK/AAY — Arrangements. Collections
Michel, Joseph
Weihnachten : elektronische Orgel / Arrangements: Josef Michel.
— Cassel : Nagel ; [London] : [Bärenreiter], 1973. — 24p ; 4to.
Contents: [Works by] Bach, Cornelius, Händel, Michel, Pachelbel, Zipoli,
[and various Christmas carols].
£1.80

(B74-50629)

Parker, John
Die Welt der Orgel : eine Sammlung für alle elektronischen
Orgeln / bearbeitet von John Parker. — Mainz ; London : Schott,
1974. — 30p ; 4to.
£2.40

(B74-50207)

Schweizer, Rolf
Orgelstücke alter Meister : elektronische Orgel / Einrichtung Rolf
Schweizer. — Cassel : Nagel ; [London] : [Bärenreiter], 1973. —
32p ; 4to.
Contents: [Works by] Bach, Fischer, Graupner, Händel, Haydn, Kuhnau,
Pachelbel, Rathgeber, Scarlatti, Speth, Telemann, Zachow.
£1.80

(B74-50630)

Sommer, Jürgen
Barock : elektronische Orgel / Arrangements Jürgen Sommer. —
Cassel : Nagel ; [London] : [Bärenreiter], 1973. — 32p ; 4to.
Contents: [Works by] Bach, Corelli, Händel, Purcell, Tartini, Telemann,
Vivaldi.
£1.80

(B74-50631)

Sommer, Jürgen
Klassik : elektronische Orgel / Arrangements Jürgen Sommer. —
Cassel : Nagel ; [London] : [Bärenreiter], 1973. — 32p ; 4to.
Contents: [Works by] Beethoven, Boccherini, Haydn, Mozart.
£1.80

(B74-50632)

Sommer, Jürgen
Oper : elektronische Orgel / Arrangements Jürgen Sommer. —
Cassel : Nagel ; [London] : [Bärenreiter], 1973. — 32p ; 4to.
Contents: [Works by] Bizet, Gluck, Lortzing, Mozart, Offenbach, Verdi,
Weber, Wagner.
£1.80

(B74-50633)

RPVK/DW/AY — Arrangements. Songs, etc. Collections
Parker, John
Opernmelodien : für elektronische Orgel / bearbeitet von John
Parker. — Mainz ; London : Schott, 1974. — 31p ; 4to.
£2.40

(B74-50208)

RPVK/DW/G/AY — Arrangements. Folk songs. Collections
Draths, Willi
Die Kinderorgel : leichte Volkslieder aus aller Welt, für
elektronische Orgel (1 Manuel) / [compiled by] Willi Draths. —
Mainz ; London : Schott, 1974. — 23p ; obl. 8vo.
£1.45

(B74-50634)

RPVK/DW/G/AYE — Arrangements. Folk songs. Collections. Germany
Sommer, Jürgen
Volkslieder : elektronische Orgel / Arrangements Jürgen Sommer.
— Cassel : Nagel ; [London] : [Bärenreiter], 1973. — 32p ; 4to.
£1.80

(B74-50635)

RPVK/DW/G/AYT — Arrangements. Folk songs. Collections. United States
Parker, John
American folk songs : für elektronische Orgel / bearbeitet von
John Parker. — Mainz ; London : Schott, 1974. — 31p ; 4to.
£2.40

(B74-50209)

RPVK/DW/GB/AY — Arrangements. Popular songs. Collections
Parker, John
Pop hits 1 : for all electronic organs / bearbeitet von John Parker.
— Mainz ; London : Schott, 1974. — 39p ; 4to.
£2.90

(B74-50636)

RPVK/DW/LC/AY — Arrangements. Spirituals. Collections
Parker, John
Spirituals für elektronische Orgel / bearbeitet von John Parker. —
Mainz ; London : Schott, 1974. — 31p ; 4to.
£2.40

(B74-50210)

RSPLTS — ACCORDION & GUITAR
RSPLX — Accordion & percussion
Fink, Siegfried
Game for two : game for accordion and percussion / by Siegfried
Fink. — Hamburg ; London : Simrock, 1974. — 15p ; 4to.
Unpriced

(B74-50211)

Fink, Siegfried
Game for two : game for accordion and percussion / by Siegfried
Fink. — Hamburg ; London : Simrock, 1974. — 15p ; 4to.
Unpriced

(B74-50212)

RSPM — UNACCOMPANIED ACCORDION SOLOS
RSPM/AY — Collections
Romani, G
Master music makers : an anthology of music by the great
composers / selected, edited and transcribed for accordion by G.
Romani. — Leicester : Charnwood Music, 1973. — 23p ; 4to.
Unpriced

(B74-51205)

RSPMHVS — Tarantellas
Parnell, Frederick
Tarantelle : accordion solo / by Frederick Parnell. — Leicester :
Charnwood Music, 1972. — 3p ; 4to.
Unpriced

(B74-51206)

RSPMJ — Miscellaneous works
Crossman, Gerald
Gruss aus Wien! = Greetings from Vienna / by Gerald
Crossman. — Leicester : Charnwood Music, 1974. — [2]p ; 4to.
Unpriced

(B74-51207)

Ebing, Hans
Kleine Spielereien : für Akkordeon mit 2. Stimme und Schlagwerk ad lib / von Hans Ebing. — Mainz ; London : Schott, 1974. — 4to.
Score (10p.) & part.
£1.44

(B74-50213)

Law, Leslie G
Two preparatory accordion solos / by Leslie G. Law. — Leicester : Charnwood Music, 1974. — 2p ; 4to.
Contents: A little impromptu - Dance-time.
Unpriced

(B74-51208)

Micallef, John
Melita romantica : accordion solo / [by] John Micallef. — Leicester : Charnwood Music, 1974. — [2]p ; 4to.
Unpriced

(B74-51209)

Parnell, Frederick
Gondoliera : accordion solo / by Frederick Parnell. — Leicester : Charnwood Music, 1972. — 2p ; 4to.
Unpriced

(B74-51210)

Parnell, Frederick
Mainly under the fingers : easy accordion solos / [by, or arranged by] Fredk. Parnell. — Leicester : Charnwood Music, 1973. — 12p ; 4to.
Unpriced

(B74-51211)

Wright, Francis
5 divertimento for accordion / by Francis Wright. — Leicester : Charnwood Music, 1974. — 7p ; 4to.
Unpriced

(B74-51212)

RSPMK — Arrangements
Useful tunes for guitar. — Leicester : Charnwood Music.
No.4 : Rigadoon, from 'Musick's hand-maid' 1689 and Jig from 'Abdalazar' / [by] Henry Purcell ; transcribed by G. Romani. — 1974. — 1 sh ; 4to.
Unpriced

(B74-51213)

No.5 : Hot cross buns : trad. and Auld lang syne : trad. / arr. Rosemary Wright. — 1974. — 1 sh ; 4to.
Unpriced

(B74-51214)

RSPMK/AAY — Arrangements. Collections
Romani, G
'Opera nights' : an album of operatic favourites / transcribed and edited for the accordion by G. Romani. — Chesham : Ricordi, 1974. — 15p ; 4to.
Unpriced

(B74-51215)

RT — CONCERTINA
RT/AC — Tutors
Butler, Frank
The concertina : a handbook and tutor for beginners on the 'English' concertina / by Frank Butler. — Duffield : Free Reed Press, 1974. — 64p ; 4to.
Unpriced

(B74-50637)

RWN — STRING ENSEMBLES
RWNS — String instruments (bowed or plucked). Quartets
Huber, Klaus
Three short meditations : for string trio and harp (1969) / by Klaus Huber. — Cassel ; London : Bärenreiter, 1973. — 12p ; fol.
£2.70

(B74-50638)

RXM — STRING ORCHESTRA
RXM/X — Canons
Penderecki, Krzysztof
[Canon for string orchestra]. Kanon für Streichorchester / von Krysztof Penderecki. — Mainz ; London : Schott, 1974. — 38p ; 4to.
Study score. — Duration 8 min.
£4.06

(B74-50639)

RXM/Y — Fugues
Lutoslawski, Witold
Preludes and fugue for 13 solo strings / by Witold Lutoslawski. — London : Chester : Hansen, 1973. — 152p ; 8vo.
Duration 34 min.
Unpriced

(B74-50640)

RXME — Sonatas
Rossini, Gioacchino Antonio
[Sonata for strings, no.2, in A major]. Sonata per archi, A-Dur : 2 Violinen, Violoncello und Kontrabass (chorisch oder solistish) / [von] Gioacchino Rossini ; herausgegeben von Walter Lebermann. — Mainz ; London : Schott, 1974. — 24p ; 4to.
£2.90
Also classified at RXNSE

(B74-51216)

Walton, *Sir* William
Sonata for string orchestra / by William Walton. — London : Oxford University Press, 1973. — 94p ; 8vo.
Duration 25 min. — This work has been adapted by the composer from his String Quartet in A minor.
ISBN 0-19-368427-6 : £3.90

(B74-50214)

RXMF — Concertos
Ginastera, Alberto
[Concerto for string orchestra. Op. 33]. Concerto per corde. Op. 33 / by Alberto Ginastera. — London : Boosey and Hawkes, 1974. — 52p ; 4to.
£3.00

(B74-50215)

Vivaldi, Antonio
[Concerto for string orchestra & basso continuo in C major. P. 27]. Concerto ripieno, C-Dur für Streichorchester und Basso continuo. PV27 / von Antonio Vivaldi ; erstmals herausgegeben von Walter Lebermann, Generalbassausführung vom Herausgeber. — Mainz ; London : Schott, 1973. — 16p ; 4to.
£1.92

(B74-50216)

RXMG — Suites
Cruft, Adrian
[Suite for strings, no.3, from Musick's Handmaid]. Third suite for strings, from Musick's Handmaid / freely arranged by Adrian Cruft, from music by Matthew Locke and Henry Purcell. — London : Chappell, 1974. — 4to.
Score (10p.) & 13 parts. — Matthew Cooke, on the covers, is a printer's error.
Unpriced

(B74-50217)

Morgan, Thomas
Suite, Love and honour : for strings and continuo / by Thomas Morgan ; edited by Richard Platt. — London : Oxford University Press, 1974. — 4to.
Score (16p.) & 4 parts.
ISBN 0-19-357824-7 : £1.75

(B74-50641)

RXMJ — Miscellaneous works
Berkeley, Lennox
Antiphon : for string orchestra / [by] Lennox Berkeley. — London : Chester, 1974. — 21p ; 8vo.
Miniature score - Duration 12 min.
Unpriced

(B74-51217)

Dodgson, Stephen
Idyll for strings / by Stephen Dodgson. — London : Chappell, 1974. — 4to.
Score (7p.) & 13 parts.
Unpriced

(B74-50218)

Gabrieli, Andrea
[Madrigali et ricercari a quattro voci, nos 6. 7]. Ricercari a quattro, nos.6 & 7 / von Andrea Gabrieli ; für zwei Violinen, Viola und Violoncello, (chorisch oder soloistisch) herausgegeben von Walter Lebermann. — Mainz ; London : Schott, 1973. — 24p ; 4to.
£1.92

(B74-50219)

Lutoslawski, Witold
Musique funèbre : for string orchestra / [by] Witold Lutoslawski. — London : Chester, 1974. — 47p ; 8vo.
Duration 13 1/2 min.
Unpriced

(B74-50642)

Mouravieff, Leon
Tanz-Metamorphosen : für Streicher / [von] Leon Mouravieff. — Frankfurt : Litolff ; London : Peters, 1974. — 27p ; 4to.
Unpriced

(B74-51218)

Stoker, Richard
Chorale for strings / by Richard Stoker. — London : Fenette Music : Breitkopf and Härtel, 1974. — 4to.
Score (4p.) & 5 parts.
Unpriced

(B74-50643)

RXMK/DW — Arrangements. Songs, etc
Dodd, Peter
An Irish idyll, The lark in the clear air / arranged for string orchestra by Peter Dodd. — London : United Music, 1971. — 4to.
Score (2p.) & 15 parts. — With several copies of various parts.
Unpriced

(B74-50644)

Villa-Lobos, Heitor
Bachianas brasileiras, no.5. Aria (Cantilena) / [by] Heitor Villa-Lobos ; arranged for string orchestra by John Krance. — New York ; London : Associated Music, 1971. — 13p ; 4to.
Unpriced

(B74-50645)

RXMP — SOLO INSTRUMENT (S) & STRING ORCHESTRA
RXMPNVVNT — Wind & string trio & string orchestra
Hummel, Johann Nepomuk
[Fantasia for viola, two clarinets & string orchestra: arr]. Fantasia for viola and string orchestra with two clarinets / [by] J.N. Hummel; arranged for viola and piano by H. Truscott. — London : Musica rara, 1974. — 4to.
Score (14p.) & part. — The main tune is the tenor aria 'Il mio tesoro intanto' from Mozart's Don Giovanni.
Unpriced

(B74-50646)

RXMPRXNTF — String trio & string orchestra. Concertos
Vivaldi, Antonio
[L'Estro armonico. Op.3, no.11]. Concerto d-Moll : für 2 Violinen, Streicher und Basso continuo / von Antonio Vivaldi ; herausgegeben von Helmut May. — Mainz ; London : Schott, 1974. — 29p ; 4to.
£4.35

(B74-50647)

RXMPSF — Violin & string orchestra. Concertos
Albinoni, Tommaso
[Concerto for violin and string orchestra in A major. Giazotto 116]. Konzert, A-Dur, für Violine, Streichorchester und Basso continuo / [von] Tomaso Albinoni ; herausgegeben von Friedrich Wanek ; Streichereingerichtet von Helmut May. — Mainz ; London : Schott, 1974. — 24p ; 4to.
£4.35

(B74-51219)

Bach, Johann Sebastian
[Concerto for violin & string orchestra in A minor. S. 1041]. Konzert, A-moll, für Violine und Streichorchester. BWV 1041 / von Joh. Seb. Bach ; nach den Quellen herausgegeben von Hans-Joachim Schulze. — Leipzig ; [London] : Peters, 1972. — 29p ; 8vo.
Miniature score.
Unpriced

(B74-51220)

RXMPSNUF — Two violins & string orchestra. Concertos
Muffat, Georg
[Exquisitioris harmoniae instrumentalis gravijucundae selectus primus. *Concerto no.9 for two violins & string orchestra, 'Victoria maesta'*]. Concerto 9, 'Victoria maesta' / von Georg Muffat ; herausgegeben von Günter Kehr. — Mainz ; London : Schott, 1973. — 12p ; 4to.
£1.92

(B74-50220)

RXMPSRF — Cello & string orchestra. Concertos
Boccherini, Luigi
[Concerto for cello & string orchestra, no.2, in D major]. Konzert No.2, D Dur für Violoncello und Streichorchester / von Luigi Boccherini ; herausgegeben und mit Kadenzen versehen von Walter Lebermann. — Mainz ; London : Schott, 1973. — 32p ; 4to.
£2.40

(B74-50221)

RXMPVRF — Flute & string orchestra. Concertos
Bach, Carl Philipp Emanuel
[Concerto for flute & string orchestra in G major. Wq.169]. Concerto in G major : for flute, strings and basso continuo. Wq.169 / by Carl Philipp Emanuel Bach ; ed. David Lasocki, realization of basso continuo by R.P. Block. — Loncon : Musica rara, 1974. — 4to.
Score (55p.) & parts.
Unpriced

(B74-50648)

Quantz, Johann Joachim
[Concerto for flute & string orchestra in D minor]. Concerto in D minor for flute, strings and continuo / [by] Johann Joachim Quantz ; edited by David Lasocki, realisation of basso continuo by R.P. Block. — London : Musica rara, 1972. — 4to.
Score (45p.) & 6 parts.
Unpriced

(B74-50649)

RXMPVRNU — Two flutes & string orchestra
Berger, Jean
Concert piece : for two flutes and string orchestra / by Jean Berger. — New York ; London : Schirmer, 1972. — 30p ; 4to.
Unpriced

(B74-50222)

RXMPVTF — Oboe & string orchestra. Concertos
Bennett, Richard Rodney
[Concerto for oboe & string orchestra]. Oboe concerto / by Richard Rodney Bennett. — London : Universal, 1974. — 40p ; 8vo.
Study score.
Unpriced

(B74-51221)

RXMPVTNUF — Two oboes & string orchestra. Concertos
Vivaldi, Antonio
[Concerto for two oboes & string orchestra in D minor. P.302]. Concerto in D minor for 2 oboes, strings and basso continuo / [by] Antonio Vivaldi ; ed. David Lasocki, realisation of basso continuo by R.P. Block. — London : Musica rara, 1973. — 4to.
Score (27p.) & 7 parts.
Unpriced

(B74-50650)

RXMPVTPLSF — Oboe, violin & string orchestra. Concertos
Vivaldi, Antonio
[Concerto for oboe, violin & string orchestra in C minor 'Lund']. Concerto in C minor for oboe, violin and strings (Lund) / [by] Antonio Vivaldi ; ed. David Lasocki, realization of basso continuo by R.P. Block. — London : Musica rara, 1973. — 4to.
Score (20p.) & 7 parts.
Unpriced

(B74-50651)

RXMPVVNUF — Two clarinets & string orchestra. Concertos
Telemann, Georg Philipp
[Concerto for two clarinets & string orchestra in D minor]. Concerto for 2 clarinets (chalumeaux) and strings / [by] G.P. Telemann ; edited by Hermann Dechant. — London : Musica rara, 1973. — 4to.
Score (24p.) & 7 parts.
Unpriced

(B74-50652)

RXMPWSE — Trumpet & string orchestra. Symphonies
Mancini, Francesco
[Idaspe. Sinfonia]. Sinfonia to 'Hydaspes' : for trumpet, strings and basso continuo / [by] Francesco Mancini ; edited by R.L. Minter. — London : Musica rara, 1974. — 4to.
Score (12p.) & 7 parts.
Unpriced

(B74-50653)

Stradella, Alessandro
[Il Barcheggio. Sinfonia]. Sinfonia to the serenata 'Il Barcheggio' : for trumpet, strings and basso continuo / [by] Alessandro Stradella ; [edited by] Robert Paul Block. — London : Musica rara.
Score (11p.) & 7 parts.
Part 1. — 1973. — 4to.
Unpriced

(B74-50654)

RXMPWT — Horn & orchestra
Cruft, Adrian
Elegy for horn and strings / [by] Adrian Cruft, with piano reduction for piano solo. — Sevenoaks : Novello, 1974. — 28p ; 4to.
£2.50
Also classified at QPK

(B74-51222)

RXMPWUU — Bass trombone & string orchestra
Andrix, George
Free forms : four pieces for brass trombone and strings / by George Andrix. — New York ; London : Schirmer, 1974. — 4to.
Score (10p.) & 6 parts.
Unpriced

(B74-51223)

RXNR — Quintets
Schubert, Franz
[Quintet for strings in C major. D.956]. Quintet, C major, for 2 violins, viola and 2 cellos. D.956 / [by] Franz Schubert ; revised by Max Hochkofler ; foreword by Roger Fiske. — London : Eulenburg, 1970. — iv,78p ; 8vo.
Miniature score.
Unpriced

(B74-51224)

RXNS — Quartets

Adler, Samuel
[Quartet for strings, no.5]. String quartet, no.5 / [by] Samuel Adler. — New York ; [London] : Boosey and Hawkes, 1974. — 40p ; 8vo.
Miniature score.
£2.50

(B74-51225)

Bainbridge, Simon
[Quartet for strings (1972)]. String quartet (1972) / [by] Simon Bainbridge. — London : United Music, 1974. — obl 4to.
Score (16p.) & 4 parts.
Unpriced

(B74-50655)

Butting, Max
[Quartet for strings, no.8. Op.96]. VIII. Streichquartett. Opus 96 / [von] Max Butting. — Leipzig ; [London] : Peters, 1973. — 68p ; 8vo.
Miniature score.
Unpriced

(B74-51226)

Carter, Elliott
[Quartet for strings, no.3]. String quartet no.3 / by Elliott Carter. — New York ; London : Associated Music, 1973. — 94p ; 8vo.
Unpriced

(B74-50656)

Jones, Douglas
Movement for string quartet / by Douglas Jones. — London : Schott, 1974. — 4to.
Score (8p.) & 4 parts.
£1.25

(B74-50223)

Kagel, Mauricio
[Quartet for strings (1965/67)]. Streichquartett (1965/67) / von Mauricio Kagel. — London : Universal, 1974. — 46p ; obl 4to.
Unpriced

(B74-50224)

Shostakovich, Dmitry
[Quartet for strings, no.7. Op.108]. Streichquartett Nr.7. Opus 108 / von Dmitri Schostakowitsch. — Leipzig ; [London] : Peters, 1974. — 4pt ; 4to.
£3.50

(B74-51227)

Shostakovich, Dmitry
[Quartet for strings, no.13. Op.138]. String quartet no.13. Op.138 / [by] Dmitri Shostakovich. — London : Boosey and Hawkes, 1974. — 8vo & 4to.
Miniature score & 4 parts.
£1.25

(B74-50657)

Street, Tison
[Quartet for strings (1972)]. String quartet (1972) / [by] Tison Street. — New York ; London : Schirmer, 1974. — 35p ; 8vo.
Study score.
Unpriced

(B74-51228)

Tchaikowsky, André
[Quartet for strings in A major. Op.3]. String quartet in A. Op.3 / [by] André Tchaikowsky. — London : Weinberger, 1974. — 8vo.
Miniature score (36p.) & 4 parts. — Duration 20 min.
Unpriced

(B74-50658)

Warren, Raymond
[Quartet for strings, no.1]. String quartet no.1 / [by] Raymond Warren. — Sevenoaks : Novello, 1974. — 52p ; 8vo.
Duration 23 min - Study score.
Unpriced

(B74-51229)

RXNSE — Quartets. Sonatas

Rossini, Gioacchino Antonio
[Sonata for strings, no.2, in A major]. Sonata per archi, A-Dur : 2 Violinen, Violoncello und Kontrabass (chorisch oder solistish) / [von] Gioacchino Rossini ; herausgegeben von Walter Lebermann. — Mainz ; London : Schott, 1974. — 24p ; 4to.
£2.90
Primary classification RXME

RXNT — Trios

Gál, Hans
[Trio for strings. Op.104]. Trio for violin, viola d'amore (or viola) and violoncello. Op.104 / [by] Hans Gál. — Hamburg ; London : Simrock, 1974. — 36p ; 8vo.
Study score.
Unpriced

(B74-51230)

S — VIOLIN

S/AC — Tutors

Cohen, Eta
[First year violin method]. Eta Cohen violin method. — Sevenoaks : Paxton.
Violin part (32p.), Piano accompaniment (2,89p.). — Piano accompaniment by Richard Drakeford.
Book 1. — 1974. — 4to.
£0.50

(B74-51231)

Doflein, Erich
Das Geigen-Schulwerk : ein Lehrgang des Violinspiels verbunden mit Musiklehre und Ubung des Zusammenspiels / von Erich und Elma Doflein. — Erweiterte Ausgabe. — Mainz ; London : Schott.
Heft 1a : Der Anfang des Geigenspiels. — 1973. — 88p ; 4to.
£2.40

(B74-50225)

S/AF — Exercises

Zámečnik, Evžen
Twelve studies for violin : for technical problems in contemporary music / by Evžen Zámečnik. — Cassel ; London : Bärenreiter, 1973. — 19p ; 4to.
£3.25

(B74-50659)

S/AL — Examinations

Associated Board of the Royal Schools of Music
Violin examinations, 1975 and 1976. — London : Associated Board of the Royal Schools of Music.
Grade 1 : Lists A and B (primary). — 1974. — 4to.
Score (11p.) & part.
£0.35

(B74-51232)

Grade II : Lists A and B (elementary). — 1974. — 4to.
Score (12p.) & part.
£0.35

(B74-51233)

Grade III : Lists A and B (transitional). — 1974. — 4to.
Score (16p.) & part.
£0.35

(B74-51234)

Grade IV : Lists A and B (lower). — 1974. — 4to.
Score (19p.) & part.
£0.35

(B74-51235)

Grade V : Lists A and B (higher). — 1974. — 4to.
Score (24p.) & part.
£0.35

(B74-51236)

Grade VI : Lists A and B (intermediate). — 1974. — 4to.
Score (28p.) & part.
£0.40

(B74-51237)

Grade VII : Lists A and B (advanced). — 1974. — 4to.
Score (36p.) & part.
£0.40

(B74-51238)

Guildhall School of Music
Violin examinations, series one. — South Croydon : Lengnick.
Score (13p.) & part.
Grade 1. — 1973. — 4to.
£0.40

(B74-50226)

Grade 2. — 1973. — 4to.
£0.40

(B74-50227)

Grade 3. — 1973. — 4to.
£0.40

(B74-50228)

Grade 4. — 1973. — 4to.
£0.60

(B74-50229)

Introductory. — 1973. — 4to.
£0.40

(B74-50230)

Junior. — 1973. — 4to.
£0.40

(B74-50231)

Preliminary. — 1973. — 4to.
£0.40

(B74-50232)

SN — VIOLIN ENSEMBLE

SNTQK/LF — Arrangements. Concertos

Vivaldi, Antonio
[L'Estro armonico, Op.3, no.11: arr]. Concerto, d-Moll : für 2 Violinen, Streicher und Basso continuo / [von] Antonio Vivaldi ; bearbeitet and herausgegeben von Walter Kolneder, Klavierauszug vom Herausgeber. — Mainz ; London : Schott, 1974. — 4to.
Score (17p.) & 2 parts.
£2.32

(B74-51239)

SP — VIOLIN & PIANO
SP/AY — Collections
Warlike Musick
[Warlike Musick for flute, violin or harpsichord]. Warlike Musick (1760) : marches and trumpet tunes, for flute or oboe or violin and basso continuo / edited by Philip Ledger. — London : Oxford University Press, 1974. — 4to.
Score (30p.) & part.
ISBN 0-19-357552-3 : £1.50
Primary classification VRP/AY

SP/W — Rondos
Head, Michael
Rondo for oboe or violin and piano / by Michael Head ; [oboe part] edited by Evelyn Barbirolli; [violin part] edited by Winifred Small. — London : Boosey and Hawkes, 1974. — 4to.
Score (8p.) & part. — The violin part is printed on the verso of the oboe part.
£0.60
Primary classification VTP/W

(B74-50781)

SPE — Sonatas
Adler, Samuel
[Sonata for violin & piano, no.3]. Third sonata for violin and piano, (in six episodes) / by Samuel Adler. — New York ; [London] : Boosey and Hawkes, 1974. — 4to.
Score (28p.) & part.
£2.50

(B74-50660)

Bavicchi, John
[Sonata for violin & piano, no.4, Op.63]. Sonata no.4 for violin and piano, Op.63 : fantasy-sonata on Lithuanian folk melodies / by John Bavicchi. — New York ; [London] : Oxford University Press, 1974. — 4to.
Score (15p.) & part.
Unpriced

(B74-50661)

Frankel, Benjamin
[Sonata for violin, no.2. Op.39]. Second sonata for solo violin. Op.39 / by Benjamin Frankel. — Sevenoaks : Novello, 1974. — 13p ; 4to.
Duration 22 min.
£0.75

(B74-50662)

Gibbs, Joseph
[Sonata for violin & basso continuo, no.3, in G major]. Violin sonata no.3 in G major / [by] Joseph Gibbs ; edited by David C. Stone ; continuo realization by Colin Tilney. — London : Schott, 1974. — 4to.
Score (12p.) & 2 parts.
Unpriced

(B74-51240)

Gibbs, Joseph
[Sonata for violin & basso continuo, no.5, in E major]. Violin sonata no.5 in E major / [by] Joseph Cooper ; edited by David C. Stone ; continuo realization by Colin Tilney. — London : Schott, 1974. — 4to.
Score (12p.) & 2 parts.
Unpriced

(B74-51241)

Hoffmeister, Franz Anton
[Sonata for flute & piano in C major. Op.13]. Sonata in C major for flute or violin and piano / by Franz Anton Hoffmeister ; edited by Hans-Peter Schmitz. — Cassel : Nagel ; London : Bärenreiter, 1973. — 4to.
Score (40p.) & part.
£3.80
Primary classification VRPE

(B74-50751)

Klebe, Giselher
[Sonata for violin & piano. Op.66]. Sonate für Violine und Klavier. Op 66 / von Giselher Klebe. — Cassel ; London : Bärenreiter, 1973. — fol.
Score (33p.) & part.
£3.60

(B74-50663)

Veracini, Francesco Maria
[Sonatas for violin & basso continuo. Op.1, nos. 1, 4, 8]. 3 sonatas for violin and piano / by Francesco Maria Veracini ; edited by Albert Lazan; bass realization by Mary Wennerstrom. — New York ; London : Associated Music, 1972. — 4to.
Score (54p.) & part.
Unpriced

(B74-50233)

Veracini, Francesco Maria
[Sonate a violino o flauto solo e basso, nos 1-3]. Three sonatas for violin (flute, treble recorder) and basso continuo / by Francesco Maria Veracini ; edited by Franz Bär. — Cassel ; [London] : Bärenreiter, 1973. — 4to.
Score (32p.) & 2 parts.
£3.60
Also classified at VRPE

(B74-50664)

SPG — Suites
Couperin, François
Concerts royaux I-IV : for flute, oboe, violin, viola da gamba and basso continuo / [by] François Couperin ; edited by David Lasocki. — London : Musica rara.
Score (8p.) & 3 parts. — With a separate leaflet of four pages containing a foreword, inserted.
No.I / realization of the basso continuo by Gerhard Krapf. — 1974. — 4to.
Unpriced
Primary classification VRPG

(B74-50754)

No.II / realization of the basso continuo by R.P. Block. — 1974. — 4to.
Unpriced
Primary classification VRPG

(B74-50755)

No.III / realization of the basso continuo by R.P. Block. — 1974. — 4to.
Unpriced
Primary classification VRPG

(B74-50756)

No.IV / realization of the basso continuo by R.P. Block. — 1974. — 4to.
Unpriced
Primary classification VRPG

(B74-50757)

Jones, Richard
[Suite for violin & basso continuo in A major. Op.3, no.1]. Suite 1 in A major for violin and basso continuo / by Richard Jones ; edited by Gwilym Beechey. — London : Oxford University Press, 1974. — 4to.
Score (11p.) & 2 parts.
ISBN 0-19-357395-4 : £1.25

(B74-50665)

Jones, Richard
[Suite for violin & basso continuo in B flat major. Op.3, no.4]. Suite 4 in B flat major for violin and basso continuo / by Richard Jones ; edited by Gwilym Beechey. — London : Oxford University Press, 1974. — 4to.
Score (9p.) & 2 parts.
ISBN 0-19-357398-9 : £1.25

(B74-50666)

Jones, Richard
[Suite for violin & basso continuo in D major. Op.3, no.3]. Suite 3 in D major for violin and basso continuo / by Richard Jones ; edited by Gwilym Beechey. — London : Oxford University Press, 1974. — 4to.
Score (9p.) & 2 parts.
ISBN 0-19-357397-0 : £1.25

(B74-50667)

Jones, Richard
[Suite for violin & basso continuo in G minor. Op.3, no.2]. Suite 2 in G minor for violin and basso continuo / by Richard Jones ; edited by Gwilym Beechey. — London : Oxford University Press, 1974. — 4to.
Score (12p.) & 2 parts.
ISBN 0-19-357396-2 : £1.25

(B74-50668)

Reger, Max
[Suite for violin & piano in F major. Op.93, 'in olden style']. Suite im alten Stil für Violine und Klavier. Opus 93, / [von] Max Reger ; bezeichnung der Violinstimme von Ulfert Thiemann. — Leipzig ; [London] : Peters, 1973. — 4to.
Score (27p.) & part.
Unpriced

(B74-51242)

SPHMV — Havanises
Saint-Saens, Camille
Havanaise for violin and piano. Op.83 / by Camille Saint-Saens ; edited by Rok Kločič. — New York ; London : Schirmer, 1973. — 4to.
Score (16p.) & part.
Unpriced

(B74-50669)

SPHVQ — Sicilianos
Standford, Patric
Siciliano : for violin and piano / by Patric Standford. — South Croydon : Lengnick, 1974. — 4to.
Score (4p.) & part.
£0.25

(B74-50234)

SPJ — Miscellaneous works
Davies, Ivor Richard
First tunes for my first finger. Op. post : violin and piano / by Ivor Richard Davies. — London : Boosey and Hawkes, 1973. — 4to.
Score (8p.) & part.
£0.70

(B74-50235)

Greaves, Terence
Four easy pieces in folk style : for violin and pianoforte / by Terence Greaves. — London : Associated Board of the Royal Schools of Music, 1974. — 4to.
Score (4p.) & part.
£0.20

(B74-51243)

Lazarof, Henri
Rhapsody for violin and piano / by Henri Lazarof. — New York ; London : Associated Music, 1972. — fol.
Score (13p.) & part.
£7.50

(B74-50670)

Nelson, Sheila M
Right from the start : twenty tunes for young violinists for violin and piano / by Sheila M. Nelson. — London : Boosey and Hawkes, 1974. — 4to.
Score (20p.) & part. — With a gramophone record.
£2.25

(B74-50671)

Schuster, Joseph
[Divertimenti for violin & keyboard, nos 1-6]. 6 divertimenti da camera for harpsichord (piano) and violin / [by] Joseph Schuster ; first printed edition, edited by Wolfgang Plath. — Cassel : Nagel ; London : Bärenreiter.
Score (36p.) & part.
1 : Divertimenti I and II. — 1971. — 4to.
£3.45

(B74-50672)

2 : Divertimenti III and IV. — 1971. — 4to.
£2.55

(B74-50673)

3 : Divertimenti V and VI. — 1971. — 4to.
£2.55

(B74-50674)

SPK — Arrangements
Beethoven, Ludwig van
[Concerto movement for violin in C major. G.148: arr]. Concerto movement for violin and chamber orchestra, 1790/92. Wo05 / by Ludwig van Beethoven ; fragment edited and completed (on the basis of Willy Hess edition) by Wilfried Fischer, editing of the solo part and cadenza Takaya Urakawa, piano score, Wilfried Fischer. — Wiesbaden : Breitkopf and Härtel ; Cassel ; London : Bärenreiter, 1972. — 4to.
Score (26p.) & part.
£3.25

(B74-50675)

Saint-Saens, Camille
[Introduction and rondo capriccioso for violin & orchestra. Opus 28: arr]. Introduktion und Rondo capriccioso. Opus 28 : für Violine und Orchester / [von] Camille Saint-Saens ; Klavierauszug von George Bizet, Violine bezeichnet von Ulfert Thiemann. — Leipzig ; [London] : Peters, 1973. — 4to.
Score (16p.) & part.
£2.40

(B74-51244)

SPK/AAY — Arrangements. Collections
Lenkei, Gabriella
Music for violin (intermediate) / edited by Gabriella Lenkei. — London : Boosey and Hawkes ; Budapest : Editio Musica, 1973. — 4to.
Score (44p.) & part.
£1.00

(B74-51245)

SPK/DW/G/AYEM — Arrangements. Folk songs. Collections.
Austria
Alt, Hansi
Red clouds : 12 folk songs from Austria, Switzerland and Tirol, for violin (or recorder or flute) and piano, with optional cello / by Hansi Alt. — New York ; [London] : Oxford University Press, 1971. — 4to.
Score & 2 parts.
Unpriced
Also classified at VRPK/DW/G/AYEM; VSRPK/DW/G/AYEM

(B74-51246)

SPK/LF — Arrangements. Concertos
Albinoni, Tommaso
[Concerto for violin & string orchestra in A major: arr]. Konzert, A-Dur für Violine, Streichorchester und Basso continuo / [von] Tomaso Albinoni ; herausgegeben von Friedrich Wanek ; Streicherstimmen eingerichtet von Helmut May. — Mainz ; London : Schott, 1974. — 4to.
Score (17p.) & part.
£2.03

(B74-51247)

Tchaikovsky, Peter
[Concerto for violin in D major. Op. 35: arr]. Konzert für Violine und Orchester. Opus 35 / von Peter Tschaikowsky ; herausgegeben von Max Rostal, Klavierauszug vom Komponisten. — Mainz ; London : Schott, 1973. — 4to.
Score (59p.) & part.
£2.40

(B74-50236)

Viotti, Giovanni Battista
[Concerto for violin & string orchestra, no.2, in E major: arr]. Konzert No.2: E-Dur für Violine und Streichorchester, zwei Oboen und zwei Hörner ad lib / von Giovanni Battista Viotti ; herausgegeben und mit Kadenz versehen von Walter Lebermann, Klavierauszug [for violin and piano]. — Mainz ; London : Schott, 1974. — 4to.
Score (35p.) & part.
£2.90

(B74-50676)

SPLSR — VIOLIN & CELLO
Hand, Colin
Discussions : for violin and cello / [by] Colin Hand. — London : Thames, 1974. — 16p ; fol.
Unpriced

(B74-51248)

SPLTS — VIOLIN & GUITAR
Carulli, Ferdinando
[Duo for flute and guitar in D major. Op. 109, no.6]. Serenade für Flöte (Violine) und Gitarre / von Ferdinando Carulli ; herausgegeben von Frank Nagel. — Mainz ; London : Schott, 1974. — 2pt ; 4to.
£1.32
Primary classification VRPLTS

(B74-50273)

SPM — UNACCOMPANIED VIOLIN
SPME — Sonatas
Standford, Patric
Sonata for violin solo. Op.36 / by Patric Standford. — Sevenoaks : Novello, 1974. — 10p ; 4to.
£0.75

(B74-50237)

SPMG — Suites
Butt, James
Soliloquy : for solo violin / [by] James Butt. — London : Thames, 1974. — 11p ; 4to.
Unpriced

(B74-51249)

SPMJ — Miscellaneous works
Rode, Pierre
24 Caprices in Etüdenform für Violine allein in den 24 Tonarten / von Pierre Rode ; revidiert und mit Vorübungen versehen von Max Rostal. — Mainz ; London : Schott, 1974. — 63p ; 4to.
With preparatory exercises (12p.).
£2.40

(B74-50238)

Telemann, Georg Philipp
[Twelve fantasias for violin]. Zwolf Fantasien für Violine ohne Bass / von G. Ph. Telemann ; nach dem Urtext herausgegeben von Manfred Fechner ; bezeichnet von Ulfert Thiemann. — Leipzig ; [London] : Peters, 1973. — 27p ; 4to.
Unpriced

(B74-51250)

SQ — VIOLA
SQK/AF — Arrangements. Exercises
Wohlfahrt, Franz
[Etudes for violin. Op.45, 54, 74. Selections: arr]. Forty selected studies in first position for the viola / by Franz Wohlfahrt ; transcribed and edited by Leonard Mogill. — New York ; London : Schirmer, 1972. — 40p ; 4to.
Unpriced

(B74-50239)

SQP — VIOLA & PIANO
SQPJ — Miscellaneous works
Applebaum, Edward
Foci for viola and piano / [by] Edward Applebaum. — London : Chester, 1973. — 4to.
Score (6p.) & part.
Unpriced

(B74-50240)

SQPK/AAY — Arrangements. Collections
Forbes, Watson
Classical and romantic pieces for viola and piano / arranged by Watson Forbes. — London : Oxford University Press, 1974. — 4to.
Score (32p.) & part. — Contents: 1: Reverie/Tchaikovsky - 2: Ballet music/Schubert - 3: Larghetto/Dvořák - 4: Song without words/Mendelssohn - 5: Giga/Handel - 6: Study/Heller - 7: Dances/Purcell - 8: Prelude/Chopin - Two elegiac melodies/Grieg.
ISBN 0-19-356501-3 : £1.30

(B74-50677)

SQPK/LF — Arrangements. Concertos
Stamitz, Anton
[Concerto for viola & string orchestra, no.4, in D major: arr]. Concerto no.4 in D major for viola and strings / by Anton Stamitz ; edited with cadences (sic) by Walter Lebermann; piano score by Ulrich Haverkampf. — Wiesbaden : Breitkopf and Härtel ; Cassel ; London : Bärenreiter, 1973. — 4to.
Score (22p.) & part.
£2.90

(B74-50678)

SQPM — UNACCOMPANIED VIOLA
SQPMG — Suites
Uhl, Alfred
Kleine Suite für Viola / von Alfred Uhl. — Mainz ; London : Schott, 1974. — 6p ; 4to.
£0.96

(B74-50241)

SQPMJ — Miscellaneous works
Block, Robert Paul
Fantasy for viola solo (1967, rev. 1973) / [by] Robert Paul Block. — London : Musica rara, 1974. — 3p ; 4to.
Printed on one side of the leaf only.
Unpriced

(B74-50679)

SQPMK — Arrangements
Rode, Pierre
24 Capricen in Etüdenform für Bratsche allein in den 24 Tonarten / von Pierre Rode ; revidiert und mit Vorübungen versehen von Max Rostal. — Mainz ; London : Schott, 1974. — 63p ; 4to.
With preparatory exercises.
£2.40

(B74-50242)

SR — CELLO
SR/AC — Tutors
Doppelbauer, Rupert
Einführung in das Violoncellospiel / von Rupert Doppelbauer. — Mainz ; London : Schott.
Heft 1. — 1973. — 47p ; 4to. —
£2.00

(B74-50243)

Heft 2. — 1973. — 48p ; 4to.
£2.40

(B74-50244)

SRN — CELLO ENSEMBLE
SRNU — Duets
Breval, Jean Baptiste
[Traite du violoncelle. Selections]. Leichte Stücke für Violoncello mit Begleitung durch 2 Violoncello / von Jean Baptiste Breval ; herausgegeben von Erich Doflein. — Mainz ; London : Schott.
Heft 1. — 1974. — 16p ; 4to.
£1.44

(B74-50245)

Heft 2. — 1974. — 16p ; 4to.
£1.44

(B74-50096)

Raoul, Jean Marie
[Méthode de violoncelle. Op.4. Leçons et exercices, nos.10-18]. Nine studies : for two cellos / by Jean-Marie Raoul ; edited by Gwilm Beechey. — London : Oxford University Press, 1974. — 9p ; 4to.
ISBN 0-19-358480-8 : £0.55

(B74-50680)

SRP — CELLO & PIANO
SRPE — Sonatas
Bertoli, Giovanni Antonio
[Compositioni musicale fatte per sonare col fagotto solo, nos 1-3]. Three sonatas for bassoon (violoncello) and basso continuo / by Giovanni Antonio Bertoli ; edited by William Kaplan. — Cassel ; London : Bärenreiter, 1973. — 4to.
Score (32p.) & 2 parts.
£3.45
Primary classification VWPE

(B74-50811)

Feld, Jindrich
[Sonata for cello & piano (1972)]. Sonate für Violoncello und Klavier (1972) / von Jindrich Feld. — Mainz ; London : Schott, 1973. — 4to.
Score (36p.) & part. — Duration 16 min.
£2.40

(B74-50246)

Marcello, Benedetto
[Sonatas for cello and basso continuo. Op.2]. Six sonatas : for cello or double bass and piano / by Marcello Benedetto ; keyboard realization and cello part edited by Analee Bacon; double bass part edited by Lucas Drew. — New York ; London : Schirmer, 1973. — 4to.
Score (38p.) & 2 parts.
£1.85
Also classified at SSPE

(B74-50681)

Reutter, Hermann
Sonata monotematica : für Violoncello (oder Fagott) und Klavier / von Hermann Reutter. — Mainz ; London : Schott, 1974. — 4to.
An edition for bassoon and piano is also available.
£1.92

(B74-50247)

SRPJ — Miscellaneous works
Head, Michael
Scherzo : for horn or bassoon (or violoncello) and piano / by Michael Head. — London : Boosey and Hawkes, 1974. — 4to.
Score (5p.) & 2 parts.
£0.60
Primary classification WTPJ

(B74-50848)

Horton, John
Five Northumbrian tunes : for cello and piano / by John Horton. — London : Schott, 1974. — 4to.
£1.00

(B74-50248)

Joubert, John
Kontakion. Opus 69 : for cello and piano / by John Joubert. — Sevenoaks : Novello, 1974. — 4to.
Score (18p.) & part. — Duration 12 min.
Unpriced

(B74-50682)

SRPK — Arrangements
Bernstein, Leonard
[Mass. Selections: arr]. Two meditations / by Leonard Bernstein ; arranged by the composer for violoncello solo and piano. — New York ; London : Amberson : Schirmer, 1972. — 4to.
Score (11p.) & part.
Unpriced

(B74-50249)

SRPK/AAY — Arrangements. Collections
Pejtsik, Árpád
Violoncello music (intermediate) : easy concert pieces in the first position / edited by Árpád Pejtsik, [and] Endre Lengyel. — London : Boosey and Hawkes ; Budapest : Editio Musica, 1973. — 4to.
Score (44p.) & part.
£1.00

(B74-51251)

SRPK/LF — Arrangements. Concertos
Boccherini, Luigi
[Concerto for cello & string orchestra in C major. Gérard 481: arr]. Konzert No.4 für Violoncello und Klavier, C-dur / [von] Luigi Boccherini ; Klavierauszug mit Kadenzen versehen von Walter Lebermann. — Mainz ; London : Schott, 1974. — 4to.
Score (23p.) & part.
£2.90

(B74-51253)

Boccherini, Luigi
[Concerto for cello & string orchestra, no.2, in D major: arr].
Konzert No.2, D Dur, für Violoncello und Streichorchester / von
Luigi Boccherini ; herausgegeben und mit Kadenzen versehen von
Walter Lebermann, Klavierauszug (vom Herausgeber). — Mainz ;
London : Schott, 1973. — 4to.
Score (28p.) & part.
£2.04

(B74-50250)

Sutermeister, Heinrich
[Concerto for cello, no.2: arr]. 2. Konzert für Violoncello und
Orchester (1971) / [von] Heinrich Sutermeister; Klavierauszug. —
Mainz ; London : Schott, 1974. — 4to.
Score (21p.) & part. — Duration 25 min.
£8.70

(B74-51254)

SRPLSS — CELLO & DOUBLE BASS
Massenet, Jules
Duo for double bass and cello / by Jules Massenet ; edited by
Rodney Slatford. — London : Yorke, 1974. — 4p ; 4to.
Published for the first time.
Unpriced

(B74-50683)

SRPLTQ — CELLO & HARP
Reimann, Aribert
Nocturnos für Violoncello und Harfe (1965) / von Aribert
Reimann. — Mainz ; London : Schott, 1974. — 4to.
Score (15p.) & part.
£1.92

(B74-50251)

SRPM — UNACCOMPANIED CELLO
SRPMFM — Cadenzas
Lazarof, Henri
[Concerto for cello & orchestra. Selections]. Cadence I : for solo
cello / by Henri Lazarof. — New York ; London : Associated
Music, 1970 [i.e. 1972]. — 3p ; fol.
£2.00

(B74-50684)

SRPMJ — Miscellaneous works
Barrell, Bernard
Soliloquys [sic]. Opus 39 : solo cello / [by] Bernard Barrell. —
London : Thames, 1974. — 7p ; fol.
Unpriced

(B74-51255)

Block, Robert Paul
Fantasy for cello solo (1973) / [by] Robert Paul Block. —
London : Musica rara, 1974. — 3p ; 4to.
Printed on one side of the leaf only.
Unpriced

(B74-50685)

SSP — DOUBLE BASS & PIANO
SSPE — Sonatas
Marcello, Benedetto
[Sonatas for cello and basso continuo. Op.2]. Six sonatas : for cello
or double bass and piano / by Marcello Benedetto ; keyboard
realization and cello part edited by Analee Bacon; double bass
part edited by Lucas Drew. — New York ; London : Schirmer,
1973. — 4to.
Score (38p.) & 2 parts.
£1.85
Primary classification SRPE

(B74-50681)

Pitfield, Thomas Baron
Sonatina for double bass and piano / by Thomas Pitfield. —
London : Yorke, 1974. — 4to.
Score (16p.) & part.

(B74-50686)

SSPHVPS — Soft shoe dances
Hoag, Charles Kelso
Soft shoe dance : for double bass and piano / by Charles K.
Hoag. — New York ; London : Schirmer, 1973. — 4to.
Score (4p.) & part.
Unpriced

(B74-50252)

SSPK/LF — Arrangements. Concertos
Lamb, Peter
[Concertante music: arr]. Concertante music : for double bass,
wind and strings; piano reduction. — London : Yorke, 1974. —
4to.
Score (11p.) & part.

(B74-51256)

SSPM — UNACCOMPANIED DOUBLE BASS
SSPMJ — Miscellaneous works
Block, Robert Paul
Fantasy for double bass solo (1973) / [by] Robert Paul Block. —
London : Musica rara, 1974. — 3p ; 4to.
Printed on one side of the leaf only.
Unpriced

(B74-50687)

STN — VIOL CONSORT
STNQR — Five viols & organ
White, William
[Fantasies for five viols. Meyer 1,3, 'Diapente']. Diapente: two
fantasies a 5. (Meyer nos. 1 and 3) : for viols or other stringed
instruments / by William White ; edited by Gordon Dodd. —
London : Peters, 1973. — 4to.
Score (19p.) & 5 parts.
Unpriced

(B74-50688)

STNS — Quartets
Parsley, Osbert
[Works, viols. Selections]. Three consort pieces : for treble, tenor
and bass viols / by Osbert Parsley ; edited by John Morehen. —
London : Oxford University Press, 1974. — 10p ; 8vo.
ISBN 0-19-358105-1 : £0.16

(B74-50689)

STNSK/DW/AYE — Arrangements. Songs, etc. Collections.
Germany
Gerle, Hans
Five pieces for four viols from 'Musica teutsch' and 'Musica und
Tabulatur' / arranged by Hans Gerle, edited by Michael Morrow
and Ian Woodfield. — London : Oxford University Press, 1974.
— 7p ; 8vo.
Contents: 1: Herr Christ der eynig Gotts Son, by Johann Walther - 2: Es
flug ein kleynes Walt Voeglein: anon - 3: Mag ich Hertz lieb erwerben dich,
by Ludwig Senfl - 4: Eyn Freulein sprach ich freuntlich zu: anon - 5:
Pacienta, by Ludwig Senfl.
ISBN 0-19-341214-4 : £0.16

(B74-51257)

STPM — UNACCOMPANIED VIOL
STUPG — Viola da gamba & piano. Suites
Marais, Marin
[Pièces de violes, liv. 4. Suite for viola da gamba, no.1, in D
minor]. Suite no.1 in D minor for viola da gamba and basso
continuo / [by] Marin Marais ; edited by George Hunter. — New
York ; London : Associated Music, 1974. — 4to.
Score (16p.) & 2 parts.
Unpriced

(B74-51258)

TMK — Plucked string instrument band. Arrangements
Astor, Bob
[Popinella : arr]. Popinella / par Bob Astor et Paul Bonneau ;
transcription et arrangement pour 'orchestra a plectre' par Sylvain
Dagosto. — Paris ; [London] : Chappell, 1971. — 6p ; 4to.
Unpriced

(B74-51259)

Veneux, Thierry
[Claire de lune: arr]. Claire de lune / [par] Thierry Veneux [et]
Jean Leroi; transcription pour 'orchestre a plectre' par Sylvain
Dagosto. — Paris ; London : Chappell, 1971. — 8p ; 4to.
Unpriced

(B74-50690)

Veneux, Thierry
[Impressions et images, suite no.3. Letter J: arr]. Impressions et
images, 3e suite. Lettre J / [par] Thierry Veneux [et] Pierre
Duclos; transcription et arrangement pour 'orchestre à plectre' par
Sylvain Dagosto. — Paris ; [London] : Chappell, 1971. — 8p ;
4to.
Unpriced

(B74-50691)

Veneux, Thierry
[Impressions et images, suite no.3. Letter K: arr]. Impressions et
images, 3e suite. Lettre K / [par] Thierry Veneux [et] Pierre
Duclos; transcription et arrangement pour 'orchestre à plectre' par
Sylvain Dagosto. — Paris ; [London] : Chappell, 1971. — 9p ;
4to.
Unpriced

(B74-50692)

Veneux, Thierry
[Le Parc aux fees. Idylle : arr]. Idylle / [par] Thierry Veneux [et]
François de Boisvallée; transcription et arrangement pour
'orchestre a plectre' par Sylvain Dagosto. — Paris ; London :
Chappell, 1971. — 12p ; 4to.
Unpriced

(B74-50693)

**TMK/AHM — Plucked string instruments band. Arrangements.
           Gavottes**
  Roger, Roger
    Gavotina / par Roger Roger ; transcription et arrangement pour
    'orchestre a plectre' par Sylvain Dagosto. — Paris ; London :
    Chappell, 1971. — 5p ; 4to.
  Unpriced

                                                              (B74-50694)

**TMK/DW — Plucked string instrument band. Arrangements. Songs,
          etc**
  Lully, Jean Baptiste
    Adieu Madras, adieu foulards / par Jean Baptiste Lully ;
    transcription et arrangement pour 'orchestre a plectre' par Sylvain
    Dagosto. — Paris ; London : Chappell, 1971. — 8p ; 4to.
  Attributed to Lully in this publication.
  Unpriced

                                                              (B74-50695)

TQ — HARP
TQ/AC — Tutors
  Griffiths, Ann
    The young harpist / [by] Ann Griffiths. — Abergavenny : Adlais,
    1974. — 26p ; fol.
  Unpriced

                                                              (B74-51260)

TQ/AF — Exercises
  Griffiths, Ann
    Seven lessons for beginners / [by] Ann Griffiths. — Abergavenny :
    Adlais, 1973. — 13p ; fol.
  Unpriced

                                                              (B74-51261)

TQCPM/T — Clarsach. Variations
  Gundry, Inglis
    In those 12 days : variations on an old Cornish carol, for clarsach
    or other harp / by Inglis Gundry. — London : Thames, 1974. —
    14p ; 4to.
  Unpriced

                                                              (B74-51262)

TQP — HARP & PIANO
TQPK/LF — Arrangements. Concertos
  Ginastera, Alberto
    [Concerto for harp. Op.25: arr]. Harp concerto. Op.25 / [by]
    Alberto Ginastera ; harp and piano reduction by Meredith Davies.
    — London : Boosey and Hawkes, 1974. — Score (58p.) & part. 4to.
  £5.00

                                                              (B74-51263)

TQPM — UNACCOMPANIED HARP
TQPMG — Suites
  Hovhaness, Alan
    Suite for harp. Op.270 / [by] Alan Hovhaness. — New York ;
    London : Associated Music, 1974. — 16p ; 4to.
  Unpriced

                                                              (B74-51264)

TQPMH — Dances
  Parrott, Ian
    Soliloquy and dance : for harp / by Ian Parrott. — London :
    Thames, 1974. — 8p ; 4to.
  Unpriced

                                                              (B74-51265)

TQPMJ — Miscellaneous works
  Griffiths, Ann
    Welsh folksong fantasies : harp / [by] Ann Griffiths. —
    Abergavenny : Adlais.
    No.1 : Sweet but simple Gwennie. — 1973. — 6p ; fol. —
  Unpriced

                                                              (B74-51266)

    No.2 : What is summer to me?. — 1973. — 7p ; fol. —
  Unpriced

                                                              (B74-51267)

TS — GUITAR
TS/AC — Tutors
  Criswick, Mary
    Guitar tutor for young children / by Mary Criswick. — London :
    Fenette Music, 1974. — 20p ; 4to.
  Unpriced

                                                              (B74-50696)

Hanlon, Allen
    Basic guitar / by Allen Hanlon. — New York ; [London] :
    Chappell.
    Book 1. — 1974. — 47p ; 4to. —
  Unpriced

                                                              (B74-51268)

Medio, Alonso
    Spanish guitar tutor : exercises, scales / by Alonso Medio ; with
    solos by different composers. — London : Clifford Essex, 1973. —
    48p ; 4to.
  £0.75

                                                              (B74-50254)

Roberts, Don
    Introduction to the 12 string guitar : 12 string guitar techniques /
    by Don Roberts. — London : Robbins Music : E M I, 1974. —
    24p ; 4to.
  This book is designed to help the 6 string guitarist exploit the special effects
  attainable on the 12 string instrument.
  Unpriced

                                                              (B74-51269)

Silverman, Jerry
    How to play the guitar : folk, blues, calypso / [by] Jerry
    Silverman. — London : Nelson, 1974. — 207p ; 8vo.
  ISBN 0-17-141039-4 : £1.95

                                                              (B74-51270)

Winters
    A teacher's guide to the guitar / by Winters. — [London] :
    Schoolmaster Publishing Co., 1971. — [3],53p : ill ; 8vo.
  Unpriced

                                                              (B74-50255)

TS/AF — Exercises
  Lester, Bryan
    Explorations in guitar playing for beginners / by Bryan Lester. —
    Chesham : Ricordi.
    Vol.1. — 1974. — 16p ; 4to. —
  Unpriced

                                                              (B74-50697)

    Vol.2. — 1974. — 13p ; 4to. —
  Unpriced

                                                              (B74-50698)

Mayes, Jerry
    12 simple studies for guitar / by Jerry Mayes. — Leicester :
    Charnwood Music, 1974. — 7p ; 4to.
  Unpriced

                                                              (B74-51271)

Shepherd, Audrey
    Eight studies for the beginner guitarist / by Audrey Shepherd. —
    Leicester : Charnwood Music, 1974. — 4p ; 8vo.
  Unpriced

                                                              (B74-51272)

TSN — GUITAR ENSEMBLE
TSNTK — Trios. Arrangements
  Vivaldi, Antonio
    [Selections: arr]. Music by Vivaldi / transcribed for three guitars
    by Theodore Norman. — New York ; London : Schirmer, 1972.
    — 47p ; 4to.
  £1.05

                                                              (B74-50256)

TSP — GUITAR & PIANO
TSPEM — Sonatinas
  Hand, Colin
    Sonatina for guitar. Opus 74 / by Colin Hand. — Sevenoaks :
    Novello, 1974. — 8p ; 4to.
  Duration 5 1/2 min.
  £0.45

                                                              (B74-50699)

TSPM — UNACCOMPANIED GUITAR
  Roe, Betty
    Sonatina dolorosa : for solo guitar / by Betty Roe ; edited by Ian
    Gammie. — London : Thames, 1974. — 7p ; 4to.
  Unpriced

                                                              (B74-51273)

TSPMH — Dances
  Martín, Juan
    The exciting sound of flamenco : guitar / by Juan Martín. —
    London : United Music, 1974. — 18p ; 4to.
  Contents: Zambra mora - Brisas habeneras (Guajiras).
  Unpriced

                                                              (B74-50700)

TSPMHVR — Tangos

Anderaos, Nelson
Tango brasileiro. 30 de maio : [guitar] / de Nelson Anderaos. — Sao Paulo : Fermata de Brasil ; [London] : [Essex Music], 1974. — 2p ; 4to.
Unpriced

(B74-51274)

TSPMJ — Miscellaneous works

Duarte, John William
Some of Noah's ark, Op.55 : six sketches for guitar / by John W. Duarte. — Chesham : Ricordi, 1974. — 8p ; 4to.
Unpriced

(B74-50701)

Romani, G
Leicester sketches : a suite for five miniatures for solo guitar / by G. Romani. — Leicester : Charnwood Music, 1974. — 10p ; 8vo.
Unpriced

(B74-51275)

Sor, Fernando
[Divertimento for guitar, no.1. Op.1]. First set of divertimenti. Op.1 / by Fernando Sor ; edited by Brian Jeffery, fingered by Hector Quine. — London : Oxford University Press, 1974. — 7p ; 4to.
ISBN 0-19-358863-3 : £0.50

(B74-50702)

Sor, Fernando
[Divertimento for guitar, no.2. Op.2]. Second set of divertimenti. Op.2 / by Fernando Sor ; edited by Brian Jeffery, fingered by Hector Quine. — London : Oxford University Press, 1974. — 7p ; 4to.
ISBN 0-19-358864-1 : £0.50

(B74-50703)

Sor, Fernando
[Divertimento for guitar, no.3. Op.8]. Third set of divertimenti. Op.8 / by Fernando Sor ; edited by Brian Jeffery, fingered by Hector Quine. — London : Oxford Universtion Press, 1974. — 6p ; 4to.
ISBN 0-19-358865-x : £0.50

(B74-50704)

Sor, Fernando
[Fantasia for guitar, no.1, in C major. Op.7]. Fantasia no.1, Op.7 / by Fernando Sor ; edited by Brian Jeffery, fingered by Hector Quine. — London : Oxford University Press, 1974. — 7p ; 8vo.
ISBN 0-19-358860-9 : £0.50

(B74-50705)

Sor, Fernando
[Fantasia for guitar, no.2, in A major. Op.4]. Fantasia no.2. Op.4 / by Fernando Sor ; edited by Brian Jeffery, fingered by Hector Quine. — London : Oxford University Press, 1974. — 5p ; 4to.
ISBN 0-19-358861-7 : £0.40

(B74-50706)

Sor, Fernando
[Fantasia for guitar, no.3, in F major. Op.10]. Fantasia no.3, Op.10 / by Fernando Sor ; edited by Brian Jeffery; fingered by Hector Quine. — London : Oxford University Press, 1974. — 7p ; 4to.
ISBN 0-19-358862-5 : Unpriced

(B74-50707)

Walton, *Sir* William
Five bagatelles for guitar / [by] William Walton ; edited by Julian Bream. — London : Oxford University Press, 1974. — 16p ; 4to.
Duration 12 1/2 min.
ISBN 0-19-359407-2 : £1.50

(B74-51276)

TSPMK — Arrangements

Albeniz, Isaac
[Suite espagnole. Sevilla]. Granada Serenata : für Gitarre / von Isaac Albeniz ; eingerichtet von Konrad Ragossnig. — Mainz ; London : Schott, 1973. — 5p ; 4to.
£0.72

(B74-50257)

Albeniz, Isaac
[Suite espagnole. *Sevilla]*. Sevilla a Sevillanas / von Isaac Albeniz ; eingerichtet für Gitarre von Konrad Ragossnig. — Mainz ; London : Schott, 1973. — 8p ; 4to.
£0.96

(B74-50258)

Bach, Carl Philipp Emanuel
[Selections: arr]. Two pieces [for solo guitar] : by C.P.E. Bach / arranged by Hector Quine. — London : Oxford University Press, 1974. — 4to.
Contents: 1: Cantabile. Wq.55, no.3: last movement - 2: Arioso 'La Philippine'. Wq.117, no.34.
ISBN 0-19-355299-x : Unpriced

(B74-51277)

Bach, Johann Sebastian
[Prelude, fugue & allegro for organ in D major. S.998: arr]. Prelude, fugue and allegro. BWV 998 / by J.S. Bach ; transcribed for solo guitar by Hector Quine. — London : Oxford University Press, 1974. — 11p ; 4to.
ISBN 0-19-355303-1 : £0.60

(B74-50708)

Useful tunes for guitar. — Leicester : Charnwood Music.
No.1 : Little brown jug : trad. and, Home on the range : trad. / arr. Rosemary Wright. — 1974. — 1 sh ; 4to.
Unpriced

(B74-51278)

No.2 : The national anthem and Jingle bells : trad. / arr. Rosemary Wright. — 1974. — 1 sh ; 4to.
Unpriced

(B74-51279)

No.3 : Minuet in G (from 'Notenbüchlein für Anna Magdelena Bach' 1725 / [by, or attributed to], J.S. Bach ; transcribed by G. Romani. — 1974. — 1 sh ; 4to.
Unpriced

(B74-51280)

TSPMK/AAY — Arrangements. Collections

Duarte, John William
A variety of guitar music / arranged for guitar by John W. Duarte. — London : Faber Music, 1973. — 32p ; 4to.
Unpriced

(B74-50259)

Sadleir, Richard
Eight solos for guitar / arranged by Dick Sadleir. — London : British and Continental, 1974. — 8p ; 4to.
Unpriced

(B74-51281)

TSPMK/AE — Arrangements. Sonatas

Albeniz, Mateo
[Sonata for piano in D major: arr]. Sonata in D / by Mateo Albeniz ; arranged for solo guitar by Ivor Mairants. — London : British and Continental Music, 1973. — 5p ; 4to.
Unpriced

(B74-50260)

Beethoven, Ludwig van
[Sonata for piano, no.2, in G major. Op.14. Andante: arr]. Andante from piano sonata Opus 14, no.2 / by Beethoven ; arranged for guitar by Edward Choppen; edited and fingered by John W. Duarte. — Sevenoaks : Novello, 1974. — 4p ; 4to.
£0.33

(B74-50709)

TSPMK/AHXJ — Arrangements. Ragtime

Joplin, Scott
[The entertainer: arr]. The entertainer : a ragtime two step / by Scott Joplin ; arranged for guitar by Douglas Rogers. — London (221a Kensington High St., W.8) : Aura Music, 1974. — 4p ; 4to.
Unpriced

(B74-51282)

TSPMK/DP/LF/AY — Arrangements. Carols. Christmas

Gavall, John
Christmas carols for beginner guitarists / arranged by John Gavall. — London : Bosworth, 1974. — 16p ; obl. 8vo.
Unpriced

(B74-51283)

TSPMK/DW/G/AY — Arrangements. Folk songs. Collections

Cammin, Heinz
Lied über die Grenze : Folklore fremder Länder / bearbeitet von Heinz Cammin ; Ausgabe für Gitarre solo mit vollstandigen Text. — Mainz ; London : Schott.
Heft II. — 1974. — 16p ; 8vo. —
£1.74

(B74-51284)

TSPMK/LF — Arrangements. Concertos

Previn, André
[Concerto for guitar: arr]. Concerto for guitar and orchestra / [by] André Previn ; reduction for guitar and piano solo, guitar edited by John Williams. — New York ; London : Schirmer, 1974. — 4to.
Score (42p.) & part.
Unpriced

(B74-51285)

TT — BANJO
TT/AC — Tutors
Shealy, Alexander
Five string banjo : picture chords, songs, exercises, diagrams and instructions / by Alexander Shealy ; illustrated by Arthur Bagas. — Carlstadt : Lewis Music ; London : Ashley-Fields, 1974. — 80p ; 4to.
Unpriced

(B74-50710)

Silverman, Jerry
Beginning the five-string banjo / by Jerry Silverman. — New York : Macmillan ; London : Collier Macmillan, 1974. — viii, 150p ; 4to.
Unpriced (hard cover), £1.95 (paperback)

(B74-50711)

TW — LUTE
TW/AZ — Collected works of individual composers
Dowland, John
The collected lute music of John Dowland / transcribed and edited by Diana Poulton and Basil Lam. — London : Faber Music in association with Faber and Faber, 1974. — xvi,317p ; fol.
ISBN 0-571-10010-4 : Unpriced

(B74-51286)

TWT — PSALTERY
TWT/AC — Appalachian dulcimer. Tutors
Gamse, Albert
The best dulcimer method yet / by Albert Gamse ; duet, rhythm and finger picking arrangements by Steve Sechak. — Carlstadt : Lewis ; [London] : [Ashley-Fields], 1974. — 97p ; 4to.
Unpriced

(B74-51287)

TWTTPMK — Arrangements
Nicholson, Roger
Musicks delight on the dulcimer, or, The New Elizabethan, wherein are contained a collection of ten pieces in tablature for the Appalachian dulcimer / by Roger Nicholson. — London : Scratchwood Music : EMI Music, 1974. — 26p ; 4to.
Unpriced

(B74-51288)

UM — WIND BAND
UMF — Concertos
Husa, Karel
Concerto for percussion and wind ensemble / by Karel Husa. — New York ; London : Associated Music, 1973. — 92p ; 4to.
Unpriced

(B74-50712)

UMG — Suites
Johnson, Stuart
French folk song suite / arranged [for] wind band by Stuart Johnson. — London : Oxford University Press, 1974. — 4to.
Score (20p.) & 20 parts. — Duration 4 min.
ISBN 0-19-365100-9 : £1.50

(B74-51289)

Rössler, Franz Anton
[Partita for wind band in F major (1785)]. Partita (1785) in F Major for two flutes, two oboes, two clarinets, three horns, and two bassoons, with double bass / [by] Antonio Rosetti; edited by Roger Hellyer. — London : Oxford University Press, 1974. — 8vo & 4to.
Score (48p.) & 12 parts. — Duration 17 min.
ISBN 0-19-358650-9 : Score £3.00, Parts unpriced

(B74-51290)

UMGM — Marches
Balent, Andrew
Century celebration. Honoring America's bicentennial : for concert band / by Andrew Balent. — New York : Warner ; [London] : [Blossom], 1974. — 4to.
Score (12p.) & 61 parts. — With several copies of various parts.
Unpriced

(B74-50713)

Balent, Andrew
Forward! : march for elementary band / by Andrew Balent. — New York : Warner ; [London] : [Blossom], 1971. — 4to.
Condensed score & 50 parts - With several copies of various parts.
Unpriced

(B74-51291)

Balent, Andrew
Spartans of tomorrow : march, for wind band / by Andrew Balent. — New York : Warner ; [London] : [Blossom], 1971. — 4to.
Score & 55 parts - With several copies of various parts.
Unpriced

(B74-51292)

Cacavas, John
March of the magnificants : for concert band / by John Cacavas. — New York ; [London] : Chappell, 1971. — 4to.
Full score, condensed score & 70 parts - With several copies of various parts.
Unpriced

(B74-51293)

UMGN — Fanfares
Gould, Morton
Fanfare for freedom : for symphonic wind ensemble / by Morton Gould. — New York : G & C Music ; New York ; [London] : [Chappell], 1971. — 4to.
Score & 24 parts.
Unpriced

(B74-51294)

UMH — Dances
Riegger, Wallingford
New dance. Op. 18c : for concert band / [by] Wallingford Riegger. — New York ; London : Associated Music, 1974. — 40p ; 4to.
Duration 5 min.
Unpriced

(B74-51295)

UMHK/T — Fandango. Variations
Surinach, Carlos
Soleriana for concert band / by Carlos Surinach ; based on the fandango by Padre Antonio Soler. — New York ; London : Associated Music, 1972. — 98p ; 4to.
Unpriced

(B74-50261)

UMJ — Miscellaneous works
Bamert, Matthias
Inkblot : for concert band / by Matthias Bamert. — New York ; London : Schirmer, 1972. — 45p ; 4to.
Duration 8 min.
Unpriced

(B74-50262)

Brunelli, Louis Jean
In memoriam : for concert band / by Louis Jean Brunelli. — New York ; [London] : Chappell, 1971. — 69p ; 4to.
Full score, condensed score & 69 parts - With several copies of various parts.
Unpriced

(B74-51296)

Cacavas, John
Make it happen : for concert band / by John Cacavas. — New York ; [London] : Athenaeum : Chappell, 1971. — 4to.
Full score, condensed score & 48 parts - With several copies of various parts.
Unpriced

(B74-51297)

Husa, Karel
Apotheosis of this earth : for concert band / by Karel Husa. — New York ; London : Associated Music, 1971. — 124p ; 4to.
Unpriced

(B74-50714)

Lai, Francis
[Love story. Theme : arr]. Theme from the film 'Love story' / by Francis Lai ; arranged for stage band by Jerry Coker. — New York : Famous Music ; [London] : [Chappell], 1971. — 4to.
Unpriced

(B74-51298)

Nystedt, Knut
Entrata festiva. Op. 60 : for concert band / by Knut Nystedt. — New York ; London : Associated Music, 1972. — 42p ; 4to.
Duration 6 min.
Unpriced

(B74-50263)

Osterling, Eric
Samaria : for concert band / by Eric Osterling. — New York ; [London] : Chappell, 1971. — 4to.
Condensed score & 4 parts.
Unpriced

(B74-51299)

Thomson, Virgil
Edges : a portrait of Robert Indiana, for band / by Virgil Thomson. — New York ; London : Schirmer, 1972. — 20p ; 4to.
Duration 2 min.
Unpriced

(B74-50264)

Thomson, Virgil
Study piece : portrait of a lady, for band / by Virgil Thomson. — New York ; London : Schirmer, 1972. — 16p ; 4to.
Duration 2 1/2 min.
Unpriced

(B74-50265)

Washburn, Robert
Chorale for band : [wind band] / [by] Robert Washburn. — New York ; [London] : Oxford University Press, 1974. — 4to.
Score (15p.) & 56 parts - With several copies of various parts.
Unpriced
(B74-51300)

UMK — Arrangements
Barber, Samuel
[The school for scandal, Op.5. Overture]. Overture to 'The school for scandal' / by Samuel Barber ; arranged for concert band by Frank M. Hudson. — New York ; [London] : Schirmer, 1971. — 46p ; 4to.
Unpriced
(B74-50715)

Bernstein, Leonard
[Mass. Almighty Father: arr]. Almighty Father : chorale from 'Mass' / by Leonard Bernstein ; arranged for wind band by Donald Hunsberger. — New York ; London : Amberson : Schirmer, 1973. — 4to.
Score (4p.) & 45 parts. — With several copies of various parts. — Duration 3 min.
£5.60(full score and parts)(extra score £0.95, extra parts £0.30 each)
(B74-50716)

Bernstein, Leonard
[Mass. Mediatation no.2 (on a sequence by Beethoven): arr]. Meditation no.2 (on a sequence by Beethoven) / by Leonard Bernstein ; arranged for wind band by Donald Hunsberger. — New York ; London : Amberson : Schirmer, 1973. — 9p ; 4to.
Unpriced
(B74-50717)

Ives, Charles
[Sonata for piano, no.2: arr]. The Alcotts / by Charles Ives ; transcribed for concert band by Richard E. Thurston. — New York ; London : Associated Music, 1972. — 20p ; 4to.
Duration 5 min.
Unpriced
(B74-50266)

Menotti, Gian Carlo
[Amahl and the night visitors. *Selections: arr*]. Introduction, march and shepherd's dance / [by] Gian Carlo Menotti ; arranged for band by Frank Erickson. — New York ; London : Schirmer, 1971. — 36p ; 4to.
Duration 6 min.
Unpriced
(B74-50718)

Renard, J
[C'est ça la France: arr]. C'est ça la France / musique de J. Renard ; arrangement pour harmonie et fanfare de Désiré Dondeyne. — Paris ; [London] : Chappell, 1973. — 8vo.
Score (6p.) & 112 parts. — Duration 3 min.
Unpriced
(B74-50719)

Schuman, William
Circus overture / by William Schuman ; arranged for band by Don Owen. — New York ; London : Schirmer, 1972. — 44p ; 4to.
Duration 6 1/2 min.
Unpriced
(B74-50267)

UMK/AE — Arrangements. Sonatas
Scarlatti, Domenico
[Sonata for harpsichord in C major. L.164: arr]. Sonata / by Domenico Scarlatti ; translated for band by Peter Phillips. — New York ; [London] : Oxford University Press, 1971. — 17p ; 4to.
Unpriced
(B74-50720)

UMK/AGM — Arrangements. Marches
Handel, George Frideric
[Scipione. March : arr]. Il Scipio : march / by George Frederick Handel ; arranged by John Cacavas. — New York ; [London] : Chappell, 1971. — 4to.
Score, conductor & 47 parts - With several copies of various parts.
Unpriced
(B74-51301)

Tchaikovsky, Peter
[Selections: arr]. Two Russian marches / by Peter I. Tchaikovsky; arranged by John Cacavas for young bands. — New York ; [London] : Chappell, 1974. — 4to. — (Citation series for young bands)
Score (22p.), conductor (8p.) & 50 parts. — Contents: Marche slave - March from the Nutcracker suite.
Unpriced
(B74-50721)

UMK/DU — Arrangements. Madrigals
Gesualdo, Carlo, *Prince of Venosa*
[Madrigali a cinque voci, libro sesto. Moro lasso : arr]. Moro lasso / by Carlo Gesualdo, Prince of Venosa ; transcribed for band by Peter Phillips. — New York ; [London] : Oxford University Press, 1971. — 9p ; 4to.
Unpriced
(B74-51302)

UMK/DW/G/AY — Arrangements. Folk songs. Collections
Koch, Johnnes Hermann Ernst
Volksmusik für Bläser / herausgegeben von Johannes H.E. Koch unter Mitarbeit von Heinrich Ehmann. — Cassel ; London : Bärenreiter, 1972. — 47p ; 8vo.
Short score.
£1.10
(B74-50722)

UMM — MILITARY BAND
UMM/T — Variations
Snyder, Randall
Variations for wind ensemble / [by] Randall Snyder. — New York ; London : Schirmer, 1974. — 4to.
Score (18p.) & 36 parts. — Various parts are in duplicate. — Duration 7 min.
Unpriced
(B74-51303)

UMMG — Suites
Osterling, Eric
Adventurous night suite : [military band] / by Eric Osterling. — New York : Warner ; [London] : [Blossom], 1974. — 4to.
Score (12p.) & 72 parts. — Contents: 1: Slumber - II: Dream - III: Nightmare - IV: Dawn.
Unpriced
(B74-50723)

Walters, Harold L
Japanese folk suite : [for military band / by] Harold L. Walters. — Miami : Rubank ; London : Novello, 1971. — 4to.
Conductor & 45 parts.
Unpriced
(B74-50724)

UMMGM — Marches
Bavicchi, John
Corley's march : for military band / by John Bavicchi. — New York ; [London] : Oxford University Press, 1971. — 8p ; 4to.
Unpriced
(B74-51304)

Frank, Marcel Gustave
Braid on parade : march, [military band] / by Marcel G. Frank. — New York : Warner ; [London] : [Blossom], 1971. — 8vo.
Conductor & 90 parts.
Unpriced
(B74-51305)

Horabin, E G
Star of Erin : quick march [for military band] / [by] E.G. Horabin. — [London] : Boosey and Hawkes, 1974. — 29 pt ; obl. 8vo.
With several copies of various parts.
£0.65
(B74-50725)

Walters, Harold L
Kneller Hall : concert march [for military band / by] Harold L. Walters. — Miami : Rubank ; London : Novello, 1971. — 4to.
Conductor & 44 parts.
Unpriced
(B74-50726)

UMMGM/KH — Regimental marches
Brush, J A
Regimental quick march, 'The Royal Highland Fusiliers' / arranged by J.A. Brush. — London : Boosey and Hawkes, 1974. — 29pt ; obl 8vo.
With several copies of various parts.
£0.65
(B74-50727)

Clark, M E
Regimental quick march 'The Royal Irish Rangers' / arranged by M.E. Clark. — London : Boosey and Hawkes, 1974. — 28pt ; obl 8vo.
With several copies of various parts.
£0.65
(B74-50728)

Gibson, John
Regimental quick march, The Queen's Lancashire Regiment, 'The attack', 'The red rose' / arranged by J. Gibson. — London : Boosey and Hawkes, 1974. — 29pt ; obl. 8vo.
£1.00
(B74-51306)

UMMJ — Miscellaneous works
Buchtel, Forrest Lawrence
Fortune's promise : overture [for military band] / by Forrest L. Buchtel. — New York : Warner ; [London] : [Blossom], 1974. — 4to.
Score (15p.) & 70 parts.
Unpriced

(B74-50729)

Grundman, Clare
March winds : [military band] / by Clare Grundman. — New York ; [London] : Boosey and Hawkes, 1971. — 4to.
Score, condensed score & 72 parts.
Unpriced

(B74-51307)

Grundman, Clare
Trumpets triumphant : pageantry for antiphonal trumpets / by Clare Grundman. — New York ; London : Boosey and Hawkes, 1974. — 8vo & obl 8vo.
Conductor & 52 parts. — With several copies of various parts.
Unpriced

(B74-50730)

Grundman, Clare
Two Irish songs : [military band] / [by] Clare Grundman. — New York ; [London] : Boosey and Hawkes, 1974. — 4to.
Score (20p.) & 73 parts.
£15.00

(B74-51308)

Sosnik, Harry
El Paseo grande = The big walk : [military band] / [by] Harry Sosnik. — New York : Warner ; [London] : [Blossom], 1971. — 19p ; 4to.
Unpriced

(B74-50731)

UMMK — Arrangements
Loesser, Frank
[Where's Charley?. The New Ashmolean Marching Society and Students Conservatory Band: arr]. The New Ashmolean Marching Society and Students Conservatory Band / by Frank Loesser ; arranged by Scott Fearing. — Boston ; London : Frank Music, 1974. — 4to.
Conductor (12p.) & 67 parts. — With several copies of various parts.
Unpriced

(B74-51309)

UMMK/AGM — Arrangements. Marches
Teike, Carl
[Alte Kameraden: arr]. Old comrades : quick march / by Carl Teike ; arranged by N. Richardson. — London : Boosey and Hawkes, 1973. — 8vo & obl. 8vo.
Conductor & 48 parts for military and brass bands.
£0.95
Also classified at WMK/AGM

(B74-50732)

UMMK/AGN — Arrangements. Fanfares
Drexler, Werner
World cup fanfare : military band / by Werner Drexler ; arr. J.H. Howe. — London : Weinberger, 1974. — 32pt ; obl. 8vo.
With several copies of various parts.
Unpriced

(B74-50733)

UMMK/DW — Arrangements. Songs, etc
Livingston, Jerry
The twelfth of never / music by Jerry Livingstone ; arranged by Andrew Balent. — Boston ; London : Frank Music, 1974. — 4to.
Conductor (9p.) & 65 parts. — With several copies of various parts.
Unpriced

(B74-51310)

UMMK/DW/JR — Arrangements. Songs, etc. Films
Loesser, Frank
[Hans Christian Andersen. The inch worm: arr]. The inch worm / by Frank Loesser ; arranged by Andrew Balent. — Boston ; London : Frank Music, 1974. — 4to.
Conductor (6p.) & 64 parts. — With several copies of various parts.
Unpriced

(B74-51311)

UMP — SOLO INSTRUMENT (S) & WIND BAND
UMPQ — Wind band & piano
Gottschalk, Louis Moreau
L'Union. [Op. 48] : paraphrase de concert sur les airs nationaux / [by] Louis Moreau Gottschalk ; arranged for piano and orchestra by Samuel Adler, edited by Eugene List. — New York ; London : Schirmer, 1972. — 37p ; 4to.
Unpriced

(B74-50734)

UMPWNR — Brass quintet & wind band
Schuller, Gunther
Diptych : for brass quintet and concert band / by Gunther Schuller. — New York ; [London] : Associated Music, 1971. — 42p ; 4to.
Duration 8 min.
Unpriced

(B74-50735)

UN — WIND ENSEMBLE
UNN — Octets
Laderman, Ezra
Octet for winds / by Ezra Laderman. — New York ; London : Oxford University Press, 1971. — 26p ; 4to.
Unpriced

(B74-50736)

UNR — Quintets
Bamert, Matthias
[Quintet for woodwind instruments]. Woodwind quintet : flute, oboe, B flat clarinet, F horn, bassoon / by Matthias Bamert. — New York ; London : Schirmer, 1972. — 4to.
Score (22p.) & 5 parts.
Unpriced

(B74-50268)

Lees, Benjamin
Two miniatures for wind quintet : flute, oboe, clarinet, horn and bassoon / by Benjamin Lees. — London : Boosey and Hawkes, 1974. — 4to.
Score (12p.) & parts.
£1.75

(B74-50737)

Washburn, Robert
Quintet for winds / by Robert Washburn. — New York ; [London] : Oxford University Press, 1971. — 4to.
Score (16p.) & 5 parts.
Unpriced

(B74-50738)

UNSFL — Quartets. Concertinos
Molter, Johann Melchior
[Concertino for trumpet, two oboes & bassoon in D major. MWV VIII, 5]. Concertino à 4, no.1 : for solo trumpet (clarino), 2 oboes and bassoon. MWV VIII, 5 / [by] Johann Melchior Molter ; [edited by] Georg Meerwein. — London : Musica rara, 1973. — 4to.
Score (8p.) & 4 parts.
Unpriced

(B74-50739)

Molter, Johann Melchior
[Concertino for trumpet, two oboes & bassoon in D major. MWV VIII, 6]. Concertino à 4, no.2 : for solo trumpet (clarino), 2 oboes and bassoon. MWV VIII, 6 / [by] Johann Melchior Molter ; [edited by] Georg Meerwein. — London : Musica rara, 1973. — 4to.
Score (8p.) & 4 parts.
Unpriced

(B74-50740)

Molter, Johann Melchior
[Concertino for trumpet, two oboes & bassoon in D major. MWV VIII, 7]. Concertino à 4, no.3 : for solo trumpet (clarino), 2 oboes and bassoon. MWV VIII, 7 / [by] Johann Melchior Molter ; [edited by] Georg Meerwein. — London : Musica rara, 1973. — 4to.
Score (8p.) & 4 parts.
Unpriced

(B74-50741)

UNUK — Arrangements
Mozart, Wolfgang Amadeus
[Duets for two horns. K.487: arr]. 12 easy duets for winds / [by] Wolfgang Amadeus Mozart ; transcribed by Henry Charles Smith. — New York ; London : Schirmer.
Volume 3 : For trombones, baritones, tubas (and cellos and basses ad lib). — 1972. — 14p ; 4to.
Unpriced

(B74-50742)

VN — WOODWIND ENSEMBLE
VNK/DW — Arrangements. Songs, etc
Villa-Lobos, Heitor
Bachianas brasileiras, no.5. Aria (Cantilena) / [by] Heitor Villa-Lobos ; arranged for woodwind choir by John Krance. — New York ; London : Associated Music, 1971. — 29p ; 4to.
Unpriced

(B74-50743)

VNR — Quintets
Zoephel, Klaus
[Quintet for wind instruments]. Quintett für Flöte, Oboe,
Klarinette in B, Horn in F und Fagott / [von] Klaus Zoephel. —
Leipzig ; [London] : Peters, 1973. — 72p ; 8vo.
Miniature score.
Unpriced
(B74-51312)

VNT — Trios
Antoni, Thomas
3 encores : for woodwind trio, flute, oboe, clarinet in B flat / [by]
Thomas Antoni. — Surbiton (167 Ewell Rd, Surbiton, Surrey) :
Camera Music, 1974. — 4to.
Score (7p.) & 3 parts.
Unpriced
(B74-51313)

Musgrave, Thea
[Impromptu for flute, oboe and clarinet, no.2]. Impromptu no.2
for flute, oboe and clarinet / [by] Thea Musgrave. — London :
Chester : Wilhelm Hansen, 1974. — 14p ; 8vo.
Study score - Duration 9 min.
Unpriced
(B74-51314)

Parfrey, Raymond
Trio for oboe, clarinet, bassoon / by Raymond Parfrey. —
Ampleforth : Emerson Edition, 1974. — 6p ; 4to.
Contents: 1: Italian madrigal - 2: Indian lament - 3: Chorale - 4: Irish jig.
£0.50
(B74-50744)

Wiseman, Charles
Trio for 2 flutes & cello or bassoon in D major / by Carlo
Wiseman; edited by John Leach. — Wendover : Roberton, 1974.
— 4to.
Score (8p.) & part.
£0.50
Primary classification NVPNT
(B74-50541)

VNTF — Trios. Concertos
Carulli, Benedetto
[Trio concertante for two clarinets & bassoon in C major. Op.1].
Trio, C-Dur. Op.1 : für zwei Klarinetten und Fagott / [von]
Benedetto Marcello ; herausgegeben von Wolfgang Stephan. —
Mainz ; London : Schott, 1974. — 4pt ; 4to.
With alternative bassoon parts in B flat and C.
£5.22
(B74-51315)

VNTGN — Trios. Fanfares
Antoni, Thomas
2 easy fanfares for woodwind trio, flute, oboe, clarinet in B flat /
by Thomas Antoni. — Surbiton : Camera Music, 1974. — 4pt ;
4to.
Short score & 3 parts.
Unpriced
(B74-50269)

VNTK — Trios. Arrangements
Bach, Johann Sebastian
[15 two-part inventions, nos 1, 4. S.772 & 775: arr]. 2 two part
inventions / by Bach; transcribed and arranged for oboe, clarinet
and bassoon by Thomas Antoni. — Surbiton : Camera Music,
1974. — 3pt ; 4to.
Unpriced
(B74-50270)

VR — FLUTE
Bach, Johann Sebastian
[Selections]. The flute solos from the Bach cantatas, passions and
oratorios / compiled and edited by Julius Baker. — New York ;
London : Schirmer, 1972. — v,110p ; 4to.
£2.35
(B74-50745)

VRN — FLUTE ENSEMBLE
VRNSK/DH/LH — Quartets. Arrangements. Motets, Anthems,
Hymns, etc. Holy Week
Bach, Johann Sebastian
[St Matthew Passion. *Aus Liebe will mein Heiland sterben: arr*].
Aria / by Johann Sebastian Bach ; transcribed for four flutes by
Julius Baker. — New York ; London : Schirmer, 1972. — 4to.
Score (7p.) & part.
Unpriced
(B74-50271)

VRNTQK/LF — Two flutes and piano. Arrangements. Concertos
Quantz, Johann Joachim
[Concerto for two flutes, no.1, in G minor: arr]. Concerto no.1 in
G minor for 2 flutes and orchestra / [by] Johann Joachim
Quantz ; edited and arranged for two flutes and piano by H.
Voxman and R.P. Block. — London : Musica rara, 1974. — 4to.
Score (28p.) & 2 parts.
Unpriced
(B74-50746)

VRNU/Y — Duets. Fugues
Hovhaness, Alan
Pastoral and fugue for two flutes / by Alan Hovhaness. — New
York ; London : Associated Music, 1974. — 6p ; 4to.
Unpriced
(B74-51316)

VRP — FLUTE & PIANO
VRP/AY — Collections
Warlike Musick
[Warlike Musick for flute, violin or harpsichord]. Warlike Musick
(1760) : marches and trumpet tunes, for flute or oboe or violin
and basso continuo / edited by Philip Ledger. — London : Oxford
University Press, 1974. — 4to.
Score (30p.) & part.
ISBN 0-19-357552-3 : £1.50
Also classified at SP/AY
(B74-51317)

VRP/AZ — Collected works of individual composers
Stanley, John
[Solos for a German flute. Op.1, 4]. Complete works for flute and
basso continuo / by John Stanley ; edited by John Caldwell. —
London : Oxford University Press.
Set 1 : Solo 1 in D minor, Solo 2 in G minor (from Eight solos, opus 1). —
1974. — 4to.
Score (22p.) & 4 parts.
ISBN 0-19-358896-x : £2.50
(B74-50747)
Set 2 : Solo 3 in G major, Solo 4 in D major (from Eight solos, opus 1). —
1974. — 4to.
Score (20p.) & 4 parts.
ISBN 0-19-358897-8 : £2.50
(B74-50748)
Set 3 : Solo 5 in C major, Solo 6 in D major (from Eight solos, opus 1). —
1974. — 4to.
Score (24p.) & 4 parts.
ISBN 0-19-358898-6 : £2.50
(B74-50749)
Set 4 : Solo 7 in D minor, Solo 8 in E minor (from Eight solos, opus 1). —
1974. — 4to.
Score (25p.) & 4 parts.
ISBN 0-19-358899-4 : £2.50
(B74-50750)

VRPE — Sonatas
Hoffmeister, Franz Anton
[Sonata for flute & piano in C major. Op.13]. Sonata in C major
for flute or violin and piano / by Franz Anton Hoffmeister ;
edited by Hans-Peter Schmitz. — Cassel : Nagel ; London :
Bärenreiter, 1973. — 4to.
Score (40p.) & part.
£3.80
Also classified at SPE
(B74-50751)

Veracini, Francesco Maria
[Sonate a violino o flauto solo e basso, nos 1-3]. Three sonatas for
violin (flute, treble recorder) and basso continuo / by Francesco
Maria Veracini ; edited by Franz Bär. — Cassel ; [London] :
Bärenreiter, 1973. — 4to.
Score (32p.) & 2 parts.
£3.60
Primary classification SPE
(B74-50664)

Vivaldi, Antonio
[Sonata for flute & basso continuo in E minor, 'Stockholm'].
Sonata in E minor : for flute and basso continuo / [by] Antonio
Vivaldi ; ed. David Lasocki, realization of basso continuo by R.P.
Block. — London : Musica rara, 1974. — 4to.
Score (8p.) & 2 parts.
Unpriced
(B74-50752)

VRPEM — Sonatinas
Lamb, Peter
Sonatina for flute and piano / by Peter Lamb. — London :
Boosey and Hawkes, 1974. — 4to.
Score (16p.) & part.
£0.85
(B74-50753)

VRPG — Suites
Couperin, François
Concerts royaux I-IV : for flute, oboe, violin, viola da gamba and
basso continuo / [by] François Couperin ; edited by David
Lasocki. — London : Musica rara.
Score (8p.) & 3 parts. — With a separate leaflet of four pages containing a
foreword, inserted.
No.I / realization of the basso continuo by Gerhard Krapf. — 1974. — 4to.
Unpriced
Also classified at SPG
(B74-50754)
No.II / realization of the basso continuo by R.P. Block. — 1974. — 4to.
Unpriced
Also classified at SPG
(B74-50755)

No.III / realization of the basso continuo by R.P. Block. — 1974. — 4to.
Unpriced
Also classified at SPG

(B74-50756)

No.IV / realization of the basso continuo by R.P. Block. — 1974. — 4to.
Unpriced
Also classified at SPG

(B74-50757)

Zamfir, Gheorghe
Suites pour flûte de Pan / par Gheorghe Zamfir. — Paris ;
[London] : Chappell, 1974. — 35p ; 4to.
Contents: Suite muntenienne - Suite maramourech - Suite banateene.
Unpriced

(B74-50758)

VRPJ — Miscellaneous works
Doppler, Albrecht Franz
Airs valaques. Op.10 : fantasie for flute with piano
accompaniment / by Franz Albrecht Doppler. — Ampleforth :
Wye Music : Emerson, 1974. — fol.
Score (14p.) & part.
Unpriced

(B74-51318)

Luening, Otto
Fantasia brevis : for flute and piano / [by] Otto Luening. — New
York : Highgate Press : Galaxy ; London : Galliard, 1974. — 4to.
Score (11p.) & part.
Unpriced

(B74-51319)

Paggi, Giovanni
Rimembranze napoletane : for flute with pianoforte
accompaniment / [by] Giovanni Paggi. — Ampleforth : Wye
Music : Emerson, 1974. — fol.
Score (17p.) & part.
Unpriced

(B74-51320)

Ridout, Alan
Three nocturnes : for flute and piano / [by] Alan Ridout. —
London : Chappell, 1974. — 4to.
Unpriced

(B74-51321)

VRPK — Arrangements
Chopin, Frédéric
[Nocturne for piano, no.20, in C sharp minor. Op. posth].
Nocturne (posthumous) / [by] Frédéric Chopin ; transcribed for
flute and piano by Julius Baker. — New York ; London :
Schirmer, 1974. — 4to.
Score (5p.) & part.
Unpriced

(B74-51322)

Debussy, Claude
Rêverie / by Claude Debussy ; arranged for flute and piano by
Harry Dexter. — London : Ashdown, 1974. — 4to.
Score (8p.) & part.
£0.30

(B74-50272)

VRPK/AE — Arrangements. Sonatas
Mozart, Wolfgang Amadeus
[Sonatas for violin & piano. K.10-15: arr]. Six sonatas for flute
and piano / by Wolfgang Amadeus Mozart ; edited by Louis
Moyse. — New York ; London : Schirmer, 1974. — 4to.
Score (65p.) & part.
Unpriced

(B74-51323)

VRPK/AG — Arrangements. Suites
Bach, Johann Sebastian
[Suite for orchestra, no.2, in B minor. S. 1067: arr]. Suite in B
minor / [by] Johann Sebastian Bach ; edited for flute and piano
and with piano reduction by Louis Moyse. — New York ;
London : Schirmer, 1974. — 4to.
Score (24p.) & part.
Unpriced

(B74-51324)

VRPK/DW/G/AYEM — Arrangements. Folk songs. Collections.
                                                            Austria
Alt, Hansi
Red clouds : 12 folk songs from Austria, Switzerland and Tirol,
for violin (or recorder or flute) and piano, with optional cello / by
Hansi Alt. — New York ; [London] : Oxford University Press,
1971. — 4to.
Score & 2 parts.
Unpriced
Primary classification SPK/DW/G/AYEM

VRPK/LF — Arrangements. Concertos
Bach, Carl Philipp Emanuel
[Concerto for flute & string orchestra in G major. Wq.169 : arr].
Concerto in G major : for flute, strings and basso continuo.
Wq.169 / by Carl Philipp Emanuel Bach ; ed. David Lasocki,
piano reduction [and] realization of basso continuo by R.P. Block.
— London : Musica rara, 1974. — 4to.
Score (18p.) & part.
Unpriced

(B74-50759)

Quantz, Johann Joachim
[Concerto for flute & string orchestra in D minor: arr]. Concerto
in D minor for flute, strings and continuo / [by] Johann Joachim
Quantz ; edited by David Lasocki, realisation of basso continuo
and piano reduction by R.P. Block. — London : Musica rara,
1972. — 4to.
Score (42p.) & part.
Unpriced

(B74-50760)

VRPLSS — FLUTE & DOUBLE BASS
VRPLSSHVHR — Flute & double bass. Rants
Dalby, Martin
Macpherson's rant : for flute and double bass / by Martin Dalby.
— London : Yorke, 1974. — 10ff ; 4to.
Unpriced

(B74-51325)

VRPLTS — FLUTE & GUITAR
Carulli, Ferdinando
[Duo for flute and guitar in D major. Op. 109, no.6]. Serenade für
Flöte (Violine) und Gitarre / von Ferdinando Carulli ;
herausgegeben von Frank Nagel. — Mainz ; London : Schott,
1974. — 2pt ; 4to.
£1.32
Also classified at SPLTS

(B74-50273)

VRPLX — FLUTE & PERCUSSION
VRPLXTRT — Vibraphone & flute
Lazarof, Henri
Asymtotes : for flute and vibraphone / by Henri Lazarof. — New
York ; London : Associated Music, 1972. — 3p ; fol.
Two copies.
£7.50

(B74-50860)

VRPM — UNACCOMPANIED FLUTE
VRPME — Sonatas
Bach, Carl Philipp Emanuel
[Sonata for flute in A minor. Wq.132]. Sonata in A minor for
flute alone / [by] Karl Philipp Emanuel Bach ; edited by Louis
Moyse. — New York ; London : Schirmer, 1974. — 7p ; 4to.
£0.70

(B74-51326)

VRPMJ — Miscellaneous works
Laderman, Ezra
Duet for flute and dancers / [by] Ezra Laderman. — New York ;
London : Oxford University Press, 1974. — 7p ; 4to.
Duration 7 min.
Unpriced

(B74-50761)

Rollin, Robert Leon
Two pieces for solo flute / by Robert Leon Rollin. — New York :
Galaxy Music ; London : Galliard, 1974. — 4p ; 4to.
Contents: 1: Idyll - 2: Country dance.
Unpriced

(B74-50762)

Stoker, Richard
Soliloquy : for solo flute / by Richard Stoker. — London :
Ashdown, 1974. — 2p ; 4to.
£0.30

(B74-50763)

VS — RECORDER
VS/AC — Tutors
Fagan, Margo
Play time : Longman first recorder course / by Margo Fagan. —
London : Longman, 1974. — 24p ; obl.8vo.
Teacher's book.
ISBN 0-582-18539-4 : £0.70

(B74-51327)

Fagan, Margo
Play time : Longman first recorder course / [by] Margo Fagan. —
London : Longman.
Stage 3 / illustrated by Peter Bailey. — 1974. — 32p : col, ill ; obl, 4to.
ISBN 0-582-18538-6 Sd : £0.30

(B74-50274)

Gamse, Albert
The best recorder method yet : charts, exercises, embellishments, solos, and ensemble music / by Albert Gamse. — Carlstadt : Lewis Music ; London : Ashley-Fields.
Book 1 : C-soprano or tenor. — 1974. — 96p ; 4to. — Unpriced
(B74-50764)

Book 2 : F-alto, F-sopranino, F-bass. — 1974. — 96p ; 4to. — Unpriced
(B74-50765)

VSM — RECORDER BAND
VSMK/AAY — Arrangements. Collections
Appleby, Benjamin William
The school recorder assembly book : sixteen hymn tunes and nine pieces for descant and treble recorders with pianoforte accompaniment / by B.W. Appleby and F. Fowler. — Leeds : Arnold, 1974. — 4to.
ISBN 0-560-00382-x : Unpriced
(B74-51328)

VSN — RECORDER ENSEMBLE
VSNK/DK — Arrangements. Anthems
Tomkins, Thomas
[Musica Deo sacra. O praise the Lord: arr]. O praise the Lord / by Thomas Tomkins ; arranged for recorder ensemble, (3 descants, 3 trebles, 3 tenors, 3 basses) by Dennis A. Bamforth. — Bury (Carne House, Parsons Lane, Bury, Lancs.) : Tomus, 1974. — 8vo.
Score (24p.) & 12 parts.
£0.75
(B74-51329)

VSNQK/DM — Arrangements. Hymns
Bach, Johann Sebastian
[Herz und Mund und That und Leben. S.147. Wohl mir dass ich Jesum habe: arr]. Jesu, joy of man's desiring / [by] J.S. Bach ; arranged for recorders, 2 descants, treble, 2 tenors, bass by Gregory Murray. — London : Oxford University Press, 1974. — 8vo & 4to.
Score (9p.) & 5 parts.
ISBN 0-19-355290-6 : Unpriced
(B74-51330)

VSNRG — Quintets. Suites
Hand, Colin
Festival overture : for recorder quintet / [by] Colin Hand. — London : Schott, 1974. — 4to.
Score (22p.) & 5 parts.
£2.50
(B74-50766)

VSNRPW — Four recorders & keyboard
Frescobaldi, Girolamo
[Canzoni da sonare, lib. 1. *Romanesca*]. Canzona on 'Romanesca' / by Girolamo Frescobaldi ; edition for four recorders and keyboard realization by Colin Sterne. — New York ; London : Associated Music, 1972. — 4to.
Score (8p.) & 4 parts.
Unpriced
(B74-50275)

VSNRQK/AH — Four recorders & piano. Arrangements. Dances
Granados, Enrique
[Spanish dances for piano, vol.2. Andaluza: arr]. Andaluza / [by] Enrique Granados ; arranged by Brian Bonsor for descant, treble (div.), tenor recorder and piano. — London : Schott, 1974. — 4to.
Score (8p.) & 3 parts.
£1.00
(B74-51331)

VSNS — Quartets
Bamforth, Dennis Anthony
[Quartet for recorders, no.1. Op.6]. Quartet no.1. Op.6 : for descant, treble, tenor and bass recorders / by Dennis A. Bamforth. — Bury (Came House, Parsons La., Bury, Lancs.) : Tomus, 1974. — 8vo.
Score (28p.) & 4 parts.
Unpriced
(B74-50276)

Ferrabosco, Alfonso, *b.1575*
[Fantasias]. Three fantasias / by Alfonso Ferrabosco II ; transcribed from Egerton Ms. 3665, setting for four recorders by J. Evan Kreider. — New York ; London : Associated Music, 1972. — 4to.
Score (8p.) & 4 parts.
Unpriced
(B74-50277)

Guami, Gioseffo
[Canzonette francese. Selections]. Canzonette francese : for recorder quartet, SATB / by Gioseffo Guami ; edited by Phillip D. Crabtree. — New York ; London : Galaxy Music, 1974. — 4to.
Score (22p.) & 4 parts. — Contents: 1: La Guamina - 2: La Ondeggiante - 3: La Vega - 4: La Todeschina.
Unpriced
(B74-50767)

Katz, Erich
Toccata for recorder consort : SATB / by Erich Katz. — New York ; London : Associated Music, 1972. — 4to.
Score (8p.) & 4 parts.
Unpriced
(B74-50278)

VSNSG — Quartets. Suites
Bamforth, Dennis Anthony
Mercer Island suite. Op.1 : for recorder quartet (descant, treble, tenor, bass) / by Dennis A. Bamforth. — Bury (Carne House, Parsons Lane, Bury) : Tomus, 1974. — 8vo.
Score (20p.) & 4 parts.
Unpriced
(B74-50768)

VSNSK/DJ — Quartets. Arrangements. Motets
Josquin des Prés
Ecce tu pulchra es : motet / by Josquin des Préz ; setting for four recorders by Erich Katz. — New York ; London : Associated Music, 1972. — 4to.
Score (4p.) & 5 parts.
Unpriced
(B74-50279)

VSNSK/DM — Quartets. Arrangements. Hymns
Bach, Johann Sebastian
[Geistliche Lieder und Schmelli's Gesangbuch und dem Notenbuch der Anna Magdalena Bach. S. 439-567. *Selections: arr*]. Geistliche Lieder / [von] Johann Sebastian Bach ; bearbeitet fur Blockflöten-Quartett, Sopran- , Alt- , Tenor- und Bassflöte von Hans Lewitus. — Mainz ; London : Schott, 1974. — 23p ; obl.8vo.
£1.45
(B74-51332)

VSNSK/DU/AY — Quartets. Arrangements. Madrigals. Colllections
Petrucci, Ottaviano dei
[Harmonice musices odhecaton. Selections]. Ten pieces from 'Harmonice musices odhecaton' / compiled by Ottaviano Petrucci; settings for four and five recorders by La Noue Davenport. — New York ; London : Associated Music, 1972. — 23p ; 4to.
Unpriced
(B74-50280)

VSNT — Trios
Touchin, Colin M
Fanfare, intermezzo and scherzo. Op.1 : for recorder trio, (descant, treble, tenor) / by Colin M. Touchin. — Bury : Tomus, 1973. — 8vo.
Score (12p.) & 3 parts.
Unpriced
(B74-50281)

VSNTG — Trios. Suites
Goldstein, David
Chanukah suite : for recorder trio, SAT / [by] David Goldstein. — New York : Galaxy ; [London] : [Galliard], 1974. — 6p ; 4to.
Unpriced
(B74-51333)

VSNTQ — Three recorders & piano
Batt, Mike
The wombling song : for recorders, descant, treble tenor and piano / by Mike Batt. — London : Chappell, 1974. — 4to.
Score (7p.) & 3 parts.
Unpriced
(B74-50282)

VSNUK — Duets. Arrangements
[Fitzwilliam Virginal Book. Selections: arr]. Six pieces from the Fitzwilliam Virginal Book / arranged for two recorders (descant and treble) by Denis Bloodworth. — London : Oxford University Press, 1974. — 5p ; 4to.
ISBN 0-19-355550-6 : £0.45
(B74-51334)

VSPLX — RECORDER & PERCUSSION
VSPLXQ — Recorder & drum
Keetman, Gunild
Pieces for recorder and drum / by Gunild Keetman. — Mainz ; London : Schott.
Book 2. — 1973. — 31p ; 4to. — £1.20
(B74-50283)

VSR — DESCANT RECORDER
VSR/AC — Tutors
Dedicott, W
The recorder for the first school / by W. Dedicott. —
Ilfracombe : Stockwell, 1974. — 31p ; 8vo.
ISBN 0-7223-0560-5 : £0.33

(B74-50769)

VSRPJ — Miscellaneous works
Gál, Hans
Three intermezzi, Op.103 : for treble recorder (or flute) and
harpsichord or pianoforte / [by] Hans Gál. — Mainz ; London :
Schott, 1974. — 4to.
Score (19p.) & part.
£2.32

(B74-51335)

VSRPK/DW/G/AYEM — Arrangements. Folk songs. Collections.
Austria
Alt, Hansi
Red clouds : 12 folk songs from Austria, Switzerland and Tirol,
for violin (or recorder or flute) and piano, with optional cello / by
Hansi Alt. — New York ; [London] : Oxford University Press,
1971. — 4to.
Score & 2 parts.
Unpriced
Primary classification SPK/DW/G/AYEM

VSRPLTSK/AH/G/AYD — Descant recorder & guitar.
Arrangements. Folk dances. Collections. England
Duarte, John William
Take your partners : easy arrangements of English country dance
tunes (from the English Dancing Master) for descant recorder and
guitar / by John W. Duarte. — Sevenoaks : Novello, 1973. —
13p ; 4to.
£0.50

(B74-50284)

VSRPMK/AHW — Unaccompanied descant recorder. Arrangements.
Waltzes
Tchaikovsky, Peter
[Selections: arr]. Waltz themes from Tchaikovsky : for descant
recorder, treble or melodica or guitar / arr. by Dick Sadleir. —
London : British and Continental Music Agencies, 1974. — 7p ;
8vo.
Unpriced
Also classified at TSPMK/AHW

(B74-50770)

VSRPMK/DW — Arrangements. Songs, etc
Sullivan, *Sir* **Arthur Seymour**
[Selections: arr]. Gilbert and Sullivan for descant recorder with
chord symbols for guitar, piano or tuned percussion / arranged by
Dick Sadleir. — London : British and Continental, 1974. — 13p ;
8vo.
Unpriced

(B74-51336)

VSRPMK/DW/AYC — Arrangements. Songs. Collections. Great
Britain
Duke, Henry
Britain sings / arranged for descant recorder by Henry Duke. —
London : British and Continental.
Book 1. — 1974. — 16p ; 4to.
Unpriced

(B74-50285)

Book 2. — 1974. — 16p ; 4to.
Unpriced

(B74-50286)

VSS — TREBLE RECORDER
VSSNTPWE/AYD — Two treble recorders & keyboard. Sonatas.
Collections. England
Ruf, Hugo
Trio sonatas by old English masters : for two treble recorders and
basso continuo / edited by Hugo Ruf. — Cassel ; London :
Bärenreiter.
Score (16p.) & 3 parts.
1. — 1973. — 4to.
£2.55

(B74-50772)

2. — 1973. — 4to.
£2.18

(B74-50771)

VSSNU — Duets
Genzmer, Harald
Tanzstücke für zwei Altblockflöten / von Harald Genzmer. —
Mainz ; London : Schott.
Heft 2. — 1973. — 13p ; 4to. —
£1.08

(B74-50287)

VSSP/T — Variations
Walter, Heinz
Variations on a theme by Georg Friedrich Handel : for soprano
recorder (flute) and harpsichord / [by] Heinz Walter. — Mainz ;
London : Schott, 1974. — 4to.
Score (12p.) & part.
£1.74

(B74-51337)

VSSPE — Sonatas
Telemann, Georg Philipp
[Der getreue Music-Meister. Sonata for treble recorder & basso
continuo in C major]. Sonata no.4 in C major : for treble recorder
and continuo / by Georg Philipp Telemann ; edited by Walter
Bergmann. — London : Schott, 1974. — 4to.
Score (6p.) & 2 parts. — The numeration of this sonata is editorial.
£0.75

(B74-50773)

Telemann, Georg Philipp
[Der getreue Music-Meister. Sonata for treble recorder & basso
continuo in F major]. Sonata no.1 in F major : for treble recorder
and continuo / by Georg Philipp Telemann ; edited by Walter
Bergmann. — London : Schott, 1974. — 4to.
Score (5p.) & 2 parts. — Numeration of this sonata is editorial.
£0.75

(B74-50774)

Telemann, Georg Philipp
[Der getreue Music-Meister. Sonata for treble recorder & basso
continuo in F minor]. Sonata no.3 in F minor : for treble recorder
and continuo / by Georg Philipp Telemann ; edited by Walter
Bergmann. — London : Schott, 1974. — 4to.
Score (11p.) & 2 parts. — The numeration of this sonata is editorial.
£0.75

(B74-50775)

Telemann, George Philipp
[Der getreue Music-Meister. Sonatas for treble recorders & basso
continuo]. Sonatas 1-4 : for treble recorder and continuo / [by]
Georg Philipp Telemann ; edited by Walter Bergmann. —
London : Schott, 1974. — 4to.
Score (27p.) & 2 parts. — Numeration of the sonatas is editorial.
£2.50

(B74-50776)

Vivaldi, Antonio
[Sonata for treble recorder & basso continuo in D minor]. Sonate
d-Moll, für Altblockflöte und Basso continuo / von Antonio
Vivaldi ; herausgegeben von Frank Nagel, Generalbassaussetzung
von Winfried Radecke. — Mainz ; London : Schott, 1973. — 4to.
Score (10p.) & 2 parts.
£1.08

(B74-50288)

VSSPE/X — Sonatas. Canons
Telemann, Georg Philipp
[Der getreue Music-Meister. Sonata for treble recorder & basso
continuo in C major (in canon)]. Sonata no.2 in C major (in
canon) : for treble recorder and continuo / by Georg Philipp
Telemann ; edited by Walter Bergmann. — London : Schott,
1974. — 4to.
Score (6p.) & 2 parts. — The numeration of this sonata is editorial.
£0.75

(B74-50777)

VSSPK/AE — Arrangements. Sonatas
Corelli, Arcangelo
[Sonata for violin & basso continuo in C minor. Op.5, no.3: arr].
Sonata in C minor. Opus 5, no.3 : for treble (alto) recorder and
basso continuo / by Arcangelo Corelli ; arranged by 'An eminent
master' (1707), edited by David Lasocki, realization of basso
continuo by R.P. Block. — London : Musica rara, 1974. — 4to.
Score (15p.) & 2 parts.
Unpriced

(B74-50778)

VST — TENOR RECORDER
VSTPMJ — Miscellaneous works
Shinohara, Makoto
Fragment : for tenor recorder / by Makoto Shinohara. —
London : Schott, 1974. — 4p ; 4to.
£0.65

(B74-50779)

VTN — OBOE ENSEMBLE
VTNTPWE — Two oboes & keyboard. Sonatas
Vivaldi, Antonio
[Sonata for two oboes & basso continuo in G minor, 'Lund']. Trio
sonata in G minor (Lund) : for 2 oboes and basso continuo / [by]
Antonio Vivaldi ; ed. David Lasocki, realisation of basso continuo
by R.P. Block. — London : Musica rara, 1973. — 4to.
Score (10p.) & 3 parts.
Unpriced

(B74-50780)

VTP — OBOE & PIANO
VTP/W — Rondos
Head, Michael
Rondo for oboe or violin and piano / by Michael Head ; [oboe part] edited by Evelyn Barbirolli; [violin part] edited by Winifred Small. — London : Boosey and Hawkes, 1974. — 4to.
Score (8p.) & part. — The violin part is printed on the verso of the oboe part.
£0.60
Also classified at SP/W

(B74-50781)

VTPE — Sonatas
Widerkehr, Jacob Christian Michael
[Sonata for oboe & piano in E minor]. Duo sonata for oboe and piano / [by] J.C.M. Widerkehr ; edited by James Brown. — London : Musica rara, 1974. — 4to.
Score (29p.) & part.
Unpriced

(B74-50782)

VTPJ — Miscellaneous works
Dodgson, Stephen
[Suite for oboe & keyboard in D major]. Suite in D : for oboe and harpsichord (piano) / by Stephen Dodgson. — London : Oxford University Press, 1974. — 4to.
Score (15p.) & part.
ISBN 0-19-356268-5 : £1.10

(B74-50783)

Johnson, Thomas Arnold
Pastorale : for oboe (or B flat clarinet) and piano / by Thomas A. Johnson. — London : British and Continental Music Agencies, 1974. — 4to.
Score (4p.) & 2 parts.
Unpriced
Also classified at VVPJ

(B74-50784)

Lancen, Serge
Fantasie concertante, no.1 : pour hautbois et piano / par Serge Lancen. — Paris ; London : Chappell, 1971. — 4to.
Score & part.
Unpriced

(B74-50785)

Maconchy, Elizabeth
Three bagatelles : for oboe and harpsichord (or piano) / by Elizabeth Maconchy. — London : Oxford University Press, 1974. — 4to.
ISBN 0-19-357720-8 : £1.00

(B74-50289)

Wen, Chi Chung
Three Chinese folksongs : for oboe and piano / [by] Chi Chung Wen. — London : Schott, 1974. — 4to.
Score (6p.) & part.
£1.00

(B74-51338)

VTPK/LF — Arrangements. Concertos
Albinoni, Tommaso
[Concerto for oboe, string quartet & basso continuo in C major. Op.9, no.5: arr]. Concerto à 5 for oboe strings and continuo. Op.9, no.5 / [by] Tommaso Albinoni ; [edited and with piano reduction by] Franz Giegling. — London : Musica rara, 1973. — 4to.
Score (18p.) & part.
Unpriced

(B74-50786)

Vivaldi, Antonio
[Concerto for two oboes & string orchestra in D minor. P.302: arr]. Concerto in D minor for 2 oboes, strings and basso continuo / [by] Antonio Vivaldi ; ed. David Lasocki, piano reduction [and] realisation of basso continuo by R.P. Block. — London : Musica rara, 1973. — 4to.
Score (14p.) & 2 parts.
Unpriced

(B74-50787)

VTPK/LFL — Arrangements. Concertinos
Kalliwoda, Jan Vaclav
[Concertino for oboe in F major. Op.110: arr]. Concertino for oboe and orchestra. Op.110 / [by] Jan Vaclav Kallowoda ; edited and with piano reduction by Han de Vries. — London : Musica rara, 1974. — 4to.
Score (21p.) & part.
Unpriced

(B74-50788)

VTPLR — Oboe & organ
Schroeder, Hermann
Drei Dialoge für Oboe und Orgel / von Hermann Schroeder. — Mainz ; London : Schott, 1973. — 4to.
Score (12p.) & part.
£1.44

(B74-50290)

VTPM — UNACCOMPANIED OBOE
VTPMJ — Miscellaneous works
Josephs, Wilfred
Solo oboe piece. Opus 84 / by Wilfred Josephs. — [Sevenoaks] : Novello, 1974. — 3p ; 4to.
£0.50

(B74-50789)

Stoker, Richard
Three pieces for oboe solo or cor anglais. Opus 29 / by Richard Stoker. — London : Peters, 1973. — 4p ; 4to.
Unpriced

(B74-50790)

VUN — SAXOPHONE ENSEMBLE
VUNS — Quartets
Jacob, Gordon
[Quartet for saxophones]. Saxophone quartet / [by] Gordon Jacob. — Ampleforth : Emerson Edition, 1974. — 5pt ; 4to.
The tenor saxophone part is in duplicate.
Unpriced

(B74-50791)

VUNTQK/LF — Arrangements. Concertos
Hoffmeister, Franz Anton
[Concerto for two clarinets in E flat major: arr]. Concerto in E flat for 2 clarinets and orchestra / [by] F.A. Hoffmeister ; 2 clarinets and piano reduction by R.P. Block. — London : Musica rara, 1973. — 4to.
Score (32p.) & 2 parts.
Unpriced

(B74-50792)

VUP — SAXOPHONE & PIANO
VUPJ — Miscellaneous works
Gallois, Olivier
Nocturnes pour un sax : [saxophone and piano] / [composed by] Olivier Gallois. — Paris ; [London] : Chappell, 1971. — 26p ; 4to.
Unpriced

(B74-51339)

VUS — ALTO SAXOPHONE
Heiden, Bernhard
Solo for alto saxophone and piano / by Bernhard Heiden. — New York ; London : Associated Music Publishers, 1973. — 4to.
Score (12p.) & part.
£1.15

(B74-50793)

VUSPK/LF — Arrangements. Concertos
Husa, Karel
[Concerto for alto saxophone and concert band: arr]. Concerto for alto saxophone and concert band / by Karel Husa; reduction for solo and piano by the composer. — New York ; London : Associated Music, 1972. — 4to.
Score (36p.) & part.
Unpriced

(B74-50291)

VV — CLARINET
VV/AC — Tutors
Couf, Herb
Let's play clarinet / by Herb Couf. — New York ; [London] : Chappell, 1974. — 64p ; 4to.
Unpriced

(B74-51340)

VVN — CLARINET ENSEMBLE
VVNK/DW — Arrangements. Songs, etc
Villa-Lobos, Heitor
Bachianas brasileiras, no.5. Aria (Cantilena) / [by] Heitor Villa-Lobos ; arranged for clarinet choir by John Krance. — New York ; London : Associated Music, 1971. — 30p ; 4to.
Unpriced

(B74-50794)

VVNS — Quartets
Harvey, Paul
Quartet for 3 B flat clarinets and bass clarinet / by Paul Harvey. — London : Schott, 1974. — 4to.
Score (20p.) & 4 parts.
£1.25

(B74-50795)

VVNSK/AAY — Arrangements. Collections
Coursey, Ralph de
Wind encores : a collection of 12 short familiar pieces arranged for four-part clarinet ensemble (2 B flat clarinets, alto clarinet (or bassoon) and bass clarinet (or bassoon)) / [arranged] by Ralph de Coursey. — New York ; London : Associated Music, 1973. — 20p ; 4to.
Unpriced

(B74-50796)

VVNTK/AAY — Trios. Arrangements. Collections
Brooks, Keith
Classical album for clarinet ensemble / arranged by Keith Brooks. — London : Boosey and Hawkes, 1974. — 4to.
Score (27p.) & part.
£2.50

(B74-50797)

VVNTQK/LE — Two clarinets & piano. Arrangements. Symphonies
Devienne, François
[Symphonie concertante for two clarinets in B flat major. Opus 25: arr]. Symphonie concertante for two clarinets and orchestra. Opus 25 / [by] François Devienne ; edited by Himie Voxman, piano reduction by R. Block. — London : Musica rara, 1973. — 4to.
Score (28p.) & 2 parts.
Unpriced

(B74-50798)

VVNTQK/LF — Two clarinets & piano. Arrangements. Concertos
Telemann, Georg Philipp
[Concerto for two clarinets & string orchestra in D minor: arr]. Concerto for 2 clarinets (chalumeaux) and strings / by G.P. Telemann ; edited with piano reduction by Hermann Dechant. — London : Musica rara, 1973. — 4to.
Score (16p.) & 2 parts.
Unpriced

(B74-50799)

VVNU — Duets
Harvey, Jonathan
Studies for two equal clarinets / by Jonathan Harvey. — Sevenoaks : Novello, 1974. — 12p ; 4to.
£0.75

(B74-50800)

Vallier, Jacques
Prelude et final : pour deux clarinettes (en si bemol) / [par] Jacques Vallier. — Paris ; [London] : Chappell, 1974. — 4to.
Two copies.
Unpriced

(B74-51341)

Walker, Eldon
Duologue : 2 clarinets / [by] Eldon Walker. — London : Thames, 1974. — 9p ; fol.
Unpriced

(B74-51342)

VVP — CLARINET & PIANO
VVPE — Sonatas
Lefevre, Jean Xavier
[Sonata for clarinet & basso continuo in B flat. Op.12, no.1]. Sonata in B flat. Opus 12, no.1 : for clarinet and piano / by Xavier Lefevre ; edited and realised by Georgina Dobree. — London : Oxford University Press, 1973. — 4to.
Score (16p.) & part.
ISBN 0-19-357548-5 : £0.75

(B74-50292)

Vanhal, Jan
[Sonata for clarinet & piano, no.2, in B flat major]. Sonata in B flat for clarinet and piano / [by] J.B. Vanhal; edited by Georgina Dobree. — London : Musica rara, 1974. — 4to.
Score (20p.) & part.
£6.50

(B74-50801)

VVPEM — Sonatinas
Richardson, Norman
Sonatina for clarinet and piano / by Norman Richardson. — London : Boosey and Hawkes, 1973. — 4to.
Score (16p.) & part.
£0.75

(B74-50293)

Vallier, Jacques
[Sonatina for clarinet & piano, no.2. Op.72]. Sonatine no.2 pour clarinette en si bemol et piano. Op.72 / [par] Jacques Vallier. — Paris ; [London] : Chappell, 1974. — 4to.
Score (12p.) & part.
Unpriced

(B74-51343)

VVPJ — Miscellaneous works
Johnson, Thomas Arnold
Pastorale : for oboe (or B flat clarinet) and piano / by Thomas A. Johnson. — London : British and Continental Music Agencies, 1974. — 4to.
Score (4p.) & 2 parts.
Unpriced
Primary classification VTPJ

(B74-50784)

Spohr, Louis
Potpourri for clarinet & piano. Op.80 / [by] Louis Spohr ; edited by Maurice F. Powell. — London : Musica rara, 1973. — 4to.
Score (19p.) & part. — This work is based on themes from 'Das unterbrochene Opferfest' by Peter von Winter.
Unpriced

(B74-50802)

VVPK — Arrangements
Bach, Johann Christian
[Sonatas for keyboard. Selections: arr]. Concerto in E flat major for clarinet and strings / [arranged for the music of] J.C. Bach by W.A. Mozart (K.107); transcribed and edited [from Mozart's version for keyboard and strings] by Yona Ettlinger; reduction for clarinet and piano. — London : Boosey and Hawkes, 1974. — 4to.
Score (26p.) & part. — The editor has contributed an additional movement from J.C. Bach's Op.17.
£1.50

(B74-50803)

Gould, Morton
[Derivations from clarinet & wind band: arr]. Derivations : for clarinet and band / by Morton Gould ; reduction for piano by Louis Brunelli. — New York ; London : Chappell, 1974. — 4to.
Score (46p.) & part. — Duration 17 1/2 min.
Unpriced

(B74-51344)

Saint-Saëns, Camille
[Le Carnival des animaux. Selections: arr]. Two pieces / [by] Camille Saint-Saëns ; arranged for clarinet and piano by Lionel Lethbridge. — London : Oxford University Press, 1974. — 4to.
Score (8p.) & part. — Contents: Fossils - The swan.
ISBN 0-19-358701-7 : £0.60

(B74-51345)

VVPK/LF — Arrangements. Concertos
Mozart, Wolfgang Amadeus
[Concerto for clarinet in A major. K.622: arr]. Concerto for clarinet and orchestra. K.622 / by W.A. Mozart ; edited by Alan Hacker; reduction for clarinet and piano. — London : Schott, 1974. — 4to.
Score (53p.) & part. — First edition for the original instrument.
£2.00

(B74-50804)

VVPLS — CLARINET & VIOLIN
VVPLSF — Concertos
Gebauer, Etienne
[Duo concertant for clarinet & violin in E flat major. Op.16, no.3]. Duo concertant for clarinet and violin. Op.16, no.3 / [by] Etienne Gebauer ; edited by Georgina Dobree. — London : Musica rara, 1973. — 19p ; 4to.
Unpriced

(B74-50805)

VVPM — UNACCOMPANIED CLARINET
VVPMJ — Miscellaneous works
Goehr, Alexander
Paraphrase on the dramatic madrigal Il Combattimento de Tancredi e Clorinda by Claudio Monteverdi. Op.28: for clarinet solo / by Alexander Goehr. — London : Schott, 1974. — 7p ; 4to.
£.25

(B74-50294)

Stoker, Richard
Triptych : for clarinet in B flat or bass clarinet / by Richard Stoker. — London : Ashdown, 1974. — 2p ; 4to.
£0.30

(B74-50806)

Vallier, Jacques
Improvisation pour clarinette (en si bemol) seule / [par] Jacques Vallier. — Paris ; [London] : Chappell, 1974. — 3p ; 4to.
Duration 6 min - Printed on one side of the leaf only.
Unpriced

(B74-51346)

VVQ — CLARINET (A)
VVQP/T — Clarinet (A) & piano. Variations
Searle, Humphrey
Cat variations : for clarinet in A and piano on a theme from Prokofiev's 'Peter and the wolf' / by Humphrey Searle. — London : Faber Music, 1974. — 4to.
Score (8p.) & part.
Unpriced

(B74-50807)

VVQPE — Sonatas
Rudolph Johann Joseph Rainer, *Archduke of Austria Cardinal Archbishop of Olmutz*
[Sonata for clarinet in A & piano in A major. Op.2]. Sonata for clarinet and piano. Op.2 / [by] Rudolph, Archduke of Austria ; edited by H. Voxman. — London : Musica rara, 1973. — 4to.
Score (35p.) & part.
Unpriced

(B74-50808)

VVQPK — Clarinet (A) & piano. Arrangements
Brahms, Johannes
[Quintet for clarinet & strings in B minor. Op. 115: arr]. Clarinet quintet in B minor / by Brahms; arranged for clarinet in A and piano by Pamela Weston. — London : Fenette Music : Breitkopf and Härtel, 1974. — 4to.
Score (35p.) & part.
Unpriced

(B74-50295)

VVTRPK — Tenor clarinet (E flat) & piano. Arrangements
Mozart, Wolfgang Amadeus
[Concerto for clarinet in A. K.622. Adagio; arr]. Adagio / by Wolfgang Amadeus Mozart ; transcribed for E flat alto clarinet with piano accompaniment by H. Voxman. — Miami : Rubank ; London : Novello, 1971. — 4to.
Score & part.
Unpriced

(B74-50809)

VWN — BASSOON ENSEMBLE
VWNS — Quartets
Ridout, Alan
Pigs : a present for Gordon Jacob, for four bassoons / by Alan Ridout. — Ampleforth : Emerson, 1973. — 4pt ; 4to.
Unpriced

(B74-50296)

VWNT — Trios
Weissenborn, Julius
Six trios for 3 bassoons. [Op.4] / [by] Julius Weissenborn ; edited by Ronald Tyree. — London : Musica rara, 1974. — 3pt ; 4to.
Unpriced

(B74-50810)

VWP — BASSOON & PIANO
VWPE — Sonatas
Bertoli, Giovanni Antonio
[Compositioni musicale fatte per sonare col fagotto solo, nos 1-3]. Three sonatas for bassoon (violoncello) and basso continuo / by Giovanni Antonio Bertoli ; edited by William Kaplan. — Cassel ; London : Bärenreiter, 1973. — 4to.
Score (32p.) & 2 parts.
£3.45
Also classified at SRPE

(B74-50811)

VWPJ — Miscellaneous works
Hughes, Eric
Six low solos : bassoon and piano / by Eric Hughes. — Ampleforth : Emerson, 1974. — 4to.
Score (12p.) & part.
Unpriced

(B74-50297)

Srebotnjak, Alojz
Six pieces for bassoon and piano / by Alojz Srebotnjak. — New York ; London : Schirmer, 1973. — 4to.
Score (16p.) & part.
£1.15

(B74-50812)

Ward-Steinman, David
Child's play : for bassoon and piano / by David Ward-Steinman. — New York : Highgate Press : Galaxy ; London : Galliard, 1974. — 20p ; 4to.
Two copies.
Unpriced

(B74-51347)

VWPK — Arrangements
Françaix, Jean
[Divertissement for bassoon & string quintet: arr.]. Divertissement pour basson et quintette à cordes / par Jean Françaix ; reduction pour piano. — Mainz ; London : Schott, 1973. — 4to.
Score (28p.) & part.
£1.92

(B74-50298)

Saint-Saëns, Camille
[Le Carnival des animaux. Selections: arr]. Two pieces / [by] Camille Saint-Saëns ; arranged for bassoon and piano by Lionel Lethbridge. — London : Oxford University Press, 1974. — 4to.
Contents: 1: Tortoises - 2: The elephant.
ISBN 0-19-358703-3 : £0.45

(B74-51348)

VWPK/LF — Arrangements. Concertos
Pleyel, Ignaz
[Concerto for bassoon in B flat: arr]. Concerto in B flat for bassoon and orchestra / [by] Ignaz Pleyel ; edited [and arranged for bassoon and piano] by R.P. Block. — London : Musica rara, 1972. — 4to.
Score (27p.) & part.
Unpriced

(B74-50813)

Vivaldi, Antonio
[Concertos for bassoon. Selections: arr]. 10 bassoon concerti / by Antonio Vivaldi ; arranged for bassoon and piano, bassoon part edited by Sol Schoenbach, piano accompaniment realized by William Winstead. — New York ; London : Schirmer.
Vol.1. — 1972. — 4to.
Score (85p.) & part.
Unpriced

(B74-50299)

Vol.2. — 1972. — 4to.
Score (81p.) & part.
Unpriced

(B74-50300)

VWPLSR — BASSOON & CELLO
Fricker, Peter Racine
Three arguments. Opus 59 : for bassoon and cello / [by] Peter Racine Fricker. — London : Fenette Music : Breitkopf and Härtel, 1974. — 9p ; obl.4to.
Unpriced

(B74-51349)

VWPM — UNACCOMPANIED BASSOON
VWPMJ — Miscellaneous works
Ridout, Alan
Caliban and Ariel : for solo bassoon / [by] Alan Ridout. — London : Chappell, 1974. — 4ff ; 4to.
Unpriced

(B74-50814)

VWPMK/AG — Arrangements. Suites
Bach, Johann Sebastian
[Suites for cello. Nos 1-2. S: 1007-8]. Two suites / by Johann Sebastian Bach ; arranged for bassoon by Paul Cammarota. — New York ; London : Schimer, 1973. — 13p ; 4to.
£1.15

(B74-50815)

VX — MOUTH ORGAN
VX/AC — Tutors
Chimes, Michael
Let's play harmonica / by Michael Chimes. — New York : Experience Music ; London : Chappell, 1974. — 62p ; 4to.
Unpriced

(B74-50816)

VY — BAGPIPES
VY/T — Variations
MacDonald, Donald
A collection of the ancient martial music of Caledonia called piobaireache / [by] Donald MacDonald. — [1st ed., reprinted] ; with a new foreword by Seumas MacNeill. — Wakefield : EP Publishing, 1974. — viii,5,8,117p ; fol.
Facsimile reprint of 1822 ed.
ISBN 0-7158-1031-6 : £4.00

(B74-50817)

WM — BRASS BAND
WM/AY — Collections
Salvation Army Brass Band Journal (Festival series). — London : Salvationist Publishing and Supplies.
Nos.353-356 : The Southern Cross: festival march, by Brian Bowen. Oh the blessed Lord: Toccata, by Wilfred Heaton. Notturno religioso, by Erik Leidzen. Songs of praise: suite, by James Curnow. — 1973. — 72p ; obl 8vo.

Unpriced

(B74-50301)

Salvation Army Brass Band Journal (General series). — London : Salvationist Publishing and Supplies.
Nos 1641-1644 : There will be God: trombone solo, by Joy Webb; arr. Ray Steadman-Allen and, When the harvest is past: flugel horn solo, by Ray Steadman-Allen; Temple 85: march, by Norman Bearcroft. The seeking heart: selection, by Charles Dove. Hallelujah!: chorus setting, by Terry Camsey, and, Troyte: hymn tune arrangement, by Brindley Boon. — 1973. — 37p ; obl 4to.
Unpriced

(B74-50818)

Nos. 1645-1648 : The Irish Salvationist march, by Walter Fletcher. The joy of Christmas suite, by Robert Redhead. Sweet little Jesus boy, negro spiritual, arr. Joy Webb, trans. Christopher Cole with David of the White Rock: Welsh melody, arr. Ray Bowes. The secret place: selection, by Neville McFarlane. — 1974. — 49p ; obl.4to.
Unpriced

(B74-50302)

Nos.1649-1652 : A shrine of quietness : meditation / [by] Derek Jordan. Congregational tunes no.8 / arr. Ray Steadman-Allen. I reckon on you : trombone ensemble / [by] Douglas Kiff ; arr. Eiliv Herikstad. Norwich citadel : march / [by] Albert Drury. — 1973. — 33p ; obl.4to. —
Unpriced

(B74-51350)

Nos.1653-1656 : Away in a manger (Normandy carol) : song transcription / [by] Robert Redhead, and, The wonder of his grace : song arrangement / [by] Howard Davies. Selection from 'Hosea' / [by] Ray Steadman-Allen, (melodies John Larsson). Melcombe : hymn tune arrangement / [by] Ray Steadman-Allen. The battle cry : march / by Bjorn Garsegg; arr. Eric Ball. — 1973. — 45p ; obl.4to. —
Unpriced

(B74-51351)

Salvation Army Brass Band Journal (Triumph series). — London : Salvationist Publishing and Supplies.
Nos 757-760 : Bognor Regis: march, by Leslie Condon. Hosea: suite, by Robert Redhead. Jesus loves me: song setting, by James Anderson. The Kiwi: march, by Ray Cresswell. — 1973. — 37p ; obl 8vo. —
Unpriced

(B74-50819)

Nos 761-764 : Joy in Bethlehem: selection, by Leslie Condon. Stainer: prelude, by Barbara Steadman-Allen, and, Hold the fort! song arrangement, by Terry Camsey. Be strong! march, by Christopher Cole. Congregational tunes: no.7, arr. by Ray Steadman-Allen. — 1973. — 33p ; obl 8vo. —
Unpriced

(B74-50820)

Nos.769-772 : Rhapsody on Danish traditional airs / [by] Erik Silferberg. A call to prayer : selection / [by] E.A. Smith. Dandenony citadel : march / [by] Allen Pengilly. March from the 'Occasional' oratorio / [by] Handel ; arr. Richard Slater, and, Nearer to thee : coronet solo / [by] Ira D. Sankey ; arr. Howard Davies. — 1974. — 37p ; obl.4to. —
Unpriced

(B74-51352)

Nos.773-776 : Jesus I come : meditation / [by] Ray Steadman-Allen. Prospects of joy : selection / by F.J. Dockerill. He came to give us life : song transcription / by John Larsson : trans. Robert Redhead. Caribbean congress : march / [by] David Wells. — 1974. — 33p ; obl.4to. —
Unpriced

(B74-51353)

WMG — Suites
Knight, Vernon
Suite for brass and percussion / by Vernon Knight. — New York ; London : Schirmer, 1972. — 4to.
Unpriced

(B74-50303)

WMGM — Marches
Ball, Eric
Torch of freedom : march for brass band / [by] Eric Ball. — London : R. Smith, 1974. — 8vo.
Short score & 25 parts.
Unpriced

(B74-50821)

WMGN — Fanfares
Brian, Havergal
[Fanfare for the orchestral brass]. Festival fanfare : 4 horns, 4 trumpets, 3 trombones and 2 tubas / by Havergal Brian. — Chelmsford : Musica Viva, 1974. — 4to.
Score (8p.) & 13 parts. — Set of parts available separately from the score.
£1.55

(B74-51354)

Copland, Aaron
Ceremonial fanfare : for brass ensemble, (4 horns, 3 trumpets, 3 trombones, tuba) / [by] Aaron Copland. — London : Boosey and Hawkes, 1974. — 4to.
Score (6p.) & 11 parts.
£1.50

(B74-51355)

Lees, Benjamin
Fanfare for a centennial : for brass timpani and percussion / by Benjamin Lees. — London : Boosey and Hawkes, 1973. — 4to.
Score (8p.) & 13 parts.
£1.75

(B74-50304)

Thomson, Virgil
Metropolitan Museum fanfare : for brass ensemble and percussion / by Virgil Thomson. — New York ; London : Schirmer, 1972. — 4to.
Score (8p.) & parts.
Unpriced

(B74-50305)

WMJ — Miscellaneous works
Beare, Cyril
Jogging along : rhythm for brass band / by Cyril T. Beare. — London : British and Continental Music, 1974. — 8vo.
Short score & 25 parts.
Unpriced

(B74-50306)

Bolton, Cecil
Mexicana / arranged by Cecil Bolton; transcribed for brass by Eric Banks. — London : Affiliated Music, 1972. — 4to.
Cornet conductor & 26 parts. — With several copies of various parts.
£1.00

(B74-50307)

Gregson, Edward
Intrada for brass band / by Edward Gregson. — London : R. Smith, 1973. — 20p ; obl. 8vo.
Duration 5 min.
Unpriced

(B74-50308)

Gregson, Edward
Patterns for brass band / by Edward Gregson. — London (210 Strand, WC2R 1AP) : R. Smith and Co. Ltd, 1974. — 20p ; obl. 4to.
Duration 5 1/2 min. — 'Specially written for the Finals of the Butlin's Youth Brass Band Championships of Great Britain, held at the Royal Albert Hall, London, October 1974' - note.
Unpriced

(B74-50822)

Hanmer, Ronald
Alice in Wonderland : fantasy [for] brass band / by Ronald Hanmer. — London : Studio Music, 1974. — 46p ; obl.4to.
Duration 10 min.
Unpriced

(B74-50309)

Johnson, Stuart
Preliminary band book / by Stuart Johnson. — London (210 Strand, WC2R 1AP) : R. Smith and Co. Ltd, 1974. — 56p ; 4to.
Unpriced

(B74-50823)

Spurgin, Anthony
Lions and martlets : fantasia for brass band / by Anthony Spurgin. — London : British and Continental, 1974. — 25p ; 8vo.
Unpriced

(B74-50310)

WMK — Arrangements
Albinoni, Tommaso
[Sonata a tre in G minor. Adagio: arr]. Adagio / by Albinoni-Giazotto ; arr for brass band by Bernard Hazelgrove. — London : Ricordi, 1974. — 16p ; obl. 4to.
£1.25

(B74-51356)

Elgar, *Sir* **Edward,** *bart*
[Chanson de matin, Op.15, no.1: arr]. Chanson de matin. Opus 15, no.1 / by Edward Elgar ; arranged for brass band by Denis Wright. — [Sevenoaks] : Paxton, 1974. — 8vo.
Conductor (4p.) & 25 parts. — With several copies of various parts.
£1.25

(B74-50824)

WMK/AGM — Arrangements. Marches
Banks, Eric
[The Red Arrows march: arr.]. The Red Arrows march / by Eric Banks and Cecil Bolton; arr. Eric Banks. — London : Affiliated Music, 1974. — 4to.
Cornet conductor & 25 parts. — With several copies of various parts.
£1.00

(B74-50311)

Teike, Carl
[Alte Kameraden: arr]. Old comrades : quick march / by Carl Teike ; arranged by N. Richardson. — London : Boosey and Hawkes, 1973. — 8vo & obl. 8vo.
Conductor & 48 parts for military and brass bands.
£0.95
Primary classification UMMK/AGM

(B74-50732)

WMK/AGN — Arrangements. Fanfares
Bliss, *Sir* **Arthur**
[Investiture antiphonal fanfares for three brass choirs: arr]. Investiture antiphonal fanfares for three brass choirs / [by] Arthur Bliss ; adapted for brass band by Roy Newsome. — Sevenoaks : Novello, 1974. — 8p ; 4to.
£0.50

(B74-51357)

Drexler, Werner
World cup fanfare : brass band / by Werner Drexler ; arr. J.H. Howe. — London : Weinberger, 1974. — 28pt ; obl. 8vo.
With several copies of various parts.
Unpriced

(B74-50825)

WMK/AHXJ — Arrangements. Ragtime
Joplin, Scott
[The entertainer: arr]. The entertainer : ragtime two-step / [by] Scott Joplin ; arr, brass band, Ronald Hanmer. — London : Studio Music, 1974. — obl.8vo.
Conductor & 24 parts - With several copies of various parts.
Unpriced

(B74-51358)

Joplin, Scott
[The entertainer: arr]. The entertainer / by Scott Joplin ; arranged for brass band by Goff Richards. — London : Chappell, 1974. — 8vo.
Conductor (7p.) & 25 parts. — With several copies of various parts.
Unpriced

(B74-51359)

Joplin, Scott
[The entertainer: arr]. The entertainer : ragtime two-step / [by] Scott Joplin ; arr. Ronald Hanmer. — London : Studio Music, 1974. — obl. 8vo.
Solo B flat cornet conductor (1p.) & 24 parts. — With several copies of various parts.
Unpriced

(B74-50826)

WMK/DW — Arrangements. Songs, etc
Campion, Thomas
[First book of ayres. Never weather-beaten sail: arr]. Never weather-beaten sail / by Thomas Campion ; arranged for brass band by Clive Bright. — London : Studio Music, 1974. — 8vo.
Conductor & 25 parts - With several copies of various parts.
Unpriced

(B74-51360)

WMK/DW — Arrangements. Songs., etc
Tiomkin, Dimitri
[High noon: arr]. Highnoon / by Dimitri Tiomkin ; arranged by Eric Banks. — London : Affiliated Music, 1973. — 4to.
Cornet conductor & 25 parts. — With several copies of various parts.
£1.00

(B74-50312)

WMK/DW/LF — Arrangements. Songs. Christmas
Pierpont, J
Jingle bells : traditional / [or rather by J Pierpont] ; arranged for brass band by Edrich Siebert. — London : Keith Prowse, 1974. — obl. 8vo.
B flat cornet conductor & 26 parts - With several copies of various parts.
Unpriced

(B74-51361)

WMP — SOLO INSTRUMENT (S) & BRASS BAND
WMPWR — Cornet & brass band
Newsome, Roy
Concorde : cornet solo [and brass band] / [by] Roy Newsome. — London : Studio Music, 1974. — 4to.
Conductor & 24 parts - Various parts are in duplicate.
Unpriced

(B74-51362)

WMPWRNU — Two cornets & brass band
Heath, Reginald
Pastorale and allegro : B flat cornet duet and brass band / by Reginald Heath. — London : R. Smith, 1974. — 8vo.
Conductor & 25 parts. — Various parts are in duplicate.
Unpriced

(B74-50313)

WMPWUN — Trombone ensemble & brass band
Binge, Ronald
Trombonioso : for trombones and band / by Ronald Binge. — London : R. Smith, 1974. — 8vo.
Duration 3 min - With several copies of various parts.
Unpriced

(B74-51363)

WN — BRASS ENSEMBLE
WNM — Nonets
Nystedt, Knut
Pia memoria : requiem for nine brass instruments [and optional chimes]. Op.65 / by Knut Nystedt. — New York ; London : Associated Music Publishers, 1973. — 4to.
Score (28p.) & 10 parts. — Duration 16 min.
£4.20

(B74-50827)

WNRG — Quintets. Suites
Lanchberry, John
Three girls for five brass : a suite for brass quintet / by John Lanchberry. — Sevenoaks : Novello, 1974. — 17p ; 4to.
Duration 5 min.
£0.75

(B74-50828)

Lazarof, Henri
Partita for brass quintet and tape / by Henri Lazarof. — New York ; London : Associated Music, 1973. — 19p ; 8vo.
Duration 12 min.
£1.40

(B74-50829)

WNSK/AH/AY — Arrangements. Dances. Collections
Burgon, Geoffrey
Four Elizabethan dance / arranged for brass quartet by Geoffrey Burgon. — New York : Galaxy ; London : Stainer and Bell, 1974. — 4to.
Score (5p.) & 5 parts.
Unpriced

(B74-50830)

WPM — UNACCOMPANIED BRASS INSTRUMENT
WPMJ — Miscellaneous works
Lehmann, Hans Ulrich
Monodie : für ein Blasinstrument (1970) / von Hans Ulrich Lehmann. — Mainz ; London : Ars Viva, 1973. — 5p(3 fold) ; 4to.
£1.44

(B74-50314)

WRN — CORNET ENSEMBLE
WRNTQ — Two cornets & piano
Heath, Reginald
Pastorale and allegro : B flat cornet duet / by Reginald Heath. — London : R. Smith, 1974. — 4to.
Unpriced

(B74-50315)

WRP — CORNET & PIANO
WRPJ — Miscellaneous works
Simon, Frank
Zillertal : for B flat cornet or trumpet with piano accompaniment / [by] Frank Simon. — Miami : Rubank ; [London] : [Novello], 1974. — 4to.
Score (7p.) & part.
Unpriced
Also classified at WSPJ

(B74-51364)

WS — TRUMPET
WS/AC — Tutors
Kaderabek, Frank
Let's play trumpet / [by] Frank Kaderabek. — New York ; [London] : Experience Music : Chappell, 1974. — 53p ; 4to.
Unpriced

(B74-51365)

WS/AF — Exercises
Burrell, Howard
Studies and exercises for unaccompanied trumpet / by Howard Burrell. — London : Oxford University Press, 1974. — 16p ; 4to.
ISBN 0-19-355758-4 : £0.80

(B74-50831)

WSM — TRUMPET BAND
WSME — Sonatas
Biber, Heinrich Ignaz Franz
[Sonata for eight trumpets, timpani & basso continuo in C major, 'Scti Polycarpi']. Sonata 'Scti Polycarpi' : for 8 trumpets, timpani and basso continuo / [by] H.I.F. Biber ; [edited by] Robert Minter. — London : Musica rara, 1974. — 4to.
Score & 10 parts.
Unpriced

(B74-50832)

WSN — TRUMPET ENSEMBLE
WSNU — Duets
Láng, István
Duo for trumpets in C / by István Láng. — London : Boosey and Hawkes, 1973. — 5p ; 4to.
£0.60

(B74-50316)

WSP — TRUMPET & PIANO
WSPF — Concertos
Genzmer, Harald
[Duo concertante for trumpet & piano]. Konzertantes Duo für Trompete in B (oder C) und Klavier / [von] Harald Genzmer. — Frankfurt : Litolff ; London : Peters, 1974. — 4to.
Score (39p.) & part.
£5.00

(B74-51366)

WSPJ — Miscellaneous works
Hanmer, Ronald
Three sketches : for trumpet or cornet and piano / by Ronald Hanmer. — Ampleforth : Emerson Edition, 1974. — 4to.
Score (8p.) & part.
£0.50

(B74-50833)

Jacob, Gordon
Four little pieces : cornet or trumpet and piano / [by] Gordon Jacob. — Ampleforth : Emerson Edition, 1974. — 4to.
Score (7p.) & part.
Unpriced

(B74-50834)

Simon, Frank
Zillertal : for B flat cornet or trumpet with piano
accompaniment / [by] Frank Simon. — Miami : Rubank ;
[London] : [Novello], 1974. — 4to.
Score (7p.) & part.
Unpriced
Primary classification WRPJ

Telemann, Georg Philipp
[Petite musique de chambre. Partita 1. *selections]*. Suite no.2 /
arranged for trumpet in B flat and piano from the music of G.P.
Telemann by Peter Wastall and Derek Hyde. — London : Boosey
and Hawkes, 1974. — 4to.
Score (9p.) & part.
£0.65

(B74-50835)

Telemann, Georg Philipp
[Petite musique de chambre. Partitas 4, 5. *selections]*. Suite no.1 :
arranged for trumpet in B flat and piano from the music of G.P.
Telemann / by Peter Wastell and Derek Hyde. — London :
Boosey and Hawkes, 1974. — 4to.
Score (8p.) & part.
£0.65

(B74-50836)

WSPK/AAY — Arrangements. Collections
Barsham, Eve
Ten trumpet tunes, with accompaniment / arranged by Eve
Garsham. — London : Oxford University Press, 1974. — 4to.
Score (14p.) & part.
ISBN 0-19-355322-8 : £0.75

(B74-50837)

WSPK/AG — Arrangements. Suites
Clarke, Jeremiah
[Selections: arr]. Suite de Clarke / arranged for trumpet and piano
by Nigel Davison. — Sevenoaks : Novello, 1974. — 4to.
Score (14p.) & part. — Suite de Clarke is found in a set of part-books for
wind instruments in the British Museum (Add. Mss.30839 and 39565-7)
which can be dated about 1700 and which may have been compiled by
James Paisible.
£0.60

(B74-51367)

WSPK/DH — Arrangements. Motets, Anthems, Hymns, etc
Handel, George Frideric
[Messiah. The trumpet shall sound: arr]. The trumpet shall
sound / [by] Handel ; arranged for trumpet in D and piano by
Philip Cranmer. — [London] : Associated Board of the Royal
Schools of Music, 1974. — 4to.
Score (8p.) & part.
£0.15

(B74-51368)

WSPK/LE — Arrangements. Sonatas
Grossi, Andrea
[Sonata for trumpet, string quartet & basso continuo in D major.
Op.3, no.11: arr]. Sonata à 5. Op.3, no.11 : for trumpet and
strings / [by] Andrea Grossi ; trumpet and piano reduction, ed.
R.P. Block. — London : Musica rara, 1973. — 4to.
Score (8p.) & 3 parts.
Unpriced

(B74-50838)

Grossi, Andrea
[Sonata for trumpet, string quartet & basso continuo in D major.
Op.3, no.12: arr]. Sonata à 5. Op.3, no.12 : for trumpet and
strings / [by] Andrea Grossi ; trumpet and piano reduction, ed.
R.P. Block. — London : Musica rara, 1973. — 4to.
Score (8p.) & 3 parts.
Unpriced

(B74-50839)

Torelli, Giuseppe
[Sonata for trumpet, string trio & basso continuo in D major. G.1:
arr]. Sonata for trumpet, strings and continuo in D. G.1 / [by]
Giuseppe Torelli ; edited and arranged by E.H. Tarr, trumpet and
piano reduction by R.P. Bolck. — London : Musica rara, 1973. —
4to.
Score (8p.) & 2 parts.
Unpriced

(B74-50840)

Torelli, Giuseppe
[Sonata for trumpet, string trio & basso continuo in D major. G.2:
arr]. Sonata for trumpet, strings and continuo in D. G.2 / [by]
Giuseppe Torelli ; edited and arranged by E.H. Tarr, trumpet and
piano reduction by R.P. Block. — London : Musica rara, 1974. —
4to.
Score (7p.) & 2 parts.
Unpriced

(B74-50841)

WSPK/LE — Arrangements. Symphonies
Mancini, Francesco
[Idaspe. Sinfonia: arr]. Sinfonia to 'Hydaspes' : for trumpet, strings
and basso continuo / [by] Francesco Mancini ; trumpet and piano
reduction, edited by R.L. Minter. — London : Musica rara, 1974.
— 4to.
Score (4p.) & 2 parts.
Unpriced

(B74-50842)

WSPK/LE — Symphonies
Stradella, Alessandro
[Il Barcheggio. Sinfonia: arr]. Sinfonia to the serenata 'Il
Barcheggio' : for trumpet, strings and basso continuo / [by]
Alessandro Stradella ; trumpet and piano reduction [edited by]
Robert Paul Block. — London : Musica rara.
Score (8p.) & 3 parts.
Part 1. — 1973. — 4to.
Unpriced

(B74-50843)

WSPLR — TRUMPET & PIANO
WSPLRK/AAY — Trumpet & organ. Arrangements. Collections
Cooper, Barry
Six voluntaries for trumpet and organ / transcribed, edited and
arranged by Barry Cooper. — London : Musica rara, 1974. —
4to.
Score (28p.) & 2 parts. — Contents: [Works by] Croft, Walond, Stubley,
Alcock, Handel, Dupuis.
Unpriced

(B74-50844)

WSPM — UNACCOMPANIED TRUMPET
WSPMJ — Miscellaneous works
Burrell, Howard
Five concert studies : for unaccompanied trumpet / [by] Howard
Burrell. — London : Oxford University Press, 1974. — 5p ; 4to.
ISBN 0-19-355759-2 : £0.60

(B74-51369)

WTN — HORN ENSEMBLE
WTNTQK/LFL — Two horns & piano. Arrangements. Concertinos
Kuhlau, Friedrich
[Concertino for two horns in F major. Op.45: arr]. Concertino for
2 horns and orchestra. Op.45 / [by] Frederic Kuhlau; ed. [and
arranged for two horns and piano] by William Blackwell and R.P.
Block. — London : Musica rara, 1974. — 4to.
Score (29p.) & 2 parts.
Unpriced

(B74-50845)

WTNU/X — Duets. Canons
Heiden, Bernhard
Five canon for two horns / by Bernhard Heiden. — New York ;
London : Associated Music, 1972. — 8p ; 4to.
£1.50

(B74-50317)

WTP — HORN & PIANO
WTP/W — Rondos
Ries, Ferdinand
[Introduction and rondo for horn & piano in E flat major. Op.113,
no.2]. Introduction and rondo for horn and piano. Opus 113,
no.2 / [by] Ferdinand Ries ; edited by Georg Meerwein. —
London : Musica rara, 1973. — 4to.
Score (18p.) & part.
Unpriced

(B74-50846)

WTPJ — Miscellaneous works
Hardy, Mabel
Moody horn : for horn and piano / by Mabel Hardy. — London :
Imperial Music, 1974. — 4to.
Score (4p.) & part.
£0.40

(B74-50847)

Head, Michael
Scherzo : for horn or bassoon (or violoncello) and piano / by
Michael Head. — London : Boosey and Hawkes, 1974. — 4to.
Score (5p.) & 2 parts.
£0.60
Also classified at SRPJ

(B74-50848)

Strauss, Richard
[Andante for horn & piano in C major. Op. posth]. Andante für
Horn und Klavier. Op. posth / von Richard Strauss. — London :
Boosey and Hawkes, 1973. — 4to.
Score (5p.) & part.
£0.65

(B74-50318)

WTPK/LF — Arrangements. Concertos
Heiden, Bernhard
[Concerto for horn: arr]. Concerto for horn and orchestra / by
Bernhard Heiden ; reduction for horn and piano by David
Wooldridge. — New York ; London : Associated Music, 1972. —
4to.
Score (24p.) & part.
Unpriced
(B74-50319)

Patterson, Paul
[Concerto for horn: arr]. Horn concerto / by Paul Patterson;
reduction for horn and piano. — London : Weinberger, 1974. —
4to.
Score (41p.) & part. — Duration 20 min.
Unpriced
(B74-50849)

WTZ — BARITONE
WTZPJ — Miscellaneous works
Simon, Frank
Zillertal : for baritone with piano accompaniment / [by] Frank
Simon. — Miami : Rubank ; [London] : [Novello], 1974. — 4to.
Score (7p.) & part.
Unpriced
(B74-51370)

WUN — TROMBONE ENSEMBLE
WUNS — Quartets
Jarre, Maurice
[Dr Zhivago. *Somewhere my love: arr*]. Somewhere by love / by
Maurice Jarre ; arranged for quartet, 4 tenor trombones (or any 4
B flat instruments) by Edrich Siebert. — London : Francis, Day
and Hunter, 1974. — obl 8vo.
Score (2p.) & 4 parts.
£0.25
(B74-50320)

WUP — TROMBONE & PIANO
WUPK/AAY — Arrangements. Collections
Richardson, Norman
Six classical solos / arranged for trombone and piano by Norman
Richardson. — London : Boosey and Hawkes, 1974. — 4to.
Score (24p.) & part.
Unpriced
(B74-51371)

WVN — TUBA ENSEMBLE
WVNU — Duets
Wekselbaltt, Herbert
First solos for the tuba player / selected and arranged for tuba
and piano (including seven duets for two tubas) by Herbert
Wekselblatt. — New York ; London : Schirmer, 1972. — 4to.
Score (36p.) & part.
£1.05
Primary classification WVPK/AAY
(B74-50321)

WVP — TUBA & PIANO
WVPK/AAY — Arrangements. Collections
Wekselbaltt, Herbert
First solos for the tuba player / selected and arranged for tuba
and piano (including seven duets for two tubas) by Herbert
Wekselblatt. — New York ; London : Schirmer, 1972. — 4to.
Score (36p.) & part.
£1.05
Also classified at WVNU
(B74-50321)

WVPM — UNACCOMPANIED TUBA
WVPMJ — Miscellaneous works
Adler, Samuel
Canto VII : tuba solo / by Samuel Adler. — New York ;
[London] : Boosey and Hawkes, 1974. — 11p ; 4to.
£1.00
(B74-50850)

Bamert, Matthias
Incon-sequenza : for one tuba-player / by Matthias Bamert. —
New York ; London : Schirmer, 1973. — 12p ; obl. 8vo.
Facsimile of the composer's manuscript.
£0.70
(B74-50851)

Muczynski, Robert
Impromptus. Op.32 : for solo tuba / by Robert Muczynski. —
New York ; London : Schirmer, 1973. — 6p ; 4to.
£0.95
(B74-50852)

WWP — EUPHONIUM & PIANO
WWP/T — Variations
Newsome, Roy
[Variations for euphonium & piano, 'The mountains of Mourne'].
The mountains of Mourne : variations for euphonium and piano
on the theme by Houston Collison (sic) / by Roy Newsome. —
London : Keith Prowse, 1974. — 4to.
Score (10p.) & part.
£0.75
(B74-50853)

WX — BASS TUBA
WXPJ — Bass tuba & piano. Miscellaneous works
Simon, Frank
Zillertal : for E flat or BB flat bass with piano accompaniment /
[by] Frank Simon. — Miami : Rubank ; [London] : [Novello],
1974. — 4to.
Score (7p.) & part.
Unpriced
(B74-51372)

X — PERCUSSION INSTRUMENTS
X/NM — Rhythm
Bobbio, Reddy
Le Guide du rythme : guide pratique des rythmiques classiques et
moderns / [par] Reddy Bobbio. — Paris ; [London] : Chappell,
1974. — viii,48p ; 8vo.
Unpriced
(B74-51373)

XHX/DZ/AF — Jazz. Improvisation. Exercises
Combe, Stuff
Anleitung zur Improvisation für Schlagzeug / von Stuff Combe ;
unter Mitarbeit von Rudi Sehring. — Mainz ; London : Schott,
1973. — 31p ; 8vo.
£1.56
(B74-50322)

XM — PERCUSSION BAND
XMJ — Miscellaneous works
Tomlinson, Geoffrey
Concourse : for percussion and other instruments / by Geoffrey
Tomlinson. — London : Boosey and Hawkes, 1973. — 4to.
Score (8p.) & 7 parts.
£1.20
(B74-50323)

XN — PERCUSSION ENSEMBLE
Lacerda, Oswaldo
Three Brazilian miniatures for percussion / by Oswaldo Lacerda.
— Mainz ; London : Schott, 1974. — 4to.
Score (15p.) & 4 parts.
£2.40
(B74-50324)

XNS — Quartets
Fink, Siegfried
12 easy studies for percussion quartet / by Siegfried Fink. —
Hamburg ; London : Simrock, 1974. — 4to.
Score (28p.) & 4 parts.
Unpriced
(B74-50325)

Stahmer, Klaus
Patterns : for percussion instruments (four or more) / [by] Klaus
Stahmer. — Mainz ; London : Schott, 1974. — 4to.
Score (12p.) & 4 parts.
£2.90
(B74-51374)

XQ — DRUM
XQ/AF — Exercises
Moisy, Heinz von
Advanced technique for the drumset / by Heinz von Moisy. —
Hamburg ; London : Simrock, 1974. — 24p ; 4to.
Unpriced
(B74-50854)

XS — BELLS
XSQMK/CB/AY — Handbell band. Arrangements. Vocal music.
Collections
Bedford, Donald A
Carol ringing and more / arranged by Donald A. and Philip
Bedford. — Chelmsford : Handbell Ringers of Great Britain,
1974. — 42p ; obl.4to.
Unpriced
(B74-51375)

XSQNK/DW/AY — Hand bell ensemble. Arrangements. Songs, etc.
Collections
Hannon, James J
50 handbell tunes / arranged by James J. Hannon. — Oxford :
Hannon, 1973. — 7p,ff 8-61 ; fol.
Pages 6, 7 and folios 8-61 are printed on one side of the leaf only.
ISBN 0-904233-00-6 : £2.70
(B74-50326)

XSR — Church bells
  Burton, Shirley
    Table for starting courses of Stedman Cinques in the Tittums / by
    Shirley Burton. — Tewkesbury (c/o 'Monsal', Bredon,
    Tewkesbury, Glos. GL20 7LY) : Central Council of Church Bell
    Ringers, Education Committee, 1974. — 16 leaves : fol. —
    (Central Council of Church Bell Ringers. Education Committee.
    Publications ; no.1)
    Campanological score. — In typescript.
    Unpriced
                                                           (B74-50855)

  Central Council of Church Bell Ringers
    Ten & twelve bell compositions / issued under the authority of
    the [Central] Council [of Church Bell Ringers]. — Tewkesbury
    (c/o 'Monsal', Bredon, Tewkesbury, Glos. GL20 7LY) : The
    Council, 1972. — [3],20p ; 8vo.
    Campanological score.
    Unpriced
                                                           (B74-50856)

  Chaddock, Norman
    Conducting Grandsire Triples / by Norman Chaddock. —
    Tewkesbury (c/o 'Monsal', Bredon, Tewkesbury, Glos. GL20
    7LY) : Central Council of Church Bell Ringers, Education
    Committee, 1974. — 4 leaves ; fol. — (Central Council of Church
    Bell Ringers. Education Committee. Publications ; no.5)
    Campanological score. — In typescript.
    Unpriced
                                                           (B74-50857)

  Chant, Harold
    Elementary method splicing / by Harold Chant. — Tewkesbury
    (c/o 'Monsal', Bredon, Tewkesbury, Glos. GL20 7LY) : Central
    Council of Church Bell Ringers, Education Committee, 1974. — 5
    leaves ; fol. — (Central Council of Church Bell Ringers.
    Publications ; no.2)
    Campanological score. — In typescript.
    Unpriced
                                                           (B74-50858)

  Chant, Harold
    Proof of Plain Bob Major / by Harold Chant. — Tewkesbury (c/o
    'Monsal', Bredon, Tewkesbury, Glos. GL20 7LY) : Central
    Council of Church Bell Ringers, Education Committee, 1974. —
    5p ; 4to. — (Central Council of Church Bell Ringers. Education
    Committee. Publications ; no.3)
    Campanological score. — typescript.
    Unpriced
                                                           (B74-50859)

XTQSP — MARIMBA & PIANO
XTQSPLRK — Marimba & organ. Arrangements
  Creston, Paul
    [Concertino for marimba. Op.21. *Second movement: arr*].
    Meditation : for marimba and organ / by Paul Creston ; second
    movement of concertino arranged by the composer. — New
    York ; London : Schirmer, 1972. — 4to.
    Score (11p.) & part.
    Unpriced
                                                           (B74-50327)

XTQSPLXTRTK/AAY — Vibraphone & marimba. Arrangements.
                  Collections
  Fink, Siegfried
    Mallet for classic : compositions by old masters / edited and
    arranged for marimba and vibraphone by Siegfried Fink. —
    Hamburg ; London : Simrock, 1973. — 28p ; 4to.
    Unpriced
                                                           (B74-50328)

XTQTPM — UNACCOMPANIED VIBRAPHONE
XTQTPMK/AAY — Arrangements. Collections
  Finkel, Ian
    Solos for the vibraphone player / selected and edited by Ian
    Finkel. — New York ; London : Schirmer, 1974. — 35p ; 4to.
    Unpriced
                                                           (B74-50861)

COMPOSER AND TITLE INDEX

2 easy fanfares for woodwind trio, flute, oboe, clarinet in B flat. (Antoni, Thomas). *Camera Music. Unpriced* VNTGN (B74-50269)

2 two part inventions. (Bach, Johann Sebastian). *Camera Music. Unpriced* VNTK (B74-50270)

3 encores : for woodwind trio, flute, oboe, clarinet in B flat. (Antoni, Thomas). *167 Ewell Rd, Surbiton, Surrey : Camera Music. Unpriced* VNT (B74-51313)

3 fables : piano solo. (Taylor, Colin). Revised ed. *Boosey and Hawkes. £0.45* QPJ (B74-50186)

3 Motets for Christmas. I sing of a maiden. I sing of a maiden. (Le Fleming, Christopher). *Roberton. Unpriced* EZDH/LF (B74-50948)

5 divertimento for accordion. (Wright, Francis). *Charnwood Music. Unpriced* RSPMJ (B74-51212)

12 easy duets for winds
Volume 3: For trombones, baritones, tubas (and cellos and basses ad lib). (Mozart, Wolfgang Amadeus). *Schirmer. Unpriced* UNUK (B74-50742)

12 easy studies for percussion quartet. (Fink, Siegfried). *Simrock. Unpriced* XNS (B74-50325)

12 simple studies for guitar. (Mayes, Jerry). *Charnwood Music. Unpriced* TS/AF (B74-51271)

15 two-part inventions, nos 1, 4. S.772 & 775: arr. 2 two part inventions. (Bach, Johann Sebastian). *Camera Music. Unpriced* VNTK (B74-50270)

17 duets on nursery tunes. (Kasschau, Howard). *Schirmer. £0.50* QNVK/DW/GK/AY (B74-50165)

24 Capricen in Etüdenform für Bratsche allein in den 24 Tonarten. (Rode, Pierre). *Schott. £2.40* SQPMK (B74-50242)

24 Caprices in Etüdenform für Violine allein in den 24 Tonarten. (Rode, Pierre). *Schott. £2.40* SPMJ (B74-50238)

50 handbell tunes. (Hannon, James J). *Hannon. £2.70* XSQNK/DW/AY (B74-50326) ISBN 0-904233-00-6

70 girls 70 : Selections. 70 girls 70. (Kander, John). *Valando. Unpriced* KDW (B74-51049)

70 girls 70. (Kander, John). *Valando. Unpriced* KDW (B74-51049)

77 newe ausserlesne liebliche zierliche Polnischer und Teutscher Art Tantze. Selections. Fifteen German and Polish dances, 1601 : for five instruments. (Demantius, Johann Christoph). *London Pro Musica. Unpriced* LNRH (B74-51081)

100 score-reading exercises. (Wilkinson, Philip George). *Novello. £1.50* LNT (B74-51083)

150 American folk songs to sing, read and play. (Erdei, Peter). *Boosey and Hawkes. £3.75* JEZDW/G/AYT (B74-50088)

'1812' overture: arr. '1812' overture : for school orchestra. (Tchaikovsky, Peter). *Bosworth. £2.10* MK (B74-50491)

'1812' overture : for school orchestra. (Tchaikovsky, Peter). *Bosworth. £2.10* MK (B74-50491)

A carol for Mary : SATB unacc. (Whitter, Mark). *Oxford University Press. £0.05* EZDP/LF (B74-50050) ISBN 0-19-343043-6

Abbreviations : piano solo. (Cines, Eugene). *Boosey and Hawkes. Unpriced* QPJ (B74-50586)

Abraham, Gerald.
Mussorgsky. (Calvocoressi, Michael Dimitri). Revised ed. *Dent. £2.75* BMU (B74-13105) ISBN 0-460-03152-x
The tradition of western music. *Oxford University Press. £1.00* A (B74-22802) ISBN 0-19-316324-1

Activity in the primary school. Hart, Muriel. Music. *Heinemann Educational. £0.80* A(VG) (B74-15369) ISBN 0-435-80606-8

Adagio for a musical clock and Rondo a capriccio 'Rage over the lost groschen'. (Beethoven, Ludwig van). *Galaxy : Galliard. Unpriced* QNUK (B74-51139)

Adams, Pamela. There was an old lady who swallowed a fly. *Restrop Manor, Purton, Wilts. : Child's Play (International) Ltd. £1.00* A/G(YSW) (B74-05270) ISBN 0-85953-021-3

Adam's apple : SATB. (Habash, John Mitri). *Robbins. Unpriced* DW (B74-50919)

Adam's apple : SSA. (Habash, John Mitri). *Robbins. Unpriced* FDW (B74-50991)

Adieu Madras, adieu foulards. (Lully, Jean Baptiste). *Chappell. Unpriced* TMK/DW (B74-50695)

Adler, Samuel.
Aleynu l'shabench : a new Friday evening service, cantor solo with mixed chorus, SATB and organ, commissioned by the Anshe Emet Synagogue, Chicago, Illinois, on the occasion of the hundredth jubilee year (1873-1973)
5: Ma toru. *Ethnic Music : Phoenix. Unpriced* DGU (B74-50888)
Canto VII : tuba solo. *Boosey and Hawkes. £1.00* WVPMJ (B74-50850)
40 studies for piano
... *Press. Unpriced* Q/AF (B74-51126)
Gradus : 40 studies for piano : by Samuel Adler
Book 1. *Oxford University Press. Unpriced* Q/AF (B74-51125)
Quartet for strings, no.5. String quartet, no.5. *Boosey and Hawkes. £2.50* RXNS (B74-51225)
Sonata for violin & piano, no.3. Third sonata for violin and piano, (in six episodes). *Boosey and Hawkes. £2.50* SPE (B74-50660)
Two songs for three years. *Boosey and Hawkes. Unpriced* KDW (B74-51045)

L'Union. Op. 48: arr. L'Union. Op.48 : paraphrase de concert sur les airs nationaux. (Gottschalk, Louis Moreau). *Schirmer. £1.40* QNUK (B74-50562)

L'Union. Op. 48 : paraphrase de concert sur les airs nationaux. (Gottschalk, Louis Moreau). *Schirmer. Unpriced* UMPQ (B74-50734)

Adoramus te = We adore thee : motet for four-part chorus of mixed voices a cappella. (Perti, Giacomo Antonio). *Schirmer. Unpriced* EZDJ (B74-50951)

Adoramus te = We adore thee : SATB a cappella. (Benjamin, Thomas). *Associated Music. Unpriced* EZDJ (B74-50042)

Adorno, Theodor Wiesengrund. Philosophy of modern music. *Sheed and Ward. £4.50* BSET (B74-09866) ISBN 0-7220-7339-9

Adriaansz, Willem. The Kumiuta and Danmono traditions of Japanese koto music. *University of California Press. £9.50* BZHPAL (B74-14313) ISBN 0-520-01785-4

Advanced technique for the drumset. (Moisy, Heinz von). *Simrock. Unpriced* XQ/AF (B74-50854)

Adventurous night suite : military band. (Osterling, Eric). *Warner : Blossom. Unpriced* UMMG (B74-50723)

African Sanctus: arr. The Lord's Prayer. (Fanshawe, David). *Chappell. Unpriced* KDTF (B74-51044)

Ager, Laurence. The rising again : a calypso for voices and piano. *Ashdown. £0.12* JFDH/LL (B74-50090)

'Air', My heart ever faithful. (Bach, Johann Sebastian). *Cramer. £0.21* RK/DH (B74-51202)

Airs valaques. Op.10 : fantasie for flute with piano accompaniment. (Doppler, Albrecht Franz). *Wye Music : Emerson. Unpriced* VRPJ (B74-51318)

Albeniz, Isaac.
Suite espagnole. Sevilla. Granada Serenata : für Gitarre. *Schott. £0.72* TSPMK (B74-50257)
Suite espagnole. *Sevilla.* Sevilla a Sevillanas. *Schott. £0.96* TSPMK (B74-50258)

Albeniz, Mateo. Sonata for piano in D major: arr. Sonata in D. *British and Continental Music. Unpriced* TSPMK/AE (B74-50260)

Albinoni, Tommaso.
Concerto for oboe, string quartet & basso continuo in C major. Op.9, no.5. Concerto à 5 for oboe strings and continuo. Op.9, no.5. *Musica rara. Unpriced* NUTNQF (B74-50527)
Concerto for oboe, string quartet & basso continuo in C major. Op.9, no.5: arr. Concerto à 5 for oboe strings and continuo. Op.9, no.5. *Musica rara. Unpriced* VTPK/LF (B74-50786)
Concerto for violin & string orchestra in A major: arr. Konzert, A-Dur für Violine, Streichorchester und Basso continuo. *Schott. £2.03* SPK/LF (B74-51247)
Concerto for violin and string orchestra in A major. Giazotto 116. Konzert, A-Dur, für Violine, Streichorchester und Basso continuo. *Schott. £4.35* RXMPSF (B74-51219)
Sonata a tre in G minor. Adagio: arr. Adagio. *Ricordi. £1.25* WMK (B74-51356)

Alcotts. (Ives, Charles). *Associated Music. Unpriced* UMK (B74-50266)

Aldine paperbacks. Dvořák. (Robertson, Alec). Revised ed. *Dent. £3.00* BDX(N) (B74-27797) ISBN 0-460-03116-3

Aldridge, Maisie.
Easy Russian piano music
Book 1. *Oxford University Press. £0.50* QP/AYM (B74-50569) ISBN 0-19-372131-7
Book 2. *Oxford University Press. £0.60* QP/AYM (B74-50570) ISBN 0-19-372132-5

Alemán, Mateo. Nocturne, Op.54 : song for medium voice and piano. (Rubbra, Edmund). *Lengnick. £0.30* KFVDW (B74-50487)

Aleynu l'shabench : a new Friday evening service, cantor solo with mixed chorus, SATB and organ, commissioned by the Anshe Emet Synagogue, Chicago, Illinois, on the occasion of the hundredth jubilee year (1873-1973)
1: Adon olam. *Ethnic Music : Phoenix. Unpriced* DGU (B74-50884)
2: Ahavat olam. *Ethnic Music : Phoenix. Unpriced* DGU (B74-50885)
3: Hashkivenu. *Ethnic Music : Phoenix. Unpriced* DGU (B74-50886)
4: Kiddush l'shabat. *Ethnic Music : Phoenix. Unpriced* DGU (B74-50887)
5: Ma toru. *Ethnic Music : Phoenix. Unpriced* DGU (B74-50888)
6: May the words. *Ethnic Music : Phoenix. Unpriced* DGU (B74-50889)
7: Psalm 150. *Ethnic Music : Phoenix. Unpriced* DGU (B74-50890)
8: Rozo d'shabos. *Ethnic Music : Phoenix. Unpriced* DGU (B74-50891)
9: Shiru ladonai shir chadash. *Ethnic Music : Phoenix. Unpriced* DGU (B74-50892)
10: Veshomru. *Ethnic Music : Phoenix. Unpriced* DGU (B74-50893)

Alice in Wonderland : fantasy for brass band. (Hanmer, Ronald). *Studio Music. Unpriced* WMJ (B74-50309)

Allanbrook, Douglas.
Psalm 131 : SATB and organ. *Boosey and Hawkes. Unpriced* DR (B74-50912)
Twelve preludes for all seasons : piano solo. *Boosey and Hawkes. £2.50* QPJ (B74-51160)

Allcock, Stephen. Three almanack verses : SATB. *Boosey and Hawkes. Unpriced* EZDW (B74-50973)

Alleluia and chorale : SATB with piano, four-hands. (Forcucci, Samuel L). *Schirmer. Unpriced* DH/LF (B74-50016)

Alleluya psallat = Sing alleluya. Op. 58 : SATB. (Mathias, William). *Oxford University Press. £0.15* DH (B74-50013) ISBN 0-19-350339-5

Allen, Ed Heron-. *See* Heron-Allen, Ed.

Allen, Kenneth. The rising again : a calypso for voices and piano. (Ager, Laurence). *Ashdown. £0.12* JFDH/LL (B74-50090)

Allen, Peter. Feed us now, O Son of God: arr. Feed us now, O Son of God. *Galaxy : Galliard. Unpriced* EZDH (B74-50386)

Alma redemptoris mater = Loving Mother of our Saviour : motet for four-part chorus of mixed voices a cappella. (Palestrina, Giovanni Pierluigi da). *Schirmer. Unpriced* EZDJ (B74-50950)

Almighty Father : chorale. (Bernstein, Leonard). *Amberson : Schirmer. Unpriced* GEZDH (B74-50434)

Almighty Father : chorale from 'Mass'. (Bernstein, Leonard). *Amberson : Schirmer. £5.60(full score and parts)(extra score £0.95, extra parts £0.30 each)* UMK (B74-50716)

Also hat Gott die Welt geliebt. S.68. Mein glaubiges Herz: arr. 'Air', My heart ever faithful. (Bach, Johann Sebastian). *Cramer. £0.21* RK/DH (B74-51202)

Alt, Hansi.
Five summer Sundays : for the piano. *Oxford University Press. Unpriced* QPJ (B74-51161)
Red clouds : 12 folk songs from Austria, Switzerland and Tirol, for violin (or recorder or flute) and piano, with optional cello. *Oxford University Press. Unpriced* SPK/DW/G/AYEM (B74-51246)

Alte Kameraden: arr. Old comrades : quick march. (Teike, Carl). *Boosey and Hawkes. £0.95* UMMK/AGM (B74-50732)

Alwyn, William.
Mirages : a song cycle for baritone and piano. *Lengnick. £1.25* KGNDW (B74-50489)
Symphony no.5, 'Hydriotaphia'. *Lengnick. £4.00* MME (B74-50133)

Am I too loud? : memoirs of an accompanist. (Moore, Gerald, *b.1899*). *Penguin. £0.60* AQ/ED(P) (B74-21540) ISBN 0-14-002480-8

Amahl and the night visitors. *Selections: arr.* Introduction, march and shepherd's dance. (Menotti, Gian Carlo). *Schirmer. Unpriced* UMK (B74-50718)

Amazin' grace : old negro hymn tune. (Whalum, Wendell). *Roberton. £0.13* DM (B74-50019)

Amazing grace. (Davis, Katherine Kennicott). *Galaxy : Galliard. Unpriced* DM (B74-50907)

Ameln, Konrad. Biblische Motetten : für das Kirchenjahr
Band 2: Darstellung des Herrn bis Trinitas. *Bärenreiter. Unpriced* EZDH/AYE (B74-50392)

America sings. (Menten, Dale). *Unichappell : Chappell. Unpriced* DW (B74-50360)

America sings: arr. America sings. (Menten, Dale). *Unichappell : Chappell. Unpriced* DW (B74-50360)

American Folklore Society. The marble threshing floor : a collection of Greek folksongs. (Frye, Ellen). *University of Texas Press for the American Folklore Society. £5.85* JEZDW/G/AYPE (B74-50451) ISBN 0-292-75005-6

American Musicological Society. Reprint series. Ornithoparchus, Andreas. Musice active micrologus. A compendium of musical practice. *Dover Publications : Constable. £7.00* A/M(XDS) (B74-11735) ISBN 0-486-20912-1

Ames, Delano. History of the piano. (Closson, Ernest). 2nd ed. *Elek. £3.50* AQ/B(X) (B74-09232) ISBN 0-236-17685-4

Amhrain Anna Sheumais. (Mackenzie, Anne). *Ann Mackenzie. Unpriced* JFEZDW/G/AYDLZL (B74-50094)

Ammer, Christine. Harper's dictionary of music. *28 Tavistock St., WC2E 7PN : Barnes and Noble. £1.60* A(C) (B74-09865) ISBN 0-06-463347-0

Amner, John.
O Lord, of whom I do depend : the humble suit of a sinner, SATB. *Royal School of Church Music. Unpriced* EZDK (B74-50046)
Sacred hymnes. My Lord is hence removed. *Vocal score.* My Lord is hence removed : SSATTB with tenor solo and viol accompaniment. *Oxford University Press. Unpriced* DH (B74-50343) ISBN 0-19-350326-3

And I am old to know : song. (Binkerd, Gordon). *Boosey and Hawkes. Unpriced* KDW (B74-51046)

Andaluza. (Granados, Enrique). *Schott. £1.00* VSNRQK/AH (B74-51331)

Andante from piano sonata Opus 14, no.2. (Beethoven, Ludwig van). *Novello. £0.33* TSPMK/AE (B74-50709)

Anderaos, Nelson. Tango brasileiro. 30 de maio : guitar. *Fermata de Brasil : Essex Music. Unpriced* TSPMHVR (B74-51274)

Andrix, George. Free forms : four pieces for brass trombone and strings. *Schirmer. Unpriced* RXMPWUU (B74-51223)

Angel scene. (Humperdinck, Engelbert). *Cramer. Unpriced* RK/DW (B74-50206)

Animals etcetera : unaccompanied voices, 4-part. (Rose, Gregory). *Boosey and Hawkes. £0.05* EZDW (B74-50061)

Anis, Fulaihan. Symphony no.2. *Boosey and Hawkes. Unpriced* MME (B74-51096)

Anleitung zur Improvisation für Schlagzeug. (Combe, Stuff). *Schott. £1.56* XHX/DZ/AF (B74-50322)

Antiphon : for string orchestra. (Berkeley, Lennox). *Chester. Unpriced* RXMJ (B74-51217)

Antoni, Thomas.

2 easy fanfares for woodwind trio, flute, oboe, clarinet in B flat. *Camera Music. Unpriced* VNTGN (B74-50269)

3 encores : for woodwind trio, flute, oboe, clarinet in B flat. *167 Ewell Rd, Surbiton, Surrey : Camera Music. Unpriced* VNT (B74-51313)

15 two-part inventions, nos 1, 4. S.772 & 775: arr. 2 two part inventions. (Bach, Johann Sebastian). *Camera Music. Unpriced* VNTK (B74-50270)

Apollo Contemporary Music. The new music : an introduction and general survey for the non-specialist. (Hellewell, David). *57 Lansdowne Rd, Bournemouth, Hants. BH1 1RN : Apollo Contemporary Music. £0.50* A(XM73) (B74-06501) ISBN 0-9503225-0-4

Apotheosis of this earth : for concert band. (Husa, Karel). *Associated Music. Unpriced* UMJ (B74-50714)

Applebaum, Edward. Foci for viola and piano. *Chester. Unpriced* SQPJ (B74-50240)

Applebaum, Max H. Servicing electronic organs. *Foulsham-Tab. £1.80* ARPV/BT (B74-27249) ISBN 0-7042-0108-9

Applebaum, Stan. Sound world : a collection of new keyboard experiences for the intermediate pianist and the advanced beginner. *Schroeder and Gunther. Unpriced* Q/AF (B74-51127)

Applebaum, Stanley. Folk music, Bach style : 21 two-part inventions. *Schroeder and Gunther. £0.50* QPJ (B74-50174)

Appleby, Benjamin William. The school recorder assembly book : sixteen hymn tunes and nine pieces for descant and treble recorders with pianoforte accompaniment. *Arnold. Unpriced* VSMK/AAY (B74-51328) ISBN 0-560-00382-x

Arch, Gwyn. That's the Spirit : musical play. *British and Continental. Unpriced* CN/L (B74-50333)

Argento, Dominick.

Letters from composers : for high voice and guitar. *Boosey and Hawkes. Unpriced* KFTE/TSDW (B74-51073)

To be sung upon the water : barcarolles and nocturnes for high voice, piano and clarinet (also bass clarinet). *Boosey and Hawkes. Unpriced* KFTE/VVDW (B74-50484)

Tria carmina paschalia : for women's voices (SSA) harp and guitar (or harpsichord). *Boosey and Hawkes. Unpriced* FE/TQPLTSDH (B74-51000)

Ariel : five poems of Sylvia Plath, for soprano clarinet and piano. (Rorem, Ned). *Boosey and Hawkes. £3.00* KFLE/VVPDW (B74-50115)

Arlesienne, 1st suite. Carillon: arr. Carillon. (Bizet, Georges). *Boosey and Hawkes. Score £1.50, Piano conductor £0.50, Set £2.50* MK/JM (B74-51091)

Armstrong, Mimi. Songs of fellowship. (Pulkingham, Betty Carr). *The Fishermen Inc., by arrangement with the Fountanin Trust. Unpriced* JE/TSDM/AY (B74-50087)

Arne, Thomas Augustine.

Concerto for keyboard, no.1, in C major. Allegro. Keyboard allegro. *Oxford University Press. £0.50* PWPJ (B74-51121) ISBN 0-19-372151-1

Sonata for harpsichord, no.3, in G. *Allegro.* Allegro. *Cramer. Unpriced* RK (B74-50205)

Arnold, Malcolm. Symphony no.6. Op.95. *Faber Music. Unpriced* MME (B74-50493)

Arnold Schoenberg, 1874 to 1951 - books, records and scores. (Lambeth Libraries). *Central Library, Brixton Oval, S.W.2 : Lambeth Libraries. Free* BSET(T) (B74-25103) ISBN 0-9501893-6-7

Arpino, Gerald. The clowns : a ballet. (Kay, Hershey). *Boosey and Hawkes. Unpriced* MM/HM (B74-51092)

Ars magna consoni et dissoni : for organ. (Speth, Johann). *Bärenreiter. £3.80* RJ (B74-50621)

Art of record buying : a list of recommended microgroove recordings

1974. *E.M.G. £2.60* A/FD(WT) (B74-02648) ISBN 0-900982-05-5

Art of singing : a manual. (Manén, Lucie). *38 Russell Sq., WC1B 5DA : Faber Music Ltd. £2.20* AB/EBE (B74-21538) ISBN 0-571-10009-0

Artman, Ruth.

God is alive : for SATB chorus and piano. *Warner Blossom. Unpriced* DH (B74-50344)

Well, what do you know? : SATB with piano accompaniment and optional violins, string bass and guitar. *Warner : Blossom. Unpriced* DW (B74-50917)

Artmann, H C.

Rosa mystica. Op. 40 : acht Gesänge für mittlere Singstimme und Orchester. (Einem, Gottfried von). *Boosey and Hawkes. Unpriced* KFVE/MDW (B74-50118)

Rosa mystica. Op.40. Vocal score. Rosa mystica. Op.40 : acht Gesänge für mittlere Singstimme und Orchester. (Einem, Gottfried von). *Boosey and Hawkes. £2.50* KFVDW (B74-50116)

Arts third level course : the development of instruments and their music.

Bray, Trevor. Music and society today. *Open University Press. Unpriced* A(Z) (B74-24207) ISBN 0-335-00869-0

Bray, Trevor. Twentieth century music, 1900-1945. *Open University Press. Unpriced* A(XM46) (B74-21535) ISBN 0-335-00866-6

Middleton, Richard. The rise of the symphony

2. *Open University Press. £1.70* AMME(X) (B74-18934) ISBN 0-335-00859-3

Olleson, Philip. The rise of the string quartet. *Open University Press. Unpriced* ARXNS(X) (B74-18935) ISBN 0-335-00862-3

Ratcliffe, Ronald V. From classical to romantic keyboard music. *Open University Press. Unpriced* AQ/B/E(XA1849) (B74-23499) ISBN 0-335-00864-x

Arts third level course: the development of instruments and their music.

Edwards, Owain. Baroque instrumental music

1: People, instruments and the continuo. *Open University Press. £2.20* AL(XE151) (B74-08077) ISBN 0-335-00852-6

Edwards, Owain. Baroque instrumental music

2: Suite, sonata and concerto. *Open University Press. Unpriced* AL(XE151) (B74-08078) ISBN 0-335-00853-4

Hendrie, Gerald. The Baroque organ (containing an introduction to units 1-2); and, Bach organ music. *Open University Press. £2.00* AR/B(XE151) (B74-07435) ISBN 0-335-00850-x

As the deer cries for flowing water : for four-part chorus of mixed voices with organ accompaniment. (Bernhard, Christoph). *Roberton. £0.26* DH (B74-50011)

As time goes by. (Taylor, Derek). *30 Gray's Inn Rd, WC1X 8JL : Abacus. £0.75* A/GB (B74-27796) ISBN 0-349-13381-6

Ashburnham, George. Summer rhapsody : for piano. *Ashburnham School of Music. Unpriced* QPJ (B74-51162)

Ashlund, Ulf Goran. Play together : for voice and guitar. *Oxford University Press. £0.65* KE/TSNDW/AY (B74-50482) ISBN 0-19-322212-4

Ashton, John, *b.1834.* Real sailor songs. 1st ed. reprinted. *15 Mortimer Terrace, N.W.5 : Broadsheet King. Unpriced* ADW/KC(YD) (B74-02415) ISBN 0-902617-10-9

Associated Board of the Royal Schools of Music.

Pianoforte examinations, 1975

Grade 1: Lists A and B (primary). *Associated Board of the Royal Schools of Music. £0.35* Q/AL (B74-51129)

Grade 2: Lists A and B (elementary). *Associated Board of the Royal Schools of Music. £0.35* Q/AL (B74-51130)

Grade 3: Lists A and B (transitional). *Associated Board of the Royal Schools of Music. £0.35* Q/AL (B74-51131)

Grade 4: Lists A and B (lower). *Associated Board of the Royal Schools of Music. £0.35* Q/AL (B74-51132)

Grade 5: List A (higher). *Associated Board of the Royal Schools of Music. £0.35* Q/AL (B74-51133)

Grade 5: List B (higher). *Associated Board of the Royal Schools of Music. £0.35* Q/AL (B74-51134)

Grade 6: List A (intermediate). *Associated Board of the Royal Schools of Music. £0.35* Q/AL (B74-51135)

Grade 6: List B (intermediate). *Associated Board of the Royal Schools of Music. £0.35* Q/AL (B74-51136)

Grade 7: List A (advanced). *Associated Board of the Royal Schools of Music. £0.35* Q/AL (B74-51137)

Grade 7 : List B (advanced). *Associated Board of the Royal Schools of Music. £0.35* Q/AL (B74-51138)

Violin examinations, 1975 and 1976

Grade 1: Lists A and B (primary). *Associated Board of the Royal Schools of Music. £0.35* S/AL (B74-51232)

Grade II: Lists A and B (elementary). *Associated Board of the Royal Schools of Music. £0.35* S/AL (B74-51233)

Grade III: Lists A and B (transitional). *Associated Board of the Royal Schools of Music. £0.35* S/AL (B74-51234)

Grade IV: Lists A and B (lower). *Associated Board of the Royal Schools of Music. £0.35* S/AL (B74-51235)

Grade V: Lists A and B (higher). *Associated Board of the Royal Schools of Music. £0.35* S/AL (B74-51236)

Grade VI: Lists A and B (intermediate). *Associated Board of the Royal Schools of Music. £0.40* S/AL (B74-51237)

Grade VII: Lists A and B (advanced). *Associated Board of the Royal Schools of Music. £0.40* S/AL (B74-51238)

Asterogenesis : piano. (Johnson, Robert Sherlaw). *Oxford University Press. £2.20* QPJ (B74-51173) ISBN 0-19-372990-3

Aston, Peter. Hodie Christus natus est = On this day, Christ the Lord is born : anthem for SATB and organ. *Novello. Unpriced* DH/LF (B74-50904)

Astor, Bob. Popinella : arr. Popinella. *Chappell. Unpriced* TMK (B74-51259)

Asymtotes : for flute and vibraphone. (Lazarof, Henri). *Associated Music. £7.50* VRPLXTRT (B74-50860)

Atkins, John. The Carter family. *33 Brunswick Gardens, W8 4AW : Old Time Music. £0.60* ADW/G(YT/P) (B74-12389) ISBN 0-904395-00-6

Atkinson, Condit. The house by the side of the road : mixed chorus and piano with optional percussion and string bass. *Galaxy : Galliard. Unpriced* DW (B74-50918)

Auden, Wystan Hugh. Works, songs. Selections. Selected songs of Thomas Campion. (Campion, Thomas). *David Godine : Bodley Head. £6.00* KDW (B74-50457) ISBN 0-370-10306-8

Aural training : a comprehensive approach. (Kliewer, Vernon Lee). *Prentice-Hall. £4.15* A/EF (B74-24904) ISBN 0-13-053231-2

Austin, William. Carol of the sun. *Vocal score.* Carol of the sun : for two-part or unison chorus. (Blake, Leonard). *Roberton. £0.10* FDP/LF (B74-50414)

Autumn cicada : ko-uta on four Japanese texts, for SSA, harp and 4 handbells. (Cole, Bruce). *Boosey and Hawkes. £0.10* FE/NYJNRDW (B74-50427)

Avant-garde flute : a handbook for composers and flutists. (Howell, Thomas). *University of California Press. £5.50* AVR/E/CY (B74-21542) ISBN 0-520-02305-6

Awakening : canon for equal voices. (Gersch, Paul J). *Chappell. Unpriced* DW/X (B74-50369)

Axenfeld, Edith Picht-. *See* Picht-Axenfeld, Edith.

Ayres, Reginald Barrett-. *See* Barrett-Ayres, Reginald.

Babe of Bethlehem : a carol for treble voices (with audience or additional choral participation). (Walters, Edmund). *Boosey and Hawkes. £0.10* FLDP/LF (B74-51011)

Baby's opera : a book of old rhymes with new dresses. (Crane, Walter). *Pan. £0.60* JFDW/GK/AYD (B74-51038) ISBN 0-330-24088-9

Bach, Carl Philipp Emanuel.

Concerto for flute & string orchestra in G major. Wq.169. Concerto in G major : for flute, strings and basso continuo. Wq.169. *Musica rara. Unpriced* RXMPVRF (B74-50648)

Concerto for flute & string orchestra in G major. Wq.169: arr. Concerto in G major : for flute, strings and basso continuo. Wq.169. *Musica rara. Unpriced* VRPK/LF (B74-50759)

Selections: arr. Two pieces for solo guitar : by C.P.E. Bach. *Oxford University Press. Unpriced* TSPMK (B74-51277) ISBN 0-19-355299-x

Sonata for flute in A minor. Wq.132. Sonata in A minor for flute alone. *Schirmer. £0.70* VRPME (B74-51326)

Bach, Johann Christian.

Sinfonia concertante for cello & oboe in F major. Sinfonia concertante in F major. *Eulenburg. £2.60* MPVTPLSRE (B74-50146)

Sinfonia concertante for cello & oboe in F major. Sinfonia concertante, F major for oboe, violoncello and orchestra. *Eulenburg. Unpriced* MPVTPLSRE (B74-50145)

Sonatas for keyboard. Selections: arr. Concerto in E flat major for clarinet and strings. *Boosey and Hawkes. £1.50* VVPK (B74-50803)

Symphony in G minor. Opus 6, no.6. Symphony, G minor. Op. 6, no.6. *Eulenburg. £0.80* MRE (B74-50147)

Bach, Johann Sebastian.

15 two-part inventions, nos 1, 4. S.772 & 775: arr. 2 two part inventions. *Camera Music. Unpriced* VNTK (B74-50270)

Also hat Gott die Welt geliebt. S.68. Mein glaubiges Herz: arr. 'Air', My heart ever faithful. *Cramer. £0.21* RK/DH (B74-51202)

Brandenburg concerto, no.1, in F major. S.1046. Menuetto: arr. Menuetto. *Warner : Blossom. Unpriced* MK/AHR (B74-50492)

Capriccio sopra la lontanza del suo fratello dilettissimo. S.992. Capriccio. *Schirmer. Unpriced* QPJ (B74-50583)

Concerto for violin & string orchestra in A minor. S. 1041. Konzert, A-moll, für Violine und Streichorchester. BWV 1041. *Peters. Unpriced* RXMPSF (B74-51220)

Geistliche Lieder und Schmelli's Gesangbuch und dem Notenbuch der Anna Magdalena Bach. S. 439-567. *Selections: arr.* Geistliche Lieder. *Schott. £1.45* VSNSK/DM (B74-51332)

Herz und Mund und That und Leben. S.147. Wohl mir dass ich Jesum habe: arr. Jesu, joy of man's desiring. *Oxford University Press. Unpriced* VSNQK/DM (B74-51330) ISBN 0-19-355290-6

Jesu, meine Freude. S.227. Vocal score. Jesu, priceless treasure : motet for two sopranos, alto, tenor and bass. *Schirmer. Unpriced* DH (B74-50010)

Prelude, fugue & allegro for organ in D major. S.998: arr. Prelude, fugue and allegro. BWV 998. *Oxford University Press. £0.60* TSPMK (B74-50708) ISBN 0-19-355303-1

St Matthew Passion. *Aus Liebe will mein Heiland sterben: arr.* Aria. *Schirmer. Unpriced* VRNSK/DH/LH (B74-50271)

Selections. The flute solos from the Bach cantatas, passions and oratorios. *Schirmer. £2.35* VR (B74-50745)

Siehe zu dass deine Gottesfurcht nicht Heuchelei sei : Kantate 179 (auf den 11 Sonntag nach Trinitis). *Eulenburg. £1.00* EMDE (B74-50028)

Suite for orchestra, no.2, in B minor. S. 1067: arr. Suite in B minor. *Schirmer. Unpriced* VRPK/AG (B74-51324)

Suites for cello. Nos 1-2. S: 1007-8. Two suites. *Schirmer. £1.15* VWPMK/AG (B74-50815)

Das wohltemperirte Clavier, Tl.1. Prelude and fugue, no.5. S.850. Praeludium V und Fuga V : Klavier (Cembalo). *Schott. £0.60* PWP/Y (B74-50554)

Das wohltemperirte Clavier, Tl.1. Prelude and fugue, no.6. S.851. Praeludium VI und Fuga VI : Klavier (Cembalo). *Schott. £0.60* PWP/Y (B74-50555)

Das wohltemperirte Clavier, Tl.1. Prelude and fugue, no.16. S.861. Praeludium XVI and Fuga XVI : Klavier (Cembalo). *Schott. £0.60* PWP/Y (B74-50556)

Das wohltemperirte Clavier, Tl.2. Prelude and fugue, no.2. S.871. Praeludium II and Fuga II : Klavier (Cembalo). *Schott. £0.60* PWP/Y (B74-50557)

Bachianas brasileiras, no.5. Aria (Cantilena). (Villa-Lobos, Heitor). *Associated Music. Unpriced* MMK/DW (B74-50508)

Bachianas brasileiras, no.5. Aria (Cantilena). (Villa-Lobos, Heitor). *Associated Music. Unpriced* RXMK/DW (B74-50645)

Bachianas brasileiras, no.5. Aria (Cantilena). (Villa-Lobos, Heitor). *Associated Music. Unpriced* VNK/DW (B74-50743)

Bachianas brasileiras, no.5. Aria (Cantilena). (Villa-Lobos, Heitor). *Associated Music. Unpriced* VVNK/DW (B74-50794)

Bacon, Analee. Sonatas for cello and basso continuo. Op.2. Six sonatas : for cello or double bass and piano. (Marcello, Benedetto). *Schirmer. £1.85* SRPE (B74-50681)

Badura-Skoda, Paul. Adagio and fugue for string quartet in C minor. K.546: arr. Adagio and fugue in C minor. K.546 and 426. (Mozart, Wolfgang Amadeus). *Schirmer. Unpriced* QNUK/Y (B74-50564)

Bagas, Arthur. Five string banjo : picture chords, songs, exercises, diagrams and instructions. (Shealy, Alex... *Lewis Music : Ashley-Fields. Unpri...*

(B74-50710)
Bagatelles. Opus 119 : piano solo. (Beethoven, Ludwig van). *Peters. Unpriced* QPJ (B74-50584)
Bailey, Andrew.
George Formby complete. (Formby, George). *Wise. Unpriced* KDW/AY (B74-50099)
The Strauss family. *Wise : Distributed by Music Sales Ltd. £1.50* QPK/AH (B74-50602)
Bailey, Leon. A shanty sequence : for 4-part chorus of mixed voices unaccompanied. *Roberton. £0.26* EZDW (B74-50056)
Bailey, Peter. Play time : Longman first recorder course Stage 3. (Fagan, Margo). *Longman. £0.30* VS/AC (B74-50274) ISBN 0-582-18538-6
Bainbridge, Simon. Quartet for strings (1972). String quartet (1972). *United Music. Unpriced* RXNS (B74-50655)
Baker, Julius.
Nocturne for piano, no.20, in C sharp minor. Op. posth. Nocturne (posthumous). (Chopin, Frédéric). *Schirmer. Unpriced* VRPK (B74-51322)
St Matthew Passion. *Aus Liebe will mein Heiland sterben: arr.* Aria. (Bach, Johann Sebastian). *Schirmer. Unpriced* VRNSK/DH/LH (B74-50271)
Selections. The flute solos from the Bach cantatas, passions and oratorios. (Bach, Johann Sebastian). *Schirmer. £2.35* VR (B74-50745)
Balent, Andrew.
Century celebration. Honoring America's bicentennial : for concert band. *Warner : Blossom. Unpriced* UMGM (B74-50713)
Forward! : march for elementary band. *Warner : Blossom. Unpriced* UMGM (B74-51291)
Hans Christian Andersen. The inch worm: arr. The inch worm. (Loesser, Frank). *Frank Music. Unpriced* UMMK/DW/JR (B74-51311)
Spartans of tomorrow : march, for wind band. *Warner Blossom. Unpriced* UMGM (B74-51292)
The twelth of never. (Livingston, Jerry). *Frank Music. Unpriced* UMMK/DW (B74-51310)
Ball, Eric. Torch of freedom : march for brass band. *R. Smith. Unpriced* WMGM (B74-50821)
Balulalow : unison voices (or solo) and piano (or organ). (Hughes-Jones, Llifon). *Thames. Unpriced* JDP/LF (B74-51023)
Bamert, Matthias.
Incon-sequenza : for one tuba-player. *Schirmer. £0.70* WVPMJ (B74-50851)
Inkblot : for concert band. *Schirmer. Unpriced* UMJ (B74-50262)
Organism : for organ solo. *Schirmer. Unpriced* RJ (B74-51192)
Quintet for woodwind instruments. Woodwind quintet : flute, oboe, B flat clarinet, F horn, bassoon. *Schirmer. Unpriced* UNR (B74-50268)
Bamforth, Dennis A. Musica Deo sacra. O praise the Lord: arr. O praise the Lord. (Tomkins, Thomas). *Carne House, Parsons Lane, Bury, Lancs. : Tomus. £0.75* VSNK/DK (B74-51329)
Bamforth, Dennis Anthony.
Mercer Island suite. Op.1 : for recorder quartet (descant, treble, tenor, bass). *Carne House, Parsons Lane, Bury : Tomus. Unpriced* VSNSG (B74-50768)
Quartet for recorders, no.1. Op.6. Quartet no.1. Op.6 : for descant, treble, tenor and bass recorders. *Came House, Parsons La., Bury, Lancs. : Tomus. Unpriced* VSNS (B74-50276)
Banks, Eric.
High noon: arr. Highnoon. (Tiomkin, Dimitri). *Affiliated Music. £1.00* WMK/DW (B74-50312)
The Red Arrows march: arr. The Red Arrows march. *Affiliated Music. £1.00* WMK/AGM (B74-50311)
Bantock, *Sir* Granville. The fighting Téméraire : TTBB. *Roberton. £0.16* GEZDW (B74-51016)
Bär, Franz. Sonate a violino o flauto solo e basso, nos 1-3. Three sonatas for violin (flute, treble recorder) and basso continuo. (Veracini, Francesco Maria). *Bärenreiter. £3.60* SPE (B74-50664)
Barber, Samuel.
Fadograph of a western scene : for orchestra. Op.44. *Schirmer. Unpriced* MMJ (B74-50139)
The school for scandal, Op.5. Overture. Overture to 'The school for scandal'. *Schirmer. Unpriced* UMK (B74-50715)
Barbirolli, Evelyn. Rondo for oboe or violin and piano. (Head, Michael). *Boosey and Hawkes. £0.60* VTP/W (B74-50781)
Barcheggio. Sinfonia. Sinfonia to the serenata 'Il Barcheggio' : for trumpet, strings and basso continuo
Part 1. (Stradella, Alessandro). *Musica rara. Unpriced* RXMPWSE (B74-50654)
Barcheggio. Sinfonia: arr. Sinfonia to the serenata 'Il Barcheggio' : for trumpet, strings and basso continuo
Part 1. (Stradella, Alessandro). *Musica rara. Unpriced* WSPK/LE (B74-50843)
Bardari, Giuseppe. Maria Stuarda. Vocal score. Maria Stuarda. (Donizetti, Gaetano). *93 Chancery La., W.C.2 : Egret House. Unpriced* CC (B74-50869)
Barham, John. Five piano solos. *Acuff-Rose. £1.00* QPJ (B74-50175)
Baring-Gould, Sabine. Folk songs of the West Country. *David and Charles. £3.25* KE/TSDW/G/AYDF (B74-50111) ISBN 0-7153-6419-7
Barnett, William. Singing joyfully, God's power proclaim : unison voices and piano or organ. (Wills, Arthur). *Boosey and Hawkes. Unpriced* JDR (B74-50446)
Barock : elektronische Orgel. (Sommer, Jürgen). *Nagel Bärenreiter. £1.80* RPVK/AAY (B74-50631)
Baroque instrumental music
1: People, instruments and the continuo. (Edwards, Owain). *Open University Press. £2.20* AL(XE151) (B74-08077) ISBN 0-335-00852-6
2: Suite, sonata and concerto. (Edwards, Owain). *Open University Press. Unpriced* AL(XE151) (B74-08078) ISBN 0-335-00853-4
Baroque organ (containing an introduction to units 1-2) and, Bach organ music. (Hendrie, Gerald). *Open University Press. £2.00* AR/B(XE151) (B74-07435) ISBN 0-335-00850-x
Barrell, Bernard. Soliloquys sic. Opus 39 : solo cello. *Thames. Unpriced* SRPMJ (B74-51255)
Barrett-Ayres, Reginald. Joseph Haydn and the string quartet. *Barrie and Jenkins. £11.00* BHEARXNS (B74-25500) ISBN 0-214-66803-7
Barricades (after Couperin) : for voice, guitar and keyboard. (Newman, Anthony). *Schirmer. Unpriced* KE/TSPDW (B74-51064)
Barsham, Eve. Ten trumpet tunes, with accompaniment. *Oxford University Press. £0.75* WSPK/AAY (B74-50837) ISBN 0-19-355322-8
Basic books in education : schooling in the middle years. Glynne-Jones, Marjorie Lilian. Music. *Macmillan. £2.60* A(VJ) (B74-21533) ISBN 0-333-12252-6
Basic goals in music
1. (Morrish, Donald James). New ed.. *McGraw-Hill. £1.10* A(VK) (B74-22799) ISBN 0-07-094430-x
2. (Morrish, Donald James). New ed.. *McGraw-Hill. £1.20* A(VK) (B74-22800) ISBN 0-07-094431-8
Book 3. (Morrish, D). *McGraw-Hill. Unpriced* C/AC (B74-50862) ISBN 0-07-094432-6
Book 4. (Morrish, D). *McGraw-Hill. Unpriced* C/AC (B74-50863) ISBN 0-07-094433-4
Book 5. (Morrish, D). *McGraw-Hill. Unpriced* C/AC (B74-50864) ISBN 0-07-094434-2
Basic guitar
Book 1. (Hanlon, Allen). *Chappell. Unpriced* TS/AC (B74-51268)
Basic string repairs : a guide for string-class teachers. (Burgan, Arthur). *Oxford University Press. £1.75* ARX/BT (B74-09234) ISBN 0-19-318509-1
Basse danse : for two pianos. (McCabe, John). *Novello. £5.00* QNUH (B74-50161)
Batt, Mike. The wombling song : for recorders, descant, treble tenor and piano. *Chappell. Unpriced* VSNTQ (B74-50282)
Battye, Ken. Welsh flavour : a selection of Welsh hymn tunes set to English words
Vol.7. *Ken Battye. Unpriced* DM/AYDK (B74-50354)
Baudelaire, Charles. L'Invitation au voyage : for four-part chorus of mixed voices with soprano, alto, tenor, and bass solos a cappella. (Corigliano, John). *Schirmer. Unpriced* EZDW (B74-50977)
Bavicchi, John.
Corley's march : for military band. *Oxford University Press. Unpriced* UMMGM (B74-51304)
Sonata for violin & piano, no.4, Op.63. Sonata no.4 for violin and piano, Op.63 : fantasy-sonata on Lithuanian folk melodies. *Oxford University Press. Unpriced* SPE (B74-50661)
BBC. *See* British Broadcasting Corporation.
Beach of Falesá : opera in three acts. (Jones, Glyn, *b.1905*). *Oxford University Press, Music Department. £0.70* BHNDAC (B74-09229) ISBN 0-19-336833-1
Beare, Cyril. Jogging along : rhythm for brass band. *British and Continental Music. Unpriced* WMJ (B74-50306)
Beat, Janet. Jephte. Vocal score. Jephte (Jephthah) : oratorio for SATB soli, SSSATB chorus, optional strings without violas, and organ continuo. (Carissimi, Giacome). *Novello. £0.55* ENXDD (B74-50378)
Beatles lyrics complete. (Beatles, The). *49 Poland St., : Futura Publications Ltd. £0.40* ADW/GB(P) (B74-20924) ISBN 0-86007-052-2
Beatles, The. The Beatles lyrics complete. *49 Poland St., : Futura Publications Ltd. £0.40* ADW/GB(P) (B74-20924) ISBN 0-86007-052-2
Beatriz's song. (Walton, *Sir* William). *Oxford University Press. £0.35* KE/TSDW/JM (B74-50481) ISBN 0-19-345866-7
Beaumont, Geoffrey. Hymn tunes : a collection of ten setting of well-loved hymns. *Weinberger. £0.50* JDM (B74-50083)
Beck, John Ness. Exhortation : for mixed chorus and piano. *Galaxy : Galliard. Unpriced* DH (B74-50894)
Bedford, Donald A. Carol ringing and more. *Handbell Ringers of Great Britain. Unpriced* XSQMK/CB/AY (B74-51375)
Bedford, Philip.
Carol ringing and more. (Bedford, Donald A). *Handbell Ringers of Great Britain. Unpriced* XSQMK/CB/AY (B74-51375)
An introduction to English handbell tune ringing. *22 Tavistock Rd, Springfield Green, Chelmsford, Essex CM1 53L : Handbell Ringers of Great Britain. £1.50* AXSQ (B74-25501) ISBN 0-904289-00-1
Beechey, Gwilym.
Méthode de violoncelle. Op.4. Leçons et exercises, nos.10-18. Nine studies : for two cellos. (Raoul, Jean Marie). *Oxford University Press. £0.55* SRNU (B74-50680) ISBN 0-19-358480-8
Suite for violin & basso continuo in A major. Op.3, no.1. Suite 1 in A major for violin and basso continuo. (Jones, Richard). *Oxford University Press. £1.25* SPG (B74-50665) ISBN 0-19-357395-4
Suite for violin & basso continuo in B flat major. Op.3, no.4. Suite 4 in B flat major for violin and basso continuo. (Jones, Richard). *Oxford University Press. £1.25* SPG (B74-50666) ISBN 0-19-357398-9
Suite for violin & basso continuo in D major. Op.3, no.3. Suite 3 in D major for violin and basso continuo. (Jones, Richard). *Oxford University Press. £1.25* SPG (B74-50667) ISBN 0-19-357397-0
Suite for violin & basso continuo in G minor. Op.3, no.2. Suite 2 in G minor for violin and basso continuo. (Jones, Richard). *Oxford University Press. £1.25* SPG (B74-50668) ISBN 0-19-357396-2
Beethoven, Ludwig van.
Bagatelles. Opus 119 : piano solo. *Peters. Unpriced* QPJ (B74-50584)
Concerto for piano, no.1, in C major. Op.15. Allegro con brio: arr. Theme from piano concerto no.1. *Leonard, Gould and Bolttler. Unpriced* QPK (B74-50594)
Concerto movement for violin in C major. G.148: arr. Concerto movement for violin and chamber orchestra, 1790/92. WoO5. *Breitkopf and Härtel : Bärenreiter. £3.25* SPK (B74-50675)
Selections : arr. Adagio for a musical clock and Rondo a capriccio 'Rage over the lost groschen'. *Galaxy : Galliard. Unpriced* QNUK (B74-51139)
Sonata for piano, no.2, in G major. Op.14. Andante: arr. Andante from piano sonata Opus 14, no.2. *Novello. £0.33* TSPMK/AE (B74-50709)
Sonatas for piano. Selections. Sonatinen und leichte Sonaten fur Klavier. *Peters. Unpriced* QPE/AY (B74-51145)
Ta, ta, ta. G.205. To Maelzel : for 4-part chorus of mixed voices unaccompanied or with wood-block. *Roberton. £0.12* EZDW/X (B74-50412)
Ta, ta, ta. K.-H 162. To Maelzel : for 4-part chorus of female voices unaccompanied or with wood-block. *Roberton. £0.10* FEZDW/X (B74-50432)
Beethoven. (Scott, Marion Margareta). Revised ed.. *Dent. £2.95* BBJ (B74-22161) ISBN 0-460-03149-x
Beethoven : studies. (Tyson, Alan). *Oxford University Press. £4.50* BBJ(D) (B74-11734) ISBN 0-19-315312-2
Beggar's opera. Selections: arr. Four songs from the Beggar's Opera. (Gay, John). *Oxford University Press. Unpriced* EZDW (B74-50978)
Beginning the five-string banjo. (Silverman, Jerry). *Macmillan : Collier Macmillan. Unpriced (hard cover), £1.95 (paperback)* TT/AC (B74-50711)
Behold now praise the Lord : anthem for SATB. (Tomblings, Philip). *St Gregory Publications. £0.15* DR (B74-50915)
Behold that star ... Rise up, shepherd an' foller! : a quodlibet. (Hudson, Hazel). *Ashdown. £0.12* FDW/LC (B74-50997)
Behold the tabernacle of God. Op.70 : anthem for SATB, with divisions and organ. (Joubert, John). *Novello. £0.16* DH (B74-50897)
Bell, Sydney. The girl with the buckles on her shoes : Irish traditional melody, unison song with piano. (Nelson, Havelock). *Roberton. £0.07* JDW (B74-50085)
Bell ringing : chimes, carillons, handbells - the world of the bell and the ringer. (Camp, John). *David and Charles. £2.95* AXSR (B74-05793) ISBN 0-7153-6088-4
Bells do ring : based on a French tune for four-part chorus of mixed voices with optional handbells. (Glarum, Leonard Stanley). *Schirmer. Unpriced* EZDP/LF (B74-50963)
Bells in our lives. (Cockett, Mary). *David and Charles. £1.60* AXS/B (B74-01380) ISBN 0-7153-6229-1
Bendusi, Francesco. Opera nova de balli, 1553 : for four instruments. *London Pro Musica. Unpriced* LNSH (B74-51082)
Benedic anima mea. Psalm 104 : for mixed voice choir, soprano and tenor soli and organ. (Saunders, Neil). *Roberton. £0.32* DR (B74-50914)
Benger, Richard. Two Christmas carols : unison or two-part. *Banks. Unpriced* JFLDP/LF (B74-51040)
Benjamin, Thomas. Adoramus te = We adore thee : SATB a cappella. *Associated Music. Unpriced* EZDJ (B74-50042)
Benjamin Britten - a complete catalogue of his published works. (Boosey and Hawkes Limited). New and revised ed.. *Boosey and Hawkes : Faber Music. £2.00* BBU(TC) (B74-03157) ISBN 0-85162-022-1
Bennett, Richard Rodney.
Concerto for oboe & string orchestra. Oboe concerto. *Universal. Unpriced* RXMPVTF (B74-51221)
Murder on the Orient Express. Theme: arr. Murder on the Orient Express : theme. *EMI. £0.25* QPK/JR (B74-51186)
Murder on the Orient Express. Waltz theme: arr. Waltz theme. *EMI. £0.25* QPK/AHW/JR (B74-51185)
Bennett, *Sir* William Sterndale. Suite de pièces. Op.24. *Stainer and Bell. Unpriced* QPG (B74-50576)
Bent, Margaret.
Gloria : TTTBB. (Power, Leonel). *Oxford University Press. Unpriced* GEZDGC (B74-50080) ISBN 0-19-341209-8
Two songs for Christmas. *Oxford University Press. Unpriced* EZDP/LF (B74-50405) ISBN 0-19-341208-x
Berger, Jean. Concert piece : for two flutes and string orchestra. *Schirmer. Unpriced* RXMPVRNU (B74-50222)
Berger, Wilhelm. Trio for clarinet, cello and piano in G minor. Opus 94. Trio in G minor for clarinet, cello and piano. Opus 94. *Musica rara. Unpriced* NUVNT (B74-50532)
Bergmann, Walter.
Der getreue Music-Meister. Sonata for treble recorder & basso continuo in C major. Sonata no.4 in C major : for treble recorder and continuo. (Telemann, Georg Philipp). *Schott. £0.75* VSSPE (B74-50773)
Der getreue Music-Meister. Sonata for treble recorder & basso continuo in C major (in canon). Sonata no.2 in C major (in canon) : for treble recorder and continuo. (Telemann, Georg Philipp). *Schott. £0.75* VSSPE/X

(B74-50777)
Der getreue Music-Meister. Sonata for treble recorder & basso continuo in F major. Sonata no.1 in F major : for treble recorder and continuo. (Telemann, Georg Philipp). *Schott. £0.75* VSSPE (B74-50774)
Der getreue Music-Meister. Sonata for treble recorder & basso continuo in F minor. Sonata no.3 in F minor : for treble recorder and continuo. (Telemann, Georg Philipp). *Schott. £0.75* VSSPE (B74-50775)
Der getreue Music-Meister. Sonatas for treble recorder & basso continuo. Sonatas 1-4 : for treble recorder and continuo. (Telemann, George Philipp). *Schott. £2.50* VSSPE (B74-50776)
Berio, Luciano. Chemins IIb-c. *Universal. Unpriced* MMJ (B74-50501)
Berkeley, Lennox.
Antiphon : for string orchestra. *Chester. Unpriced* RXMJ (B74-51217)
Three Latin motets : for five voices. *Chester. Unpriced* EZDJ (B74-50394)
'Berkshire Archaeological Journal'. The church bells of Berkshire : their inscriptions and founders, arranged alphabetically by parishes ... (Sharpe, Frederick). 2nd ed. *Kingsmead Reprints. £4.00* AXSR/B(YDEU) (B74-05271) ISBN 0-901571-46-6
Berlioz, Hector.
Symphonie fantastique. *Breitkopf and Härtel : Bärenreiter. £13.20* MME (B74-50494)
Te Deum. *Breitkopf and Härtel : Bärenreiter. £13.20* EMDGKHB (B74-50374)
Waverley. Op.1 : overture. *Eulenberg. Unpriced* MMJ (B74-50502)
Berlitz, Maximilian Delphinus. Berlitz: introduction to French : for voice and piano. (Fennimore, Joseph). *Schirmer. Unpriced* KDW (B74-51047)
Berlitz: introduction to French : for voice and piano. (Fennimore, Joseph). *Schirmer. Unpriced* KDW (B74-51047)
Bernhard, Christoph. Geistlicher Harmonien, erster Teil. *Wie der Hirsch schreiet.* As the deer cries for flowing water : for four-part chorus of mixed voices with organ accompaniment. *Roberton. £0.26* DH (B74-50011)
Bernstein, Leonard.
Mass. Almighty Father: arr. Almighty Father : chorale. *Amberson : Schirmer. Unpriced* GEZDH (B74-50434)
Mass. Almighty Father: arr. Almighty Father : chorale from 'Mass'. *Amberson : Schirmer. £5.60(full score and parts)(extra score £0.95, extra parts £0.30 each)* UMK (B74-50716)
Mass. *Gloria tibi: arr.* Gloria tibi : for two-part chorus of treble voices with tenor solo and piano and bongo accompaniment. *Amberson : Schirmer. Unpriced* ENYLDH (B74-50033)
Mass. Mediatation no.2 (on a sequence by Beethoven): arr. Meditation no.2 (on a sequence by Beethoven). *Amberson : Schirmer. Unpriced* UMK (B74-50717)
Mass. Selections: arr. Two meditations. *Amberson : Schirmer. Unpriced* SRPK (B74-50249)
Works, songs. Collections. Collected songs. *Amberson : Schirmer. Unpriced* KDW/AZ (B74-50473)
Bernstein, Seymour.
Birds 2 : a second suite of nine impressionistic studies for piano solo. *Schroeder and Gunther. Unpriced* QPG (B74-50577)
Concerto for piano, 'For our time': arr. Concerto ('For our time'). *Schroeder and Gunther. Unpriced* QNUK/LF (B74-50163)
Bernstein, Walter Heinz. Concerto for oboe, strings & basso continuo in C minor. Concerto a 5 für Oboe, Streicher und Basso continuo C-moll. (Telemann, Georg Philipp). *Litolff : Peters. £2.80* NUTNRF (B74-51117)
Berthold, G. Duets for two cats : for 2-part chorus of female voices or SA duet with piano. (Rossini, Gioachino Antonio). *Roberton. £0.12* FDW (B74-50422)
Berthomieu, Marc. Jardins de Paris : pour voix moyenne. *Chappell. Unpriced* KFVDW (B74-50485)
Bertoli, Giovanni Antonio. Compositioni musicale fatte per sonare col fagotto solo, nos 1-3. Three sonatas for bassoon (violoncello) and basso continuo. *Bärenreiter. £3.45* VWPE (B74-50811)
Berton, Ralph. Remembering Bix : a memoir of the jazz age. *W.H. Allen. £4.95* 788.10924 (B74-27250) ISBN 0-491-01951-3
Best dulcimer method yet. (Gamse, Albert). *Lewis Ashley-Fields. Unpriced* TWT/AC (B74-51287)
Best of Gilbert and Sullivan : songs from operettas arranged with piano accompaniment. (Sullivan, *Sir* Arthur Seymour). *Chappell. Unpriced* KDW (B74-50468)
Best recorder method yet : charts, exercises, embellishments, solos, and ensemble music
Book 1: C-soprano or tenor. (Gamse, Albert). *Lewis Music : Ashley-Fields. Unpriced* VS/AC (B74-50764)
Book 2: F-alto, F-sopranino, F-bass. (Gamse, Albert). *Lewis Music : Ashley-Fields. Unpriced* VS/AC (B74-50765)
Bhajeb : for organ. (Newman, Anthony). *Schirmer. Unpriced* RJ (B74-51194)
Biber, Heinrich Ignaz Franz. Sonata for eight trumpets, timpani & basso continuo in C major, 'Scti Polycarpi'. Sonata 'Scti Polycarpi' : for 8 trumpets, timpani and basso continuo. *Musica rara. Unpriced* WSME (B74-50832)
Biblische Motetten : für das Kirchenjahr
Band 2: Darstellung des Herrn bis Trinitas. (Ameln, Konrad). *Bärenreiter. Unpriced* EZDH/AYE (B74-50392)
Bibri, Vladimir. Via crucis : a cycle of fifteen saetas, for four-part chorus of mixed voices and Spanish guitar. (Surinach, Carlos). *Associated Music. Unpriced* ETSDE (B74-50380)
Bierley, Paul E. John Philip Sousa - a descriptive catalog of his work. *University of Illinois Press. £4.75* BSK(TC) (B74-11345) ISBN 0-252-00297-0
Big band jazz. (McCarthy, Albert). *Barrie and Jenkins. £5.00* AMT(XMT56) (B74-17388) ISBN 0-214-66894-0
Binge, Ronald. Trombonioso : for trombones and band. *R. Smith. Unpriced* WMPWUN (B74-51363)
Binkerd, Gordon.
And I am old to know : song. *Boosey and Hawkes. Unpriced* KDW (B74-51046)
Concert set for piano : arr. Concert set for organ. *Boosey and Hawkes. £3.75* RK (B74-51198)
Eternitie : SSATB. *Boosey and Hawkes. Unpriced* EZDH (B74-50943)
Hope is the thing with feathers : SSAA. *Boosey and Hawkes. Unpriced* FEZDW (B74-51004)
Infant joy : SSAA. *Boosey and Hawkes. Unpriced* FEZDW (B74-51005)
The lamb : SATB. *Boosey and Hawkes. Unpriced* EZDW (B74-50974)
Bird - the legend of Charlie Parker. (Reisner, Robert George). *Quartet Books. £3.95* AMT(P) (B74-27252) ISBN 0-7043-2063-0
Birds 2 : a second suite of nine impressionistic studies for piano solo. (Bernstein, Seymour). *Schroeder and Gunther. Unpriced* QPG (B74-50577)
Birds : extravaganza in one act after Aristophanes. (Maconchy, Elizabeth). *Boosey and Hawkes. £2.75* CC (B74-50870)
Birds : extravaganza in one act after Aristophanes. (Maconchy, Elizabeth). *Boosey and Hawkes. Unpriced* CQC (B74-50873)
Birds. Vocal score. The birds : extravaganza in one act after Aristophanes. (Maconchy, Elizabeth). *Boosey and Hawkes. £2.75* CC (B74-50870)
Birtwistle, Harrison. An imaginary landscape : orchestra. *Universal. Unpriced* MMJ (B74-50140)
Bix - man & legend. (Sudhalter, Richard M). *Quartet Books. £4.95* AMT(P) (B74-27251) ISBN 0-7043-2070-3
Bizet, Georges.
L'Arlesienne, 1st suite. Carillon: arr. Carillon. *Boosey and Hawkes. Score £1.50, Piano conductor £0.50, Set £2.50* MK/JM (B74-51091)
Introduction and rondo capriccioso for violin & orchestra. Opus 28: arr. Introduktion und Rondo capriccioso. Opus 28 : für Violine und Orchester. (Saint-Saens, Camille). *Peters. £2.40* SPK (B74-51244)
Symphony in C major. Symphony, C major. *Eulenburg. Unpriced* MME (B74-51097)
Blacher, Boris. Vokalisen für Kammerchor. *Boosey and Hawkes. £0.30* EZDW (B74-50057)
Black and white : eight tunes for young pianists. (Last, Joan). *Oxford University Press. £0.45* QPJ (B74-50178) ISBN 0-19-373104-5
Black November turkey : for four-part chorus of mixed voices with soprano and alto solos a cappella. (Corigliano, John). *Schirmer. Unpriced* EZDW (B74-50059)
Blacking, John. How musical is man? *University of Washington Press. £3.25* BZNR (B74-30188) ISBN 0-295-95218-0
Blackwell, William. Concertino for two horns in F major. Op.45: arr. Concertino for 2 horns and orchestra. Op.45. (Kuhlau, Friedrich). *Musica rara. Unpriced* WTNTQK/LFL (B74-50845)
Blackwood, Alan, *b.1932.* A trip to the concert. *36 Park St., W1Y 4DE : Nelson Young World. £0.45* AM (B74-13709) ISBN 0-7238-0946-1
Blake, Leonard. Carol of the sun. *Vocal score.* Carol of the sun : for two-part or unison chorus. *Roberton. £0.10* FDP/LF (B74-50414)
Blake, William.
Infant joy : SSAA. (Binkerd, Gordon). *Boosey and Hawkes. Unpriced* FEZDW (B74-51005)
The lamb : SATB. (Binkerd, Gordon). *Boosey and Hawkes. Unpriced* EZDW (B74-50974)
Blarr, Oskar Gottlieb. Oekumenische Beatmesse : Liebe ist nicht nur ein Wort. *Bosse : Bärenreiter. £1.60* ELDE (B74-50372)
Blaydon races : variations for orchestra. (Russell, Leslie). *Boosey and Hawkes. £10.50* MM/T (B74-51095)
Blessed be he. Op. 147 : SATB. (Rubbra, Edmund). *Lengnick. £0.12* EZDH (B74-50040)
Blezard, William. Hours of the day : a suite of six piano pieces for young people with supplementary exercises. *167 Ewell Rd, Surbiton, Surrey : Camera Music. Unpriced* QPG (B74-51148)
Bliss, *Sir* Arthur. Investiture antiphonal fanfares for three brass choirs: arr. Investiture antiphonal fanfares for three brass choirs. *Novello. £0.50* WMK/AGN (B74-51357)
Bloch (Ernest) lectures. *See* Ernest Bloch lectures.
Block, Paul. Concerto for oboe, violin & string orchestra in C minor, 'Lund': arr. Concerto in C minor for oboe, violin and strings (Lund). (Vivaldi, Antonio). *Musica rara. Unpriced* NUTNTK/LF (B74-50530)
Block, Robert Paul.
Il Barcheggio. Sinfonia. Sinfonia to the serenata 'Il Barcheggio' : for trumpet, strings and basso continuo
Part 1. (Stradella, Alessandro). *Musica rara. Unpriced* RXMPWSE (B74-50654)
Il Barcheggio. Sinfonia: arr. Sinfonia to the serenata 'Il Barcheggio' : for trumpet, strings and basso continuo
Part 1. (Stradella, Alessandro). *Musica rara. Unpriced* WSPK/LE (B74-50843)
Concertino for two horns in F major. Op.45: arr. Concertino for 2 horns and orchestra. Op.45. (Kuhlau, Friedrich). *Musica rara. Unpriced* WTNTQK/LFL (B74-50845)
Concerto for bassoon in B flat: arr. Concerto in B flat for bassoon and orchestra. (Pleyel, Ignaz). *Musica rara. Unpriced* VWPK/LF (B74-50813)
Concerto for flute & string orchestra in D minor. Concerto in D minor for flute, strings and continuo. (Quantz, Johann Joachim). *Musica rara. Unpriced* RXMPVRF (B74-50649)
Concerto for flute & string orchestra in D minor: arr. Concerto in D minor for flute, strings and continuo. (Quantz, Johann Joachim). *Musica rara. Unpriced* VRPK/LF (B74-50760)
Concerto for flute & string orchestra in G major. Wq.169. Concerto in G major : for flute, strings and basso continuo. Wq.169. (Bach, Carl Philipp Emanuel). *Musica rara. Unpriced* RXMPVRF (B74-50648)
Concerto for flute & string orchestra in G major. Wq.169: arr. Concerto in G major : for flute, strings and basso continuo. Wq.169. (Bach, Carl Philipp Emanuel). *Musica rara. Unpriced* VRPK/LF (B74-50759)
Concerto for oboe, violin & string orchestra in C minor 'Lund'. Concerto in C minor for oboe, violin and strings (Lund). (Vivaldi, Antonio). *Musica rara. Unpriced* RXMPVTPLSF (B74-50651)
Concerto for treble recorder, oboe, violin, bassoon and basso continuo in G major. P.105. Concerto in G major : for treble recorder (flute), oboe, violin, bassoon and basso continuo. P.105. (Vivaldi, Antonio). *Musica rara. Unpriced* NUPNRF (B74-50525)
Concerto for treble recorder, oboe, violin, bassoon & basso continuo in G minor. P.403. Concerto in G minor : for treble recorder (flute), oboe, violin, bassoon and basso continuo. P.403. (Vivaldi, Antonio). *Musica rara. Unpriced* NUPNRF (B74-50526)
Concerto for two clarinets in E flat major: arr. Concerto in E flat for 2 clarinets and orchestra. (Hoffmeister, Franz Anton). *Musica rara. Unpriced* VUNTQK/LF (B74-50792)
Concerto for two flutes, no.1, in G minor: arr. Concerto no.1 in G minor for 2 flutes and orchestra. (Quantz, Johann Joachim). *Musica rara. Unpriced* VRNTQK/LF (B74-50746)
Concerto for two oboes & string orchestra in D minor. P.302. Concerto in D minor for 2 oboes, strings and basso continuo. (Vivaldi, Antonio). *Musica rara. Unpriced* RXMPVTNUF (B74-50650)
Concerto for two oboes & string orchestra in D minor. P.302: arr. Concerto in D minor for 2 oboes, strings and basso continuo. (Vivaldi, Antonio). *Musica rara. Unpriced* VTPK/LF (B74-50787)
Concerto for woodwind & string quartet & basso continuo in B flat major. Op.8, no.3. Concerto in B flat for 2 oboes or violins, 2 violins or oboes and basso continuo. Opus 8, no.3. (Pepusch, Johann Christoph). *Musica rara. Unpriced* NUTNRF (B74-50528)
Concerto for woodwind quartet & basso continuo in G major. Op.8, no.2. Concerto in G for 2 flutes, 2 oboes, violins and basso continuo. Op.8, no.2. (Pepusch, Johann Christoph). *Musica rara. Unpriced* NWPNRF (B74-50546)
Concertos for woodwind quartet & basso continuo. Op.8, nos. 1, 4-6. 4 concerti for 2 treble recorders, 2 flutes, tenor recorders, oboes, violins & basso continuo. Op.8, nos. 1, 4, 5, 6
Opus 8, no.4 in F major. (Pepusch, Johann Christoph). *Musica rara. Unpriced* NWPNRF (B74-50549)
Concertos for woodwind quartet & basso continuo. Op.8, nos. 1, 4-6. 4 concerti for 2 treble recorders, 2 flutes, tenor recorders, oboes, violins & basso continuo. Op.8, nos. 1, 4, 5, 6
Opus 8, no.6: in F major. (Pepusch, Johann Christoph). *Musica rara. Unpriced* NWPNRF (B74-50548)
Concertos for woodwind quartet & basso continuo. Op.8, nos. 1, 4-6. 4 concerti for 2 treble recorders, 2 flutes, tenor recorders, oboes, violins & basso continuo. Op.8, nos. 1,4,5,6
Opus 8, no.5 in C major. (Pepusch, Johann Christoph). *Musica rara. Unpriced* NWPNRF (B74-50550)
Concertos for woodwind quartet & basso continuo. Op.8, nos. 1, 4-6. 4 concerti for 2 treble recorders, 2 flutes, tenor recorders, oboes, violins & basso continuo. Op.8, nos. 1,4,5,6
Opus 8, no.1: in B flat major. (Pepusch, Johann Christoph). *Musica rara. Unpriced* NWPNRF (B74-50547)
Concerts royaux I-IV : for flute, oboe, violin, viola da gamba and basso continuo
No.II. (Couperin, François). *Musica rara. Unpriced* VRPG (B74-50755)
No.III. (Couperin, François). *Musica rara. Unpriced* VRPG (B74-50756)
No.IV. (Couperin, François). *Musica rara. Unpriced* VRPG (B74-50757)
Fantasy for cello solo (1973). *Musica rara. Unpriced* SRPMJ (B74-50685)
Fantasy for double bass solo (1973). *Musica rara. Unpriced* SSPMJ (B74-50687)
Fantasy for viola solo (1967, rev. 1973). *Musica rara. Unpriced* SQPMJ (B74-50679)
Qunitet for flute & strings in A major. Op.51, no.3. Quintet in A for flute and strings. Op.51, no.3. (Kuhlau, Friedrich). *Musica rara. Unpriced* NVRNR (B74-50542)

Sinfonia concertante for flute, oboe, horn, bassoon, no.5, in F major: arr. Symphonie concertante no.5 in F major : for flute, oboe (clarinet), horn, bassoon and orchestra. (Pleyel, Ignaz). *Musica rara. Unpriced* MPUNSE (B74-50516)
Sonata for flute & basso continuo in E minor, 'Stockholm'.

Sonata in E minor : for flute and basso continuo. (Vivaldi, Antonio). *Musica rara. Unpriced* VRPE (B74-50752)

Sonata for trumpet, string quartet & basso continuo in D major. Op.3, no.11. Sonata a 5. Op.3, no.11 : for trumpet and strings. (Grossi, Andrea). *Musica rara. Unpriced* NUXSNQE (B74-50533)

Sonata for trumpet, string quartet & basso continuo in D major. Op.3, no.11: arr. Sonata à 5. Op.3, no.11 : for trumpet and strings. (Grossi, Andrea). *Musica rara. Unpriced* WSPK/LE (B74-50838)

Sonata for trumpet, string quartet & basso continuo in D major. Op.3, no.12. Sonata à 5. Op.3, no.12 : for trumpet and strings. (Grossi, Andrea). *Musica rara. Unpriced* NUXSNQE (B74-50534)

Sonata for trumpet, string quartet & basso continuo in D major. Op.3, no.12: arr. Sonata à 5. Op.3, no.12 : for trumpet and strings. (Grossi, Andrea). *Musica rara. Unpriced* WSPK/LE (B74-50839)

Sonata for trumpet, string trio & basso continuo in D major. G.1: arr. Sonata for trumpet, strings and continuo in D. G.1. (Torelli, Giuseppe). *Musica rara. Unpriced* WSPK/LE (B74-50840)

Sonata for trumpet, string trio & basso continuo in D major. G.2: arr. Sonata for trumpet, strings and continuo in D. G.2. (Torelli, Giuseppe). *Musica rara. Unpriced* WSPK/LE (B74-50841)

Sonata for two oboes & basso continuo in G minor, 'Lund'. Trio sonata in G minor (Lund) : for 2 oboes and basso continuo. (Vivaldi, Antonio). *Musica rara. Unpriced* VTNTPWE (B74-50780)

Sonata for two trumpets, bassoon, string quintet & basso continuo in C major. Sonata à 8 in C for 2 trumpets, bassoon, strings and continuo. (Höffner, Anton). *Musica rara. Unpriced* NUNME (B74-50521)

Sonata for two trumpets, bassoon, string quintet & basso continuo in C major. Sonata à 8 in C for 2 trumpets, bassoon, strings and continuo. (Höffner, Anton). *Musica rara. Unpriced* NUNTK/LE (B74-50524)

Sonata for violin & basso continuo in C minor. Op.5, no.3: arr. Sonata in C minor. Opus 5, no.3 : for treble (alto) recorder and basso continuo. (Corelli, Arcangelo). *Musica rara. Unpriced* VSSPK/AE (B74-50778)

Symphonie concertante for two clarinets in B flat major. Opus 25: arr. Symphonie concertante for two clarinets and orchestra. Opus 25. (Devienne, François). *Musica rara. Unpriced* VVNTQK/LE (B74-50798)

Bloodworth, Denis. Fitzwilliam Virginal Book. Selections: arr. Six pieces from the Fitzwilliam Virginal Book. *Oxford University Press. £0.45* VSNUK (B74-51334) ISBN 0-19-355550-6

Bloomster, Wesley V. Philosophy of modern music. (Adorno, Theodor Wiesengrund). *Sheed and Ward. £4.50* BSET (B74-09866) ISBN 0-7220-7339-9

Bluetes, 1, a serie

album no.1. Op.31 (de 1 a 10) : piano. (Miguez, Leopoldo). *Arthur Napoleão : Essex Music. Unpriced* QPJ (B74-51178)

Blunt, Wilfrid. On wings of song : a biography of Felix Mendelssohn. *Hamilton. £5.50* BMJ(N) (B74-14969) ISBN 0-241-02455-2

Blyton, Carey. Ladies only. Op.58 : five songs for SSA unaccompanied. *Novello. Unpriced* FEZDW (B74-51006)

Boalch, Donald Howard. Makers of the harpsichord and clavichord, 1440-1840. 2nd ed. *Clarendon Press. £9.75* APW/BC(XCS401/C) (B74-21541) ISBN 0-19-816123-9

Boatwright, Howard. Serenade : for two strings and two winds. *Oxford University Press. Unpriced* NVNS (B74-50540) ISBN 0-19-385008-7

Bob Dylan : a retrospective. (McGregor, Craig). *Angus and Robertson. £0.75* AKDW/GB/E(P) (B74-17386) ISBN 0-207-12675-5

Bobbio, Reddy. Le Guide du rythme : guide pratique des rythmiques classiques et moderns. *Chappell. Unpriced* X/NM (B74-51373)

Bobri, Vladimir. The Segovia technique. *Macmillan : Collier Macmillan. £5,45* ATS/E/CY (B74-13713) ISBN 0-02-511990-7

Boccherini, Luigi.

Concerto for cello & string orchestra in C major. Gérard 481: arr. Konzert No.4 für Violoncello und Klavier, C-dur. *Schott. £2.90* SRPK/LF (B74-51253)

Concerto for cello & string orchestra, no.2, in D major. Konzert No.2, D Dur für Violoncello und Streichorchester. *Schott. £2.40* RXMPSRF (B74-50221)

Concerto for cello & string orchestra, no.2, in D major: arr. Konzert No.2, D Dur, für Violoncello und Streichorchester. *Schott. £2.04* SRPK/LF (B74-50250)

Boissier, Auguste. Technische Studien. *Selections.* The Liszt studies : essential selections from the technical studies for the piano, including the first English edition of the legendary Liszt Pedagogue, a lesson-diary of the master as teacher as kept by Mme August Boisser, 1831-2. (Liszt, Franz). *Associated Music. Unpriced* Q/AF (B74-50558)

Boisvallée, François de. Le Parc aux fees. Idylle: arr. Idylle. (Veneux, Thierry). *Chappell. Unpriced* TMK (B74-50693)

Bolton, Cecil.

Mexicana. *Affiliated Music. £1.00* WMJ (B74-50307)

The Red Arrows march: arr. The Red Arrows march. (Banks, Eric). *Affiliated Music. £1.00* WMK/AGM (B74-50311)

Bonhoeffer, Dietrich. Four stations on the road to freedom, Opus 73 : for SSAATTBB soli or chorus (unaccompanied). (Joubert, John). *Novello. Unpriced* JNEZAYDE (B74-50456)

Bónis, Ferenc. The selected writings of Zoltán Kodály. (Kodály, Zoltán). *Boosey and Hawkes. £3.95* A(D) (B74-21534) ISBN 0-85162-021-3

Bononcini, Antonio. Stabat mater : for SATB soli and chorus, string orchestra and organ continuo. *Novello. £1.25* EMDGKADD/LK (B74-50373)

Bonsor, Brian. Spanish dances for piano, vol.2. Andaluza: arr. Andaluza. (Granados, Enrique). *Schott. £1.00* VSNRQK/AH (B74-51331)

Boosey and Hawkes Limited. Benjamin Britten - a complete catalogue of his published works. New and revised ed.. *Boosey and Hawkes : Faber Music. £2.00* BBU(TC) (B74-03157) ISBN 0-85162-022-1

Borge, Victor. My favourite intermissions. *See* Borge, Victor. My favourite intervals.

Borge, Victor. My favourite intervals. *Woburn Press. £2.25* A/D(YB/M) (B74-09227) ISBN 0-7130-0126-7

Boucourechliev, André. Grodek d'apres Georg Trakl (1963, revision 1969) : for soprano voice, flute and percussion. *Universal. Unpriced* KFLE/NYHRDX (B74-51068)

Bourgeois, Louis. The Old Hundreth Psalm tune ('All people that on earth do dwell') : anthem for unison or mixed (SATB) choir accompanied by organ with band and/or orchestra. (Vaughan Williams, Ralph). *Oxford University Press. Unpriced* EUMDM (B74-50381)

Bownas, Geoffrey. Autumn cicada : ko-uta on four Japanese texts, for SSA, harp and 4 handbells. (Cole, Bruce). *Boosey and Hawkes. £0.10* FE/NYJNRDW (B74-50427)

Box of toys and entertainment for speech and percussion. (Russell-Smith, Geoffry). *Novello. £1.02* FHYE/XMDX (B74-50077)

Boy fights alligator : fugue, for orchestra. (Thomson, Virgil). *Schirmer. Unpriced* MM/Y/JR (B74-50132)

Boyd, Jack. Must I now = Muss i denn : German folk song. *Warner : Blossom. Unpriced* ESSPLRSDW (B74-50379)

Boyle, John S. The concert piano in Scotland : a report to the Scottish Arts Council. (Piano Panel). *19 Charlotte Sq., Edinburgh EH2 4DF : Scottish Arts Council. £0.25* AQ(W/YDL) (B74-09233) ISBN 0-902989-13-8

Brace, Geoffrey. Metyelitsa : SATB unaccompanied Russian folk song. (Hopkins, Ewart). *Roberton. £0.07* EZDW (B74-50410)

Bradshaw, Lloyd.

Basic goals in music

Book 3. (Morrish, D L). *McGraw-Hill. Unpriced* C/AC (B74-50862) ISBN 0-07-094432-6

Book 4. (Morrish, D L). *McGraw-Hill. Unpriced* C/AC (B74-50863) ISBN 0-07-094433-4

Book 5. (Morrish, D L). *McGraw-Hill. Unpriced* C/AC (B74-50864) ISBN 0-07-094434-2

Brahms, Johannes.

Quintet for clarinet & strings in B minor. Op. 115: arr. Clarinet quintet in B minor. *Fenette Music : Breitkopf and Härtel. Unpriced* VVQPK (B74-50295)

Songs of Ophelia, nos. 3, 4. Christmas cradle song. *Novello. Unpriced* EZDP/LF (B74-50959)

Zigeunerlieder = Gypsy songs. Op.103 : for four-part chorus of mixed voices with soprano and tenor solos and piano accompaniment. *Schirmer. Unpriced* DW (B74-50357)

Brahms chamber music. (Keys, Ivor). *British Broadcasting Corporation. £0.45* BBTAN (B74-14311) ISBN 0-563-10168-7

Braid on parade : march, military band. (Frank, Marcel Gustave). *Warner : Blossom. Unpriced* UMMGM (B74-51305)

Brand, Jim. The wild rover : the story of the Prodigal Son: a musical play for children. (O'Gorman, Denis). *Grail Publications. £0.50* BOFGACN (B74-11053) ISBN 0-901829-22-6

Brandenburg concerto, no.1, in F major. S.1046. Menuetto: arr. Menuetto. (Bach, Johann Sebastian). *Warner : Blossom. Unpriced* MK/AHR (B74-50492)

Brannen, Ann. E.H. Grieg's 'Peer Gynt'. (Suzuki, Yoshiharu). *F. Warne. £1.75* BGTAM/JMBN (B74-26152) ISBN 0-7232-1784-x

Brass bands of Yorkshire. (Cooper, Thomas Leonard). *Dalesman. £1.60* AWM(QB/YDGJ) (B74-09231) ISBN 0-85206-195-1

Brauel, Henning. Concerto for violin, no.2. Vocal score. 2nd violin concerto for solo violin, tape, voices and 33 instrumentalists. (Henze, Hans Werner). *Schott. £7.20* KGE/SPDX (B74-50119)

Bray, Roger. O Lord arise : anthem for seven voices, S.S.A.A.T.B.B. (Weelkes, Thomas). *Oxford University Press. £0.20* EZDK (B74-50955) ISBN 0-19-352126-1

Bray, Trevor.

Music and society today. *Open University Press. Unpriced* A(Z) (B74-24207) ISBN 0-335-00869-0

Twentieth century music, 1900-1945. *Open University Press. Unpriced* A(XM46) (B74-21535) ISBN 0-335-00866-6

Bream, Julian. Five bagetelles for guitar. (Walton, *Sir* William). *Oxford University Press. £1.50* TSPMJ (B74-51276) ISBN 0-19-359407-2

Breathnach, Diarmuid. Lámhleabhar gineárálta don cheoltóir. (Cecily, *Sister, OP*). *Folens. £0.48* A (B74-11047) ISBN 0-902592-58-0

Brecht, Bertold. Lehrstuch (1929). Vocal score. Lehrstuck (1929). (Hindemith, Paul). *Schott. £4.35* DX (B74-50929)

Brecht, Bertolt. Children's crusade = Kinderkreuzzug. Op.82 : a ballad for children's voices and orchestra. (Britten, Benjamin). *Faber Music : Faber. £15.00* BBUADX (B74-21537) ISBN 0-571-10370-7

Brejean, Philippe. Quand la chance est là. This old world = Quand la chance est là : for SATB chorus accompanied. *Chappell. Unpriced* DW (B74-50358)

Breval, Jean Baptiste.

Traite du violoncello. Selections. Leichte Stücke für Violoncello mit Begleitung durch 2 Violoncello

Heft 1. *Schott. £1.44* SRNU (B74-50245)

Traite du violoncello. Selections. Leichte Stücke für Violoncello mit Begleitung durch 2 Violoncello

Heft 2. *Schott. £1.44* (B74-50096)

Brian, Havergal.

Fanfare for the orchestral brass. Festival fanfare : 4 horns, 4 trumpets, 3 trombones and 2 tubas. *Musica Viva. £1.55* WMGN (B74-51354)

Psalm 23. Vocal score. Psalm 23 : tenor solo, chorus (SATB) and orchestra. *Musica Viva. £1.20* DR (B74-50022)

Brief biographies. Rowland-Entwistle, Theodore. Famous composers. *David and Charles. £2.50* A/D(YB/M) (B74-09226) ISBN 0-7153-6375-1

Bright, Clive. First book of ayres. Never weather-beaten sail: arr. Never weather-beaten sail. (Campion, Thomas). *Studio Music. Unpriced* WMK/DW (B74-51360)

Brimhall, John. The entertainer. (Joplin, Scott). *California Music : Chappell. Unpriced* KDW (B74-50460)

Brisman, Heskel. Jerusalem city of gold : songs of modern and ancient Israel. *Chappell. Unpriced* KDW/AYVD (B74-50472)

Britain sings

Book 1. (Duke, Henry). *British and Continental. Unpriced* VSRPMK/DW/AYC (B74-50285)

Book 2. (Duke, Henry). *British and Continental. Unpriced* VSRPMK/DW/AYC (B74-50286)

British Broadcasting Corporation. Music guides.

Keys, Ivor. Brahms chamber music. *British Broadcasting Corporation. £0.45* BBTAN (B74-14311) ISBN 0-563-10168-7

Piggott, Patrick. Rachmaninov orchestral music. *British Broadcasting Corporation. £0.45* BRCAM (B74-14309) ISBN 0-563-12468-7

British Broadcasting Corporation. Songs for 'Singing Together' : fifty songs from around the world taken from the BBC's music programme Singing Together. (Coombes, Douglas). *British Broadcasting Corporation. £1.25* JFDW/G/AY (B74-51036) ISBN 0-563-13189-6

British Federation of Music Festivals. Year book

1974. *106 Gloucester Place, W1H 3DB : The Federation. £0.60* A(YC/WE/Q) (B74-12386) ISBN 0-901532-05-3

Britten, Benjamin. Children's crusade = Kinderkreuzzug. Op.82 : a ballad for children's voices and orchestra. *Faber Music : Faber. £15.00* BBUADX (B74-21537) ISBN 0-571-10370-7

Broadwood, Lucy Etheldred. English traditional songs and carols. *Rowman and Littlefield : EP Publishing. Unpriced* KDW/G/AYD (B74-50474) ISBN 0-7158-1025-1

Brokering, Herbert. Trilogy of praise : for four-part chorus of mixed voices a cappella. (Wetzler, Robert). *Schirmer. Unpriced* EZDE (B74-50037)

Brooks, Keith. Classical album for clarinet ensemble. *Boosey and Hawkes. £2.50* VVNTK/AAY (B74-50797)

Brown, Christopher. Strawberry fair : two-part. *Oxford University Press. £0.08* FDW (B74-50990) ISBN 0-19-341509-7

Brown, David. First evening service. Magnificat and Nunc dimittis : SSAATB. (Weelkes, Thomas). *Oxford University Press. £0.30* DGPP (B74-50342) ISBN 0-19-351646-2

Brown, David, *b.1929.*

Mikhail Glinka : a biographical and critical study. *Oxford University Press. £7.00* BGL(N) (B74-03503) ISBN 0-19-315311-4

Wilbye. *Oxford University Press. £1.65* BWNRB (B74-13708) ISBN 0-19-315220-7

Brown, Frank Edwin. Cramer's carols : for male voice choir. *Cramer. Unpriced* GEZDP/LF/AY (B74-51015)

Brown, Howard Mayer. Mon mary m'a diffamée : chanson, S.T.T. *Oxford University Press. Unpriced* ETWDU (B74-50035) ISBN 0-19-341203-9

Brown, James. Sonata for oboe & piano in E minor. Duo sonata for oboe and piano. (Widerkehr, Jacob Christian Michael). *Musica rara. Unpriced* VTPE (B74-50782)

Brown, Maurice John Edwin. Chopin. (Hedley, Arthur). Revised ed. *Dent. £2.50* BCE (B74-13109) ISBN 0-460-03154-6

Brown, Rosemary. The Rosemary Brown piano album : 7 pieces inspired by Beethoven, Schubert, Chopin, Schumann, Brahms and Liszt. *Paxton. £0.60* QPJ (B74-50585)

Brown gal in de ring : 12 Jamaican folk-songs. (Lewin, Olive). *Oxford University Press. £0.40* JFDW/GS/AYULD (B74-51039) ISBN 0-19-330544-5

Browne, Michael Dennis. Nonsongs : six songs about nothing in particular for voices, descant recorders, pitched and unpitched percussion and piano. (Lord, David). *Universal. Unpriced* JE/NYFSRDW (B74-51025)

Brückner, H. Sonata for two trumpets, two violins & basso continuo. Sonata for 2 cornetti (trumpets), 2 violins and basso continuo. *Musica rara. Unpriced* NUXSNRE (B74-50537)

Brunelli, Louis. Derivations from clarinet & wind band: arr. Derivations : for clarinet and band. (Gould, Morton). *Chappell. Unpriced* VVPK (B74-51344)

Brunelli, Louis Jean. In memoriam : for concert band. *Chappell. Unpriced* UMJ (B74-51296)

Brush, J A. Regimental quick march, 'The Royal Highland Fusiliers'. *Boosey and Hawkes. £0.65* UMMGM/KH (B74-50727)

Brydson, John Callis. Fantasy : suite of five pieces for

pianoforte. *Freeman. £0.35* QPG (B74-50168)
Buchtel, Forrest Lawrence. Fortune's promise : overture for military band. *Warner : Blossom. Unpriced* UMMJ (B74-50729)
Built on the rock : anthem for unison choir or solo voice and organ. (Lindeman, Ludvig Matthias). *Oxford University Press. Unpriced* JDH (B74-51017)
Bullard, Alan. Air and gigue for clavichord (or piano). *Oxford University Press. Unpriced* QTPHP (B74-51188) ISBN 0-19-372394-8
Bulmer, Dave. Music from Ireland
Vol.1. *154 Bamburgh Ave, South Shields : Dave Bulmer. Unpriced* LPM/AYDM (B74-51087)
Burgan, Arthur. Basic string repairs : a guide for string-class teachers. *Oxford University Press. £1.75* ARX/BT (B74-09234) ISBN 0-19-318509-1
Burgon, Geoffrey. Four Elizabethan dance. *Galaxy : Stainer and Bell. Unpriced* WNSK/AH/AY (B74-50830)
Burkhard, Willy
Concerto for viola and orchestra. Konzert für Viola und Orchester. *Bärenreiter. £2.55* MPSQF (B74-50515)
Die schwarze Spinne, Op.80a : Suite für Orchester. *Bärenreiter. £3.25* MMG (B74-50498)
Burns, Robert. The kindling fire : twelve Burns songs, arranged for high voice using the airs to which Burns set his verses. (Liddell, Claire). *Roberton. £1.00* KFTDW/AY (B74-51072)
Burrell, Howard.
Five concert studies : for unaccompanied trumpet. *Oxford University Press. £0.60* WSPMJ (B74-51369) ISBN 0-19-355759-2
Studies and exercises for unaccompanied trumpet. *Oxford University Press. £0.80* WS/AF (B74-50831) ISBN 0-19-355758-4
Burt, James.
The world of your 100 best tunes requested by listeners to the popular BBC radio series devised and presented by Alan Keith, easy-to-play piano album, piano arrangements by James Burt
Vol.4. (Keith, Alan). *Chappell. Unpriced* QPK/AAY (B74-50598)
The world of your 100 best tunes requested by listeners to the popular BBC radio series
Vol.1. (Keith, Alan). *Chappell. £0.50* QPK/AAY (B74-50599)
Vol.2. (Keith, Alan). *Chappell. £0.50* QPK/AAY (B74-50600)
Vol.3. (Keith, Alan). *Chappell. £0.95* QPK/AAY (B74-50601)
Burton, Shirley. Table for starting courses of Stedman Cinques in the Tittums. *c/o 'Monsal', Bredon, Tewkesbury, Glos. GL20 7LY : Central Council of Church Bell Ringers, Education Committee. Unpriced* XSR (B74-50855)
Bush, Geoffrey. Suite de pièces. Op.24. (Bennett, *Sir* William Sterndale). *Stainer and Bell. Unpriced* QPG (B74-50576)
Busoni, Ferruccio Benvenuto. Works, organ. Selections. Praeludium, Basso ostinato. Op.7, and Doppelfuge zum Choral. Op.76. *Cranz. £0.60* R/Y (B74-50614)
Butler, Frank. The concertina : a handbook and tutor for beginners on the 'English' concertina. *Free Reed Press. Unpriced* RT/AC (B74-50637)
Butt, James. Soliloquy : for solo violin. *Thames. Unpriced* SPMG (B74-51249)
Butterworth, Neil. Christmas day : SATB unacc. *Banks. Unpriced* EZDP/LF (B74-50960)
Butting, Max. Quartet for strings, no.8. Op.96. VIII. Streichquartett. Opus 96. *Peters. Unpriced* RXNS (B74-51226)
Byrd, William.
Gradualia, lib.1. Sacerdotes Domini. Sacerdotes Domini = Then did priests make offering : SATB. Revised ed. *Oxford University Press. Unpriced* EZDGKAF (B74-50038) ISBN 0-19-352008-7
Gradulia, lib 2. Victimae paschali. Victimae paschali = Unto Christ the victim : motet for five voices, SSAT unacc. *Oxford University Press. £0.30* DGKADD/LL (B74-50879) ISBN 0-19-352010-9
Liber primus sacrarum cantionum. Vigilate. Vigilate = Be ye watchful : motet for five voices S.A.T.Ba.B. *Oxford University Press. £0.20* EZDJ (B74-50395) ISBN 0-19-352056-7
Cacavas, John.
Make it happen : for concert band. *Athenaeum : Chappell. Unpriced* UMJ (B74-51297)
March of the magnificants : for concert band. *Chappell. Unpriced* UMGM (B74-51293)
Scipione. March : arr. Il Scipio : march. (Handel, George Frideric). *Chappell. Unpriced* UMK/AGM (B74-51301)
Selections: arr. Two Russian marches. (Tchaikovsky, Peter). *Chappell. Unpriced* UMK/AGM (B74-50721)
Cadence I : for solo cello. (Lazarof, Henri). *Associated Music. £2.00* SRPMFM (B74-50684)
Cage, John. John Cage. (Kostelanetz, Richard). *Allen Lane. £2.00* BCBG (B74-11048) ISBN 0-7139-0762-2
Calamus. Op.104 : mixed chorus of brass-percussion ensemble or piano : music by Paul Creston. (Creston, Paul). *Schirmer. Unpriced* DX (B74-50927)
Calamus. Op.104. Vocal score. Calamus. Op.104 : mixed chorus of brass-percussion ensemble or piano : music by Paul Creston. (Creston, Paul). *Schirmer. Unpriced* DX (B74-50927)
Calder, Robert. Pity me not : SATB a cappella. *Associated Music. Unpriced* EZDW (B74-50058)
Caldwell, John.
Solos for a German flute. Op.1, 4. Complete works for flute and basso continuo
Set 1: Solo 1 in D minor, Solo 2 in G minor (from Eight solos, opus 1). (Stanley, John). *Oxford University Press. £2.50* VRP/AZ (B74-50747) ISBN 0-19-358896-x
Solos for a German flute. Op.1, 4. Complete works for flute and basso continuo
Set 2: Solo 3 in G major, Solo 4 in D major (from Eight solos, opus 1). (Stanley, John). *Oxford University Press. £2.50* VRP/AZ (B74-50748) ISBN 0-19-358897-8
Solos for a German flute. Op.1, 4. Complete works for flute and basso continuo
Set 3: Solo 5 in C major, Solo 6 in D major (from Eight solos, opus 1). (Stanley, John). *Oxford University Press. £2.50* VRP/AZ (B74-50749) ISBN 0-19-358898-6
Solos for a German flute. Op.1, 4. Complete works for flute and basso continuo
Set 4: Solo 7 in D minor, Solo 8 in E minor (from Eight solos, opus 1). (Stanley, John). *Oxford University Press. £2.50* VRP/AZ (B74-50750) ISBN 0-19-358899-4
Caliban and Ariel : for solo bassoon. (Ridout, Alan). *Chappell. Unpriced* VWPMJ (B74-50814)
California University. *See* University of California.
Caligaverunt oculi mei = My eyes are blinded by my weeping : Lenten motet for four-part chorus of mixed voices a cappella. (Ingegneri, Marco Antonio). *Schirmer. Unpriced* FEZDGKH/LHL (B74-50073)
Callers' choice : a selection of recently composed dances
Book 1. (Matthews, Nibs). *English Folk Dance and Song Society. Unpriced* LH/H/AY (B74-50121) ISBN 0-85418-035-4
Calvocoressi, Michael Dimitri. Mussorgsky. Revised ed. *Dent. £2.75* BMU (B74-13105) ISBN 0-460-03152-x
Cambridge University. *See* University of Cambridge.
Cameo. Paganelli, Sergio. Musical instruments from the Renaissance to the 19th century. *Hamlyn. £0.50* AL/B(XD401) (B74-20189) ISBN 0-600-31853-2
Camilleri, Charles.
Due canti : two songs for piano solo. *Roberton. £0.40* QPJ (B74-51163)
Etudes : pianoBook 1. *Roberton. £0.75* QPJ (B74-51164)
Book 2. *Roberton. £0.75* QPJ (B74-51165)
Book 3. *Roberton. £0.55* QPJ (B74-51166)
Hemda : for piano solo. *Fairfield, Distributed by Novello. £0.40* QPJ (B74-50176)
Mantra : for piano solo. *Fairfield, Distributed by Novello. £1.00* QPJ (B74-50177)
Sonatina classica : piano. *Roberton. £0.50* QPEM (B74-51146)
Sonatina for piano, no.1. Sonatine number one : piano. *Roberton. £0.60* QPEM (B74-51147)
Three African sketches : piano. *Roberton. £0.40* QPJ (B74-51167)
Times of day : five Southern impressions, piano. *Roberton. £0.60* QPJ (B74-51168)
Cammarota, Paul. Suites for cello. Nos 1-2. S: 1007-8. Two suites. (Bach, Johann Sebastian). *Schimer. £1.15* VWPMK/AG (B74-50815)
Cammin, Heinz.
Lied über die Grenze : Folklore fremder Länder für drei gleiche Stimmen mit Begleitung
Heft II. *Schott. £2.61* FDW/G/AY (B74-50996)
Lied über die Grenze : Folklore fremder Länder
Heft II. *Schott. £1.74* TSPMK/DW/G/AY (B74-51284)
Camp, John. Bell ringing : chimes, carillons, handbells - the world of the bell and the ringer. *David and Charles. £2.95* AXSR (B74-05793) ISBN 0-7153-6088-4
Camp, Leonard Van. Weltspiegel. *O Musika du edle Kunst.* O Musica, thou noble art : for five-part chorus of mixed voices a cappella. (Peuerl, Paul). *Roberton. £0.10* EZDW (B74-50060)
Campion, Thomas.
First book of ayres. Never weather-beaten sail: arr. Never weather-beaten sail. *Studio Music. Unpriced* WMK/DW (B74-51360)
Works, songs. Selections. Selected songs of Thomas Campion. *David Godine : Bodley Head. £6.00* KDW (B74-50457) ISBN 0-370-10306-8
Candlelight : a cycle of nursery jingles. (Warlock, Peter). *Thames Music. Unpriced* KDW (B74-51054)
Canenon llafar gwlad = Songs from oral tradition
Vol.1. (Saer, D Roy). *National Museum of Wales, Welsh Folk Museum. Unpriced* JEZDW/G/AYDK (B74-51033) ISBN 0-85485-026-0
Cantata for Easter : four part chorus of mixed voices with organ accompaniment. (Effinger, Cecil). *Schirmer. Unpriced* DE/LL (B74-50876)
Cantate rag : for S.A.T.B., piano and percussion. (Sansom, Clive A). *Paterson. Unpriced* ENYLDE (B74-50935)
Canticle of fire : for chorus (SATB) and organ. (Williamson, Malcolm). *Weinberger. Unpriced* DE (B74-50875)
Cantico del sole : for unaccompanied mixed voices. (Walton, *Sir* William). *Oxford University Press. £0.50* EZDH (B74-50947) ISBN 0-19-338490-6
Cantilena no.1 : piano. (Lombardi, Nilson). *Arthur Napoleão : Essex Music. Unpriced* QPJ (B74-51177)
Cantiones sacrae. Deus misereatur nostri. Deus misereatur nostri = God be merciful unto us : for four-part chorus of mixed voices a cappella. (Schütz, Heinrich). *Schirmer. Unpriced* EZDR (B74-50407)
Cantiones sacrae. In te Domine, speravi. In te Domine, speravi = Lord in thee do I put my trust : motet for four-part chorus of mixed voices a cappella. (Schütz, Heinrich). *Schirmer. Unpriced* EZDJ (B74-50398)
Cantiones sacrae. Quoniam ad te clamabo, Domine. Quoniam ad te clamabo, Domine = Now behold to thee I cry, O Lord : motet for four-part chorus of mixed voices a cappella. (Schütz, Heinrich). *Chappell. Unpriced* EZDJ (B74-50399)
Cantiones sacrae. Verbum caro factum est. Verbum caro factum est = And the Word became flesh : motet for six-part chorus of mixed voices a cappella. (Hassler, Hans Leo). *Schirmer. Unpriced* EZDJ (B74-50949)
Canto VII : tuba solo. (Adler, Samuel). *Boosey and Hawkes. £1.00* WVPMJ (B74-50850)
Canzona for piano. Op.28. (Tcherepnin, Alexander). New ed. *Simrock. Unpriced* QPJ (B74-50187)
Canzona on 'Romanesca'. (Frescobaldi, Girolamo). *Associated Music. Unpriced* VSNRPW (B74-50275)
Canzonette francese : for recorder quartet, SATB. (Guami, Gioseffo). *Galaxy Music. Unpriced* VSNS (B74-50767)
Canzonette francese. Selections. Canzonette francese : for recorder quartet, SATB. (Guami, Gioseffo). *Galaxy Music. Unpriced* VSNS (B74-50767)
Canzoni da sonare, lib. 1. *Romanesca.* Canzona on 'Romanesca'. (Frescobaldi, Girolamo). *Associated Music. Unpriced* VSNRPW (B74-50275)
Capell, Richard. Schubert's songs. 3rd ed. *Duckworth. £4.95* BSFAKDW (B74-05269) ISBN 0-7156-0735-9
Capriccio. (Bach, Johann Sebastian). *Schirmer. Unpriced* QPJ (B74-50583)
Capriccio sopra la lontanza del suo fratello dilettissimo. S.992. Capriccio. (Bach, Johann Sebastian). *Schirmer. Unpriced* QPJ (B74-50583)
Carcasio, Giuseppe. Sonata for two trumpets, two oboes & basso continuo, no.1, in D major. Sonata for 2 trumpets, 2 oboes, ad lib and organ-basso continuo, no.1. *Musica rara. Unpriced* NWNRE (B74-50545)
Carillon. (Bizet, Georges). *Boosey and Hawkes. Score £1.50, Piano conductor £0.50, Set £2.50* MK/JM (B74-51091)
Carissimi, Giacome. Jephte. Vocal score. Jephte (Jephthah) : oratorio for SATB soli, SSSATB chorus, optional strings without violas, and organ continuo. *Novello. £0.55* ENXDD (B74-50378)
Carissimi, Giacomo. Nisi Dominus. Psalm 127 : motet for SSATB and organ continuo. *Novello. £0.20* DR (B74-50913)
Carnival des animaux : grande fantasie zoologique. (Saint-Saëns, Camille). *Peters. Unpriced* MMJ (B74-51104)
Carnival des animaux. Selections: arr. Two pieces. (Saint-Saëns, Camille). *Oxford University Press. £0.60* VVPK (B74-51345) ISBN 0-19-358701-7
Carnival des animaux. Selections: arr. Two pieces. (Saint-Saëns, Camille). *Oxford University Press. £0.45* VWPK (B74-51348) ISBN 0-19-358703-3
Carol of the sun : for two-part or unison chorus. (Blake, Leonard). *Roberton. £0.10* FDP/LF (B74-50414)
Carol of the sun. *Vocal score.* Carol of the sun : for two-part or unison chorus. (Blake, Leonard). *Roberton. £0.10* FDP/LF (B74-50414)
Carol ringing and more. (Bedford, Donald A). *Handbell Ringers of Great Britain. Unpriced* XSQMK/CB/AY (B74-51375)
Carper, Virginia Speiden. Water music. Selections: arr. Three pieces. (Handel, George Frideric). *Schirmer. Unpriced* QNTZNK (B74-50160)
Carr, Ian, *b.1933.* Music outside : contemporary jazz in Britain. *Latimer New Dimensions. £3.00* AMT(M) (B74-01930) ISBN 0-901539-25-2
Carter, Andrew.
Down in yon forest : English traditional carol, SSAATBB unacc. *Banks. Unpriced* EZDP/LF (B74-50961)
Two traditional carols : SATB unacc. *Banks. Unpriced* EZDP/LF/AY (B74-50969)
Carter, Anthony. '1812' overture: arr. '1812' overture : for school orchestra. (Tchaikovsky, Peter). *Bosworth. £2.10* MK (B74-50491)
Carter, Elliot. Voyage : for medium voice and piano. *Associated Music Publishers. £0.40* KFVDW (B74-50486)
Carter, Elliott.
Concerto for orchestra. *Associated Music. Unpriced* MMF (B74-50136)
Pocohontas : orchestral suite from the ballet. *Associated Music. Unpriced* MMG/HM (B74-50138)
Quartet for strings, no.3. String quartet no.3. *Associated Music. Unpriced* RXNS (B74-50656)
Tell me where is fancy bred : for voice and guitar. *Associated Music. Unpriced* KE/TSDW (B74-50110)
Carter, Sydney. Green print for song. *Galliard, Stainer and Bell. Unpriced* JDP (B74-51022) ISBN 0-85249-284-7
Carter family. (Atkins, John). *33 Brunswick Gardens, W8 4AW : Old Time Music. £0.60* ADW/G(YT/P) (B74-12389) ISBN 0-904395-00-6
Carulli, Benedetto. Trio concertante for two clarinets & bassoon in C major. Op.1. Trio, C-Dur. Op.1 : für zwei Klarinetten und Fagott. *Schott. £5.22* VNTF (B74-51315)
Carulli, Ferdinando. Duo for flute and guitar in D major. Op. 109, no.6. Serenade für Flöte (Violine) und Gitarre. *Schott. £1.32* VRPLTS (B74-50273)
Cassey, Chuck. We're all in this together : arr. We're all in this together : for mixed chorus (SATB). (Hague, Albert). *Chappell. Unpriced* DW (B74-50924)
Cat variations : for clarinet in A and piano on a theme from Prokofiev's 'Peter and the wolf'. (Searle, Humphrey). *Faber Music. Unpriced* VVQP/T (B74-50807)
Caterina Cornaro. (Donizetti, Gaetano). *Egret House : (Under the auspices of the Donizetti Society). Unpriced* CC (B74-50867)
Caterina Cornaro. Vocal score. Caterina Cornaro. (Donizetti, Gaetano). *Egret House : (Under the auspices of the Donizetti Society). Unpriced* CC (B74-50867)
Cathedral Church of the Blessed Virgin Mary and St Chad, *Lichfield. See* Lichfield Cathedral.
Cavern : unison song. (Davies, Laurence Hector). *Ashdown. £0.05* JFDW (B74-50091)
Cazzati, Mauritio. Sonata for strings & basso continuo in G minor. Op.35, 'La Sampiera'. Sonata 'La Sampiera' : for strings and continuo. *Schott. £1.50* NXNRE

(B74-50155)

Cecil Sharp's collection of English folk songs. (Karpeles, Maud). *Oxford University Press. £44 for set* JEZDW/G/AYD (B74-51032) ISBN 0-19-313125-0

Cecily, *Sister, OP.* Lámhleabhar ginearálta don cheoltóir. *Folens. £0.48* A (B74-11047) ISBN 0-902592-58-0

Celtic dances. Opus 60 : for orchestra. (Mathias, William). *Oxford University Press. £3.50* MMH (B74-51100) ISBN 0-19-365572-1

Center for the Study of Armament and Disarmament. *See* University of California at Los Angeles. *Center for the Study of Armament and Disarmament.*

Central Council of Church Bell Ringers. Publications. Chant, Harold. Elementary method splicing. *c/o 'Monsal', Bredon, Tewkesbury, Glos. GL20 7LY : Central Council of Church Bell Ringers, Education Committee. Unpriced* XSR (B74-50858)

Central Council of Church Bell Ringers. Ten & twelve bell compositions. *c/o 'Monsal', Bredon, Tewkesbury, Glos. GL20 7LY : The Council. Unpriced* XSR (B74-50856)

Central Council of Church Bell Ringers. *Education Committee.* Publications.

Burton, Shirley. Table for starting courses of Stedman Cinques in the Tittums. *c/o 'Monsal', Bredon, Tewkesbury, Glos. GL20 7LY : Central Council of Church Bell Ringers, Education Committee. Unpriced* XSR (B74-50855)

Chaddock, Norman. Conducting Grandsire Triples. *c/o 'Monsal', Bredon, Tewkesbury, Glos. GL20 7LY : Central Council of Church Bell Ringers, Education Committee. Unpriced* XSR (B74-50857)

Chant, Harold. Proof of Plain Bob Major. *c/o 'Monsal', Bredon, Tewkesbury, Glos. GL20 7LY : Central Council of Church Bell Ringers, Education Committee. Unpriced* XSR (B74-50859)

Century celebration. Honoring America's bicentennial : for concert band. (Balent, Andrew). *Warner : Blossom. Unpriced* UMGM (B74-50713)

Ceremonial fanfare : for brass ensemble, (4 horns, 3 trumpets, 3 trombones, tuba). (Copland, Aaron). *Boosey and Hawkes. £1.50* WMGN (B74-51355)

Ceremonial music for organ

Book 2. (Dearnley, Christopher). *Oxford University Press. £0.50* RK/AAY (B74-50627) ISBN 0-19-375345-6

Ceremonial. Op.103 : for percussion ensemble and piano. (Creston, Paul). *Schirmer. Unpriced* NYLNN (B74-50553)

C'est ça la France. (Renard, J). *Chappell. Unpriced* UMK (B74-50719)

Chaddock, Norman. Conducting Grandsire Triples. *c/o 'Monsal', Bredon, Tewkesbury, Glos. GL20 7LY : Central Council of Church Bell Ringers, Education Committee. Unpriced* XSR (B74-50857)

Chamber music for beginners : for two melodic instruments and bass, with continuo. (Máriássy, István). *Boosey and Hawkes : Editio Musica. £1.25* LNTQ/AY (B74-51084)

Chambers, George Bennet. Folksong - plainsong : a study in origins and musical relationships. 2nd ed. *Merlin Press. £3.00* ADT(ZF) (B74-20191) ISBN 0-85036-195-8

Chanson de matin. Opus 15, no.1. (Elgar, *Sir* Edward, *bart*). *Paxton. £1.25* WMK (B74-50824)

Chant, Harold.

Elementary method splicing. *c/o 'Monsal', Bredon, Tewkesbury, Glos. GL20 7LY : Central Council of Church Bell Ringers, Education Committee. Unpriced* XSR (B74-50858)

Proof of Plain Bob Major. *c/o 'Monsal', Bredon, Tewkesbury, Glos. GL20 7LY : Central Council of Church Bell Ringers, Education Committee. Unpriced* XSR (B74-50859)

Chanukah suite : for recorder trio, SAT. (Goldstein, David). *Galaxy : Galliard. Unpriced* VSNTG (B74-51333)

Chappell, Herbert. Psalms for today. *Chappell. Unpriced* JDR (B74-50445)

Chapple, Brian. Hallelujahs : for two choirs and organ. *Chester : Hansen. Unpriced* DH (B74-50895)

Charade. Op.28 : for orchestra. (Muczynski, Robert). *Schirmer. Unpriced* MMJ (B74-51103)

Chasseur maudit. (Franck, César). *Eulenburg. Unpriced* MMJ (B74-50505)

Chavez, Carlos. Discovery = Descubrimiento : for orchestra. *Schirmer. £2.35* MMJ (B74-50503)

Chemins IIb-c. (Berio, Luciano). *Universal. Unpriced* MMJ (B74-50501)

Child is born to us : a Christmas choral cycle for full chorus of treble voices a cappella. (Davye, John J). *Associated Music. Unpriced* FLEZDP/LF (B74-50433)

Child of wonder. Alleluia and chorale. Alleluia and chorale : SATB with piano, four-hands. (Forcucci, Samuel L). *Schirmer. Unpriced* DH/LF (B74-50016)

Children of David. Op.37 : five modern psalms, for mixed chorus and organ

1: Psalm. (Mechem, Kirke). *Boosey and Hawkes. Unpriced* DH (B74-50898)

2: Joy. (Mechem, Kirke). *Boosey and Hawkes. Unpriced* DH (B74-50899)

3: The song of David. (Mechem, Kirke). *Boosey and Hawkes. Unpriced* DH (B74-50900)

4: Man of my own people. (Mechem, Kirke). *Boosey and Hawkes. Unpriced* DH (B74-50901)

5: Pied beauty. (Mechem, Kirke). *Boosey and Hawkes. Unpriced* DH (B74-50902)

Children's crusade = Kinderkreuzzug. Op.82 : a ballad for children's voices and orchestra. (Britten, Benjamin). *Faber Music : Faber. £15.00* BBUADX (B74-21537) ISBN 0-571-10370-7

Child's play : for bassoon and piano. (Ward-Steinman, David). *Highgate Press : Galaxy : Galliard. Unpriced* VWPJ (B74-51347)

Chimes, Michael. Let's play harmonica. *Experience Music : Chappell. Unpriced* VX/AC (B74-50816)

Choksy, Lois. The Kodály method : comprehensive music education from infant to adult. *Prentice-Hall. £2.60* A(VC) (B74-23950) ISBN 0-13-516757-4

Chopin, Frédéric. Nocturne for piano, no.20, in C sharp minor. Op. posth. Nocturne (posthumous). *Schirmer. Unpriced* VRPK (B74-51322)

Chopin. (Hedley, Arthur). Revised ed. *Dent. £2.50* BCE (B74-13109) ISBN 0-460-03154-6

Choppen, Edward. Sonata for piano, no.2, in G major. Op.14. Andante: arr. Andante from piano sonata Opus 14, no.2. (Beethoven, Ludwig van). *Novello. £0.33* TSPMK/AE (B74-50709)

Chorale for band : wind band. (Washburn, Robert). *Oxford University Press. Unpriced* UMJ (B74-51300)

Chorale for strings. (Stoker, Richard). *Fenette Music : Breitkopf and Härtel. Unpriced* RXMJ (B74-50643)

Chorbajian, John.

Dark house : for full chorus of mixed voices a cappella. *Schirmer. Unpriced* EZDW (B74-50975)

The silver swan : for full chorus of mixed voices a cappella. *Schirmer. Unpriced* EZDW (B74-50976)

When David heard that his son was slain : for full chorus of mixed voices a cappella. *Schirmer. Unpriced* EZDK (B74-50954)

Christmas carols for beginner guitarists. (Gavall, John). *Bosworth. Unpriced* TSPMK/DP/LF/AY (B74-51283)

Christmas child : for unison, SA or SAB chorus and piano. (Rocherolle, Eugenie R). *Warner : Blossom. Unpriced* JDW/LF (B74-50448)

Christmas cradle song. (Brahms, Johannes). *Novello. Unpriced* EZDP/LF (B74-50959)

Christmas day : SATB unacc. (Butterworth, Neil). *Banks. Unpriced* EZDP/LF (B74-50960)

Christopher Columbus. Beatriz's song: arr. Beatriz's song. (Walton, *Sir* William). *Oxford University Press. £0.35* KE/TSDW/JM (B74-50481) ISBN 0-19-345866-7

Christus natus est : unison with descant. (Wilcock, Anthea). *Chappell. Unpriced* FDP/LF (B74-50989)

Christus : Oratorium nach Texten aus der heligen Schrift und der katholischen Liturgie : Soli, Chor, Orgel und grosses Orchester. (Liszt, Franz). *Gregg. £7.80* EMDE (B74-50932) ISBN 0-576-28232-4

Chromatic poem : for organ (1969). (Slonimski, Sergei). *Peters. Unpriced* RJ (B74-51196)

Church bells of Berkshire : their inscriptions and founders, arranged alphabetically by parishes ... (Sharpe, Frederick). 2nd ed. *Kingsmead Reprints. £4.00* AXSR/B(YDEU) (B74-05271) ISBN 0-901571-46-6

Churchill, John.

Three songs from eastern Canada : for mixed voice S.A.T.B. and piano

1: Les trois canes (Cheticamp, N.S.). *Lengnick. £0.12* DW/G/AYSXC (B74-50025)

2: Ave maris stella (Acadian 17th cent.). *Lengnick. £0.12* DW/G/AYSXC (B74-50026)

3: I'se the b'y (Newfoundland). *Lengnick. £0.12* DW/G/AYSXC (B74-50027)

Churchill, Sarah. Songs. *Sparta Florida : Chappell. Unpriced* KDW (B74-50458)

Churchley, Frank.

Basic goals in music

Book 3. (Morrish, D L). *McGraw-Hill. Unpriced* C/AC (B74-50862) ISBN 0-07-094432-6

Book 4. (Morrish, D L). *McGraw-Hill. Unpriced* C/AC (B74-50863) ISBN 0-07-094433-4

Book 5. (Morrish, D L). *McGraw-Hill. Unpriced* C/AC (B74-50864) ISBN 0-07-094434-2

Ciampa, Carmela Marie. Harper's dictionary of music. (Ammer, Christine). *28 Tavistock St., WC2E 7PN : Barnes and Noble. £1.60* A(C) (B74-09865) ISBN 0-06-463347-0

Cines, Eugene. Abbreviations : piano solo. *Boosey and Hawkes. Unpriced* QPJ (B74-50586)

Circus overture. (Schuman, William). *Schirmer. Unpriced* UMK (B74-50267)

Citation series for young bands. Tchaikovsky, Peter. Selections: arr. Two Russian marches. *Chappell. Unpriced* UMK/AGM (B74-50721)

Claire de lune. (Veneux, Thierry). *Chappell. Unpriced* TMK (B74-50690)

Claire de lune: arr. Claire de lune. (Veneux, Thierry). *Chappell. Unpriced* TMK (B74-50690)

Clark, M E. Regimental quick march 'The Royal Irish Rangers'. *Boosey and Hawkes. £0.65* UMMGM/KH (B74-50728)

Clarke, Frank. Four stations on the road to freedom, Opus 73 : for SSAATTBB soli or chorus (unaccompanied). (Joubert, John). *Novello. Unpriced* JNEZAYDE (B74-50456)

Clarke, Jeremiah. Suite de Clarke. *Novello. £0.60* WSPK/AG (B74-51367)

Class piano. (McLain, Margaret Starr). *Indiana University Press. £2.80* AQ/E(VC) (B74-22162) ISBN 0-253-31357-0

Classical album for clarinet ensemble. (Brooks, Keith). *Boosey and Hawkes. £2.50* VVNTK/AAY (B74-50797)

Classical and romantic pieces for viola and piano. (Forbes, Watson). *Oxford University Press. £1.30* SQPK/AAY (B74-50677) ISBN 0-19-356501-3

Classical Chinese plays. (Hung, Josephine Huang). 2nd ed. *Vision Press. £3.80* BZHAC (B74-13707) ISBN 0-85478-302-4

Classics for the young pianist. (Lake, Ian). *Chappell. Unpriced* QP/AY (B74-51142)

Claudia theme. (Devor, Don). *Edwin H. Morris. Unpriced* QPK/JR (B74-50604)

Clayton, Desmond. Concerto for violin, no.2. Vocal score. 2nd violin concerto for solo violin, tape, voices and 33 instrumentalists. (Henze, Hans Werner). *Schott. £7.20* KGE/SPDX (B74-50119)

Clemenicic, René. Old musical instruments. *Octopus Books. £0.99* AL/B(XD351) (B74-07433) ISBN 0-7064-0057-7

Clements, John. Come, dark-eyed sleep : S.S.C. and pianoforte. *Ashdown. £0.10* FDW (B74-50416)

Closson, Ernest. History of the piano. 2nd ed. *Elek. £3.50* AQ/B(X) (B74-09232) ISBN 0-236-17685-4

Clowns : a ballet. (Kay, Hershey). *Boosey and Hawkes. Unpriced* MM/HM (B74-51092)

Coburn, Oliver. Great singers from the seventeenth century to the present day. (Pahlen, Kurt). *W.H. Allen. £4.75* AK/E(M/XM71) (B74-00870) ISBN 0-491-01361-2

Cockett, Mary. Bells in our lives. *David and Charles. £1.60* AXS/B (B74-01380) ISBN 0-7153-6229-1

Coelius, Sedulius. Songs of Ophelia, nos. 3, 4. Christmas cradle song. (Brahms, Johannes). *Novello. Unpriced* EZDP/LF (B74-50959)

Coeuroy, André. Le Chasseur maudit. (Franck, César). *Eulenburg. Unpriced* MMJ (B74-50505)

Cohen, Eta. First year violin method. Eta Cohen violin method

Book 1. *Paxton. £0.50* S/AC (B74-51231)

Cohn, Nik. Rock dreams. (Peellaert, Guy). *Pan Books. £1.95* ADW/GB/E(M/XPM22/EM) (B74-07429) ISBN 0-330-24008-0

Coker, Jerry. Love story. Theme : arr. Theme from the film 'Love story'. (Lai, Francis). *Famous Music : Chappell. Unpriced* UMJ (B74-51298)

Cole, Bruce. Autumn cicada : ko-uta on four Japanese texts, for SSA, harp and 4 handbells. *Boosey and Hawkes. £0.10* FE/NYJNRDW (B74-50427)

Cole, Hugo. Sounds and signs : aspects of musical notation. *Oxford University Press. £1.50* A(QU) (B74-02414) ISBN 0-19-317105-8

Cole, Tony. Take me high : song album. *Coronado Music. £0.75* KDW/JR (B74-50108)

Coleridge-Taylor, Samuel. Quintet for clarinet and strings. *Musica rara. Unpriced* NVVNR (B74-50544)

Collection of organ music. (Thiman, Eric Harding). *Novello. £1.50* RJ (B74-50622)

Collection of the ancient martial music of Caledonia called piobaireache. (MacDonald, Donald). 1st ed., reprinted. *EP Publishing. £4.00* VY/T (B74-50817) ISBN 0-7158-1031-6

College outline series. Jones, George Thaddeus. Music theory. *28 Tavistock St., WC2E 7PN : Barnes and Noble. £1.95* A/AM (B74-25492) ISBN 0-06-460137-4

Collier, Graham, *b.1937.* Inside jazz. *Quartet Books. £2.75* AMT (B74-00162) ISBN 0-7043-2028-2

Collisson, Houston. Variations for euphonium & piano, 'The mountains of Mourne'. The mountains of Mourne : variations for euphonium and piano on the theme by Houston Collison (sic). (Newsome, Roy). *Keith Prowse. £0.75* WWP/T (B74-50853)

Columbia Broadcasting System. Main alphabetical & numerical catalogue : including CBS, CBS Harmony Series, Embassy, Epic, Monument, Mums, Philadelphia International

1974-75. *28 Theobalds Rd, WC1X 8PB : CBS Records. Unpriced* A/FD(WM) (B74-30308) ISBN 0-904456-01-3

Combe, Stuff. Anleitung zur Improvisation für Schlagzeug. *Schott. £1.56* XHX/DZ/AF (B74-50322)

Combellack, Myrna May. A survey of musical activities in Cornwall. *Trevenson House, Pool, Redruth, Cornwall : Institute of Cornish Studies. £0.30* A(YDFR) (B74-22803) ISBN 0-903686-05-8

Come, dark-eyed sleep : S.S.C. and pianoforte. (Clements, John). *Ashdown. £0.10* FDW (B74-50416)

Come down, O love divine : anthem for SSA (unaccompanied) suitable for Whitsun or general use. (Nelson, Havelock). *Elkin. £0.07* FEZDH (B74-50074)

Communion service in E, series 3 : for congregational use. (Walker, Robert). *Novello. £0.16* JDGS (B74-50441)

Compendium of musical practice. (Ornithoparchus, Andreas). *Dover Publications : Constable. £7.00* A/M(XDS) (B74-11735) ISBN 0-486-20912-1

Composer's voice. (Cone, Edward T). *University of California Press. £5.50* A/D (B74-28312) ISBN 0-520-02508-3

Compositioni musicale fatte per sonare col fagotto solo, nos 1-3. Three sonatas for bassoon (violoncello) and basso continuo. (Bertoli, Giovanni Antonio). *Bärenreiter. £3.45* VWPE (B74-50811)

Concert piano in Scotland : a report to the Scottish Arts Council. (Piano Panel). *19 Charlotte Sq., Edinburgh EH2 4DF : Scottish Arts Council. £0.25* AQ(W/YDL) (B74-09233) ISBN 0-902989-13-8

Concert piece : for two flutes and string orchestra. (Berger, Jean). *Schirmer. Unpriced* RXMPVRNU (B74-50222)

Concert set for organ. (Binkerd, Gordon). *Boosey and Hawkes. £3.75* RK (B74-51198)

Concert song companion : a guide to the classical repertoire. (Osborne, Charles, *b.1927*). *Gollancz. £4.00* AKDW(XEXK301) (B74-24211) ISBN 0-575-01825-9

Concertante music : for double bass, wind and strings; piano reduction. (Lamb, Peter). *Yorke. Unpriced* SSPK/LF (B74-51256)

Concertina : a handbook and tutor for beginners on the 'English' concertina. (Butler, Frank). *Free Reed Press. Unpriced* RT/AC (B74-50637)

Concerto movement for violin and chamber orchestra, 1790/92. Wo05. (Beethoven, Ludwig van). *Breitkopf and Härtel : Bärenreiter. £3.25* SPK (B74-50675)

Concerto movement for violin in C major. G.148: arr. Concerto movement for violin and chamber orchestra,

1790/92. Wo05. (Beethoven, Ludwig van). *Breitkopf and Härtel : Bärenreiter. £3.25* SPK (B74-50675)

Concerts royaux I-IV : for flute, oboe, violin, viola da gamba and basso continuo
No.I. (Couperin, François). *Musica rara. Unpriced* VRPG (B74-50754)
No.II. (Couperin, François). *Musica rara. Unpriced* VRPG (B74-50755)
No.III. (Couperin, François). *Musica rara. Unpriced* VRPG (B74-50756)
No.IV. (Couperin, François). *Musica rara. Unpriced* VRPG (B74-50757)

Concise history of music : from primitive times to the present. (Young, Percy Marshall). *E. Benn. £2.00* A(X) (B74-13103) ISBN 0-510-37312-7

Concorde : cornet solo and brass band. (Newsome, Roy). *Studio Music. Unpriced* WMPWR (B74-51362)

Concourse : for percussion and other instruments. (Tomlinson, Geoffrey). *Boosey and Hawkes. £1.20* XMJ (B74-50323)

Condon, Eddie. The Eddie Condon scrapbook of jazz. *Hale. £4.80* AMT(P) (B74-13108) ISBN 0-7091-4476-8

Conducting Grandsire Triples. (Chaddock, Norman). *c/o 'Monsal', Bredon, Tewkesbury, Glos. GL20 7LY : Central Council of Church Bell Ringers, Education Committee. Unpriced* XSR (B74-50857)

Cone, Edward T. The composer's voice. *University of California Press. £5.50* A/D (B74-28312) ISBN 0-520-02508-3

Conrat, Hugo. Ziguenerlieder = Gypsy songs. Op.103 : for four-part chorus of mixed voices with soprano and tenor solos and piano accompaniment. (Brahms, Johannes). *Schirmer. Unpriced* DW (B74-50357)

Constant Lambert. (Shead, Richard). *c/o Lutterworth Press, Luke House, Farnham Rd, Guildford, Surrey : Simon Publications. £2.95* BLBP(N) (B74-05266) ISBN 0-903620-01-4

Contemporary contrabass. (Turetzky, Bertram). *University of California Press. £4.40* ASS/E/CY (B74-28317) ISBN 0-520-02291-2

Cook, Georgina. Blessed be he. Op. 147 : SATB. (Rubbra, Edmund). *Lengnick. £0.12* EZDH (B74-50040)

Cooke, Jean. Famous composers. (Rowland-Entwistle, Theodore). *David and Charles. £2.50* A/D(YB/M) (B74-09226) ISBN 0-7153-6375-1

Coombes, Douglas. Songs for 'Singing Together' : fifty songs from around the world taken from the BBC's music programme Singing Together. *British Broadcasting Corporation. £1.25* JFDW/G/AY (B74-51036) ISBN 0-563-13189-6

Cooper, Barry.
Six voluntaries for trumpet and organ. *Musica rara. Unpriced* WSPLRK/AAY (B74-50844)
Sonata for two trumpets, two oboes & basso continuo, no.1, in D major. Sonata for 2 trumpets, 2 oboes, ad lib and organ-basso continuo, no.1. (Carcasio, Giuseppe). *Musica rara. Unpriced* NWNRE (B74-50545)

Cooper, Martin. The new Oxford history of music
Vol.10: The modern age, 1890-1960. *Oxford University Press. £9.50* A(X) (B74-22160) ISBN 0-19-316310-1

Cooper, Thomas Leonard. Brass bands of Yorkshire. *Dalesman. £1.60* AWM(QB/YDGJ) (B74-09231) ISBN 0-85206-195-1

Copland, Aaron.
Ceremonial fanfare : for brass ensemble, (4 horns, 3 trumpets, 3 trombones, tuba). *Boosey and Hawkes. £1.50* WMGN (B74-51355)
In evening air : piano solo. *Boosey and Hawkes. £0.40* QPJ (B74-51169)
Music for radio (1937). Prairie journal : for orchestra. *Boosey and Hawkes. £15.00* MMJ (B74-51101)
Our town : music from the film score. *Boosey and Hawkes. £6.75* MM/JR (B74-51094)

Copley, Ian. Let joybells ring. (Hitchcock, Gordon). *David and Charles. £2.95* JDP/LF/AY (B74-51024) ISBN 0-7153-6712-9

Corelli, Arcangelo. Sonata for violin & basso continuo in C minor. Op.5, no.3: arr. Sonata in C minor. Opus 5, no.3 : for treble (alto) recorder and basso continuo. *Musica rara. Unpriced* VSSPK/AE (B74-50778)

Corigliano, John.
A black November turkey : for four-part chorus of mixed voices with soprano and alto solos a cappella. *Schirmer. Unpriced* EZDW (B74-50059)
L'Invitation au voyage : for four-part chorus of mixed voices with soprano, alto, tenor, and bass solos a cappella. *Schirmer. Unpriced* EZDW (B74-50977)
Poem in October. Vocal score. Poem in October : for voice and orchestra. *Schirmer. Unpriced* KDX (B74-51059)

Corke, Philip. A trip to the concert. (Blackwood, Alan, *b.1932*). *36 Park St., W1Y 4DE : Nelson Young World. £0.45* AM (B74-13709) ISBN 0-7238-0946-1

Corley's march : for military band. (Bavicchi, John). *Oxford University Press. Unpriced* UMMGM (B74-51304)

Cornish, William. Pleasure it is : for unaccompanied mixed chorus. (Kechley, Gerald). *Galaxy : Galliard. Unpriced* EZDP (B74-50958)

Corrette, Michel. Premier livre d'orgue. *Selections.* Magnificat du 3e et 4e ton : for organ. *Novello. Unpriced* RDFF (B74-50617)

Cott, Jonathan.
Stockhausen : conversations with the composer. *Pan Books. £0.95* BSNK (B74-27248) ISBN 0-330-24165-6
Stockhausen : conversations with the composer. *28 Poland St., W1V 3DB : Robson Books Ltd. £3.50* BSNK (B74-10399) ISBN 0-903895-12-9

Couf, Herb. Let's play clarinet. *Chappell. Unpriced* VV/AC (B74-51340)

Couperin, François.
Concerts royaux I-IV : for flute, oboe, violin, viola da gamba and basso continuo
No.I. *Musica rara. Unpriced* VRPG (B74-50754)
No.II. *Musica rara. Unpriced* VRPG (B74-50755)
No.III. *Musica rara. Unpriced* VRPG (B74-50756)
No.IV. *Musica rara. Unpriced* VRPG (B74-50757)

Coursey, Ralph de. Wind encores : a collection of 12 short familiar pieces arranged for four-part clarinet ensemble (2 B flat clarinets, alto clarinet (or bassoon) and bass clarinet (or bassoon)). *Associated Music. Unpriced* VVNSK/AAY (B74-50796)

Crabtree, Phillip D. Canzonette francese. Selections. Canzonette francese : for recorder quartet, SATB. (Guami, Gioseffo). *Galaxy Music. Unpriced* VSNS (B74-50767)

Craig, Douglas. Koanga. Vocal score. Koanga : opera in three acts with prologue and epilogue. (Delius, Frederick). *Boosey and Hawkes. Unpriced* CC (B74-50866)

Cramer's carols : for male voice choir. (Brown, Frank Edwin). *Cramer. Unpriced* GEZDP/LF/AY (B74-51015)

Crane, Hart. Voyage : for medium voice and piano. (Carter, Elliot). *Associated Music Publishers. £0.40* KFVDW (B74-50486)

Crane, Walter. The baby's opera : a book of old rhymes with new dresses. *Pan. £0.60* JFDW/GK/AYD (B74-51038) ISBN 0-330-24088-9

Crawdad song : based on a folksong from the Kentucky Mountains. (Dexter, Harry). *Ashdown. £0.12* FDW (B74-50417)

Creative music making and the young school leaver. (North West Regional Curriculum Development Project). *Blackie. £1.40* A(VK/YDJC/XQG4) (B74-20922) ISBN 0-216-89673-8

Crees, Kathleen. Jonathan and the magic clavichord : a children's story with music. *Autocylus. Unpriced* PWPJ (B74-50158)

Creighton, Basil. Gustav Mahler : memories and letters. (Werfel, Alma Mahler). 3rd ed. *J. Murray. £5.00* BME(N) (B74-00161) ISBN 0-7195-2944-1

Creston, Paul.
Calamus. Op.104. Vocal score. Calamus. Op.104 : mixed chorus of brass-percussion ensemble or piano : music by Paul Creston. *Schirmer. Unpriced* DX (B74-50927)
Ceremonial. Op.103 : for percussion ensemble and piano. *Schirmer. Unpriced* NYLNN (B74-50553)
Concertino for marimba. Op.21. *Second movement: arr.* Meditation : for marimba and organ. *Schirmer. Unpriced* XTQSPLRK (B74-50327)

Criswick, Mary. Guitar tutor for young children. *Fenette Music. Unpriced* TS/AC (B74-50696)

Croce, Giovanni. Exaudi Deus = Oh hear me Lord God : general motet, for four-part chorus of mixed voices a cappella. *Schirmer. Unpriced* EZDJ (B74-50043)

Crocker, John, *b.1925.* Robinson Crusoe : a pantomime. *Evans Plays. £0.50* BCQRACPP (B74-12388) ISBN 0-237-74975-0

Crosse, Gordon, *b.1937.* The story of Vasco : opera in three acts. *Oxford University Press, Music Department. £0.70* BCRAC (B74-09228) ISBN 0-19-335702-x

Crossman, Gerald. Gruss aus Wien! = Greetings from Vienna. *Charnwood Music. Unpriced* RSPMJ (B74-51207)

Cruft, Adrian.
Elegy for horn and strings. *Novello. £2.50* RXMPWT (B74-51222)
Meditation on the Passion chorale. Op.72 : for organ. *Chappell. Unpriced* RJ (B74-50198)
Suite for strings, no.3, from Musick's Handmaid. Third suite for strings, from Musick's Handmaid. *Chappell. Unpriced* RXMG (B74-50217)

Cruger, Johann. Two hymns of praise : with introductory fanfares
1: Now thank we all our God. (Rutter, John). *Oxford University Press. £1.00* EWMDM/AY (B74-50938) ISBN 0-19-367376-2

Crumb, George. Makrokosmos
Volume 1 : for amplified piano. *Peters. £6.00* QPJ (B74-51170)

Crump, Peter. Unum ex illorum sabbatorum : piano. *Thames. Unpriced* QPJ (B74-51171)

Cumming, Richard.
The mock marriage. Man is for the woman made: arr. Man is for the woman made. (Purcell, Henry). *Boosey and Hawkes. Unpriced* DW (B74-50365)
Plaisir d'amour: arr. Plaisir d'amour. (Martini, Giovanni). *Boosey and Hawkes. Unpriced* DW (B74-50359)

Cummings, Edward Estlin.
Three settings of E.E. Cummings
1: Buffalo Bill's: TTBB a cappella. (Yannatos, James). *Associated Music. Unpriced* GEZDW (B74-50081)
2: The rose: SSAA a capella. (Yannatos, James). *Associated Music. Unpriced* FEZDW (B74-50076)
3: In just- : SSATB a cappella. (Yannatos, James). *Associated Music. Unpriced* EZDW (B74-50065)

Da Palestrina, Giovanni Pierluigi. *See* Palestrina, Giovanni Pierluigi da.

Da Siena, Bianco. Come down, O love divine : anthem for SSA (unaccompanied) suitable for Whitsun or general use. (Nelson, Havelock). *Elkin. £0.07* FEZDH (B74-50074)

Dagosto, Sylvain.
Adieu Madras, adieu foulards. (Lully, Jean Baptiste). *Chappell. Unpriced* TMK/DW (B74-50695)
Claire de lune: arr. Claire de lune. (Veneux, Thierry). *Chappell. Unpriced* TMK (B74-50690)
Gavotina. (Roger, Roger). *Chappell. Unpriced* TMK/AHM (B74-50694)
Impressions et images, suite no.3. Letter J: arr. Impressions et images, 3e suite. Lettre J. (Veneux, Thierry). *Chappell. Unpriced* TMK (B74-50691)
Impressions et images, suite no.3. Letter K: arr. Impressions et images, 3e suite. Lettre K. (Veneux, Thierry). *Chappell. Unpriced* TMK (B74-50692)
Le Parc aux fees. Idylle: arr. Idylle. (Veneux, Thierry). *Chappell. Unpriced* TMK (B74-50693)
Popinella : arr. Popinella. (Astor, Bob). *Chappell. Unpriced* TMK (B74-51259)

Dalby, Martin. Macpherson's rant : for flute and double bass. *Yorke. Unpriced* VRPLSSHVHR (B74-51325)

Dallas, Karl. One hundred songs of toil : with guitar chords. *Wolfe. £1.75* KE/TSDW/GM/AYC (B74-50112) ISBN 0-7234-0525-5

Dance band era : the dancing decades from ragtime to swing, 1910-1950. (McCarthy, Albert). *Spring Books. £1.95* AMT(M/XMK41) (B74-30607) ISBN 0-600-32907-0

Dance of life : song. (Previn, André). *Chappell. Unpriced* KDW (B74-50464)

Dancing day : a cycle of traditional Christmas carols. (Rutter, John). *Oxford University Press. £1.50* FE/TQDPDE/LF (B74-50999) ISBN 0-19-338065-x

Danforth, Samuel. Three almanack verses : SATB. (Allcock, Stephen). *Boosey and Hawkes. Unpriced* EZDW (B74-50973)

Danz (John) lectures. *See* John Danz lectures.

Dark house : for full chorus of mixed voices a cappella. (Chorbajian, John). *Schirmer. Unpriced* EZDW (B74-50975)

Davenport, La Noue. Harmonice musices odhecaton. Selections. Ten pieces from 'Harmonice musices odhecaton'. (Petrucci, Ottaviano dei). *Associated Music. Unpriced* VSNSK/DU/AY (B74-50280)

David Essex story. (Tremlett, George). *49 Poland St., W1A 2LG : Futura Publications Ltd. £0.40* AKDW/GB/E(P) (B74-26609) ISBN 0-86007-092-1

Davidson, Charles. Aleynu l'shabench : a new Friday evening service, cantor solo with mixed chorus, SATB and organ, commissioned by the Anshe Emet Synagogue, Chicago, Illinois, on the occasion of the hundredth jubilee year (1873-1973)
8: Rozo d'shabos. *Ethnic Music : Phoenix. Unpriced* DGU (B74-50891)

Davies, Ivor Richard. First tunes for my first finger. Op. post : violin and piano. *Boosey and Hawkes. £0.70* SPJ (B74-50235)

Davies, Laurence Hector. The Cavern : unison song. *Ashdown. £0.05* JFDW (B74-50091)

Davis, Alfred.
Duets for two cats : for 2-part chorus of female voices or SA duet with piano. (Rossini, Gioachino Antonio). *Roberton. £0.12* FDW (B74-50422)
Ta, ta, ta. G.205. To Maelzel : for 4-part chorus of mixed voices unaccompanied or with wood-block. (Beethoven, Ludwig van). *Roberton. £0.12* EZDW/X (B74-50412)
Ta, ta, ta. K.-H 162. To Maelzel : for 4-part chorus of female voices unaccompanied or with wood-block. (Beethoven, Ludwig van). *Roberton. £0.10* FEZDW/X (B74-50432)

Davis, Katherine Kennicott.
Amazing grace. *Galaxy : Galliard. Unpriced* DM (B74-50907)
The shot heard round the world : for SATB chorus, organ and optional B flat trumpets. *Warner : Blossom. Unpriced* DH (B74-50345)

Davis, Lorrie. Letting down my hair. *Elek. £3.50* BMBDACM (B74-28314) ISBN 0-236-31072-0

Davison, Nigel. Suite de Clarke. (Clarke, Jeremiah). *Novello. £0.60* WSPK/AG (B74-51367)

Davye, John J. A Child is born to us : a Christmas choral cycle for full chorus of treble voices a cappella. *Associated Music. Unpriced* FLEZDP/LF (B74-50433)

Dawes, Frank.
Sinfonia concertante for cello & oboe in F major. Sinfonia concertante in F major. (Bach, Johann Christian). *Eulenburg. £2.60* MPVTPLSRE (B74-50146)
Sinfonia concertante for cello & oboe in F major. Sinfonia concertante, F major for oboe, violoncello and orchestra. (Bach, Johann Christian). *Eulenburg. Unpriced* MPVTPLSRE (B74-50145)
Works, organ. Collections. Organ works. (Hart, Philip). *Hinrichsen. Unpriced* R/AZ (B74-50613)

Day's play. (Last, Joan). *Forsyth. Unpriced* QPJ (B74-51176)

D.B. Kabalevsky's 'Joey the clown' ('The comedians'). (Watanabe, Saburo). *F. Warne. £1.75* BKDBAM/HMBN (B74-26153) ISBN 0-7232-1783-1

De Boisvallée, François. *See* Boisvallée, François de.

De Coursey, Ralph. *See* Coursey, Ralph de.

De Jong, Conrad. *See* Jong, Conrad de.

De la Fontaine, Jean. *See* Fontaine, Jean de la.

De La Grange, Henry-Louis. *See* La Grange, Henry-Louis de.

De Machaut, Guillaume. *See* Machaut, Guillaume de.

De Manchicourt, Pierre de. *See* Manchicourt, Pierre de.

De Prevaux, Blandine Ollivier. *See* Prevaux, Blandine Ollivier de.

De temporum fine comoedia = Das Spiel vom Ende der Zeiten Vigilia. (Orff, Carl). *Schott. Unpriced* EMDX (B74-50933)

De Victoria, Tomas Luis. *See* Victoria, Tomas Luis de.

De Vries, Han. *See* Vries, Han de.

Dean-Myatt, William. Bix - man & legend. (Sudhalter, Richard M). *Quartet Books. £4.95* AMT(P) (B74-27251) ISBN 0-7043-2070-3

Dearnley, Christopher. Ceremonial music for organ
Book 2. *Oxford University Press. £0.50* RK/AAY

(B74-50627) ISBN 0-19-375345-6
Debussy, Claude.
Rêverie. *Ashdown. £0.30* VRPK (B74-50272)
World's favourite best known Debussy piano music. *Ashley : Phoenix. Unpriced* QPJ (B74-50587)
Decca Group records & tapes, main catalogue (alphabetical & numerical)
1974: up to and including September 1973. *Decca Record Co. Unpriced* A/FD(WM) (B74-13392) ISBN 0-901364-05-3
Dechan, Hermann. Concerto for two clarinets & string orchestra in D minor: arr. Concerto for 2 clarinets (chalumeaux) and strings. (Telemann, Georg Philipp). *Musica rara. Unpriced* VVNTQK/LF (B74-50799)
Dechant, Hermann. Concerto for two clarinets & string orchestra in D minor. Concerto for 2 clarinets (chalumeaux) and strings. (Telemann, Georg Philipp). *Musica rara. Unpriced* RXMPVVNUF (B74-50652)
Dedicott, W. The recorder for the first school. *Stockwell. £0.33* VSR/AC (B74-50769) ISBN 0-7223-0560-5
Deep river : spiritual for full female voice choir unaccompanied, S.S.A.. (Lees, Heath). *Roberton. £0.08* FEZDW/LC (B74-51009)
Deg o ganenon gwerin i blant. *See* Lewis, Esme. Ten Welsh folk-songs for juniors.
Dei Petrucci, Ottavanio. *See* Petrucci, Ottavanio dei.
Dekker, Thomas. Spring cantata : SATB
V: July. (Washburn, Robert). *Boosey and Hawkes. Unpriced* EZDX (B74-50985)
Del Tredici, David. *See* Tredici, David del.
Delius, Frederick. Koanga. Vocal score. Koanga : opera in three acts with prologue and epilogue. *Boosey and Hawkes. Unpriced* CC (B74-50866)
Demantius, Johann Christoph. 77 newe ausserlesne liebliche zierliche Polnischer und Teutscher Art Tantze. Selections. Fifteen German and Polish dances, 1601 : for five instruments. *London Pro Musica. Unpriced* LNRH (B74-51081)
Denisoff, R Serge. Songs of protest, war and peace : a bibliography & discography. Revised ed. *30 Cornmarket St., Oxford OX1 3EY : ABC-Clio Inc. £1.45* ADW/KJWX(T) (B74-16447) ISBN 0-87436-121-4
Derivations : for clarinet and band. (Gould, Morton). *Chappell. Unpriced* VVPK (B74-51344)
Derivations from clarinet & wind band: arr. Derivations : for clarinet and band. (Gould, Morton). *Chappell. Unpriced* VVPK (B74-51344)
Des Prés, Josquin. *See* Josquin des Prés.
Deus misereatur nostri = God be merciful unto us : for four-part chorus of mixed voices a cappella. (Schütz, Heinrich). *Schirmer. Unpriced* EZDR (B74-50407)
Deutsche Liturgie. Heilig. Heilig = Holy holy holy : for double chorus of mixed voices a cappella. (Mendelssohn, Felix). *Schirmer. Unpriced* EZDH (B74-50944)
Devienne, François. Symphonie concertante for two clarinets in B flat major. Opus 25: arr. Symphonie concertante for two clarinets and orchestra. Opus 25. *Musica rara. Unpriced* VVNTQK/LE (B74-50798)
Devor, Don. From the mixed-up files of Mrs. Basil E. Frankweiler. Claudia theme: arr. Claudia theme. *Edwin H. Morris. Unpriced* QPK/JR (B74-50604)
Dexter, Harold. Rêverie. (Debussy, Claude). *Ashdown. £0.30* VRPK (B74-50272)
Dexter, Harry.
The crawdad song : based on a folksong from the Kentucky Mountains. *Ashdown. £0.12* FDW (B74-50417)
The first year organist : eleven famous melodies for all organs. *Ashdown. £0.80* RK/AAY (B74-51199)
Joshua fought the battle of Jericho : negro spiritual. *Ashdown. Unpriced* FDW/LC (B74-50423)
Listen to the lambs : negro spiritual. *Ashdown. £0.12* FDW/LC (B74-50072)
The peanut song : an adaptation of a popular American folksong. *Ashdown. £0.12* FDW (B74-50418)
Di Lasso, Orlando. *See* Lasso, Orlando di.
Diapente: two fantasies a 5. (Meyer nos. 1 and 3) : for viols or other stringed instruments. (White, William). *Peters. Unpriced* STNQR (B74-50688)
Dickinson, Emily.
Hope is the thing with feathers : SSAA. (Binkerd, Gordon). *Boosey and Hawkes. Unpriced* FEZDW (B74-51004)
Winter afternoons : cantata for six solo voices and double bass. (Dickinson, Peter). *Novello. £0.50* ESSDE (B74-50937)
Dickinson, Peter. Winter afternoons : cantata for six solo voices and double bass. *Novello. £0.50* ESSDE (B74-50937)
Dictionary of contemporary music. *See* Vinton, John.
Dictionary of twentieth-century music. (Vinton, John). *Thames and Hudson. £9.50* A(C/XM71) (B74-24905) ISBN 0-500-01100-1
Diemer, Emma Lou. Rondo concertante : for orchestra. *Boosey and Hawkes. Unpriced* MMF/W (B74-51099)
DiLello, Richard. The longest cocktail party. *37 Soho Sq., W.1 : Charisma Books. £1.90* A/GB(Q/YC) (B74-18700) ISBN 0-85947-006-7
Ding-dong-doh : a carol for unison treble voices (with optional second and third parts). (Walters, Edmund). *Boosey and Hawkes. £0.10* JFLDP/LF (B74-51041)
Dinham, Kenneth J.
O my lord : negro spiritual. *Banks. Unpriced* EZDP/LF (B74-50962)
Three kings came to Bethlehem Town : solo, unison or two-part (or mixed voices), with accompaniment for guitar or piano ad lib. *Banks. Unpriced* KE/TSDP/LF (B74-51062)
Dinklage, Carol. The children of David. Op.37 : five modern psalms, for mixed chorus and organ
1: Psalm. (Mechem, Kirke). *Boosey and Hawkes. Unpriced* DH (B74-50898)
Diptych : for brass quintet and concert band. (Schuller, Gunther). *Associated Music. Unpriced* UMPWNR (B74-50735)
Disabled Living Foundation. Report of Joint Study Conference on Music and the Physically Handicapped, held on April 6th, 1970, at the Goldsmiths' Hall, London, E.C.2 ... (Joint Study Conference on Music and the Physically Handicapped, *London, 1970*). *346 Kensington High St., W.14 : Disabled Living Foundation. £0.50* A(Z/D) (B74-16560) ISBN 0-901908-02-9
Discographies : a bibliography of catalogues of recordings, mainly relating to specific musical subjects, composers and performers. (Foreman, Ronald Lewis Edmund). *10e Prior Bolton St., N.1 : Triad Press. £1.60* A/FD(T/WT) (B74-03642) ISBN 0-902070-08-8
Discovering Indian music. (Menon, Raghava Raghava). *Abacus Press. £2.40* BZF (B74-02979) ISBN 0-85626-033-9
Discovery = Descubrimiento : for orchestra. (Chavez, Carlos). *Schirmer. £2.35* MMJ (B74-50503)
Discussions : for violin and cello. (Hand, Colin). *Thames. Unpriced* SPLSR (B74-51248)
Dobree, Georgina.
Duo concertant for clarinet & violin in E flat major. Op.16, no.3. Duo concertant for clarinet and violin. Op.16, no.3. (Gebauer, Etienne). *Musica rara. Unpriced* VVPLSF (B74-50805)
Sonata for clarinet & basso continuo in B flat. Op.12, no.1. Sonata in B flat. Opus 12, no.1 : for clarinet and piano. (Lefevre, Jean Xavier). *Oxford University Press. £0.75* VVPE (B74-50292) ISBN 0-19-357548-5
Sonata for clarinet & piano, no.2, in B flat major. Sonata in B flat for clarinet and piano. (Vanhal, Jan). *Musica rara. £6.50* VVPE (B74-50801)
Documentary monographs in modern art. Kostelanetz, Richard. John Cage. *Allen Lane. £2.00* BCBG (B74-11048) ISBN 0-7139-0762-2
Dodd, Gordon. Fantasies for five viols. Meyer 1,3, 'Diapente'. Diapente: two fantasies a 5. (Meyer nos. 1 and 3) : for viols or other stringed instruments. (White, William). *Peters. Unpriced* STNQR (B74-50688)
Dodd, Peter. An Irish idyll, The lark in the clear air. *United Music. Unpriced* RXMK/DW (B74-50644)
Dodgson, Stephen.
Idyll for strings. *Chappell. Unpriced* RXMJ (B74-50218)
Six inventions for harpsichord
Set 1. *Chappell. Unpriced* QRPJ (B74-50606)
Set 2. *Chappell. Unpriced* QRPJ (B74-50607)
Set 3. *Chappell. Unpriced* QRPJ (B74-50608)
Suite for clavichord, no.1, in C. Suite no.1 in C for clavichord. *Chappell. Unpriced* QTPG (B74-50610)
Suite for clavichord, no.2, in E flat. Suite no.2 in E flat. *Chappell. Unpriced* QTPG (B74-50611)
Suite for oboe & keyboard in D major. Suite in D : for oboe and harpsichord (piano). *Oxford University Press. £1.10* VTPJ (B74-50783) ISBN 0-19-356268-5
Zigeunerlieder = Gypsy songs. Op.103 : for four-part chorus of mixed voices with soprano and tenor solos and piano accompaniment. *Chappell. Unpriced* MMJ (B74-50504)
Doe, Paul.
English sacred music
1: Anthems. (Tallis, Thomas). *Stainer and Bell. Unpriced* CB/LD (B74-50329)
2: Service music. (Tallis, Thomas). *Stainer and Bell. Unpriced* CB/LD (B74-50330)
Doflein, Elma. Das Geigen-Schulwerk : ein Lehrgang des Violinspiels verbunden mit Musiklehre und Übung des Zusammenspiels
Heft 1a: Der Anfang des Geigenspiels. (Doflein, Erich). Erweiterte Ausgabe. *Schott. £2.40* S/AC (B74-50225)
Doflein, Erich.
Das Geigen-Schulwerk : ein Lehrgang des Violinspiels verbunden mit Musiklehre und Übung des Zusammenspiels
Heft 1a: Der Anfang des Geigenspiels. Erweiterte Ausgabe. *Schott. £2.40* S/AC (B74-50225)
Traite du violoncello. Selections. Leichte Stücke für Violoncello mit Begleitung durch 2 Violoncello
Heft 1. (Breval, Jean Baptiste). *Schott. £1.44* SRNU (B74-50245)
Traite du violoncello. Selections. Leichte Stücke für Violoncello mit Begleitung durch 2 Violoncello
Heft 2. (Breval, Jean Baptiste). *Schott. £1.44* JRNU (B74-50096)
Donald, Mike. Travelling the northern road. *EFDS. Unpriced* JE/TSDW (B74-51027)
Dondeyne, Désiré. C'est ça la France: arr. C'est ça la France. (Renard, J). *Chappell. Unpriced* UMK (B74-50719)
Donington, Robert.
The interpretation of early music. New version. *Faber. £10.00* A(YB/XDXJ151) (B74-21536) ISBN 0-571-04789-0
Wagner's 'Ring' and its symbols : the music and the myth. 3rd ed. *Faber. £3.95* BWCAC (B74-09867) ISBN 0-571-04825-0
Donizetti, Gaetano.
Caterina Cornaro. Vocal score. Caterina Cornaro. *Egret House : (Under the auspices of the Donizetti Society). Unpriced* CC (B74-50867)
Lucrezia Borgia. Vocal score. Lucrezia Borgia. *93 Chancery La., W.C.2 : Egret House. Unpriced* CC (B74-50868)
Maria Stuarda. Vocal score. Maria Stuarda. *93 Chancery La., W.C.2 : Egret House. Unpriced* CC (B74-50869)
Requiem. Vocal score. Messa di requiem. *Egret House : (Under the auspices of the Donizetti Society). Unpriced* DGKAV (B74-50880)
Donizetti Society.
The Journal of the Donizetti Society
Issue no.1-. *The Secretary, 56 Harbut Rd, SW11 2RB : The Society. £2.50* BDR(B) (B74-13107) ISBN 0-9503333-0-1
Lucrezia Borgia. Vocal score. Lucrezia Borgia. (Donizetti, Gaetano). *93 Chancery La., W.C.2 : Egret House. Unpriced* CC (B74-50868)
Maria Stuarda. Vocal score. Maria Stuarda. (Donizetti, Gaetano). *93 Chancery La., W.C.2 : Egret House. Unpriced* CC (B74-50869)
Donlon, Kenneth Lew. Harper's dictionary of music. (Ammer, Christine). *28 Tavistock St., WC2E 7PN : Barnes and Noble. £1.60* A(C) (B74-09865) ISBN 0-06-463347-0
Donne, John.
Hymn to God the Father : anthem for 4-part chorus of mixed voices SATB, unaccompanied. (Eldridge, Guy). *Roberton. £0.12* EZDH (B74-50387)
Nativitie : SATB a cappella. (O'Neal, Barry). *Associated Music. Unpriced* EZDH/LF (B74-50041)
Doppelbauer, Rupert.
Einführung in das Violoncellospiel
Heft 1. *Schott. £2.00* SR/AC (B74-50243)
Heft 2. *Schott. £2.40* SR/AC (B74-50244)
Doppler, Albrecht Franz. Airs valaques. Op.10 : fantasie for flute with piano accompaniment. *Wye Music : Emerson. Unpriced* VRPJ (B74-51318)
Dorati, Antal. Night music : for solo flute and small orchestra. *Chester : Hansen. Unpriced* MPVR (B74-51111)
Doving, Carl. Melodien til Landstads Salmebog. Kirken den er et. Built on the rock : anthem for unison choir or solo voice and organ. (Lindeman, Ludvig Matthias). *Oxford University Press. Unpriced* JDH (B74-51017)
Dowland, John.
The collected lute music of John Dowland. *Faber Music in association with Faber and Faber. Unpriced* TW/AZ (B74-51286) ISBN 0-571-10010-4
Musice active micrologus. A compendium of musical practice. (Ornithoparchus, Andreas). *Dover Publications : Constable. £7.00* A/M(XDS) (B74-11735) ISBN 0-486-20912-1
Down in yon forest : English traditional carol, SSAATBB unacc. (Carter, Andrew). *Banks. Unpriced* EZDP/LF (B74-50961)
Dr Zhivago. *Somewhere my love: arr.* Somewhere by love. (Jarre, Maurice). *Francis, Day and Hunter. £0.25* WUNS (B74-50320)
Draths, Willi. Die Kinderorgel : leichte Volkslieder aus aller Welt, für elektronische Orgel (1 Manuel). *Schott. £1.45* RPVK/DW/G/AY (B74-50634)
Drayton, Paul.
My soul, there is a country : SATB. *Oxford University Press. £0.12* DH (B74-50896) ISBN 0-19-350348-4
Now glad of heart be every one : Easter carol, for SATB and organ. *Novello. £0.10* DP/LL (B74-50021)
Drehorgelstücklein aus dem 18. Jahrhundert in Originalen, zubereitet für Flötlein sowie für Klavier oder andere Tasteninstrumente. (Zeraschi, Helmut). *Peters. Unpriced* PWPK/AY(XF101) (B74-51122)
Drei Dialoge für Oboe und Orgel. (Schroeder, Hermann). *Schott. £1.44* VTPLR (B74-50290)
Drew, Lucas. Sonatas for cello and basso continuo. Op.2. Six sonatas : for cello or double bass and piano. (Marcello, Benedetto). *Schirmer. £1.85* SRPE (B74-50681)
Drexler, Werner.
World cup fanfare : brass band. *Weinberger. Unpriced* WMK/AGN (B74-50825)
World cup fanfare : military band. *Weinberger. Unpriced* UMMK/AGN (B74-50733)
Drinker, Henry S. Siehe zu dass deine Gottesfurcht nicht Heuchelei sei : Kantate 179 (auf den 11 Sonntag nach Trinitis). (Bach, Johann Sebastian). *Eulenburg. £1.00* EMDE (B74-50028)
Drinkrow, John. The vintage musical comedy book. *Osprey Publishing. £1.95* ACMBN (B74-04045) ISBN 0-85045-103-5
Dryden, John. A time's passing : SATB a cappella. (Woolf, Gregory). *Associated Music. Unpriced* EZDW (B74-50064)
Duarte, John William.
Some of Noah's ark, Op.55 : six sketches for guitar. *Ricordi. Unpriced* TSPMJ (B74-50701)
Sonata for piano, no.2, in G major. Op.14. Andante: arr. Andante from piano sonata Opus 14, no.2. (Beethoven, Ludwig van). *Novello. £0.33* TSPMK/AE (B74-50709)
Take your partners : easy arrangements of English country dance tunes (from the English Dancing Master) for descant recorder and guitar. *Novello. £0.50* VSRPLTSK/AH/G/AYD (B74-50284)
A variety of guitar music. *Faber Music. Unpriced* TSPMK/AAY (B74-50259)
Duchesne, Janet. Bells in our lives. (Cockett, Mary). *David and Charles. £1.60* AXS/B (B74-01380) ISBN 0-7153-6229-1
Duclos, Pierre.
Impressions et images, suite no.3. Letter J: arr. Impressions et images, 3e suite. Lettre J. (Veneux, Thierry). *Chappell. Unpriced* TMK (B74-50691)
Impressions et images, suite no.3. Letter K: arr. Impressions et images, 3e suite. Lettre K. (Veneux, Thierry). *Chappell. Unpriced* TMK (B74-50692)
Due canti : two songs for piano solo. (Camilleri, Charles). *Roberton. £0.40* QPJ (B74-51163)

Duets for two cats : for 2-part chorus of female voices or SA duet with piano. (Rossini, Gioachino Antonio). *Roberton. £0.12* FDW (B74-50422)
Duets for two horns. K.487: arr. 12 easy duets for winds
Volume 3: For trombones, baritones, tubas (and cellos and basses ad lib). (Mozart, Wolfgang Amadeus). *Schirmer. Unpriced* UNUK (B74-50742)
Duke, Henry.
Britain sings
Book 1. *British and Continental. Unpriced* VSRPMK/DW/AYC (B74-50285)
Book 2. *British and Continental. Unpriced* VSRPMK/DW/AYC (B74-50286)
Haydn. (Haydn, Joseph). *Freeman. Unpriced* QPK (B74-51183)
Duke, John. When I was one and twenty : for voice and piano. *Schirmer. Unpriced* KDW (B74-50098)
Duologue : 2 clarinets. (Walker, Eldon). *Thames. Unpriced* VVNU (B74-51342)
Dvořák, Antonin. Te Deum. Op.103. Vocal score. Te Deum. Op.103 : for full chorus of mixed voices with soprano and bass soli accompaniment. *Schirmer. Unpriced* DGKHB (B74-50881)
Dvořák. (Robertson, Alec). Revised ed. *Dent. £3.00* BDX(N) (B74-27797) ISBN 0-460-03116-3
Early English Church Music.
Tallis, Thomas. English sacred music
1: Anthems. *Stainer and Bell. Unpriced* CB/LD (B74-50329)
Tallis, Thomas. English sacred music
2: Service music. *Stainer and Bell. Unpriced* CB/LD (B74-50330)
Early music in facsimile.
A fifteenth century song book : Cambridge University Library Add.MS 5943. *5 Albert Grove, Leeds 6 : Boethius Press. £4.60* AELDW(YD/XCQ) (B74-04046) ISBN 0-904263-01-0
A fifteenth century song book : Cambridge University Library Add.MS 5943. *5 Albert Grove, Leeds 6 : Boethius Press. £4.60* 784.3063 (B74-04046) ISBN 0-904263-01-0
The Turpyn book of lute songs : King's College, Cambridge, Rowe MS 2. *5 Albert Grove, Leeds 6 : Boethius Press. £8.70* AKE/TWDW(YD/XDZS14) (B74-03504) ISBN 0-904263-00-2
Easter day : anthem for female or boys' voices and organ. (Rose, Michael). *Novello. £0.14* DH/LL (B74-50018)
Easy Russian piano music
Book 1. (Aldridge, Maisie). *Oxford University Press. £0.50* QP/AYM (B74-50569) ISBN 0-19-372131-7
Book 2. (Aldridge, Maisie). *Oxford University Press. £0.60* QP/AYM (B74-50570) ISBN 0-19-372132-5
Ebb, Fred. 70 girls 70 : Selections. 70 girls 70. (Kander, John). *Valando. Unpriced* KDW (B74-51049)
Eberl, Anton. Trio for clarinet, cello & piano in E flat major, Op.36. Grand trio for piano, clarinet and violoncello. Op.36. *Musica rara. £2.85* NUVNT (B74-50531)
Ebing, Hans. Kleine Spielereien : für Akkordeon mit 2. Stimme und Schlagwerk ad lib. *Schott. £1.44* RSPMJ (B74-50213)
Ecce tu pulchra es : motet. (Josquin des Prés). *Associated Music. Unpriced* VSNSK/DJ (B74-50279)
Ecloga VIII (Vergili 'Bucolica') : for 6 male voices (1972). (Penderecki, Krzysztof). *Schott. £2.40* JNGEZAZDX (B74-50095)
Eddie Condon scrapbook of jazz. (Condon, Eddie). *Hale. £4.80* AMT(P) (B74-13108) ISBN 0-7091-4476-8
Eden, Walter. Glory choruses
No.3; arranged by Walter Eden and Norman Wicker. (Turner, Roy). *112a Beacon Hill Rd, Newark : Henri's Evangelical Revival Association. Unpriced* JDM (B74-51021)
Edges : a portrait of Robert Indiana, for band. (Thomson, Virgil). *Schirmer. Unpriced* UMJ (B74-50264)
Edges : a portrait of Robert Indiana for piano. (Thomson, Virgil). *Schirmer. Unpriced* QPJ (B74-50592)
Edwardes, Richard. Spring cantata : SATB
III: May. (Washburn, Robert). *Boosey and Hawkes. Unpriced* EZDX (B74-50983)
Edwards, Owain.
Baroque instrumental music
1: People, instruments and the continuo. *Open University Press. £2.20* AL(XE151) (B74-08077) ISBN 0-335-00852-6
2: Suite, sonata and concerto. *Open University Press. Unpriced* AL(XE151) (B74-08078) ISBN 0-335-00853-4
Effinger, Cecil. A cantata for Easter : four part chorus of mixed voices with organ accompaniment. *Schirmer. Unpriced* DE/LL (B74-50876)
E.H. Grieg's 'Peer Gynt'. (Suzuki, Yoshiharu). *F. Warne. £1.75* BGTAM/JMBN (B74-26152) ISBN 0-7232-1784-x
Ehmann, Heinrich. Volksmusik für Bläser. (Koch, Johnnes Hermann Ernst). *Bärenreiter. £1.10* UMK/DW/G/AY (B74-50722)
Ehret, Walter.
Selva morale e spirituale. Messa a 4 da capella. Agnus Dei. Vocal score. Lamb of God = Agnus dei. (Monteverdi, Claudio). *Schirmer. Unpriced* DGF (B74-50878)
Selva morale e spirituale. Messa a 4 da capella. Sanctus. Vocal score. Holy holy holy = Sanctus. (Monteverdi, Claudio). *Schirmer. Unpriced* DGE (B74-50877)
Eight for Christmas : French carols with English words. (Ratcliffe, Desmond). *Novello. Unpriced* EZDP/LF/AYH (B74-50970)
Eight Russian folksongs. Op. 58, nos. 1, 2, 4: arr. Russian folksongs, set 1. (Liadov, Anatoly). *Boosey and Hawkes. Score £1.50, Piano conductor £0.50, Set £2.50* MK (B74-51090)
Eight Russian folksongs. Op.58, nos. 6-8: arr. Russian folksongs. Set 2. (Liadov, Anatoly). *Boosey and Hawkes. £4.50* MH (B74-51088)
Eight studies for the beginner guitarist. (Shepherd, Audrey). *Charnwood Music. Unpriced* TS/AF (B74-51272)
Eighteenth-century French cantata. (Tunley, David). *Dobson. £6.00* ADX(YH/XF71) (B74-25495) ISBN 0-234-77070-8
Einem, Gottfried von.
Geistliche Sonate : für Sopran, Trompete und Orgel. Op.38. *Boosey and Hawkes. Unpriced* KFLE/WSPLRDE (B74-51070)
Reifliches Divertimento. Op. 35a : Variationen über Thema aus dem 3. Bild der Oper 'Der Besuch der alten dame'. *Boosey and Hawkes. £1.50* NUXTNS/T (B74-50152)
Rosa mystica. Op. 40 : acht Gesänge für mittlere Singstimme und Orchester. *Boosey and Hawkes. Unpriced* KFVE/MDW (B74-50118)
Rosa mystica. Op.40. Vocal score. Rosa mystica. Op.40 : acht Gesänge für mittlere Singstimme und Orchester. *Boosey and Hawkes. £2.50* KFVDW (B74-50116)
Die träumenden Knaben, Op.41 : Cantata für vierstimmigen gemischten Chor, Klarinette und Fagott. *Boosey and Hawkes. Unpriced* EVVPLVWDX (B74-50383)
Einführung in das Violoncellospiel
Heft 1. (Doppelbauer, Rupert). *Schott. £2.00* SR/AC (B74-50243)
Heft 2. (Doppelbauer, Rupert). *Schott. £2.40* SR/AC (B74-50244)
E.J. Moeran. (Wild, Stephen). *10e Prior Bolton St., N.1 : Triad Press. £1.50* BMLE (B74-08075) ISBN 0-902070-09-6
Eldridge, Guy.
Hymn to God the Father : anthem for 4-part chorus of mixed voices SATB, unaccompanied. *Roberton. £0.12* EZDH (B74-50387)
The shield of faith : anthem for unison voices with accompaniment for organ or piano. *Cramer. £0.09* JDK (B74-51019)
Elegy and Le Motif : organ. (Laxton, Alwyn). *Paxton. £0.35* RJ (B74-50202)
Elegy for horn and strings. (Cruft, Adrian). *Novello. £2.50* RXMPWT (B74-51222)
Elementaria : first acquaintance with Orff-Schulwerk. (Keetman, Gunild). *48 Great Marlborough St., W1V 2BN : Schott and Co. Ltd. £4.50* A(VG) (B74-13706) ISBN 0-901938-04-1
Elementary method splicing. (Chant, Harold). *c/o 'Monsal', Bredon, Tewkesbury, Glos. GL20 7LY : Central Council of Church Bell Ringers, Education Committee. Unpriced* XSR (B74-50858)
Elgar, *Sir* Edward, *bart.* Chanson de matin, Op.15, no.1: arr. Chanson de matin. Opus 15, no.1. *Paxton. £1.25* WMK (B74-50824)
Ellington, Duke. Music is my mistress. *W.H. Allen. £5.50* AMT(P) (B74-20925) ISBN 0-491-01720-0
Ellington, Edward Kennedy. *See* Ellington, Duke.
Ellinwood, Leonard.
English sacred music
1: Anthems. (Tallis, Thomas). *Stainer and Bell. Unpriced* CB/LD (B74-50329)
2: Service music. (Tallis, Thomas). *Stainer and Bell. Unpriced* CB/LD (B74-50330)
Elvin, Laurence. The Harrison story : Harrison and Harrison, organ builders, Durham. *10 Almond Ave., Swanpool, Lincoln : The author. £5.95* AR/BC(YD/P) (B74-15898) ISBN 0-9500049-2-8
Elvis. (Hopkins, Jerry). *Abacus. £1.00* AKDW/HK/E(P) (B74-04795) ISBN 0-349-11717-9
Emerson, Ralph Waldo. The shot heard round the world : for SATB chorus, organ and optional B flat trumpets. (Davis, Katherine Kennicott). *Warner : Blossom. Unpriced* DH (B74-50345)
En la fuente del rosel = 'Neath the rosebush in the stream : for four-part chorus of mixed voices a cappella. (Vasquez, Juan). *Roberton. £0.10* EZDU (B74-50055)
English church music : a collection of essays
1974. *Addington Palace, Croydon CR9 5AD : Royal School of Church Music. £1.12* AD/LD(YD/D) (B74-20190) ISBN 0-85402-057-8
English Folk Dance and Song Society.
Folk directory
1974. *The Society. £1.25 (£0.75 to members)* A/G(BC) (B74-13106) ISBN 0-85418-096-6
Jim's yolk songs. (Garrett, John M). *English Folk Dance and Song Society. £0.45* KE/TSDW (B74-50479) ISBN 0-85418-103-2
Join the band : a selection of folk dance tunes for beginners, with second parts. (Wood, Barbara). *English Folk Dance and Song Society. Unpriced* LNUH/G/AY (B74-50490) ISBN 0-85418-079-6
English Folk Dance and Song Society. *Vaughan Williams Memorial Library. See* Vaughan Williams Memorial Library.
English Harpsichord Magazine. *For earlier publications of this magazine see* Harpsichord Magazine.
English Harpsichord Magazine, and early keyboard instrument review
Vol.1, no.2- ; Apr. 1974-. *Rose Cottage, Bois La., Chesham Bois, Amersham, Bucks. HP6 6BP : Edgar Hunt. £0.55* APW(B) (B74-12390)
English National Opera Limited. A history of Sadler's Wells Opera : an illustrated booklet, published in the centenary year of Lilian Baylis's birth, to mark the change of the Company's name to the English National Opera. *London Coliseum, St Martin's La., WC2N 4ES : English National Opera Ltd. £1.00* AC/E(YC/QB/X) (B74-26029) ISBN 0-9503681-0-5
English sacred music
1: Anthems. (Tallis, Thomas). *Stainer and Bell. Unpriced* CB/LD (B74-50329)
2: Service music. (Tallis, Thomas). *Stainer and Bell. Unpriced* CB/LD (B74-50330)
English song, Dowland to Purcell. (Spink, Ian). *Batsford. £5.50* ADW(YD/XE101) (B74-06503) ISBN 0-7134-0756-5
English traditional songs and carols. (Broadwood, Lucy Etheldred). *Rowman and Littlefield : EP Publishing. Unpriced* KDW/G/AYD (B74-50474) ISBN 0-7158-1025-1
Enoch, Yvonne. Group piano-teaching. *Oxford University Press. £2.30* AQ/E(VC) (B74-15524) ISBN 0-19-318421-4
Enstone, R. Concerto for piano, no.1, in C major. Op.15. Allegro con brio: arr. Theme from piano concerto no.1. (Beethoven, Ludwig van). *Leonard, Gould and Bolttler. Unpriced* QPK (B74-50594)
Entertainer. (Joplin, Scott). *California Music : Chappell. Unpriced* KDW (B74-50460)
Entertainer. (Joplin, Scott). *Lewis Music : Ashley-Fields. Unpriced* QPHXJ (B74-51154)
Entertainer. (Joplin, Scott). *Chappell. Unpriced* WMK/AHXJ (B74-51359)
Entertainer : a rag time two step. (Joplin, Scott). *Lewis Music : Ashley Fields. Unpriced* QPHXJ (B74-51153)
Entertainer : a ragtime two step. (Joplin, Scott). *221a Kensington High St., W.8 : Aura Music. Unpriced* TSPMK/AHXJ (B74-51282)
Entertainer : a ragtime two step : composed by Scott Joplin. (Joplin, Scott). *Lewis Music : Ashley Fields. Unpriced* QPHXJ (B74-51155)
Entertainer : a ragtime two step : composed by Scott Joplin. (Joplin, Scott). *Lewis Music : Ashley-Fields. Unpriced* RK/AHXJ (B74-51201)
Entertainer : a ragtime two step, for piano. (Joplin, Scott). *Chappell. Unpriced* QPHXJ (B74-50172)
Entertainer: arr. The entertainer. (Joplin, Scott). *Lewis Music : Ashley-Fields. Unpriced* QPHXJ (B74-51154)
Entertainer: arr. The entertainer. (Joplin, Scott). *Chappell. Unpriced* WMK/AHXJ (B74-51359)
Entertainer: arr. The entertainer : a ragtime two step : composed by Scott Joplin. (Joplin, Scott). *Lewis Music : Ashley Fields. Unpriced* QPHXJ (B74-51155)
Entertainer: arr. The entertainer : a ragtime two step : composed by Scott Joplin. (Joplin, Scott). *Lewis Music Ashley-Fields. Unpriced* RK/AHXJ (B74-51201)
Entertainer: arr. The entertainer : piano solo. (Joplin, Scott). *Belwin-Mills. £0.30* QPHXJ (B74-50579)
Entertainer: arr. The entertainer : piano solo. (Joplin, Scott). *Bosworth. Unpriced* QPHX (B74-51152)
Entertainer: arr. The entertainer : ragtime two step. (Joplin, Scott). *Lewis Music : Ashley Fields. Unpriced* QPHXJ (B74-51156)
Entertainer: arr. The entertainer : ragtime two step. (Joplin, Scott). *Lewis Music : Ashley Fields. Unpriced* QPHXJ (B74-51157)
Entertainer: arr. The entertainer : ragtime two-step. (Joplin, Scott). *Studio Music. Unpriced* WMK/AHXJ (B74-51358)
Entertainer : piano solo. (Joplin, Scott). *Belwin-Mills. £0.30* QPHXJ (B74-50579)
Entertainer : piano solo. (Joplin, Scott). *Bosworth. Unpriced* QPHX (B74-51152)
Entertainer : ragtime two-step. (Joplin, Scott). *Studio Music. Unpriced* WMK/AHXJ (B74-50826)
Entertainer : ragtime two step. (Joplin, Scott). *Lewis Music : Ashley Fields. Unpriced* QPHXJ (B74-51156)
Entertainer : ragtime two step. (Joplin, Scott). *Lewis Music : Ashley Fields. Unpriced* QPHXJ (B74-51157)
Entertainer : ragtime two-step. (Joplin, Scott). *Studio Music. Unpriced* WMK/AHXJ (B74-51358)
Entrata festiva. Op. 60 : for concert band. (Nystedt, Knut). *Associated Music. Unpriced* UMJ (B74-50263)
Entwistle, Theodore Rowland-. *See* Rowland-Entwistle, Theodore.
Enzenberger, Hans Magnus. Concerto for violin, no.2. Vocal score. 2nd violin concerto for solo violin, tape, voices and 33 instrumentalists. (Henze, Hans Werner). *Schott. £7.20* KGE/SPDX (B74-50119)
Epilogue to evensong : organ solo. (Turvey, A W). *Cramer. Unpriced* RJ (B74-50623)
Epithalamios : choruses for organ. (Hamilton, Alasdair). *Roberton. £0.30* R/KDD (B74-50197)
Erber, Gerhard. Sonatas for piano. Selections. Sonatinen und leichte Sonaten fur Klavier. (Beethoven, Ludwig van). *Peters. Unpriced* QPE/AY (B74-51145)
Erdei, Peter. 150 American folk songs to sing, read and play. *Boosey and Hawkes. £3.75* JEZDW/G/AYT (B74-50088)
Erdmann, Veit. Exercises and pieces for orchestra groups. *Schott. £1.20* M/AF (B74-50129)
Erickson, Frank. Amahl and the night visitors. *Selections: arr.* Introduction, march and shepherd's dance. (Menotti, Gian Carlo). *Schirmer. Unpriced* UMK (B74-50718)
Ernest Bloch lectures. Cone, Edward T. The composer's voice. *University of California Press. £5.50* A/D (B74-28312) ISBN 0-520-02508-3
Erskine, Thomas, *Earl of Kelly.* Periodical overture, no.17, in E flat major. Symphony in E flat major, Periodical overture 17 : for flutes, clarinets/oboes, bassoon, horns, strings and continuo. *Oxford University Press. £2.75* MRE (B74-50518) ISBN 0-19-365170-x

Espaces : for chamber ensemble. (Lazarof, Henri). *Associated Music. Unpriced* MRJ (B74-50151)
Essercizii musici, trio 12. Sonata for instruments in E flat major. Sonata Es-Dur, für Oboe, obligates Cembalo und Basso continuo. (Telemann, Georg Philipp). *Schott. £2.61* NWNTE (B74-51118)
Esslinger Sankt Pauls-Messe nach Texten aus den Briefen des Apostels Paulus : für vierstimmigen gemischten Chor, Gemeinde, Orgel und (ad libitum) Rhythmusgruppe, Orgel (oder Klavier). (Krol, Bernhard). *Simrock. Unpriced* DG (B74-50336)
Estro armonico. Op.3, no.11. Concerto d-Moll : für 2 Violinen, Streicher und Basso continuo. (Vivaldi, Antonio). *Schott. £4.35* RXMPRXNTF (B74-50647)
Eta Cohen violin method
Book 1. (Cohen, Eta). *Paxton. £0.50* S/AC (B74-51231)
Eternitie : SSATB. (Binkerd, Gordon). *Boosey and Hawkes. Unpriced* EZDH (B74-50943)
'Etudes : pianoBook 1. (Camilleri, Charles). *Roberton. £0.75* QPJ (B74-51164)
Book 2. (Camilleri, Charles). *Roberton. £0.75* QPJ (B74-51165)
Book 3. (Camilleri, Charles). *Roberton. £0.55* QPJ (B74-51166)
Etzkorn, K. Peter. Music and society : the later writings of Paul Honigsheim. (Honigsheim, Paul). *Wiley-Interscience. £8.50* A(Z) (B74-07432) ISBN 0-471-24680-8
Evans, Edward G. The experience of music. (Reimer, Bennett). *Prentice-Hall. £6.00* A/C (B74-16180) ISBN 0-13-294553-3
Evans, Meredydd. Canenon llafar gwlad = Songs from oral tradition
Vol.1. (Saer, D Roy). *National Museum of Wales, Welsh Folk Museum. Unpriced* JEZDW/G/AYDK (B74-51033) ISBN 0-85485-026-0
Evans, Philip R. Bix - man & legend. (Sudhalter, Richard M). *Quartet Books. £4.95* AMT(P) (B74-27251) ISBN 0-7043-2070-3
Evening hymn. (Handel, George Frideric). *Oxford University Press. Unpriced* DH (B74-50012) ISBN 0-19-351119-3
Evening with angels : nine movements for chamber ensemble, woodwind, brass and strings. (Holloway, Robin). *Oxford University Press. £5.00* MRJ (B74-51114) ISBN 0-19-357238-9
Everyday handbooks. Ammer, Christine. Harper's dictionary of music. *28 Tavistock St., WC2E 7PN : Barnes and Noble. £1.60* A(C) (B74-09865) ISBN 0-06-463347-0
Examination in pianoforte playing and singing sight reading tests as set throughout 1973. Grades I-VIII and diplomas. (London College of Music). *Ashdown. £0.35* Q/EG/AL (B74-50159)
Exaudi Deus = Oh hear me Lord God : general motet, for four-part chorus of mixed voices a cappella. (Croce, Giovanni). *Schirmer. Unpriced* EZDJ (B74-50043)
Exciting sound of flamenco : guitar. (Martín, Juan). *United Music. Unpriced* TSPMH (B74-50700)
Exhortation : for mixed chorus and piano. (Beck, John Ness). *Galaxy : Galliard. Unpriced* DH (B74-50894)
Exile symphony, (Symphony no.1). Op.17, no.2. (Hovhaness, Alan). *Peters. £7.50* MME (B74-51098)
Experience of music. (Reimer, Bennett). *Prentice-Hall. £6.00* A/C (B74-16180) ISBN 0-13-294553-3
Experimental music : Cage and beyond. (Nyman, Michael). *Studio Vista. £3.75* A(XPK24) (B74-23495) ISBN 0-289-70182-1
Explorations in guitar playing for beginners
Vol.1. (Lester, Bryan). *Ricordi. Unpriced* TS/AF (B74-50697)
Vol.2. (Lester, Bryan). *Ricordi. Unpriced* TS/AF (B74-50698)
Exquisitioris harmoniae instrumentalis gravijucundae selectus primus. *Concerto no.9 for two violins & string orchestra, 'Victoria maesta'.* Concerto 9, 'Victoria maesta'. (Muffat, Georg). *Schott. £1.92* RXMPSNUF (B74-50220)
Exultate Deo. Sing aloud with gladness = Exultate Deo : SATB a cappella. (Scarlatti, Alessandro). *Royal School of Church Music. £0.32* EZDJ (B74-50952)
Faber Music Limited. Benjamin Britten - a complete catalogue of his published works. (Boosey and Hawkes Limited). New and revised ed.. *Boosey and Hawkes : Faber Music. £2.00* BBU(TC) (B74-03157) ISBN 0-85162-022-1
Fables. Fables : five very short operas. (Rorem, Ned). *Boosey and Hawkes. £3.25* CC (B74-50871)
Fables : five very short operas. (Rorem, Ned). *Boosey and Hawkes. £3.25* CC (B74-50871)
Fadograph of a western scene : for orchestra. Op.44. (Barber, Samuel). *Schirmer. Unpriced* MMJ (B74-50139)

Fafnir and the knights, and other settings of poems by Stevie Smith : for treble voices and piano duet. (Pehkonen, Elis). *Lengnick. £2.00* FLDX (B74-50079)
Fagan, Margo.
Play time : Longman first recorder course. *Longman. £0.70* VS/AC (B74-51327) ISBN 0-582-18539-4
Play time : Longman first recorder course
Stage 3. *Longman. £0.30* VS/AC (B74-50274) ISBN 0-582-18538-6
Fair Organ Preservation Society. Organ parade. *c/o K. Redfern, 3 Bentley Rd, Denton, Manchester M34 3AZ : Fair Organ Preservation Society. £1.50 (Free to members)* A/FM(EM) (B74-07436) ISBN 0-9502701-1-3
Famous composers. (Rowland-Entwistle, Theodore). *David and Charles. £2.50* A/D(YB/M) (B74-09226) ISBN 0-7153-6375-1
Fanfare for a centennial : for brass timpani and percussion. (Lees, Benjamin). *Boosey and Hawkes. £1.75* WMGN (B74-50304)
Fanfare for freedom : for symphonic wind ensemble. (Gould, Morton). *G & C Music : Chappell. Unpriced* UMGN (B74-51294)
Fanfare for the orchestral brass. Festival fanfare : 4 horns, 4 trumpets, 3 trombones and 2 tubas. (Brian, Havergal). *Musica Viva. £1.55* WMGN (B74-51354)
Fanfare, intermezzo and scherzo. Op.1 : for recorder trio, (descant, treble, tenor). (Touchin, Colin M). *Tomus. Unpriced* VSNT (B74-50281)
Fanshawe, David. African Sanctus: arr. The Lord's Prayer. *Chappell. Unpriced* KDTF (B74-51044)
Fantasia brevis : for flute and piano. (Luening, Otto). *Highgate Press : Galaxy : Galliard. Unpriced* VRPJ (B74-51319)
Fantasia for viola and string orchestra with two clarinets. (Hummel, Johann Nepomuk). *Musica rara. Unpriced* RXMPNVVNT (B74-50646)
Fantasia for viola, two clarinets & string orchestra: arr. Fantasia for viola and string orchestra with two clarinets. (Hummel, Johann Nepomuk). *Musica rara. Unpriced* RXMPNVVNT (B74-50646)
Fantasia pictorial, stories from famous music.
Hatsuyama, Shigeru. P.I. Tchaikovsky's 'Swan Lake'. *F. Warne. £1.75* BTDAM/HMBN (B74-26150) ISBN 0-7232-1759-9
Hori, Fumiko. P.I. Tchaikovsky's 'The nutcracker'. *F. Warne. £1.75* BTDAM/HMBN (B74-26151) ISBN 0-7232-1760-2
Suzuki, Yoshiharu. E.H. Grieg's 'Peer Gynt'. *F. Warne. £1.75* BGTAM/JMBN (B74-26152) ISBN 0-7232-1784-x
Watanabe, Saburo. D.B. Kabalevsky's 'Joey the clown' ('The comedians'). *F. Warne. £1.75* BKDBAM/HMBN (B74-26153) ISBN 0-7232-1783-1
Fantasie concertante, no.1 : pour hautbois et piano. (Lancen, Serge). *Chappell. Unpriced* VTPJ (B74-50785)
Fantasy and fugue on 'Edward Cuthbert Bairstow' : for organ. (Marshall, Philip). *Ashdown. £0.40* R/Y (B74-50616)
Fantasy for cello solo (1973). (Block, Robert Paul). *Musica rara. Unpriced* SRPMJ (B74-50685)
Fantasy for double bass solo (1973). (Block, Robert Paul). *Musica rara. Unpriced* SSPMJ (B74-50687)
Fantasy for viola solo (1967, rev. 1973). (Block, Robert Paul). *Musica rara. Unpriced* SQPMJ (B74-50679)
Fantasy : suite of five pieces for pianoforte. (Brydson, John Callis). *Freeman. £0.35* QPG (B74-50168)
Fauré, Gabriel. Gabriel Fauré - his greater piano solos. *Copa : Phoenix. Unpriced* QPJ (B74-50588)
Fearing, Scott. Where's Charley?. The New Ashmolean Marching Society and Students Conservatory Band: arr. The New Ashmolean Marching Society and Students Conservatory Band. (Loesser, Frank). *Frank Music. Unpriced* UMMK (B74-51309)
Feather, Leonard. From Satchmo to Miles. *Quartet Books. £2.95* AMT(M/XN54) (B74-21539) ISBN 0-7043-2055-x
Fechner, Manfred. Twelve fantasias for violin. Zwolf Fantasien für Violine ohne Bass. (Telemann, Georg Philipp). *Peters. Unpriced* SPMJ (B74-51250)
Fedtke, Traugott. Ars magna consoni et dissoni : for organ. (Speth, Johann). *Bärenreiter. £3.80* RJ (B74-50621)
Feed us now, O Son of God. (Allen, Peter). *Galaxy : Galliard. Unpriced* EZDH (B74-50386)
Feed us now, O Son of God: arr. Feed us now, O Son of God. (Allen, Peter). *Galaxy : Galliard. Unpriced* EZDH (B74-50386)
Feld, Jindrich. Sonata for cello & piano (1972). Sonate für Violoncello und Klavier (1972). *Schott. £2.40* SRPE (B74-50246)
Fellowes, Edmund Horace.
O Lord arise : anthem for seven voices, S.S.A.A.T.B.B. (Weelkes, Thomas). *Oxford University Press. £0.20* EZDK (B74-50955) ISBN 0-19-352126-1
Organists and Masters of the Choristers of St George's Chapel in Windsor Castle. *S.P.C.K. House, Northumberland Ave., W.C.2 : Society for the Promotion of Christian Knowledge for the Dean and Canons of St George's Chapel in Windsor Castle. Unpriced* AR/E(YDEUW) (B74-23496)
Fenby, Eric. Koanga. Vocal score. Koanga : opera in three acts with prologue and epilogue. (Delius, Frederick). *Boosey and Hawkes. Unpriced* CC (B74-50866)
Fennimore, Joseph. Berlitz: introduction to French : for voice and piano. *Schirmer. Unpriced* KDW (B74-51047)

Ferdinand : for speaker and solo violin. (Ridout, Alan). *Chappell. Unpriced* KHYE/SPM (B74-51080)
Ferguson, Edwin Earle. We pause beside this door : anthem for the New Year, for four-part chorus of mixed voices with organ accompaniment. *Roberton. £0.10* DH/LFM (B74-50017)
Ferrabosco, Alfonso, *b.1575.* Fantasias. Three fantasias. *Associated Music. Unpriced* VSNS (B74-50277)
Festival fanfare : 4 horns, 4 trumpets, 3 trombones and 2 tubas. (Brian, Havergal). *Musica Viva. £1.55* WMGN (B74-51354)
Festival folk : songs in folk song style. *EFDS. Unpriced* JE/TSDW/AY (B74-51028)
Festival mass for unison (or mixed) choir congregation and organ. (Gelineau, Joseph). *Boosey and Hawkes. Unpriced* JDG (B74-50438)
Festival overture : for recorder quintet. (Hand, Colin). *Schott. £2.50* VSNRG (B74-50766)
Festival service books
7: The journey: a meditation. (Royal School of Church Music). *Royal School of Church Music. Unpriced* DGM (B74-50340)
Field, Michael. Come, dark-eyed sleep : S.S.C. and pianoforte. (Clements, John). *Ashdown. £0.10* FDW (B74-50416)
Fifteen German and Polish dances, 1601 : for five instruments. (Demantius, Johann Christoph). *London Pro Musica. Unpriced* LNRH (B74-51081)
Fifteenth century song book : Cambridge University Library Add.MS 5943. *5 Albert Grove, Leeds 6 : Boethius Press. £4.60* AELDW(YD/XCQ) (B74-04046) ISBN 0-904263-01-0
Fifteenth century song book : Cambridge University Library Add.MS 5943. *5 Albert Grove, Leeds 6 : Boethius Press. £4.60* 784.3063 (B74-04046) ISBN 0-904263-01-0
Fighting Téméraire : TTBB. (Bantock, *Sir* Granville). *Roberton. £0.16* GEZDW (B74-51016)
Fingers and thumbs : a project of preliminary exercises at the pianoforte. (Symons, Mary). *60 Muswell Rd, N.10 : C.W. Daniel. Unpriced* Q/ELM/AF (B74-50560) ISBN 0-85207-112-4
Fink, Siegfried.
12 easy studies for percussion quartet. *Simrock. Unpriced* XNS (B74-50325)
Game for two : game for accordion and percussion. *Simrock. Unpriced* RSPLX (B74-50211)
Game for two : game for accordion and percussion. *Simrock. Unpriced* RSPLX (B74-50212)
Mallet for classic : compositions by old masters. *Simrock. Unpriced* XTQSPLXTRTK/AAY (B74-50328)
Finkel, Ian. Solos for the vibraphone player. *Schirmer. Unpriced* XTQTPMK/AAY (B74-50861)
Firebird. Selections: arr. L'Oiseau de feu = Der Feuervogel. (Stravinsky, Igor). *Schott. £1.44* QPK/HM (B74-50194)
First book of ayres. Never weather-beaten sail: arr. Never weather-beaten sail. (Campion, Thomas). *Studio Music. Unpriced* WMK/DW (B74-51360)
First evening service. Magnificat and Nunc dimittis : SSAATB. (Weelkes, Thomas). *Oxford University Press. £0.30* DGPP (B74-50342) ISBN 0-19-351646-2
First set of divertimenti. Op.1. (Sor, Fernando). *Oxford University Press. £0.50* TSPMJ (B74-50702) ISBN 0-19-358863-3
First solos for the tuba player. (Wekselbaltt, Herbert). *Schirmer. £1.05* WVPK/AAY (B74-50321)
First tunes for my first finger. Op. post : violin and piano. (Davies, Ivor Richard). *Boosey and Hawkes. £0.70* SPJ (B74-50235)
First year organist : eleven famous melodies for all organs. (Dexter, Harry). *Ashdown. £0.80* RK/AAY (B74-51199)
First year violin method. Eta Cohen violin method
Book 1. (Cohen, Eta). *Paxton. £0.50* S/AC (B74-51231)
Fischer, Wilfried. Concerto movement for violin in C major. G.148: arr. Concerto movement for violin and chamber orchestra, 1790/92. Wo05. (Beethoven, Ludwig van). *Breitkopf and Härtel : Bärenreiter. £3.25* SPK (B74-50675)
Fiske, Roger. Water music. (Handel, George Frideric). *Eulenburg. £0.70* MRG (B74-50148)
Fitzpatrick, Horace. Georg Philipp Telemann. (Petzoldt, Richard). *E. Benn. £3.25* BTE (B74-26608) ISBN 0-510-35905-1
Fitzwilliam Museum. Handel and the Fitzwilliam : a collection of essays and a catalogue of an exhibition of Handeliana in the Fitzwilliam Museum in May and June 1974 on the occasion of three concerts of the music of Handel and some of his contemporaries. *Trumpington St., Cambridge : Fitzwilliam Museum. £0.75* BHC(WJ) (B74-16446) ISBN 0-904454-00-2
Fitzwilliam Virginal Book. Selections: arr. Six pieces from the Fitzwilliam Virginal Book. *Oxford University Press. £0.45* VSNUK (B74-51334) ISBN 0-19-355550-6
Five 17th century songs. (Gammie, Ian). *Thames. Unpriced* KFVE/TSDW (B74-51075)
Five canon for two horns. (Heiden, Bernhard). *Associated Music. £1.50* WTNU/X (B74-50317)
Five childhood lyrics : for unaccompanied mixed voices. (Rutter, John). *Oxford University Press. £0.80* EZDW (B74-50980) ISBN 0-19-343716-3
Five Northumbrian tunes : for cello and piano. (Horton, John). *Schott. £1.00* SRPJ (B74-50248)
Five piece suite : for piano. (Jacques, Michael). *Roberton. £0.40* QPG (B74-51149)
Five pieces for four viols from 'Musica teutsch' and 'Musica und Tabulatur'. (Gerle, Hans). *Oxford University Press. £0.16* STNSK/DW/AYE (B74-51257) ISBN 0-19-341214-4
Five string banjo : picture chords, songs, exercises, diagrams and instructions. (Shealy, Alexander). *Lewis Music : Ashley-Fields. Unpriced* TT/AC (B74-50710)
Five summer Sundays : for the piano. (Alt, Hansi). *Oxford University Press. Unpriced* QPJ (B74-51161)
Fleming, Christopher le. *See* Le Fleming, Christopher.
Flibberty and the penguin : a musical play. (Wood, David, *b.1944*). *French. £0.50* BWPDACN (B74-22805) ISBN 0-573-05033-3
Flute solos from the Bach cantatas, passions and oratorios. (Bach, Johann Sebastian). *Schirmer. £2.35* VR (B74-50745)
Foci for viola and piano. (Applebaum, Edward). *Chester. Unpriced* SQPJ (B74-50240)
Foggy dew : more English folk songs from the Hammond Gardiner Mss. (Purslow, Frank). *E.F.D.S. £0.90* KEZDW/G/AYD (B74-50113)
Folk and traditional music of the Western continents. (Nettl, Bruno). 2nd ed. *Prentice-Hall. £4.70* A/G (B74-16181) ISBN 0-13-322941-6
Folk directory
1974. *The Society. £1.25 (£0.75 to members)* A/G(BC)

(B74-13106) ISBN 0-85418-096-6
Folk music, Bach style : 21 two-part inventions. (Applebaum, Stanley). *Schroeder and Gunther. £0.50* QPJ (B74-50174)
Folk songs of the West Country. (Baring-Gould, Sabine). *David and Charles. £3.25* KE/TSDW/G/AYDF (B74-50111) ISBN 0-7153-6419-7
Folksong - plainsong : a study in origins and musical relationships. (Chambers, George Bennet). 2nd ed. *Merlin Press. £3.00* ADT(ZF) (B74-20191) ISBN 0-85036-195-8
Fong-Torres, Ben. The 'Rolling Stone' rock 'n' roll reader. *Bantam. £0.75* A/GB(XQG4) (B74-15523) ISBN 0-552-67483-4
Fontaine, Jean de la. Fables. Fables : five very short operas. (Rorem, Ned). *Boosey and Hawkes. £3.25* CC (B74-50871)
For children : piano solos
Book 1. (Kirkby-Mason, Barbara). *Keith Prowse Music. Unpriced* QPJ (B74-51174)
Book 2. (Kirkby-Mason, Barbara). *Keith Prowse Music. Unpriced* QPJ (B74-51175)
For two to play : early English duets for keyboard, four hands, or for organ (two players, two manuals). (Goebels, Franzpeter). *Nagel : Bärenreiter. £1.45* QNV/AY (B74-50567)
Forbes, Watson. Classical and romantic pieces for viola and piano. *Oxford University Press. £1.30* SQPK/AAY (B74-50677) ISBN 0-19-356501-3
Forcucci, Samuel L. Child of wonder. Alleluia and chorale. Alleluia and chorale : SATB with piano, four-hands. *Schirmer. Unpriced* DH/LF (B74-50016)
Foreman, Lewis. Systematic discography. *Bingley. £3.00* A/FD(U) (B74-25104) ISBN 0-85157-161-1
Foreman, Ronald Lewis Edmund. Discographies : a bibliography of catalogues of recordings, mainly relating to specific musical subjects, composers and performers. *10e Prior Bolton St., N.1 : Triad Press. £1.60* A/FD(T/WT) (B74-03642) ISBN 0-902070-08-8
Formby, George. George Formby complete. *Wise. Unpriced* KDW/AY (B74-50099)
Forte, Allen.
The structure of atonal music. *Yale University Press. £4.95* A/PN/PF (B74-11052) ISBN 0-300-01610-7
Tonal harmony in concept and practice. 2nd ed. *Holt, Rinehart and Winston. £6.95* A/R (B74-14970) ISBN 0-03-077495-0
Fortune's promise : overture for military band. (Buchtel, Forrest Lawrence). *Warner : Blossom. Unpriced* UMMJ (B74-50729)
Forty nine trio preludes for organ based on Sarum plainsong hymn melodies. (Henriksen, Josef). *St Gregory. £1.65* RJ (B74-50200)
Forward! : march for elementary band. (Balent, Andrew). *Warner : Blossom. Unpriced* UMGM (B74-51291)
Foss, Peter. George Formby complete. (Formby, George). *Wise. Unpriced* KDW/AY (B74-50099)
Foster, Anthony. Jonah and the whale : an entertainment for junior choirs and audience with piano and optional instruments. *Oxford University Press. £1.59* JDX (B74-50449) ISBN 0-19-336120-5
Foster, George Murphy. *See* Foster, Pops.
Foster, Pops. Pops Foster - the autobiography of a New Orleans jazzman. *University of California Press. £1.65* AMT(P) (B74-03506) ISBN 0-520-02355-2
Four Celtic Christmas carols : for four-part chorus of mixed voices (a cappella). (Gomer, Llywelyn). *Schirmer. Unpriced* EZDP/AYDKLM (B74-50048)
Four easy pieces in folk style : for violin and pianoforte. (Greaves, Terence). *Associated Board of the Royal Schools of Music. £0.20* SPJ (B74-51243)
Four Elizabethan dance. (Burgon, Geoffrey). *Galaxy : Stainer and Bell. Unpriced* WNSK/AH/AY (B74-50830)
Four little pieces : cornet or trumpet and piano. (Jacob, Gordon). *Emerson Edition. Unpriced* WSPJ (B74-50834)
Four little pieces : for piano. (Shaw, Francis). *Ashdown. Unpriced* QPJ (B74-50183)
Four motets. Op.268 : SATB a cappella
1: Blessed is the man that trusteth in the Lord; text from Jeremiah 17. (Hovhaness, Alan). *Associated Music. £0.20* EZDH (B74-50388)
2: Help, Lord, for the godly man ceaseth; text from Psalm 12. (Hovhaness, Alan). *Associated Music. £0.15* EZDH (B74-50389)
3: Lord, who shall abide in thy tabernacle? Text from Psalm 15. (Hovhaness, Alan). *Associated Music. £0.20* EZDH (B74-50390)
4: The fool hath said in his heart; text from Psalm 14. (Hovhaness, Alan). *Associated Music. £0.15* EZDH (B74-50391)
Four note opera : an opera in one act for soprano, contralto, tenor, baritone and bass with piano accompaniment. (Johnson, Tom). *Associated Music. Unpriced* CC (B74-50331)
Four pieces of the late fifteenth century : for four instruments ATTB. (Thomas, Bernard). *Pro Musica. Unpriced* LNS (B74-50123)
Four sisters : part-song for SSA and piano. (Hogben, Dorothy). *Oxford University Press. Unpriced* FDW (B74-50419)
Four songs on poems of James Joyce : for voice and piano. (Tredici, David Del). *Boosey and Hawkes. £2.25* KDW (B74-50469)
Four stations on the road to freedom, Opus 73 : for SSAATTBB soli or chorus (unaccompanied). (Joubert, John). *Novello. Unpriced* JNEZAYDE (B74-50456)
Fowke, Edith. The Penguin book of Canadian folk songs. *Penguin. £0.75* JEZDW/G/AYSX (B74-50452) ISBN 0-14-070842-1
Fox-Strangeways, A H. Now glad of heart be every one : Easter carol, for SATB and organ. (Drayton, Paul). *Novello. £0.10* DP/LL (B74-50021)
Fragment : for tenor recorder. (Shinohara, Makoto). *Schott. £0.65* VSTPMJ (B74-50779)
Françaix, Jean. Divertissement for bassoon & string quintet: arr. Divertissement pour basson et quintette à cordes. *Schott. £1.92* VWPK (B74-50298)
Francis, *Saint, of Assisi*. Cantico del sole : for unaccompanied mixed voices. (Walton, *Sir* William). *Oxford University Press. £0.50* EZDH (B74-50947) ISBN 0-19-338490-6
Franck, César. Le Chasseur maudit. *Eulenburg. Unpriced* MMJ (B74-50505)
Frank, Florence Kiper. The children of David. Op.37 : five modern psalms, for mixed chorus and organ
4: Man of my own people. (Mechem, Kirke). *Boosey and Hawkes. Unpriced* DH (B74-50901)
Frank, Marcel Gustave. Braid on parade : march, military band. *Warner : Blossom. Unpriced* UMMGM (B74-51305)
Frankel, Benjamin. Sonata for violin, no.2. Op.39. Second sonata for solo violin. Op.39. *Novello. £0.75* SPE (B74-50662)
Franz Schubert and the essence of melody. (Gal, Hans). *Gollancz. £3.50* BSF (B74-04794) ISBN 0-575-01559-4
Fraser, Shena. Full fathom five : for SAB chorus, soprano and tenor soloists and piano. *Thames. £0.75* DX (B74-50928)
Free forms : four pieces for brass trombone and strings. (Andrix, George). *Schirmer. Unpriced* RXMPWUU (B74-51223)
Freed, Arnold.
Adam's apple : SATB. (Habash, John Mitri). *Robbins. Unpriced* DW (B74-50919)
Adam's apple : SSA. (Habash, John Mitri). *Robbins. Unpriced* FDW (B74-50991)
The sea of life : SATB. (Habash, John Mitri). *Robbins. Unpriced* DW (B74-50920)
The sea of life : SSA. (Habash, John Mitri). *Robbins. Unpriced* FDW (B74-50992)
Silent spring : SATB. (Habash, John Mitri). *Robbins. Unpriced* DW (B74-50921)
Silent spring : SSA. (Habash, John Mitri). *Robbins. Unpriced* FDW (B74-50993)
Smokey smokestack : SATB. (Habash, John Mitri). *Robbins. Unpriced* DW (B74-50922)
Freedland, Michael. Irving Berlin. *W.H. Allen. £3.50* BBLN(N) (B74-05268) ISBN 0-491-01112-1
French folk song suite. (Johnson, Stuart). *Oxford University Press. £1.50* UMG (B74-51289) ISBN 0-19-365100-9
French piano music : for the young musician. (Solymos, Peter). *Boosey and Hawkes. £1.00* PWP/AYH (B74-50157)
French's acting editions.
Wood, David, *b.1944*. Flibberty and the penguin : a musical play. *French. £0.50* BWPDACN (B74-22805) ISBN 0-573-05033-3
Wood, David, *b.1944*. Hijack over Hygenia : a musical play for children. *French. £0.75* BWPDACN (B74-28315) ISBN 0-573-05034-1
Frescobaldi, Girolamo. Canzoni da sonare, lib. 1. *Romanesca*. Canzona on 'Romanesca'. *Associated Music. Unpriced* VSNRPW (B74-50275)
Frick, Ottmar. Elementaria : first acquaintance with Orff-Schulwerk. (Keetman, Gunild). *48 Great Marlborough St., W1V 2BN : Schott and Co. Ltd. £4.50* A(VG) (B74-13706) ISBN 0-901938-04-1
Fricker, Peter Racine.
Intrada : for organ. Op.64. *Faber Music. Unpriced* RJ (B74-50199)
Three arguments. Opus 59 : for bassoon and cello. *Fenette Music : Breitkopf and Härtel. Unpriced* VWPLSR (B74-51349)
From classical to romantic keyboard music. (Ratcliffe, Ronald V). *Open University Press. Unpriced* AQ/B/E(XA1849) (B74-23499) ISBN 0-335-00864-x
From Satchmo to Miles. (Feather, Leonard). *Quartet Books. £2.95* AMT(M/XN54) (B74-21539) ISBN 0-7043-2055-x
From the mixed-up files of Mrs. Basil E. Frankweiler. Claudia theme: arr. Claudia theme. (Devor, Don). *Edwin H. Morris. Unpriced* QPK/JR (B74-50604)
From the psalms : for soprano and piano. (Laderman, Ezra). *Oxford University Press. Unpriced* KFLDH (B74-50483)
Fromm, Herbert. Aleynu l'shabench : a new Friday evening service, cantor solo with mixed chorus, SATB and organ, commissioned by the Anshe Emet Synagogue, Chicago, Illinois, on the occasion of the hundredth jubilee year (1873-1973)
2: Ahavat olam. *Ethnic Music : Phoenix. Unpriced* DGU (B74-50885)
Frucht des Geistes ist Liebe. The fruit of the spirit is love = Die Frucht des Geistes ist Liebe : SATB chorus, flute and organ. (Geisler, Johann Christian). Moramus ed. *Boosey and Hawkes. Unpriced* EVRPLRDH (B74-50382)
Fruit of the spirit is love = Die Frucht des Geistes ist Liebe : SATB chorus, flute and organ. (Geisler, Johann Christian). Moramus ed. *Boosey and Hawkes. Unpriced* EVRPLRDH (B74-50382)
Frye, Ellen. The marble threshing floor : a collection of Greek folksongs. *University of Texas Press for the American Folklore Society. £5.85* JEZDW/G/AYPE (B74-50451) ISBN 0-292-75005-6
Full fathom five : for SAB chorus, soprano and tenor soloists and piano. (Fraser, Shena). *Thames. £0.75* DX (B74-50928)
Fürwahr, Er trug uns're Krankheit: arr. Surely he has borne our sorrows = Fürwahr, Er trug uns're Krankheit S.A.T.B. with accompaniment. (Herbst, Johannes). Moramus ed. *Boosey and Hawkes. Unpriced* DH (B74-50346)
Gabriel Fauré - his greater piano solos. (Fauré, Gabriel). *Copa : Phoenix. Unpriced* QPJ (B74-50588)
Gabrieli, Andrea. Madrigali et ricercari a quattro voci, nos 6. 7. Ricercari a quattro, nos.6 & 7. *Schott. £1.92* RXMJ (B74-50219)
Gal, Hans. Franz Schubert and the essence of melody. *Gollancz. £3.50* BSF (B74-04794) ISBN 0-575-01559-4
Gál, Hans.
Three intermezzi, Op.103 : for treble recorder (or flute) and harpsichord or pianoforte. *Schott. £2.32* VSRPJ (B74-51335)
Trio for strings. Op.104. Trio for violin, viola d'amore (or viola) and violoncello. Op.104. *Simrock. Unpriced* RXNT (B74-51230)
Gallagher, Rachel. Letting down my hair. (Davis, Lorrie). *Elek. £3.50* BMBDACM (B74-28314) ISBN 0-236-31072-0
Gallois, Olivier. Nocturnes pour un sax : saxophone and piano. *Chappell. Unpriced* VUPJ (B74-51339)
Game for two : game for accordion and percussion. (Fink, Siegfried). *Simrock. Unpriced* RSPLX (B74-50211)
Game for two : game for accordion and percussion. (Fink, Siegfried). *Simrock. Unpriced* RSPLX (B74-50212)
Gammie, Ian.
Five 17th century songs. *Thames. Unpriced* KFVE/TSDW (B74-51075)
Sonatina dolorosa : for solo guitar. (Roe, Betty). *Thames. Unpriced* TSPMEM (B74-51273)
Gamse, Albert.
The best dulcimer method yet. *Lewis : Ashley-Fields. Unpriced* TWT/AC (B74-51287)
The best recorder method yet : charts, exercises, embellishments, solos, and ensemble music
Book 1: C-soprano or tenor. *Lewis Music : Ashley-Fields. Unpriced* VS/AC (B74-50764)
Book 2: F-alto, F-sopranino, F-bass. *Lewis Music : Ashley-Fields. Unpriced* VS/AC (B74-50765)
Ganz, Rudolph. The literature of the piano : a guide for amateur and student. (Hutcheson, Ernest). 3rd ed., revised. *Hutchinson. £4.75* AQ (B74-17389) ISBN 0-09-119120-3
Gárdonyi, Zoltan. Piano works
Vol.4: Hungarian rhapsodies II, nos 10-19. (Liszt, Franz). *Bärenreiter. £2.90* QP/AZ (B74-50571)
Garrett, John M. Jim's yolk songs. *English Folk Dance and Song Society. £0.45* KE/TSDW (B74-50479) ISBN 0-85418-103-2
Garrigue, John. Lala and la : SSA. (Kennedy, John Brodbin). *Boosey and Hawkes. Unpriced* FEZDW (B74-51007)
Gatsby era greats : songs with photographs from the film 'The great Gatsby'. *Chappell. Unpriced* KDW/GB/AY (B74-50475)
Gavall, John. Christmas carols for beginner guitarists. *Bosworth. Unpriced* TSPMK/DP/LF/AY (B74-51283)
Gavotina. (Roger, Roger). *Chappell. Unpriced* TMK/AHM (B74-50694)
Gay, John. Beggar's opera. Selections: arr. Four songs from the Beggar's Opera. *Oxford University Press. Unpriced* EZDW (B74-50978)
Gebauer, Etienne. Duo concertant for clarinet & violin in E flat major. Op.16, no.3. Duo concertant for clarinet and violin. Op.16, no.3. *Musica rara. Unpriced* VVPLSF (B74-50805)
Geigen-Schulwerk : ein Lehrgang des Violinspiels verbunden mit Musiklehre und Übung des Zusammenspiels
Heft 1a: Der Anfang des Geigenspiels. (Doflein, Erich). Erweiterte Ausgabe. *Schott. £2.40* S/AC (B74-50225)
Geisler, Johann Christian. Die Frucht des Geistes ist Liebe. The fruit of the spirit is love = Die Frucht des Geistes ist Liebe : SATB chorus, flute and organ. Moramus ed. *Boosey and Hawkes. Unpriced* EVRPLRDH (B74-50382)
Geistliche Chormusik. Verleih uns Frieden genadiglich. Verleih uns Frieden genadiglich = Lord grant us peace : for five-part chorus of mixed voices a cappella. (Schutz, Heinrich). *Schirmer. Unpriced* EZDH (B74-50946)
Geistliche Concerten, Tl.2. Dialogus. Kommt her ihr Gesegneten meines Vaters = Come ye blessed ones of my Father : dialogue for five voices (SATTB) and continuo. (Scheidt, Samuel). *Novello. £1.00* JNBDH (B74-51043)
Geistliche Lieder. (Bach, Johann Sebastian). *Schott. £1.45* VSNSK/DM (B74-51332)
Geistliche Lieder und Schmelli's Gesangbuch und dem Notenbuch der Anna Magdalena Bach. S. 439-567. *Selections: arr.* Geistliche Lieder. (Bach, Johann Sebastian). *Schott. £1.45* VSNSK/DM (B74-51332)
Geistliche Sonate : für Sopran, Trompete und Orgel. Op.38. (Einem, Gottfried von). *Boosey and Hawkes. Unpriced* KFLE/WSPLRDE (B74-51070)
Geistlicher Harmonien, erster Teil. *Wie der Hirsch schreiet*. As the deer cries for flowing water : for four-part chorus of mixed voices with organ accompaniment. (Bernhard, Christoph). *Roberton. £0.26* DH (B74-50011)
Gelineau, Joseph. Festival mass for unison (or mixed) choir congregation and organ. *Boosey and Hawkes. Unpriced* JDG (B74-50438)
General Bass : für kontinuerliche Instrumentalklange.

(Kagel, Mauricio). *Universal. Unpriced* LPMJ (B74-50128)
Genzmer, Harald.
Duo concertante for trumpet & piano. Konzertantes Duo für Trompete in B (oder C) und Klavier. *Litolff : Peters. £5.00* WSPF (B74-51366)
Tanzstücke für zwei Altblockflöten
Heft 2. *Schott. £1.08* VSSNU (B74-50287)
Georg Philipp Telemann. (Petzoldt, Richard). *E. Benn. £3.25* BTE (B74-26608) ISBN 0-510-35905-1
George Formby complete. (Formby, George). *Wise. Unpriced* KDW/AY (B74-50099)
George Gershwin - for piano. (Gershwin, George). *Chappell. Unpriced* QPJ (B74-50589)
Gerber, Rudolf. Concerto for clarinet in A major. K.622. Concerto, A major, for clarinet and orchestra. K.622. (Mozart, Wolfgang Amadeus). *Eulenburg. £0.85* MPVVF (B74-51112)
Gerdes, Johannes. Concerto for violin in E minor. Konzert, E-moll, für Violine, zwei Oboen, Streicher und Basso continuo, (Fagott ad libitum). (Telemann, Georg Philipp). *Peters. Unpriced* MPSF (B74-51109)
Gerle, Hans. Five pieces for four viols from 'Musica teutsch' and 'Musica und Tabulatur'. *Oxford University Press. £0.16* STNSK/DW/AYE (B74-51257) ISBN 0-19-341214-4
Gersch, Paul J. The awakening : canon for equal voices. *Chappell. Unpriced* DW/X (B74-50369)
Gershwin, George. Selections. George Gershwin - for piano. *Chappell. Unpriced* QPJ (B74-50589)
Gershwin : his life and music. (Schwartz, Charles). *Abelard-Schuman. £4.90* BGH(N) (B74-20923) ISBN 0-200-72129-1
Gershwin years. (Jablonski, Edward). *Robson Books. £6.95* BGH(N) (B74-27798) ISBN 0-903895-19-6
Gershwins. (Kimball, Robert). *Cape. £9.50* BGH(N) (B74-24209) ISBN 0-224-01014-x
Gery, H T Wade-. *See* Wade-Gery, H T.
Gesualdo, Carlo, *Prince of Venosa.* Madrigali a cinque voci, libro sesto. Moro lasso : arr. Moro lasso. *Oxford University Press. Unpriced* UMK/DU (B74-51302)
Getreue Music-Meister. Sonata for treble recorder & basso continuo in C major. Sonata no.4 in C major : for treble recorder and continuo. (Telemann, Georg Philipp). *Schott. £0.75* VSSPE (B74-50773)
Getreue Music-Meister. Sonata for treble recorder & basso continuo in C major (in canon). Sonata no.2 in C major (in canon) : for treble recorder and continuo. (Telemann, Georg Philipp). *Schott. £0.75* VSSPE/X (B74-50777)
Getreue Music-Meister. Sonata for treble recorder & basso continuo in F major. Sonata no.1 in F major : for treble recorder and continuo. (Telemann, Georg Philipp). *Schott. £0.75* VSSPE (B74-50774)
Getreue Music-Meister. Sonata for treble recorder & basso continuo in F minor. Sonata no.3 in F minor : for treble recorder and continuo. (Telemann, Georg Philipp). *Schott. £0.75* VSSPE (B74-50775)
Getreue Music-Meister. Sonatas for treble recorders & basso continuo. Sonatas 1-4 : for treble recorder and continuo. (Telemann, George Philipp). *Schott. £2.50* VSSPE (B74-50776)
Ghosts, fire, water : for alto solo and unaccompanied mixed voices. (Mews, Douglas). *Oxford University Press. £0.30* EZDE (B74-50036) ISBN 0-19-343670-1
Gibbs, Joseph.
Sonata for violin & basso continuo, no.3, in G major. Violin sonata no.3 in G major. *Schott. Unpriced* SPE (B74-51240)
Sonata for violin & basso continuo, no.5, in E major. Violin sonata no.5 in E major. *Schott. Unpriced* SPE (B74-51241)
Gibson, Arthur J. Sonata for harpsichord, no.3, in G. *Allegro.* Allegro. (Arne, Thomas Augustine). *Cramer. Unpriced* RK (B74-50205)
Gibson, John. Regimental quick march, The Queen's Lancashire Regiment, 'The attack', 'The red rose'. *Boosey and Hawkes. £1.00* UMMGM/KH (B74-51306)
Giegling, Franz.
Concerto for oboe, string quartet & basso continuo in C major. Op.9, no.5. Concerto à 5 for oboe strings and continuo. Op.9, no.5. (Albinoni, Tommaso). *Musica rara. Unpriced* NUTNQF (B74-50527)
Concerto for oboe, string quartet & basso continuo in C major. Op.9, no.5: arr. Concerto à 5 for oboe strings and continuo. Op.9, no.5. (Albinoni, Tommaso). *Musica rara. Unpriced* VTPK/LF (B74-50786)
Gigue de Pan : organ with optional drums. (Mews, Donald). *Oxford University Press. £0.60* RHP (B74-51190) ISBN 0-19-375565-3
Gilbert, William Schwenk. Works, operettas. Selections: arr. The best of Gilbert and Sullivan : songs from operettas arranged with piano accompaniment. (Sullivan, *Sir* Arthur Seymour). *Chappell. Unpriced* KDW (B74-50468)
Gilbert and Sullivan for descant recorder with chord symbols for guitar, piano or tuned percussion. (Sullivan, *Sir* Arthur Seymour). *British and Continental. Unpriced* VSRPMK/DW (B74-51336)
Gilder, Eric. Robinson Crusoe : a pantomime. (Crocker, John, *b.1925*). *Evans Plays. £0.50* BCQRACPP (B74-12388) ISBN 0-237-74975-0
Gillett, Charlie. Rock file
2. *Panther. £0.50* ADW/GB (B74-18933) ISBN 0-586-04087-0
Ginastera, Alberto.
Concerto for harp. Op.25. Harp concerto. Op.25. *Boosey and Hawkes. £7.50* MPTQF (B74-51110)
Concerto for harp. Op.25: arr. Harp concerto. Op.25. *Boosey and Hawkes. £3.00* TQPK/LF (B74-51263)
Concerto for string orchestra. Op. 33. Concerto per corde. Op. 33. *Boosey and Hawkes. £3.00* RXMF (B74-50215)
Girl guide song book : unison voices
Book 1. *Girl Guides Association. Unpriced* JFDW/AY (B74-51034)
Book 2. *Girl Guides Association. Unpriced* JFDW/AY (B74-51035)
Girl with the buckles on her shoes : Irish traditional melody, unison song with piano. (Nelson, Havelock). *Roberton. £0.07* JDW (B74-50085)
Gladiolus rag. (Joplin, Scott). *Chappell. Unpriced* QPHXJ (B74-51158)
Glarum, Leonard Stanley. The bells do ring : based on a French tune for four-part chorus of mixed voices with optional handbells. *Schirmer. Unpriced* EZDP/LF (B74-50963)
Gloria: arr. Gloria : for four-part chorus of mixed voices, two solo sopranos and solo alto. (Vivaldi, Antonio). *Schirmer. £0.95* DGC (B74-50339)
Gloria : for choir, SATB and piano, with two players, one at the keyboard and the other manipulating the strings. (Patterson, Paul). *Weinberger. Unpriced* DE (B74-50874)
Gloria : for four-part chorus of mixed voices, two solo sopranos and solo alto. (Vivaldi, Antonio). *Schirmer. £0.95* DGC (B74-50339)
Gloria. Opus 49 : rhapsodische Fantasie für Orgel. (Korn, Peter Jona). *Litolff : Peters. £4.20* RJ (B74-51193)
Gloria tibi : for two-part chorus of treble voices with tenor solo and piano and bongo accompaniment. (Bernstein, Leonard). *Amberson : Schirmer. Unpriced* ENYLDH (B74-50033)
Glory choruses
No.3; arranged by Walter Eden and Norman Wicker. (Turner, Roy). *112a Beacon Hill Rd, Newark : Henri's Evangelical Revival Association. Unpriced* JDM (B74-51021)
Glory of the dove : for S.A., T.B., or SATB (unaccompanied). (Stoker, Richard). *Ashdown. Unpriced* EZDW (B74-50409)
Glynne-Jones, Marjorie Lilian. Music. *Macmillan. £2.60* A(VJ) (B74-21533) ISBN 0-333-12252-6
God is alive : for SATB chorus and piano. (Artman, Ruth). *Warner : Blossom. Unpriced* DH (B74-50344)
Godden, Rumer. St Jerome and the lion : a legend for voices, piano and optional recorders and percussion. (Parry, William Howard). *Keith Prowse Music. £0.75* JFDE (B74-50089)
Goebels, Franzpeter. For two to play : early English duets for keyboard, four hands, or for organ (two players, two manuals). *Nagel : Bärenreiter. £1.45* QNV/AY (B74-50567)
Goehr, Alexander. Paraphrase on the dramatic madrigal Il Combattimento de Tancredi e Clorinda by Claudio Monteverdi. Op.28: for clarinet solo. *Schott. £.25* VVPMJ (B74-50294)
Goldbeck, Frederick. Twentieth century composers
Vol.4: France, Italy and Spain. *Weidenfeld and Nicolson. £4.50* AD(YB/M/XM) (B74-29004) ISBN 0-297-76793-3
Goldberger, David. Capriccio sopra la lontanza del suo fratello dilettissimo. S.992. Capriccio. (Bach, Johann Sebastian). *Schirmer. Unpriced* QPJ (B74-50583)
Golding, Robin. History of the piano. (Closson, Ernest). 2nd ed. *Elek. £3.50* AQ/B(X) (B74-09232) ISBN 0-236-17685-4
Goldman, Maurice. Aleynu l'shabench : a new Friday evening service, cantor solo with mixed chorus, SATB and organ, commissioned by the Anshe Emet Synagogue, Chicago, Illinois, on the occasion of the hundredth jubilee year (1873-1973)
1: Adon olam. *Ethnic Music : Phoenix. Unpriced* DGU (B74-50884)
Goldstein, David. Chanukah suite : for recorder trio, SAT. *Galaxy : Galliard. Unpriced* VSNTG (B74-51333)
Goldthorpe, Ruth. The awakening : canon for equal voices. (Gersch, Paul J). *Chappell. Unpriced* DW/X (B74-50369)
Gomer, Llywelyn. Four Celtic Christmas carols : for four-part chorus of mixed voices (a cappella). *Schirmer. Unpriced* EZDP/AYDKLM (B74-50048)
Gondoliera : accordion solo. (Parnell, Frederick). *Charnwood Music. Unpriced* RSPMJ (B74-51210)
Good companions. (Previn, André). *Chappell. Unpriced* KDW (B74-51052)
Good companions. Good companions: arr. Good companions : song. (Previn, André). *Chappell. Unpriced* KDW (B74-50462)
Good companions. *Selections: arr.* The good companions. (Previn, André). *Chappell. Unpriced* KDW (B74-51052)
Good companions. Slippin' around the corner. Slippin' around the corner. (Previn, André). *Chappell. Unpriced* DW (B74-50363)
Good companions : song. (Previn, André). *Chappell. Unpriced* KDW (B74-50462)
Good companions. Stage struck. Stage struck : song. (Previn, André). *Chappell. Unpriced* DW (B74-50364)
Good companions. Ta luv: arr. Ta luv : song. (Previn, André). *Chappell. Unpriced* KDW (B74-50463)
Good companions. The dance of life: arr. The dance of life : song. (Previn, André). *Chappell. Unpriced* KDW (B74-50464)
Good companions. The pleasure of your company: arr. The pleasure of your company : song. (Previn, André). *Chappell. Unpriced* KDW (B74-50465)
Goodnight, my someone. (Willson, Meredith). *Frank Music. Unpriced* FDW (B74-50995)
Gordon, Philip. Brandenburg concerto, no.1, in F major. S.1046. Menuetto: arr. Menuetto. (Bach, Johann Sebastian). *Warner : Blossom. Unpriced* MK/AHR (B74-50492)
Gottschalk, Louis Moreau.
Piano music of Louis Moreau Gottschalk : 26 complete pieces from original editions. *Dover : Constable. £3.36* QPJ (B74-50590) ISBN 0-486-21683-7
L'Union. Op. 48: arr. L'Union. Op.48 : paraphrase de concert sur les airs nationaux. *Schirmer. £1.40* QNUK (B74-50562)
L'Union. Op. 48 : paraphrase de concert sur les airs nationaux. *Schirmer. Unpriced* UMPQ (B74-50734)
Gould, Morton.
Derivations from clarinet & wind band: arr. Derivations : for clarinet and band. *Chappell. Unpriced* VVPK (B74-51344)
Fanfare for freedom : for symphonic wind ensemble. *G & C Music : Chappell. Unpriced* UMGN (B74-51294)
Gould, Sabine Baring-. *See* Baring-Gould, Sabine.
Gradualia, lib.1. Sacerdotes Domini. Sacerdotes Domini = Then did priests make offering : SATB. (Byrd, William). Revised ed. *Oxford University Press. Unpriced* EZDGKAF (B74-50038) ISBN 0-19-352008-7
Gradulia, lib 2. Victimae paschali. Victimae paschali = Unto Christ the victim : motet for five voices, SSAT unacc. (Byrd, William). *Oxford University Press. £0.30* DGKADD/LL (B74-50879) ISBN 0-19-352010-9
Gradus : 40 studies for piano
Book 2. (Adler, Samuel). *Oxford University Press. Unpriced* Q/AF (B74-51126)
Gradus : 40 studies for piano : by Samuel Adler
Book 1. (Adler, Samuel). *Oxford University Press. Unpriced* Q/AF (B74-51125)
Granada Serenata : für Gitarre. (Albeniz, Isaac). *Schott. £0.72* TSPMK (B74-50257)
Granados, Enrique. Spanish dances for piano, vol.2. Andaluza: arr. Andaluza. *Schott. £1.00* VSNRQK/AH (B74-51331)
Grand tradition : seventy years of singing on record. (Steane, John Barry). *Duckworth. £10.00* AB/FD (B74-15525) ISBN 0-7156-0661-1
Grange, Henry-Louis de La. *See* La Grange, Henry-Louis de.
Grant, Lawrence.
The entertainer: arr. The entertainer : a ragtime two step : composed by Scott Joplin. (Joplin, Scott). *Lewis Music : Ashley Fields. Unpriced* QPHXJ (B74-51155)
The entertainer: arr. The entertainer : a ragtime two step : composed by Scott Joplin. (Joplin, Scott). *Lewis Music Ashley-Fields. Unpriced* RK/AHXJ (B74-51201)
More classic to contemporary piano music in its original form. *Ashley : Phoenix. Unpriced* QP/AY (B74-50568)
Selections: arr. Scott Joplin : the king of ragtime writers: easy piano. (Joplin, Scott). *Lewis Music : Ashley-Fields. Unpriced* QPHXJ (B74-51159)
World's favorite contemporary music for all organs. *Ashley : Phoenix. Unpriced* RK/AAY (B74-51200)
World's favorite preludes : offertories and postludes for the piano
Vol.1. *Ashley : Phoenix. Unpriced* QPK/AAY (B74-50596)
Vol.2. *Ashley : Phoenix. Unpriced* QPK/AAY (B74-50597)
World's favorite wedding music for piano. *Ashley : Phoenix. Unpriced* QPK/KDD/AY (B74-50605)
Gray, Andy. My top pop book. *Hamlyn. £0.85* AKDW/GB/E(M) (B74-30606) ISBN 0-600-37073-9
Great American popular singers. (Pleasants, Henry). *Gollancz. £3.75* AKDW/GB/E(M/YT/XN54) (B74-28316) ISBN 0-575-01774-0
Great composers. Holst, Imogen. Holst. *Faber. £2.30* BHP(N) (B74-06502) ISBN 0-571-09967-x
Great Gatsby : the songs of the twenties from the film of the seventies. *EMI Music. Unpriced* KDW/JR (B74-50476)
Great is the Lord : SATB a cappella. (Whitcomb, Robert). *Associated Music. Unpriced* EZDK (B74-50956)
Great ones
1: Great film music. *Wise. £1.50* C/AY (B74-50000)
2: Seventeen exciting singer songwriters. *Wise. £1.50* C/AY (B74-50001)
3: Great groups. *Wise. £1.50* C/AY (B74-50002)
4: Nineteen famous singers and their songs & 17 more songs. *Wise. £1.50* C/AY (B74-50003)
Great singers from the seventeenth century to the present day. (Pahlen, Kurt). *W.H. Allen. £4.75* AK/E(M/XM71) (B74-00870) ISBN 0-491-01361-2
Great songs of the 60's. *Wise. Unpriced* KDW/GB/AY (B74-50102)
Great TV themes : piano arrangements. (Simpson, Dudley). *Affiliated Music. £0.75* QPK/JS/AY (B74-50195)
Greaves, Terence. Four easy pieces in folk style : for violin and pianoforte. *Associated Board of the Royal Schools of Music. £0.20* SPJ (B74-51243)
Green print for song. (Carter, Sydney). *Galliard, Stainer and Bell. Unpriced* JDP (B74-51022) ISBN 0-85249-284-7
Greene, Maurice.
Overture no.5 in D major. *Eulenburg. £1.50* MRJ (B74-50149)
Overture no.6 in E flat major. *Eulenburg. £1.50* MRJ (B74-50150)
Greenfield, Robert. Stones Touring Party : a journey through America with the Rolling Stones. *Joseph. £3.00* AKDW/GB/E(P) (B74-25497) ISBN 0-7181-1249-0
Greenfield, Robert. STP. *See* Greenfield, Robert. Stones Touring Party.
Greening, Richard. The organs of Lichfield Cathedral. *c/o 28 Walsall Rd, Lichfield, Staffs. WS13 8AB : Dean and*

Chapter of Lichfield. £0.45 AR/B(YDHNLB) (B74-13712) ISBN 0-9503008-1-0
Gregg, Humphrey Procter-. *See* Procter-Gregg, Humphrey.
Gregson, Edward.
Intrada for brass band. *R. Smith. Unpriced* WMJ (B74-50308)
Patterns for brass band. *210 Strand, WC2R 1AP : R. Smith and Co. Ltd. Unpriced* WMJ (B74-50822)
Grieg. (Horton, John). *Dent. £2.95* BGT (B74-13104) ISBN 0-460-03135-x
Griffiths, Ann.
Seven lessons for beginners. *Adlais. Unpriced* TQ/AF (B74-51261)
Welsh folksong fantasies : harp
No.1: Sweet but simple Gwennie. *Adlais. Unpriced* TQPMJ (B74-51266)
No.2: What is summer to me? *Adlais. Unpriced* TQPMJ (B74-51267)
The young harpist. *Adlais. Unpriced* TQ/AC (B74-51260)

Grimsey, John. La Périchole. Vocal score. La Périchole : operetta in three acts: music. (Offenbach, Jacques). *Weinberger. Unpriced* CF (B74-50332)
Grischkat, Hans. Siehe zu dass deine Gottesfurcht nicht Heuchelei sei : Kantate 179 (auf den 11 Sonntag nach Trinitis). (Bach, Johann Sebastian). *Eulenburg. £1.00* EMDE (B74-50028)
Grodek d'apres Georg Trakl (1963, revision 1969) : for soprano voice, flute and percussion. (Boucourechliev, André). *Universal. Unpriced* KFLE/NYHRDX (B74-51068)
Grossi, Andrea.
Sonata for trumpet, string quartet & basso continuo in D major. Op.3, no.11. Sonata a 5. Op.3, no.11 : for trumpet and strings. *Musica rara. Unpriced* NUXSNQE (B74-50533)
Sonata for trumpet, string quartet & basso continuo in D major. Op.3, no.11: arr. Sonata à 5. Op.3, no.11 : for trumpet and strings. *Musica rara. Unpriced* WSPK/LE (B74-50838)
Sonata for trumpet, string quartet & basso continuo in D major. Op.3, no.12. Sonata à 5. Op.3, no.12 : for trumpet and strings. *Musica rara. Unpriced* NUXSNQE (B74-50534)
Sonata for trumpet, string quartet & basso continuo in D major. Op.3, no.12: arr. Sonata à 5. Op.3, no.12 : for trumpet and strings. *Musica rara. Unpriced* WSPK/LE (B74-50839)
Group piano-teaching. (Enoch, Yvonne). *Oxford University Press. £2.30* AQ/E(VC) (B74-15524) ISBN 0-19-318421-4
Grundman, Clare.
March winds : military band. *Boosey and Hawkes. Unpriced* UMMJ (B74-51307)
Trumpets triumphant : pageantry for antiphonal trumpets. *Boosey and Hawkes. Unpriced* UMMJ (B74-50730)
Two Irish songs : military band. *Boosey and Hawkes. £15.00* UMMJ (B74-51308)
Zoo illogical : for solo voice, or voices in unison or octaves, with instrumental ensemble woodwind, brass & percussion, (optional piano). *Boosey and Hawkes. Unpriced* JE/NYHNMDE (B74-50450)
Zoo illogical. *Vocal score.* Zoo illogical : for solo voice, or voices in unison or octaves with piano. *Boosey and Hawkes. Unpriced* JDW (B74-50447)
Grundtvig, N F S. Melodien til Landstads Salmebog. Kirken den er et. Built on the rock : anthem for unison choir or solo voice and organ. (Lindeman, Ludvig Matthias). *Oxford University Press. Unpriced* JDH (B74-51017)
Gruss aus Wien! = Greetings from Vienna. (Crossman, Gerald). *Charnwood Music. Unpriced* RSPMJ (B74-51207)
Guami, Francesco.
Ricercari a due voci, nos. 1-3, 6-10, 16-23. Ten ricercari, 1588 : for two instruments, A.T. *Pro Musica. Unpriced* LNU (B74-50126)
Ricercari for two instruments. *Selections.* Seven ricercari, 1588 : for two instruments, S.A. *London Pro Musica. Unpriced* LNU (B74-51085)
Guami, Gioseffo. Canzonette francese. Selections. Canzonette francese : for recorder quartet, SATB. *Galaxy Music. Unpriced* VSNS (B74-50767)
Guarnieri, Mozart Camargo.
Sonatina for piano, no.4. Sonatina no.4 for piano. *Associated Music. Unpriced* QPEM (B74-50574)
Sonatina for piano, no.6. Sonatina no.6 for piano. *Associated Music. Unpriced* QPEM (B74-50575)
Guest, Donald. The wedding responses : SATB unacc. *Oxford University Press. £0.06* DGMM/KDD (B74-50341) ISBN 0-19-351649-7
Guide du rythme : guide pratique des rythmiques classiques et moderns. (Bobbio, Reddy). *Chappell. Unpriced* X/NM (B74-51373)
Guildhall School of Music.
Violin examinations, series one
Grade 1. *Lengnick. £0.40* S/AL (B74-50226)
Grade 2. *Lengnick. £0.40* S/AL (B74-50227)
Grade 3. *Lengnick. £0.40* S/AL (B74-50228)
Grade 4. *Lengnick. £0.60* S/AL (B74-50229)
Introductory. *Lengnick. £0.40* S/AL (B74-50230)
Junior. *Lengnick. £0.40* S/AL (B74-50231)
Preliminary. *Lengnick. £0.40* S/AL (B74-50232)
Guitar : from the Renaissance to the present day. (Turnbull, Harvey). *Batsford. £4.00* ATS(X) (B74-14312) ISBN 0-7134-2784-1
Guitar repair : a manual of repair for guitars and fretted instruments. (Sloane, Irving). *Nelson. £2.50* ATR/BT (B74-28318) ISBN 0-17-149062-2
Guitar song book
Book 1. (Whyton, Wally). *Durham Music. £1.25* JE/TSDW/AY (B74-51029)
Guitar tutor for young children. (Criswick, Mary). *Fenette Music. Unpriced* TS/AC (B74-50696)
Gumer, Bob. The entertainer: arr. The entertainer. (Joplin, Scott). *Lewis Music : Ashley-Fields. Unpriced* QPHXJ (B74-51154)
Gundry, Inglis. In those 12 days : variations on an old Cornish carol, for clarsach or other harp. *Thames. Unpriced* TQCPM/T (B74-51262)
Gustav Holst - letters to W.G. Whittaker. (Holst, Gustav). *The University, Glasgow G12 8QG : University of Glasgow Press. £4.00* BHP(N) (B74-26028) ISBN 0-85261-106-4
Gustav Mahler : memories and letters. (Werfel, Alma Mahler). 3rd ed. *J. Murray. £5.00* BME(N) (B74-00161) ISBN 0-7195-2944-1
Gŵr wrth gerdd : John Hughes, 1896-1968. (Hughes, Hugh John). *Gwasg Gomer. £0.90* AD/EC(P/D) (B74-04044) ISBN 0-85088-217-6
Gypsy baron suite. (Strauss, Johann, *b.1825*). *Boosey and Hawkes. £15.00* MMK (B74-50143)
Habash, John Mitri.
Adam's apple : SATB. *Robbins. Unpriced* DW (B74-50919)
Adam's apple : SSA. *Robbins. Unpriced* FDW (B74-50991)
The sea of life : SATB. *Robbins. Unpriced* DW (B74-50920)
The sea of life : SSA. *Robbins. Unpriced* FDW (B74-50992)
Silent spring : SATB. *Robbins. Unpriced* DW (B74-50921)

Silent spring : SSA. *Robbins. Unpriced* FDW (B74-50993)

Smokey smokestack : SATB. *Robbins. Unpriced* DW (B74-50922)
Smokey smokestack : SSA. *Robbins. Unpriced* FDW (B74-50994)
To you, my love : four part SATB. *Robbins. Unpriced* DW (B74-50923)
Hacker, Alan. Concerto for clarinet in A major. K.622: arr. Concerto for clarinet and orchestra. K.622. (Mozart, Wolfgang Amadeus). *Schott. £2.00* VVPK/LF (B74-50804)
Hague, Albert. We're all in this together : arr. We're all in this together : for mixed chorus (SATB). *Chappell. Unpriced* DW (B74-50924)
Halápy, Lili.
Musical reading and writing
Vol.1. (Szönyi, Erzsébet). *Boosey and Hawkes. £2.95* A(VC/QU) (B74-25493) ISBN 0-85162-011-6
The selected writings of Zoltán Kodály. (Kodály, Zoltán). *Boosey and Hawkes. £3.95* A(D) (B74-21534) ISBN 0-85162-021-3
Half a fortnight : seven songs for group music making. (Kelly, Bryan). *Novello. £1.60* JFE/XMDW (B74-50093)
Halffter, Cristóbal.
Pinturas negras : concierto para organo y orquesta (1972). *Universal. Unpriced* MPRF (B74-51108)
Procesional : para dos pianos solistas y orquesta. *Universal. Unpriced* MPQNU (B74-51107)
Hall, Martin.
Geistliche Sonate : für Sopran, Trompete und Orgel. Op.38. (Einem, Gottfried von). *Boosey and Hawkes. Unpriced* KFLE/WSPLRDE (B74-51070)
Hallelujahs : for two choirs and organ. (Chapple, Brian). *Chester : Hansen. Unpriced* DH (B74-50895)
Hamilton, Alasdair.
Epithalamios : choruses for organ. *Roberton. £0.30* R/KDD (B74-50197)
The plumes of time : 4 songs for medium voice and piano. *Roberton. £0.50* KFVDW (B74-50117)
Hand, Colin.
Discussions : for violin and cello. *Thames. Unpriced* SPLSR (B74-51248)
Festival overture : for recorder quintet. *Schott. £2.50* VSNRG (B74-50766)
Sonatina for guitar. Opus 74. *Novello. £0.45* TSPEM (B74-50699)
Handbell Ringers of Great Britain. An introduction to English handbell tune ringing. (Bedford, Philip). *22 Tavistock Rd, Springfield Green, Chelmsford, Essex CM1 53L : Handbell Ringers of Great Britain. £1.50* AXSQ (B74-25501) ISBN 0-904289-00-1
Handel, George Frideric.
Concertos for organ. Op.7. Organ concertos. Op.7
No.1: B flat major. *Eulenburg. £0.80* MPRF (B74-50509)
Concertos for organ. Op.7. Organ concertos. Op.7
No.2: A major. *Eulenburg. £0.80* MPRF (B74-50510)
Concertos for organ. Op.7. Organ concertos. Op.7
No.3: B flat major. *Eulenburg. £0.80* MPRF (B74-50511)
Concertos for organ. Op.7. Organ concertos. Op.7
No.4: D minor. *Eulenburg. £0.80* MPRF (B74-50512)
Concertos for organ. Op.7. Organ concertos. Op.7
No.5: G minor. *Eulenburg. £0.80* MPRF (B74-50513)
Concertos for organ. Op.7. Organ concertos. Op.7
No.6: B flat major. *Eulenburg. £0.80* MPRF (B74-50514)
Fugue for organ in E major. Fugue in E major. *Novello. Unpriced* R/Y (B74-50615)
Messiah. Handel's conducting score of 'Messiah' : reproduced in facsimile from the manuscript in the library of St Michael's College, Tenbury Wells. *Scolar Press for the Royal Musical Association. £37.50* BHCADD (B74-24210) ISBN 0-85967-158-5
Messiah. The trumpet shall sound: arr. The trumpet shall sound. *Associated Board of the Royal Schools of Music. £0.15* WSPK/DH (B74-51368)
Rinaldo. Lascia ch'io panga: arr. Evening hymn. *Oxford University Press. Unpriced* DH (B74-50012) ISBN 0-19-351119-3
Scipione. March : arr. Il Scipio : march. *Chappell. Unpriced* UMK/AGM (B74-51301)
Water music. *Eulenburg. £0.70* MRG (B74-50148)
Water music. Selections: arr. Three pieces. *Schirmer. Unpriced* QNTZNK (B74-50160)
Handel and the Fitzwilliam : a collection of essays and a catalogue of an exhibition of Handeliana in the Fitzwilliam Museum in May and June 1974 on the occasion of three concerts of the music of Handel and some of his contemporaries. (Fitzwilliam Museum). *Trumpington St., Cambridge : Fitzwilliam Museum. £0.75* BHC(WJ) (B74-16446) ISBN 0-904454-00-2
Handl, Jacob.
Tomus primis operis musici. *Hodie Christus natus est.* Hodie Christus natus est = Christ was born today : song, for full chorus of mixed voices a cappella. *Roberton. £0.10* EZDJ/LF (B74-50045)
Tomus primus operis musici. Omnes de Saba venient. Omnes de Saba venient : motet for Epiphany, SATTB unacc. *Oxford University Press. £0.08* EZDJ/LFP (B74-50403) ISBN 0-19-350342-5
Hanlon, Allen. Basic guitar
Book 1. *Chappell. Unpriced* TS/AC (B74-51268)
Hanmer, Ronald.
Alice in Wonderland : fantasy for brass band. *Studio Music. Unpriced* WMJ (B74-50309)
The entertainer: arr. The entertainer : ragtime two-step. (Joplin, Scott). *Studio Music. Unpriced* WMK/AHXJ (B74-50826)
The entertainer: arr. The entertainer : ragtime two-step. (Joplin, Scott). *Studio Music. Unpriced* WMK/AHXJ (B74-51358)
La Périchole. Vocal score. La Périchole : operetta in three acts: music. (Offenbach, Jacques). *Weinberger. Unpriced* CF (B74-50332)
Three sketches : for trumpet or cornet and piano. *Emerson Edition. £0.50* WSPJ (B74-50833)
Hannahs, Roger C.
Two Christmas motets : SSA a cappella
1: When all the world - introit in Christmas-tide. *Associated Music. Unpriced* FEZDJ/LF (B74-51002)
2: A hallowed day - alleluia for Christmas Day. *Associated Music. Unpriced* FEZDJ/LF (B74-51003)
Hannon, James J. 50 handbell tunes. *Hannon. £2.70* XSQNK/DW/AY (B74-50326) ISBN 0-904233-00-6
Hans Christian Andersen. The inch worm: arr. The inch worm. (Loesser, Frank). *Frank Music. Unpriced* UMMK/DW/JR (B74-51311)
Hänsel und Gretel. *Abends will ich schlafen gehen: arr.* Angel scene. (Humperdinck, Engelbert). *Cramer. Unpriced* RK/DW (B74-50206)
Hanson, Pauline. And I am old to know : song. (Binkerd, Gordon). *Boosey and Hawkes. Unpriced* KDW (B74-51046)
Happitaphs. Op.81 : 12 happy epitaphs for children's or adult voices and piano. (Josephs, Wilfred). *Boosey and Hawkes. £0.30* FDW (B74-50071)
Hardy, Mabel. Moody horn : for horn and piano. *Imperial Music. £0.40* WTPJ (B74-50847)
Harmonice musices odhecaton. Selections. Ten pieces from 'Harmonice musices odhecaton'. (Petrucci, Ottaviano dei). *Associated Music. Unpriced* VSNSK/DU/AY (B74-50280)
Harper, Jeanne. Sound of living waters : songs of revival. (Pulkingham, Betty). *Hodder and Stoughton. Unpriced* DM/AY (B74-50908) ISBN 0-340-18893-6
Harper's dictionary of music. (Ammer, Christine). *28 Tavistock St., WC2E 7PN : Barnes and Noble. £1.60* A(C) (B74-09865) ISBN 0-06-463347-0
Harpsichord Magazine. *For later publications of this magazine see* English Harpsichord Magazine.
Harpsichord Magazine, and early keyboard instrument review
Vol.1, no.1; Oct. 1973. *Rose Cottage, Bois La., Chesham Bois, Amersham, Bucks. HP6 6BP : Edgar Hunt. £0.50* APW(B) (B74-12391)
Harris, Jerry Weseley.
Magnificat. Esurientes implevit. Vocal score. He hath filled the hungry = Esurientes implevit : for two-part chorus of treble voices, s.A.. (Vivaldi, Antonio). *Roberton. £0.12* FDH (B74-50987)
Tomus primis operis musici. *Hodie Christus natus est.* Hodie Christus natus est = Christ was born today : song, for full chorus of mixed voices a cappella. (Handl, Jacob). *Roberton. £0.10* EZDJ/LF (B74-50045)
Harris, Kenn. Opera recordings : a critical guide. *David and Charles. £3.95* AC/FD (B74-00871) ISBN 0-7153-6362-x
Harrison story : Harrison and Harrison, organ builders, Durham. (Elvin, Laurence). *10 Almond Ave., Swanpool, Lincoln : The author. £5.95* AR/BC(YD/P) (B74-15898) ISBN 0-9500049-2-8
Hart, Muriel. Music. *Heinemann Educational. £0.80* A(VG) (B74-15369) ISBN 0-435-80606-8
Hart, Philip. Works, organ. Collections. Organ works. *Hinrichsen. Unpriced* R/AZ (B74-50613)
Harvey, Jonathan.
Round the star and back : for piano and a small number of other instruments capable of reasonable blend. *Novello. £1.50* QPJ (B74-50591)
Studies for two equal clarinets. *Novello. £0.75* VVNU (B74-50800)

Harvey, Paul. Quartet for 3 B flat clarinets and bass clarinet. *Schott. £1.25* VVNS (B74-50795)
Harvey, Trevor. Jonah and the whale : an entertainment for junior choirs and audience with piano and optional instruments. (Foster, Anthony). *Oxford University Press. £1.59* JDX (B74-50449) ISBN 0-19-336120-5
Hassler, Hans Leo. Cantiones sacrae. Verbum caro factum est. Verbum caro factum est = And the Word became flesh : motet for six-part chorus of mixed voices a cappella. *Schirmer. Unpriced* EZDJ (B74-50949)
Hatsuyama, Shigeru. P.I. Tchaikovsky's 'Swan Lake'. *F. Warne. £1.75* BTDAM/HMBN (B74-26150) ISBN 0-7232-1759-9
Hatton, Graham. Psalm 23. Vocal score. Psalm 23 : tenor solo, chorus (SATB) and orchestra. (Brian, Havergal). *Musica Viva. £1.20* DR (B74-50022)
Haufrecht, Herbert.
Das klagende Lied, no.1. Waldmärchen. Vocal score. Waldmärchen = A forest legend (Das klagende Lied: 1). (Mahler, Gustav). *Belwin-Mills. Unpriced* DX (B74-50371)
Square set : for two pianos. *Associated Music. Unpriced* QNUHG (B74-50162)
Hauschild, Peter. Sonatas for piano. Selections. Sonatinen und leichte Sonaten fur Klavier. (Beethoven, Ludwig van). *Peters. Unpriced* QPE/AY (B74-51145)
Havanaise for violin and piano. Op.83. (Saint-Saens, Camille). *Schirmer. Unpriced* SPHMV (B74-50669)
Havas, Kato. Stage fright : its causes and cures, with special reference to violin playing. *Bosworth. £2.50* AS/E/CS (B74-12392) ISBN 0-900180-69-2
Haverkampf, Ulrich. Concerto for viola & string orchestra, no.4, in D major: arr. Concerto no.4 in D major for viola and strings. (Stamitz, Anton). *Breitkopf and Härtel : Bärenreiter. £2.90* SQPK/LF (B74-50678)
Haydn, Joseph.
Haydn. *Freeman. Unpriced* QPK (B74-51183)
Mass, no.1, in B flat major, 'Heiligmesse'. Vocal score. Missa Sancti Bernardi de Offida, 'Heiligmesse' : for four-part chorus of mixed voices. *Schirmer. Unpriced* DG (B74-50007)
Mass, no.8, in B flat major, 'Sancti Joannis de Deo'. Vocal score. Missa brevis Sancti Joannis de Deo, 'Small organ mass' : for four-part chorus of mixed voices. *Schirmer. Unpriced* DG (B74-50008)
Mass, no.15, in C major, 'Mariazellermesse'. Vocal score. Missa Cellensis in C, 'Mariazellermesse' : for four-part chorus of mixed voices. *Schirmer. Unpriced* DG (B74-50009)
Quartet for strings, no.17, in B flat major. Op.3, no.5. Serenade: arr. Serenade. *Oxford University Press. Unpriced* MK (B74-51089) ISBN 0-19-364179-8
Haydn, Michael. Litaniae de S.S. Nomine Jesu. Litany in B flat (In nomine Jesu) for four-part chorus of mixed voices, soprano, alto, tenor and bass soli. *Schirmer. Unpriced* DS/LDB (B74-50916)
Hazelgrove, Bernard. Sonata a tre in G minor. Adagio: arr. Adagio. (Albinoni, Tommaso). *Ricordi. £1.25* WMK (B74-51356)
He hath filled the hungry = Esurientes implevit : for two-part chorus of treble voices, s.A.. (Vivaldi, Antonio). *Roberton. £0.12* FDH (B74-50987)
Head, Michael.
Rondo for oboe or violin and piano. *Boosey and Hawkes. £0.60* VTP/W (B74-50781)
Scherzo : for horn or bassoon (or violoncello) and piano. *Boosey and Hawkes. £0.60* WTPJ (B74-50848)
Heath, Reginald.
Pastorale and allegro : B flat cornet duet. *R. Smith. Unpriced* WRNTQ (B74-50315)
Pastorale and allegro : B flat cornet duet and brass band. *R. Smith. Unpriced* WMPWRNU (B74-50313)
Heber, Reginald. Hosanna to the living Lord : unison. (Hunter, Ian). *Thames. Unpriced* JDM (B74-51020)
Hebraic rhapsody, no.2 : piano. (Herschel, Yossel Ben). *Pandian Press : Galliard. Unpriced* QPJ (B74-51172)
Hedges, Anthony. To music. *Vocal score.* To music : for tenor solo, SATB and orchestra. *Chappell. Unpriced* DX (B74-50370)
Hedley, Arthur. Chopin. Revised ed. *Dent. £2.50* BCE (B74-13109) ISBN 0-460-03154-6
Heiden, Bernhard.
Concerto for horn: arr. Concerto for horn and orchestra. *Associated Music. Unpriced* WTPK/LF (B74-50319)
Five canon for two horns. *Associated Music. £1.50* WTNU/X (B74-50317)
Solo for alto saxophone and piano. *Associated Music Publishers. £1.15* VUSPJ (B74-50793)
Heilig = Holy holy holy : for double chorus of mixed voices a cappella. (Mendelssohn, Felix). *Schirmer. Unpriced* EZDH (B74-50944)
Heine, Heinrich. Softly and gently. Op.4, no.3 : for voice and piano. (Holst, Gustav). *Bosworth. Unpriced* KDW (B74-51048)
Hell-bound train : a cowboy songbook. (Ohrlin, Glenn). *University of Illinois Press. £4.30* JEZDW/GNF/AY (B74-50453) ISBN 0-252-00190-7
Hellewell, David. The new music : an introduction and general survey for the non-specialist. *57 Lansdowne Rd, Bournemouth, Hants. BH1 1RN : Apollo Contemporary Music. £0.50* A(XM73) (B74-06501) ISBN 0-9503225-0-4
Hellman, Neal. Life is like a mountain dulcimer : songs. *Ludlow Music : Essex Music. Unpriced* KE/TWTTDW/AY (B74-51065)
Hellyer, Roger. Partita for wind band in F major (1785). Partita (1785) in F Major for two flutes, two oboes, two clarinets, three horns, and two bassoons, with double bass. (Rössler, Franz Anton). *Oxford University Press. Score £3.00, Parts unpriced* UMG (B74-51290) ISBN 0-19-358650-9
Helyer, Marjorie. Eight duets : for piano. *Ashdown. Unpriced* QNV (B74-50565)
Hemda : for piano solo. (Camilleri, Charles). *Fairfield, Distributed by Novello. £0.40* QPJ (B74-50176)
Hendrie, Gerald.
The Baroque organ (containing an introduction to units 1-2); and, Bach organ music. *Open University Press. £2.00* AR/B(XE151) (B74-07435) ISBN 0-335-00850-x
From classical to romantic keyboard music. (Ratcliffe, Ronald V). *Open University Press. Unpriced* AQ/B/E(XA1849) (B74-23499) ISBN 0-335-00864-x
Henriksen, Josef. Forty nine trio preludes for organ based on Sarum plainsong hymn melodies. *St Gregory. £1.65* RJ (B74-50200)
Henshilwood, Donald. Humming bird : waltz song. (Stephens, Hugh). *Hambly Music. £0.20* KDW (B74-50467)
Henze, Hans Werner. Concerto for violin, no.2. Vocal score. 2nd violin concerto for solo violin, tape, voices and 33 instrumentalists. *Schott. £7.20* KGE/SPDX (B74-50119)
Herbert, George. Prayer : anthem for SATB and organ. (Wills, Arthur). *Novello. £0.12* DH (B74-50903)
Herbst, Johannes.
Fürwahr, Er trug uns're Krankheit: arr. Surely he has borne our sorrows = Fürwahr, Er trug uns're Krankheit : S.A.T.B. with accompaniment. Moramus ed. *Boosey and Hawkes. Unpriced* DH (B74-50346)
Höret alle die ihr von Hause: arr. Listen all who enter these portals = Höret alle die ihr von Hause : S.A.T.B. with accompaniment. Moramus ed. *Boosey and Hawkes. Unpriced* DH (B74-50347)
Here's Jupiter : SATB a capella (or improvised rock accompaniment ad lib.). (Kent, Richard). *Warner Blossom. Unpriced* EZDW (B74-50979)
Hermges, David. Old musical instruments. (Clemenicic, René). *Octopus Books. £0.99* AL/B(XD351) (B74-07433) ISBN 0-7064-0057-7
Heron-Allen, Edward. Violin-making as it was and is : being a historical, theoretical and practical treatise on the science and art of violin-making for the use of violin makers and players, amateur and professional. 2nd ed. *Ward Lock. £4.50* AS/BC (B74-02416) ISBN 0-7063-1045-4
Herrick, Robert.
Eternitie : SSATB. (Binkerd, Gordon). *Boosey and Hawkes. Unpriced* EZDH (B74-50943)
Spring cantata : SATB
I: The succession of the four sweet months. (Washburn, Robert). *Boosey and Hawkes. Unpriced* EZDX (B74-50981)
Herring, Ann King.
D.B. Kabalevsky's 'Joey the clown' ('The comedians'). (Watanabe, Saburo). *F. Warne. £1.75* BKDBAM/HMBN (B74-26153) ISBN 0-7232-1783-1
P.I. Tchaikovsky's 'Swan Lake'. (Hatsuyama, Shigeru). *F. Warne. £1.75* BTDAM/HMBN (B74-26150) ISBN 0-7232-1759-9
P.I. Tchaikovsky's 'The nutcracker'. (Hori, Fumiko). *F. Warne. £1.75* BTDAM/HMBN (B74-26151) ISBN 0-7232-1760-2
Herrmann, Bernard. Portrait of Hitch : a musical portrait of Alfred Hitchcock, for orchestra. *Novello. Unpriced* MMJ (B74-51102)
Herrmann, William. Gloria: arr. Gloria : for four-part chorus of mixed voices, two solo sopranos and solo alto. (Vivaldi, Antonio). *Schirmer. £0.95* DGC (B74-50339)
Herschel, Yossel Ben. Hebraic rhapsody, no.2 : piano. *Pandian Press : Galliard. Unpriced* QPJ (B74-51172)
Herz und Mund und That und Leben. S.147. Wohl mir dass ich Jesum habe: arr. Jesu, joy of man's desiring. (Bach, Johann Sebastian). *Oxford University Press. Unpriced* VSNQK/DM (B74-51330) ISBN 0-19-355290-6
Heute ist Christus der Herr geboren = Jesus our Lord on this day was born : motet for Christmas, for three-part chorus of women's voices with continuo (or piano) accompaniment. (Schütz, Heinrich). *Schirmer. Unpriced* FDH/LF (B74-50413)
Hewitt, Leslie.
A fifteenth century song book : Cambridge University Library Add.MS 5943. *5 Albert Grove, Leeds 6 : Boethius Press. £4.60* AELDW(YD/XCQ) (B74-04046) ISBN 0-904263-01-0
A fifteenth century song book : Cambridge University Library Add.MS 5943. *5 Albert Grove, Leeds 6 : Boethius Press. £4.60* 784.3063 (B74-04046) ISBN 0-904263-01-0
The Turpyn book of lute songs : King's College, Cambridge, Rowe MS 2. *5 Albert Grove, Leeds 6 : Boethius Press. £8.70* AKE/TWDW(YD/XDZS14) (B74-03504) ISBN 0-904263-00-2
Hidden face of music. (Whone, Herbert). *Gollancz. £3.00* A/CC (B74-12385) ISBN 0-575-01739-2
Higginbottom, Edward. Premier livre d'orgue. *Selections.* Magnificat du 3e et 4e ton : for organ. (Corrette, Michel). *Novello. Unpriced* RDFF (B74-50617)
High noon: arr. Highnoon. (Tiomkin, Dimitri). *Affiliated Music. £1.00* WMK/DW (B74-50312)
Highnoon. (Tiomkin, Dimitri). *Affiliated Music. £1.00* WMK/DW (B74-50312)
Hijack over Hygenia : a musical play for children. (Wood, David, *b.1944*). *French. £0.75* BWPDACN (B74-28315) ISBN 0-573-05034-1
Hilton, Everett Jay. Melodien til Landstads Salmebog. Kirken den er et. Built on the rock : anthem for unison choir or solo voice and organ. (Lindeman, Ludvig Matthias). *Oxford University Press. Unpriced* JDH (B74-51017)
Hilty, Everett Jay. O come, O come Emmanuel = Veni Emmanuel : Advent anthem for unison or 2-part mixed chorus and organ. *Oxford University Press. Unpriced* JDP/LEZ (B74-50444)
Hindemith, Paul. Lehrstuch (1929). Vocal score. Lehrstuck (1929). *Schott. £4.35* DX (B74-50929)
Histoire de Vasco. *See* Schehadé, Georges.
Historical monographs relating to St George's Chapel, Windsor Castle. Fellowes, Edmund Horace. Organists and Masters of the Choristers of St George's Chapel in Windsor Castle. *S.P.C.K. House, Northumberland Ave., W.C.2 : Society for the Promotion of Christian Knowledge for the Dean and Canons of St George's Chapel in Windsor Castle. Unpriced* AR/E(YDEUW) (B74-23496)
History of Sadler's Wells Opera : an illustrated booklet, published in the centenary year of Lilian Baylis's birth, to mark the change of the Company's name to the English National Opera. (English National Opera Limited). *London Coliseum, St Martin's La., WC2N 4ES : English National Opera Ltd. £1.00* AC/E(YC/QB/X) (B74-26029) ISBN 0-9503681-0-5
History of the piano. (Closson, Ernest). 2nd ed. *Elek. £3.50* AQ/B(X) (B74-09232) ISBN 0-236-17685-4
Hitchcock, Gordon.
Folk songs of the West Country. (Baring-Gould, Sabine). *David and Charles. £3.25* KE/TSDW/G/AYDF (B74-50111) ISBN 0-7153-6419-7
Let joybells ring. *David and Charles. £2.95* JDP/LF/AY (B74-51024) ISBN 0-7153-6712-9
Hitchcock, Hugh Wiley. Music in the United States : a historical introduction. 2nd ed. *Prentice-Hall. £3.65* A(YT/X) (B74-28313) ISBN 0-13-608398-6
Hoag, Charles Kelso. Soft shoe dance : for double bass and piano. *Schirmer. Unpriced* SSPHVPS (B74-50252)
Hochkofler, Max.
Quintet for strings in C major. D.956. Eight studies for the beginner guitarist. (Shepherd, Audrey). *Charnwood Music. Unpriced* TS/AF (B74-51272)
Quintet for strings in C major. D.956. Quintet, C major, for 2 violins, viola and 2 cellos. D.956. (Schubert, Franz). *Eulenburg. Unpriced* RXNR (B74-51224)
Hoddinott, Alun.
The beach of Falesá : opera in three acts. (Jones, Glyn, *b.1905*). *Oxford University Press, Music Department. £0.70* BHNDAC (B74-09229) ISBN 0-19-336833-1
Sonata for piano, no.6. Op.78, no.3. Sonata no.6. Opus 78, no.3. *Oxford University Press. £1.25* QPE (B74-50572) ISBN 0-19-372840-0
Hodie Christus natus est = Christ was born today : song, for full chorus of mixed voices a cappella. (Handl, Jacob). *Roberton. £0.10* EZDJ/LF (B74-50045)
Hodie Christus natus est = On this day, Christ the Lord is born : anthem for SATB and organ. (Aston, Peter). *Novello. Unpriced* DH/LF (B74-50904)
Hodie Christus natus est = On this day Christ the Lord is born : motet for six-part chorus of mixed voices. (Schütz, Heinrich). *Schirmer. Unpriced* DH/LF (B74-50351)
Hodie Christus natus est. S.W.V.456. *Vocal score.* Hodie Christus natus est = On this day Christ the Lord is born : motet for six-part chorus of mixed voices. (Schütz, Heinrich). *Schirmer. Unpriced* DH/LF (B74-50351)
Hodson, Keith.
The wigwam tune book : 20 exciting modern tunes to your favourite hymns. *Wigwam Publications. Unpriced* JDM/AY (B74-50084)
The world belongs to Jesus : nine contemporary songs of worship. *the Baptist Church, Rochdale Rd, Heywood, Lancs. OL10 1LG : Wigwam Publications for Songcrafts. Unpriced* JDM (B74-50442) ISBN 0-904434-00-1
Hoffmeister, Franz Anton.
Concerto for two clarinets in E flat major: arr. Concerto in E flat for 2 clarinets and orchestra. *Musica rara. Unpriced* VUNTQK/LF (B74-50792)
Sonata for flute & piano in C major. Op.13. Sonata in C major for flute or violin and piano. *Nagel : Bärenreiter. £3.80* VRPE (B74-50751)
Höffner, Anton.
Sonata for two trumpets, bassoon, string quintet & basso continuo in C major. Sonata à 8 in C for 2 trumpets, bassoon, strings and continuo. *Musica rara. Unpriced* NUNME (B74-50521)
Sonata for two trumpets, bassoon, string quintet & basso continuo in C major. Sonata à 8 in C for 2 trumpets, bassoon, strings and continuo. *Musica rara. Unpriced* NUNTK/LE (B74-50524)
Hofmann, Klaus. Sonata for oboe, violin & basso continuo in G major. Sonata in Gmajor for oboe, violin and basso continuo. (Telemann, Georg Philipp). *Bärenreiter. £1.80* NUTNTE (B74-50529)
Hofstetter, Romanus. Quartet for strings, no.17, in B flat major. Op.3, no.5. Serenade: arr. Serenade. (Haydn, Joseph). *Oxford University Press. Unpriced* MK (B74-51089) ISBN 0-19-364179-8
Hogben, Dorothy. The four sisters : part-song for SSA and piano. *Oxford University Press. Unpriced* FDW (B74-50419)
Hogwood, Christopher. Concerto for keyboard, no.1, in C major. Allegro. Keyboard allegro. (Arne, Thomas Augustine). *Oxford University Press. £0.50* PWPJ (B74-51121) ISBN 0-19-372151-1
Hohensee, Wolfgang. Drei Lieder : für Bariton und Klavier. *Peters. Unpriced* KGNDW (B74-51077)
Holden, Sally. Life is like a mountain dulcimer : songs. (Hellman, Neal). *Ludlow Music : Essex Music. Unpriced* KE/TWTTDW/AY (B74-51065)
Hollander, John. Works, songs. Selections. Selected songs of

Thomas Campion. (Campion, Thomas). *David Godine : Bodley Head. £6.00* KDW (B74-50457) ISBN 0-370-10306-8

Holloway, Robin. Evening with angels : nine movements for chamber ensemble, woodwind, brass and strings. *Oxford University Press. £5.00* MRJ (B74-51114) ISBN 0-19-357238-9

Holst, Gustav.

Gustav Holst - letters to W.G. Whittaker. *The University, Glasgow G12 8QG : University of Glasgow Press. £4.00* BHP(N) (B74-26028) ISBN 0-85261-106-4

The planets. Jupiter. *Selections: arr.* Joybringer : song based on 'Jupiter' by Gustav Holst. *Feldman. £0.25* KDW (B74-50459)

Softly and gently. Op.4, no.3 : for voice and piano. *Bosworth. Unpriced* KDW (B74-51048)

Holst, Imogen.

Holst. *Faber. £2.30* BHP(N) (B74-06502) ISBN 0-571-09967-x

A thematic catalogue of Gustav Holst's music. *38 Russell Sq., WC1B 5DA : Faber Music Ltd : G. and I. Holst Ltd. £15.00* BHP(TD) (B74-21167) ISBN 0-571-10004-x

Holst. (Holst, Imogen). *Faber. £2.30* BHP(N) (B74-06502) ISBN 0-571-09967-x

Holy holy holy = Sanctus. (Monteverdi, Claudio). *Schirmer. Unpriced* DGE (B74-50877)

Holzweissig, Christa. Klavierschule für den Elementarunterricht. (Holzweissig, Erika). *Peters. Unpriced* Q/AC (B74-51123)

Holzweissig, Erika. Klavierschule für den Elementarunterricht. *Peters. Unpriced* Q/AC (B74-51123)

Honigsheim, Paul. Music and society : the later writings of Paul Honigsheim. *Wiley-Interscience. £8.50* A(Z) (B74-07432) ISBN 0-471-24680-8

Hope is the thing with feathers : SSAA. (Binkerd, Gordon). *Boosey and Hawkes. Unpriced* FEZDW (B74-51004)

Hopkins, Ewart. Metyelitsa : SATB unaccompanied Russian folk song. *Roberton. £0.07* EZDW (B74-50410)

Hopkins, Gerard Manley.

The children of David. Op.37 : five modern psalms, for mixed chorus and organ

5: Pied beauty. (Mechem, Kirke). *Boosey and Hawkes. Unpriced* DH (B74-50902)

Three motets : SATB and organ. (Rorem, Ned). *Boosey and Hawkes. Unpriced* DH (B74-50350)

Hopkins, Jerry. Elvis. *Abacus. £1.00* AKDW/HK/E(P) (B74-04795) ISBN 0-349-11717-9

Horabin, E G. Star of Erin : quick march for military band. *Boosey and Hawkes. £0.65* UMMGM (B74-50725)

Höret alle die ihr von Hause: arr. Listen all who enter these portals = Höret alle die ihr von Hause : S.A.T.B. with accompaniment. (Herbst, Johannes). Moramus ed. *Boosey and Hawkes. Unpriced* DH (B74-50347)

Hori, Fumiko. P.I. Tchaikovsky's 'The nutcracker'. *F. Warne. £1.75* BTDAM/HMBN (B74-26151) ISBN 0-7232-1760-2

Horizon overture : for chamber orchestra. (Horovitz, Joseph). *Novello. Unpriced* MRJ (B74-50520)

Horovitz, Joseph.

Horizon overture : for chamber orchestra. *Novello. Unpriced* MRJ (B74-50520)

Horrortorio. Vocal score. Horrortorio : a choral extravaganza for SATB soli & chorus and orchestra. *Novello. £0.65* EMDX (B74-50375)

Horrortorio : a choral extravaganza for SATB soli & chorus and orchestra. (Horovitz, Joseph). *Novello. £0.65* EMDX (B74-50375)

Horse of wood : a pop-style cantata. (Withams, Eric L). *Universal. Unpriced* FDX (B74-50998)

Horton, John.

Five Northumbrian tunes : for cello and piano. *Schott. £1.00* SRPJ (B74-50248)

Grieg. *Dent. £2.95* BGT (B74-13104) ISBN 0-460-03135-x

Hosanna to the living Lord : unison. (Hunter, Ian). *Thames. Unpriced* JDM (B74-51020)

Hours of the day : a suite of six piano pieces for young people with supplementary exercises. (Blezard, William). *167 Ewell Rd, Surbiton, Surrey : Camera Music. Unpriced* QPG (B74-51148)

House by the side of the road : mixed chorus and piano with optional percussion and string bass. (Atkinson, Condit). *Galaxy : Galliard. Unpriced* DW (B74-50918)

Housman, Alfred Edward. When I was one and twenty : for voice and piano. (Duke, John). *Schirmer. Unpriced* KDW (B74-50098)

Hovhaness, Alan.

Four motets. Op.268 : SATB a cappella

1: Blessed is the man that trusteth in the Lord; text from Jeremiah 17. *Associated Music. £0.20* EZDH (B74-50388)

2: Help, Lord, for the godly man ceaseth; text from Psalm 12. *Associated Music. £0.15* EZDH (B74-50389)

3: Lord, who shall abide in thy tabernacle? Text from Psalm 15. *Associated Music. £0.20* EZDH (B74-50390)

4: The fool hath said in his heart; text from Psalm 14. *Associated Music. £0.15* EZDH (B74-50391)

Four songs, Opus 238 and Four songs, Opus 242 : low voice and piano. *Peters. £6.00* KFXDW (B74-51076)

Pastoral and fugue for two flutes. *Associated Music. Unpriced* VRNU/Y (B74-51316)

Suite for harp. Op.270. *Associated Music. Unpriced* TQPMG (B74-51264)

Symphony no.1. Op.17, no.2 (Exile). Exile symphony, (Symphony no.1). Op.17, no.2. *Peters. £7.50* MME (B74-51098)

How musical is man? (Blacking, John). *University of Washington Press. £3.25* BZNR (B74-30188) ISBN 0-295-95218-0

How pleasant to know Mr. Lear : for narrator and orchestra. (Roxburgh, Edwin). *United Music. Unpriced* KHYE/M (B74-50120)

How to make musical sounds. (Southworth, Mary). *Studio Vista. £1.25* AL/BC (B74-05792) ISBN 0-289-70405-7

How to play the guitar : folk, blues, calypso. (Silverman, Jerry). *Nelson. £1.95* TS/AC (B74-51270) ISBN 0-17-141039-4

How to repair musical instrument amplifiers. (Wels, Byron Gerald). *Yeovil Rd, Slough, Bucks. SL1 4JH : Foulsham-Tab Ltd. £1.50* APV/BT (B74-05794) ISBN 0-7042-0050-3

Howe, James Hakin.

World cup fanfare : brass band. (Drexler, Werner) *Weinberger. Unpriced* WMK/AGN (B74-50825)

World cup fanfare : military band. (Drexler, Werner). *Weinberger. Unpriced* UMMK/AGN (B74-50733)

Howell, Thomas. The avant-garde flute : a handbook for composers and flutists. *University of California Press. £5.50* AVR/E/CY (B74-21542) ISBN 0-520-02305-6

Howes, Frank. The music of William Walton. 2nd ed. *Oxford University Press. £3.00* BWJ (B74-00528) ISBN 0-19-315431-5

Huber, Klaus.

Kleine deutsche Messe (1969). *Vocal score.* Kleine deutsche Messe = Missa brevissima (1969) : für Chor und Orgel (Gemeinde und Schlagzeug ad libitum) oder für Chor a cappella (Schlagzeug ad libitum) oder Originalfassung, für Chor, Orgel, Streichtrio und Harfe (Gemeinde und Schlagzeng ad libitum). *Bärenreiter. £1.80* DG (B74-50335)

Three short meditations : for string trio and harp (1969). *Bärenreiter. £2.70* RWNS (B74-50638)

Hudson, Frank M. The school for scandal, Op.5. Overture. Overture to 'The school for scandal'. (Barber, Samuel). *Schirmer. Unpriced* UMK (B74-50715)

Hudson, Hazel.

Behold that star ... Rise up, shepherd an' foller! : a quodlibet. *Ashdown. £0.12* FDW/LC (B74-50997)

Mary Ann - Jamaica farewell : a quodlibet for two-part singing with piano accompaniment and optional parts for percussion with or without descant recorder. *Ashdown. £0.10* FDW (B74-50070)

The shepherds : a Spanish Christmas carol sequence for voices with optional parts for guitar, tuned and untuned percussion and piano. *Ashdown. £0.40* FDP/LF/AYK (B74-50415)

Hufstader, Robert. Jesu, meine Freude. S.227. Vocal score. Jesu, priceless treasure : motet for two sopranos, alto, tenor and bass. (Bach, Johann Sebastian). *Schirmer. Unpriced* DH (B74-50010)

Hughes, Donald Jefferson. Loth to depart : eleven songs for mixed voices. *Oxford University Press. £0.35* EZDW/AY (B74-50411) ISBN 0-19-330492-9

Hughes, Edward. Out of the depths, based on Psalm 129 (130) : (SATB). *Campbell, Connelly. Unpriced* DH (B74-50348)

Hughes, Eric. Six low solos : bassoon and piano. *Emerson. Unpriced* VWPJ (B74-50297)

Hughes, Hugh John. Gŵr wrth gerdd : John Hughes, 1896-1968. *Gwasg Gomer. £0.90* AD/EC(P/D) (B74-04044) ISBN 0-85088-217-6

Hughes, Ted. The story of Vasco : opera in three acts. (Crosse, Gordon, *b.1937*). *Oxford University Press, Music Department. £0.70* BCRAC (B74-09228) ISBN 0-19-335702-x

Hughes-Jones, Llifon. Balulalow : unison voices (or solo) and piano (or organ). *Thames. Unpriced* JDP/LF (B74-51023)

Hummel, Johann Nepomuk. Fantasia for viola, two clarinets & string orchestra: arr. Fantasia for viola and string orchestra with two clarinets. *Musica rara. Unpriced* RXMPNVVNT (B74-50646)

Humming bird : waltz song. (Stephens, Hugh). *Hambly Music. £0.20* KDW (B74-50467)

Humperdinck, Engelbert. Hänsel und Gretel. *Abends will ich schlafen gehen: arr.* Angel scene. *Cramer. Unpriced* RK/DW (B74-50206)

Hundred score-reading exercises. 100 score-reading exercises. (Wilkinson, Philip George). *Novello. £1.50* LNT (B74-51083)

Hung, Josephine Huang. Classical Chinese plays. 2nd ed. *Vision Press. £3.80* BZHAC (B74-13707) ISBN 0-85478-302-4

Hungarian children's songs : for piano. (Sugár, Rezsö). *Boosey and Hawkes. £0.85* QPJ (B74-50185)

Hungarian children's songs : for piano duet. (Sugár, Rezso). *Boosey and Hawkes. £0.85* QNV (B74-50566)

Hunsberger, Donald.

Mass. Almighty Father: arr. Almighty Father : chorale from 'Mass'. (Bernstein, Leonard). *Amberson : Schirmer. £5.60(full score and parts)(extra score £0.95, extra parts £0.30 each)* UMK (B74-50716)

Mass. Mediatation no.2 (on a sequence by Beethoven): arr. Meditation no.2 (on a sequence by Beethoven). (Bernstein, Leonard). *Amberson : Schirmer. Unpriced* UMK (B74-50717)

Hunter, George.

Pièces de violes, liv. 4. Suite for viola da gamba, no.1, in D minor. Suite no.1 in D minor for viola da gamba and basso continuo. (Marais, Marin). *Associated Music. Unpriced* STUPG (B74-51258)

Salve regina : for four-part chorus of mixed voices a cappella. (Okeghem, Jean). *Associated Music. Unpriced* EZDJ (B74-50397)

Tu solus, qui facis mirabilia : for four-part chorus of mixed voices a cappella. (Josquin Des Prés). *Associated Music. Unpriced* EZDJ (B74-50396)

Hunter, Ian. Hosanna to the living Lord : unison. *Thames. Unpriced* JDM (B74-51020)

Huray, Peter le. *See* Le Huray, Peter.

Husa, Karel.

Apotheosis of this earth : for concert band. *Associated Music. Unpriced* UMJ (B74-50714)

Concerto for alto saxophone and concert band: arr. Concerto for alto saxophone and concert band. *Associated Music. Unpriced* VUSPK/LF (B74-50291)

Concerto for percussion and wind ensemble. *Associated Music. Unpriced* UMF (B74-50712)

Hussey, Dyneley. Verdi. Revised ed.. *Dent. £2.50* BVE(N) (B74-17892) ISBN 0-460-03151-1

Hutcheson, Ernest. The literature of the piano : a guide for amateur and student. 3rd ed., revised. *Hutchinson. £4.75* AQ (B74-17389) ISBN 0-09-119120-3

Hyde, Derek.

Petite musique de chambre. Partita 1. *selections.* Suite no.2. (Telemann, Georg Philipp). *Boosey and Hawkes. £0.65* WSPJ (B74-50835)

Petite musique de chambre. Partitas 4, 5. *selections.* Suite no.1 : arranged for trumpet in B flat and piano from the music of G.P. Telemann. (Telemann, Georg Philipp). *Boosey and Hawkes. £0.65* WSPJ (B74-50836)

Hymn to God the Father : anthem for 4-part chorus of mixed voices SATB, unaccompanied. (Eldridge, Guy). *Roberton. £0.12* EZDH (B74-50387)

Hymns for celebration : a supplement for use at Holy Communion today. (Routley, Erik). *Royal School of Church Music. Unpriced* DM/AY (B74-50353) ISBN 0-85402-055-1

I hear an army : for soprano and string quartet. (Tredici, David del). *Boosey and Hawkes. £2.00* KFLE/RXNSDX (B74-51069)

I sing of a Maiden : arr. I sing of a Maiden. (Shaw, Martin). *Oxford University Press. Unpriced* EZDP/LF (B74-50967)

I sing of a maiden. (Le Fleming, Christopher). *Roberton. Unpriced* EZDH/LF (B74-50948)

I sing of a Maiden. (Shaw, Martin). *Oxford University Press. Unpriced* EZDP/LF (B74-50967)

I thought Terry Dene was dead. (Wooding, Dan). *Coverdale House. £0.50* AKDW/GB/E(P) (B74-25498) ISBN 0-902088-55-6

Ich waiss mir Meidlein = I know a fair maiden : madrigal, for four-part chorus of mixed voices a cappella. (Lasso, Orlando di). *Schirmer. Unpriced* EZDU (B74-50054)

Idaspe. Sinfonia. Sinfonia to 'Hydaspes' : for trumpet, strings and basso continuo. (Mancini, Francesco). *Musica rara. Unpriced* RXMPWSE (B74-50653)

Idaspe. Sinfonia: arr. Sinfonia to 'Hydaspes' : for trumpet, strings and basso continuo. (Mancini, Francesco). *Musica rara. Unpriced* WSPK/LE (B74-50842)

Idyll for strings. (Dodgson, Stephen). *Chappell. Unpriced* RXMJ (B74-50218)

Idylle. (Veneux, Thierry). *Chappell. Unpriced* TMK (B74-50693)

Imaginary landscape : orchestra. (Birtwistle, Harrison). *Universal. Unpriced* MMJ (B74-50140)

Impressions et images, 3e suite. Lettre J. (Veneux, Thierry). *Chappell. Unpriced* TMK (B74-50691)

Impressions et images, 3e suite. Lettre K. (Veneux, Thierry). *Chappell. Unpriced* TMK (B74-50692)

Impressions : piano solos. (Pope, Roger Hugh). *196 Grays Inn Rd WC IX 8EW : Warren and Phillips. Unpriced* QPJ (B74-51179)

Impromptu for the organ. (Waters, Charles Frederick). *Cramer. £0.24* RJ (B74-50203)

Impromptus. Op.32 : for solo tuba. (Muczynski, Robert). *Schirmer. £0.95* WVPMJ (B74-50852)

Improvisation on a Mormon hymn: arr. Improvisation on a Mormon hymn: Come, come ye saints. (Johannesen, Grant). *Oxford University Press. Unpriced* RK (B74-50626)

Improvisation on a Mormon hymn: Come, come ye saints. (Johannesen, Grant). *Oxford University Press. Unpriced* RK (B74-50626)

Improvisation pour clarinette (en si bemol) seule. (Vallier, Jacques). *Chappell. Unpriced* VVPMJ (B74-51346)

In Bethlehem, that fair city : Christmas carol for mixed chorus unaccompanied. (Payne, Mary Monroe). *Oxford University Press. Unpriced* EZDP/LF (B74-50406)

In evening air : piano solo. (Copland, Aaron). *Boosey and Hawkes. £0.40* QPJ (B74-51169)

In memoriam : for concert band. (Brunelli, Louis Jean). *Chappell. Unpriced* UMJ (B74-51296)

In memoriam N.N : cantata. (Lang, Istvan). *Boosey and Hawkes. £2.50* EMDX (B74-50030)

In te Domine, speravi = Lord in thee do I put my trust : motet for four-part chorus of mixed voices a cappella. (Schütz, Heinrich). *Schirmer. Unpriced* EZDJ (B74-50398)

In those 12 days : variations on an old Cornish carol, for clarsach or other harp. (Gundry, Inglis). *Thames. Unpriced* TQCPM/T (B74-51262)

In venisti enim gratiam = You have been acclaimed the chosen one. The Annunciation : for four-part chorus of mixed voices a cappella. (Victoria, Tomàs Luis de). *Schirmer. Unpriced* EZDJ (B74-50400)

Inayat, David. Rise eagle rise. (Schäfer, Karl-Heinz). *Maneges, Chappell : Chappell. Unpriced* KDW (B74-50466)

Incantation : 4th piano concerto. (Martinu, Bohuslav). *Supraphon : Bärenreiter. £3.60* QNUK/LF (B74-50563)

Inch worm. (Loesser, Frank). *Frank Music. Unpriced* UMMK/DW/JR (B74-51311)

Incon-sequenza : for one tuba-player. (Bamert, Matthias). *Schirmer. £0.70* WVPMJ (B74-50851)

Infant holy : Polish carol. (Shirley, Nancy). *Roberton. £0.07* FEZDP/LF (B74-50075)
Infant joy : SSAA. (Binkerd, Gordon). *Boosey and Hawkes. Unpriced* FEZDW (B74-51005)
Ingegneri, Marco Antonio. Responsoria hebdomadae sanctae. Caligaverunt oculi mei. Caligaverunt oculi mei = My eyes are blinded by my weeping : Lenten motet for four-part chorus of mixed voices a cappella. *Schirmer. Unpriced* FEZDGKH/LHL (B74-50073)
Inkblot : for concert band. (Bamert, Matthias). *Schirmer. Unpriced* UMJ (B74-50262)
Inside jazz. (Collier, Graham, *b.1937*). *Quartet Books. £2.75* AMT (B74-00162) ISBN 0-7043-2028-2
Institute of Cornish Studies. Special reports. Combellack, Myrna May. A survey of musical activities in Cornwall. *Trevenson House, Pool, Redruth, Cornwall : Institute of Cornish Studies. £0.30* A(YDFR) (B74-22803) ISBN 0-903686-05-8
Intermediate cellist. (Stanfield, Milly Bernardine). *Oxford University Press. £2.00* ASR/E (B74-03505) ISBN 0-19-318508-3
Interpretation of early music. (Donington, Robert). New version. *Faber. £10.00* A(YB/XDXJ151) (B74-21536) ISBN 0-571-04789-0
Intonazione : for two piano. (Lazarof, Henri). *Associated Music. £12.00* QNU (B74-50561)
Intrada for brass band. (Gregson, Edward). *R. Smith. Unpriced* WMJ (B74-50308)
Intrada : for organ. Op.64. (Fricker, Peter Racine). *Faber Music. Unpriced* RJ (B74-50199)
Introduction and rondo capriccioso for violin & orchestra. Opus 28: arr. Introduktion und Rondo capriccioso. Opus 28 : für Violine und Orchester. (Saint-Saens, Camille). *Peters. £2.40* SPK (B74-51244)
Introduction, march and shepherd's dance. (Menotti, Gian Carlo). *Schirmer. Unpriced* UMK (B74-50718)
Introduction to English handbell tune ringing. (Bedford, Philip). *22 Tavistock Rd, Springfield Green, Chelmsford, Essex CM1 53L : Handbell Ringers of Great Britain. £1.50* AXSQ (B74-25501) ISBN 0-904289-00-1
Introduction to musical history. (Westrup, *Sir* Jack Allan). 2nd ed. *Hutchinson. £1.50* A(XB) (B74-04792) ISBN 0-09-031591-x
Introduction to the 12 string guitar : 12 string guitar techniques. (Roberts, Don). *Robbins Music : E M I. Unpriced* TS/AC (B74-51269)
Introduktion und Rondo capriccioso. Opus 28 : für Violine und Orchester. (Saint-Saens, Camille). *Peters. £2.40* SPK (B74-51244)
Investiture antiphonal fanfares for three brass choirs. (Bliss, *Sir* Arthur). *Novello. £0.50* WMK/AGN (B74-51357)
Investiture antiphonal fanfares for three brass choirs: arr. Investiture antiphonal fanfares for three brass choirs. (Bliss, *Sir* Arthur). *Novello. £0.50* WMK/AGN (B74-51357)
Invisible drummer : five preludes for piano. (Previn, André). *Boosey and Hawkes. £1.50* QPHX (B74-51151)
Invitation au voyage : for four-part chorus of mixed voices with soprano, alto, tenor, and bass solos a cappella. (Corigliano, John). *Schirmer. Unpriced* EZDW (B74-50977)
Irish folk music : a fascinating hobby, with some account of allied subjects including O'Farrell's treatise on the Irish or Union pipes and Touhey's hints to amateur pipers. (O'Neill, Francis). 1st ed. reprinted. *EP Publishing. £3.00* A/G(YDM/XA1909) (B74-12387) ISBN 0-85409-910-7
Irish idyll, The lark in the clear air. (Dodd, Peter). *United Music. Unpriced* RXMK/DW (B74-50644)
Irving Berlin. (Freedland, Michael). *W.H. Allen. £3.50* BBLN(N) (B74-05268) ISBN 0-491-01112-1
Isle of the dead. Op. 29 : symphonic poem. (Rachmaninoff, Sergei). *Boosey and Hawkes. £1.25* MMJ (B74-50141)
Ives, Charles.
Easter carol : solo quartet, SATB and organ. *Associated Music. Unpriced* DP/LL (B74-50355)
Memos. *Calder and Boyars. £5.00* BIV(N) (B74-01379) ISBN 0-7145-0953-1
Sonata for piano, no.2: arr. The Alcotts. *Associated Music. Unpriced* UMK (B74-50266)
Ivor Novello song album. (Novello, Ivor). *Chappell. Unpriced* KDW (B74-51050)
Jablonski, Edward. The Gershwin years. *Robson Books. £6.95* BGH(N) (B74-27798) ISBN 0-903895-19-6
Jackson, Francis.
Sing a new song to the Lord. Op.36, no.4 : anthem for soprano solo, SATB with divisions and organ. *Novello. Unpriced* DR (B74-50356)
Sonata giocosa per la renascita di una cattedrale. Opus 42 : organ. *Oxford University Press. £1.80* RE (B74-51189)
Jackson, Richard. Piano music of Louis Moreau Gottschalk : 26 complete pieces from original editions. (Gottschalk, Louis Moreau). *Dover : Constable. £3.36* QPJ (B74-50590) ISBN 0-486-21683-7
Jackson, Stanley, *b.1910.* Monsieur Butterfly : the story of Puccini. *W.H. Allen. £3.50* BPU(N) (B74-05267) ISBN 0-491-01162-8
Jacob, Gordon.
Four little pieces : cornet or trumpet and piano. *Emerson Edition. Unpriced* WSPJ (B74-50834)
Quartet for saxophones. Saxophone quartet. *Emerson Edition. Unpriced* VUNS (B74-50791)
Jacobs, Robert Louis. Wagner. Revised ed.. *Dent. £2.75* BWC(N) (B74-25494) ISBN 0-460-03153-8
Jacques, Michael. Five piece suite : for piano. *Roberton. £0.40* QPG (B74-51149)
Janetzky, Kurt. Concerto for oboe, strings & basso continuo in C minor. Concerto a 5 für Oboe, Streicher und Basso continuo C-moll. (Telemann, Georg Philipp). *Litolff : Peters. £2.80* NUTNRF (B74-51117)
Japanese folk suite : for military band. (Walters, Harold L). *Rubank : Novello. Unpriced* UMMG (B74-50724)
Jardins de Paris : pour voix moyenne. (Berthomieu, Marc). *Chappell. Unpriced* KFVDW (B74-50485)
Jarman, Richard. A history of Sadler's Wells Opera : an illustrated booklet, published in the centenary year of Lilian Baylis's birth, to mark the change of the Company's name to the English National Opera. (English National Opera Limited). *London Coliseum, St Martin's La., WC2N 4ES : English National Opera Ltd. £1.00* AC/E(YC/QB/X) (B74-26029) ISBN 0-9503681-0-5
Jarre, Maurice. Dr Zhivago. *Somewhere my love: arr.* Somewhere by love. *Francis, Day and Hunter. £0.25* WUNS (B74-50320)
Jeffers, Robinson. The children of David. Op.37 : five modern psalms, for mixed chorus and organ
2: Joy. (Mechem, Kirke). *Boosey and Hawkes. Unpriced* DH (B74-50899)
Jeffery, Brian.
Divertimento for guitar, no.1. Op.1. First set of divertimenti. Op.1. (Sor, Fernando). *Oxford University Press. £0.50* TSPMJ (B74-50702) ISBN 0-19-358863-3
Divertimento for guitar, no.2. Op.2. Second set of divertimenti. Op.2. (Sor, Fernando). *Oxford University Press. £0.50* TSPMJ (B74-50703) ISBN 0-19-358864-1
Divertimento for guitar, no.3. Op.8. Third set of divertimenti. Op.8. (Sor, Fernando). *Oxford Universtion Press. £0.50* TSPMJ (B74-50704) ISBN 0-19-358865-x
Fantasia for guitar, no.1, in C major. Op.7. Fantasia no.1, Op.7. (Sor, Fernando). *Oxford University Press. £0.50* TSPMJ (B74-50705) ISBN 0-19-358860-9
Fantasia for guitar, no.2, in A major. Op.4. Fantasia no.2. Op.4. (Sor, Fernando). *Oxford University Press. £0.40* TSPMJ (B74-50706) ISBN 0-19-358861-7
Fantasia for guitar, no.3, in F major. Op.10. Fantasia no.3, Op.10. (Sor, Fernando). *Oxford University Press. Unpriced* TSPMJ (B74-50707) ISBN 0-19-358862-5
Jennings, Trevor Stanley. A short history of Surrey bells and ringing customs. *'Marchants', 53 Latchmere La., Kingston-upon-Thames, Surrey KT2 5SF : The author. £1.00* AXSR/E(YDCH) (B74-18432) ISBN 0-9500076-3-3
Jephte (Jephthah) : oratorio for SATB soli, SSSATB chorus, optional strings without violas, and organ continuo. (Carissimi, Giacome). *Novello. £0.55* ENXDD (B74-50378)
Jephte. Vocal score. Jephte (Jephthah) : oratorio for SATB soli, SSSATB chorus, optional strings without violas, and organ continuo. (Carissimi, Giacome). *Novello. £0.55* ENXDD (B74-50378)
Jerusalem city of gold : songs of modern and ancient Israel. *Chappell. Unpriced* KDW/AYVD (B74-50472)
Jessel, Camilla. Thames pageant : a cantata for young players and singers. (Panufnik, Andrzej). *Boosey and Hawkes. £1.50* FE/MDX (B74-50424)
Jesu child : SATB. (Rutter, John). *Oxford University Press. £0.20* DP/LF (B74-50910) ISBN 0-19-343045-2
Jesu, joy of man's desiring. (Bach, Johann Sebastian). *Oxford University Press. Unpriced* VSNQK/DM (B74-51330) ISBN 0-19-355290-6
Jesu, meine Freude. S.227. Vocal score. Jesu, priceless treasure : motet for two sopranos, alto, tenor and bass. (Bach, Johann Sebastian). *Schirmer. Unpriced* DH (B74-50010)
Jesu, priceless treasure : motet for two sopranos, alto, tenor and bass. (Bach, Johann Sebastian). *Schirmer. Unpriced* DH (B74-50010)
Jesus folk : a new collection of folk songs. (Smith, Peter). *Galliard : Stainer and Bell. Unpriced* JE/TSDM/AY (B74-51026) ISBN 0-85249-304-5
Jesus is alive today : unison hymn. (Mills, Betty Lou). *32a Fore St., St Austell, Cornwell : Good News Crusade. £0.20* JDM (B74-50443)
Jim's yolk songs. (Garrett, John M). *English Folk Dance and Song Society. £0.45* KE/TSDW (B74-50479) ISBN 0-85418-103-2
Jingle bells : traditional. (Pierpont, J). *Keith Prowse. Unpriced* WMK/DW/LF (B74-51361)
Joey the clown. *See* Watanabe, Saburo.
Jogging along : rhythm for brass band. (Beare, Cyril). *British and Continental Music. Unpriced* WMJ (B74-50306)
Johannesen, Grant. Improvisation on a Mormon hymn: arr. Improvisation on a Mormon hymn: Come, come ye saints. *Oxford University Press. Unpriced* RK (B74-50626)
John, Donald A. Servicing electronic organs. (Applebaum, Max H). *Foulsham-Tab. £1.80* ARPV/BT (B74-27249) ISBN 0-7042-0108-9
John Cage. (Kostelanetz, Richard). *Allen Lane. £2.00* BCBG (B74-11048) ISBN 0-7139-0762-2
John Danz lectures. Blacking, John. How musical is man? *University of Washington Press. £3.25* BZNR (B74-30188) ISBN 0-295-95218-0
John o' the North. The king's daughter : SA and piano. (Nelson, Havelock). *Lengnick. £0.12* FDW (B74-50420)
John Philip Sousa - a descriptive catalog of his work. (Bierley, Paul E). *University of Illinois Press. £4.75* BSK(TC) (B74-11345) ISBN 0-252-00297-0
Johnny Cash - winners got scars too. (Wren, Christopher, *b.1936*). *Abacus. £0.60* AKDW/GCW(P) (B74-11737) ISBN 0-349-13740-4
Johnson, David. Periodical overture, no.17, in E flat major. Symphony in E flat major, Periodical overture 17 : for flutes, clarinets/oboes, bassoon, horns, strings and continuo. (Erskine, Thomas, *Earl of Kelly*). *Oxford University Press. £2.75* MRE (B74-50518) ISBN 0-19-365170-x
Johnson, Hunter. Past the evening sun : orchestra. *Galaxy : Galliard. Unpriced* MMJ (B74-50506)
Johnson, Robert Sherlaw. Asterogenesis : piano. *Oxford University Press. £2.20* QPJ (B74-51173) ISBN 0-19-372990-3
Johnson, Stuart.
French folk song suite. *Oxford University Press. £1.50* UMG (B74-51289) ISBN 0-19-365100-9
Preliminary band book. *210 Strand, WC2R 1AP : R. Smith and Co. Ltd. Unpriced* WMJ (B74-50823)
Quartet for strings, no.17, in B flat major. Op.3, no.5. Serenade: arr. Serenade. (Haydn, Joseph). *Oxford University Press. Unpriced* MK (B74-51089) ISBN 0-19-364179-8
Johnson, Thomas Arnold. Pastorale : for oboe (or B flat clarinet) and piano. *British and Continental Music Agencies. Unpriced* VTPJ (B74-50784)
Johnson, Tom. The four note opera : an opera in one act for soprano, contralto, tenor, baritone and bass with piano accompaniment. *Associated Music. Unpriced* CC (B74-50331)
Johnstone, H Diack. Fugue for organ in E major. Fugue in E major. (Handel, George Frideric). *Novello. Unpriced* R/Y (B74-50615)
Join the band : a selection of folk dance tunes for beginners, with second parts. (Wood, Barbara). *English Folk Dance and Song Society. Unpriced* LNUH/G/AY (B74-50490) ISBN 0-85418-079-6
Joint Study Conference on Music and the Physically Handicapped, *London, 1970.* Report of Joint Study Conference on Music and the Physically Handicapped, held on April 6th, 1970, at the Goldsmiths' Hall, London, E.C.2 ... *346 Kensington High St., W.14 : Disabled Living Foundation. £0.50* A(Z/D) (B74-16560) ISBN 0-901908-02-9
Jonah and the whale : an entertainment for junior choirs and audience with piano and optional instruments. (Foster, Anthony). *Oxford University Press. £1.59* JDX (B74-50449) ISBN 0-19-336120-5
Jonathan and the magic clavichord : a children's story with music. (Crees, Kathleen). *Autocylus. Unpriced* PWPJ (B74-50158)
Jones, Douglas. Movement for string quartet. *Schott. £1.25* RXNS (B74-50223)
Jones, George Thaddeus. Music theory. *28 Tavistock St., WC2E 7PN : Barnes and Noble. £1.95* A/AM (B74-25492) ISBN 0-06-460137-4
Jones, Glyn, *b.1905.* The beach of Falesá : opera in three acts. *Oxford University Press, Music Department. £0.70* BHNDAC (B74-09229) ISBN 0-19-336833-1
Jones, Jonathan Barrie. From classical to romantic keyboard music. (Ratcliffe, Ronald V). *Open University Press. Unpriced* AQ/B/E(XA1849) (B74-23499) ISBN 0-335-00864-x
Jones, Llifon Hughes-. *See* Hughes-Jones, Llifon.
Jones, Marjorie Lilian Glynne-. *See* Glynne-Jones, Marjorie Lilian.
Jones, Richard.
Suite for violin & basso continuo in A major. Op.3, no.1. Suite 1 in A major for violin and basso continuo. *Oxford University Press. £1.25* SPG (B74-50665) ISBN 0-19-357395-4
Suite for violin & basso continuo in B flat major. Op.3, no.4. Suite 4 in B flat major for violin and basso continuo. *Oxford University Press. £1.25* SPG (B74-50666) ISBN 0-19-357398-9
Suite for violin & basso continuo in D major. Op.3, no.3. Suite 3 in D major for violin and basso continuo. *Oxford University Press. £1.25* SPG (B74-50667) ISBN 0-19-357397-0
Suite for violin & basso continuo in G minor. Op.3, no.2. Suite 2 in G minor for violin and basso continuo. *Oxford University Press. £1.25* SPG (B74-50668) ISBN 0-19-357396-2
Jong, Conrad de. Little suite : for piano. *Schroeder and Gunther. Unpriced* QPG (B74-50169)
Jongen, Joseph. Petit prelude. Aria : organ. *Oxford University Press. £0.35* RJ (B74-50619) ISBN 0-19-375495-9
Joplin, Scott.
The entertainer. *California Music : Chappell. Unpriced* KDW (B74-50460)
The entertainer : a rag time two step. *Lewis Music Ashley Fields. Unpriced* QPHXJ (B74-51153)
The entertainer : a ragtime two step, for piano. *Chappell. Unpriced* QPHXJ (B74-50172)
The entertainer: arr. The entertainer. *Lewis Music Ashley-Fields. Unpriced* QPHXJ (B74-51154)
The entertainer: arr. The entertainer. *Chappell. Unpriced* WMK/AHXJ (B74-51359)
The entertainer: arr. The entertainer : a ragtime two step. *221a Kensington High St., W.8 : Aura Music. Unpriced* TSPMK/AHXJ (B74-51282)
The entertainer: arr. The entertainer : a ragtime two step : composed by Scott Joplin. *Lewis Music : Ashley Fields. Unpriced* QPHXJ (B74-51155)
The entertainer: arr. The entertainer : a ragtime two step : composed by Scott Joplin. *Lewis Music : Ashley-Fields. Unpriced* RK/AHXJ (B74-51201)
The entertainer: arr. The entertainer : piano solo. *Belwin-Mills. £0.30* QPHXJ (B74-50579)
The entertainer: arr. The entertainer : piano solo. *Bosworth. Unpriced* QPHX (B74-51152)
The entertainer: arr. The entertainer : ragtime two-step. *Studio Music. Unpriced* WMK/AHXJ (B74-50826)
The entertainer: arr. The entertainer : ragtime two step. *Lewis Music : Ashley Fields. Unpriced* QPHXJ (B74-51156)
The entertainer: arr. The entertainer : ragtime two step.

Lewis Music : Ashley Fields. Unpriced QPHXJ (B74-51157)
The entertainer: arr. The entertainer : ragtime two-step. *Studio Music. Unpriced* WMK/AHXJ (B74-51358)
Gladiolus rag. *Chappell. Unpriced* QPHXJ (B74-51158)
Piano rags. *Chappell. Unpriced* QPHXJ (B74-50173)
Piano rags. *Novello. £0.55* QPHXJ (B74-50580)
Pine apple rag : piano. *Chappell. Unpriced* QPHXJ (B74-50581)
Selections: arr. Scott Joplin : the king of ragtime writers: easy piano. *Lewis Music : Ashley-Fields. Unpriced* QPHXJ (B74-51159)
Solace : a Mexican serenade, for piano. *Chappell. Unpriced* QPHXJ (B74-50582)
Joseph Haydn and the string quartet. (Barrett-Ayres, Reginald). *Barrie and Jenkins. £11.00* BHEARXNS (B74-25500) ISBN 0-214-66803-7
Josephs, Wilfred.
Happitaphs, Op.81 : 12 happy epitaphs for children's or adult voices and piano. *Boosey and Hawkes. £0.30* FDW (B74-50071)
Lady Glencora's waltz : from 'The Pallisers' BBC television series. *Weinberger. £0.25* QPK/AHW/JS (B74-50191)
Solo oboe piece. Opus 84. *Novello. £0.50* VTPMJ (B74-50789)
Joshua fought the battle of Jericho : negro spiritual. (Dexter, Harry). *Ashdown. Unpriced* FDW/LC (B74-50423)
Josquin des Prés. Ecce tu pulchra es : motet. *Associated Music. Unpriced* VSNSK/DJ (B74-50279)
Josquin Des Prés. Tu solus, qui facis mirabilia : for four-part chorus of mixed voices a cappella. *Associated Music. Unpriced* EZDJ (B74-50396)
Joubert, John.
Behold the tabernacle of God. Op.70 : anthem for SATB, with divisions and organ. *Novello. £0.16* DH (B74-50897)
Four stations on the road to freedom, Opus 73 : for SSAATTBB soli or chorus (unaccompanied). *Novello. Unpriced* JNEZAYDE (B74-50456)
Kontakion. Opus 69 : for cello and piano. *Novello. Unpriced* SRPJ (B74-50682)
Journey to the centre of the earth. (Wakeman, Rick). *Rondor : Music Sales. Unpriced* QPK/DW (B74-50603)
Journey to the centre of the earth: arr. Journey to the centre of the earth. (Wakeman, Rick). *Rondor : Music Sales. Unpriced* QPK/DW (B74-50603)
Joy to the world : treble voices. (Smith, Peter Melville). *Banks. Unpriced* FLDP/LF (B74-51010)
Joybringer : song based on 'Jupiter' by Gustav Holst. (Holst, Gustav). *Feldman. £0.25* KDW (B74-50459)
Joyce, James.
Four songs on poems of James Joyce : for voice and piano. (Tredici, David Del). *Boosey and Hawkes. £2.25* KDW (B74-50469)
I hear an army : for soprano and string quartet. (Tredici, David del). *Boosey and Hawkes. £2.00* KFLE/RXNSDX (B74-51069)
Jubilate Deo = Sing to God : motet for four-part chorus of mixed voices a cappella. (Lasso, Orlando di). *Schirmer. Unpriced* EZDJ (B74-50044)
Jubilate Deo : simple Gregorian chants for the faithful to learn as recommended in the Second Vatican Council's Constitution on the Sacred Liturgy. *Catholic Truth Society. Unpriced* JEZDTDM (B74-51031)
Jung, Hans Rudolf. Concerto for violin in E minor. Konzert, E-moll, für Violine, zwei Oboen, Streicher und Basso continuo, (Fagott ad libitum). (Telemann, Georg Philipp). *Peters. Unpriced* MPSF (B74-51109)
Junior ensemble series. Kersey, Robert E. Just five : a collection of pentatonic songs
Book 1. *Belwin-Mills. £0.40* JFEZDW/PP/AY (B74-50454)
Just five : a collection of pentatonic songs
Book 1. (Kersey, Robert E). *Belwin-Mills. £0.40* JFEZDW/PP/AY (B74-50454)
Book 2. (Kersey, Robert E). *Belwin-Mills. £0.40* JFEZDW/PP/AY (B74-50455)
Kaderabek, Frank. Let's play trumpet. *Experience Music : Chappell. Unpriced* WS/AC (B74-51365)
Kagel, Mauricio.
General Bass : für kontinuerliche Instrumentalklange. *Universal. Unpriced* LPMJ (B74-50128)
Quartet for strings (1965/67). Streichquartett (1965/67). *Universal. Unpriced* RXNS (B74-50224)
Recitativarie : für singende Cembalistin, 1971/72. *Universal. Unpriced* KHYE/QRP (B74-51079)
Unguis incarnatus est : für Klavier und ... *Universal. Unpriced* LPJ (B74-50127)
Kaiser, Ernst. Letters of Arnold Schoenberg. (Schoenberg, Arnold). *Faber. £2.95* BSET(N) (B74-04793) ISBN 0-571-10514-9
Kalib, Sholom. Aleynu l'shabench : a new Friday evening service, cantor solo with mixed chorus, SATB and organ, commissioned by the Anshe Emet Synagogue, Chicago, Illinois, on the occasion of the hundredth jubilee year (1873-1973)
4: Kiddush l'shabat. *Ethnic Music : Phoenix. Unpriced* DGU (B74-50887)
Kallin, Anna. Twentieth century composers
Vol.4: France, Italy and Spain. *Weidenfeld and Nicolson. £4.50* AD(YB/M/XM) (B74-29004) ISBN 0-297-76793-3
Kalliwoda, Jan Vaclav. Concertino for oboe in F major. Op.110: arr. Concertino for oboe and orchestra. Op.110. *Musica rara. Unpriced* VTPK/LFL (B74-50788)
Kameke, Ernst Ulrich von. Osterpsalm für gemischten Chor. *Bärenreiter. £0.75* EZDR/LL (B74-50408)
Kander, John. 70 girls 70 : Selections. 70 girls 70. *Valando. Unpriced* KDW (B74-51049)
Kaplan, William. Compositioni musicale fatte per sonare col fagotto solo, nos 1-3. Three sonatas for bassoon (violoncello) and basso continuo. (Bertoli, Giovanni Antonio). *Bärenreiter. £3.45* VWPE (B74-50811)
Károlyi, Pál. Triphtongas 1 : for organ. *Boosey and Hawkes. £0.75* RJ (B74-50201)
Karpeles, Maud. Cecil Sharp's collection of English folk songs. *Oxford University Press. £44 for set* JEZDW/G/AYD (B74-51032) ISBN 0-19-313125-0
Kasschau, Howard.
Seventeen duets on nursery tunes. 17 duets on nursery tunes. *Schirmer. £0.50* QNVK/DW/GK/AY (B74-50165)
Three singing duets. *Schirmer. Unpriced* QNVK/DW/AY (B74-50164)
Katz, Erich.
Ecce tu pulchra es : motet. (Josquin des Prés). *Associated Music. Unpriced* VSNSK/DJ (B74-50279)
Toccata for recorder consort : SATB. *Associated Music. Unpriced* VSNS (B74-50278)
Kavanagh, Priscilla. Lámhleabhar ginearálta don cheoltóir. (Cecily, *Sister, OP*). *Folens. £0.48* A (B74-11047) ISBN 0-902592-58-0
Kay, Hershey. The clowns : a ballet. *Boosey and Hawkes. Unpriced* MM/HM (B74-51092)
Kechley, Gerald. Pleasure it is : for unaccompanied mixed chorus. *Galaxy : Galliard. Unpriced* EZDP (B74-50958)
Keetman, Gunild.
Elementaria : first acquaintance with Orff-Schulwerk. *48 Great Marlborough St., W1V 2BN : Schott and Co. Ltd. £4.50* A(VG) (B74-13706) ISBN 0-901938-04-1
Pieces for recorder and drum
Book 2. *Schott. £1.20* VSPLXQ (B74-50283)
Keetman, Peter. Elementaria : first acquaintance with Orff-Schulwerk. (Keetman, Gunild). *48 Great Marlborough St., W1V 2BN : Schott and Co. Ltd. £4.50* A(VG) (B74-13706) ISBN 0-901938-04-1
Kehr, Günter. Exquisitioris harmoniae instrumentalis gravijucundae selectus primus. *Concerto no.9 for two violins & string orchestra, 'Victoria maesta'.* Concerto 9, 'Victoria maesta'. (Muffat, Georg). *Schott. £1.92* RXMPSNUF (B74-50220)
Keith, Alan.
The world of your 100 best tunes requested by listeners to the popular BBC radio series devised and presented by Alan Keith, easy-to-play piano album, piano arrangements by James Burt
Vol.4. *Chappell. Unpriced* QPK/AAY (B74-50598)
The world of your 100 best tunes requested by listeners to the popular BBC radio series
Vol.1. *Chappell. £0.50* QPK/AAY (B74-50599)
Vol.2. *Chappell. £0.50* QPK/AAY (B74-50600)
Vol.3. *Chappell. £0.95* QPK/AAY (B74-50601)
Keller, Hans. Children's crusade = Kinderkreuzzug. Op.82 : a ballad for children's voices and orchestra. (Britten, Benjamin). *Faber Music : Faber. £15.00* BBUADX (B74-21537) ISBN 0-571-10370-7
Keller, Hermann. Bagatelles. Opus 119 : piano solo. (Beethoven, Ludwig van). *Peters. Unpriced* QPJ (B74-50584)
Kelly, Bryan. Half a fortnight : seven songs for group music making. *Novello. £1.60* JFE/XMDW (B74-50093)
Kennedy, John Brodbin.
Lala and la : SSA. *Boosey and Hawkes. Unpriced* FEZDW (B74-51007)
Two reflections : SSA unaccompanied. *Boosey and Hawkes. Unpriced* FEZDW (B74-51008)
Kennedy, Michael, *b.1926.* Mahler. *Dent. £2.75* BME(N) (B74-16725) ISBN 0-460-03141-4
Kennerley, Peter. Little camel boy : a carol for treble voices with audience (or choral) participation. (Walters, Edmund). *Boosey and Hawkes. £0.15* FLDP/LF (B74-51012)
Kent, Richard. Here's Jupiter : SATB a capella (or improvised rock accompaniment ad lib.). *Warner Blossom. Unpriced* EZDW (B74-50979)
Kersey, Robert E.
Just five : a collection of pentatonic songs
Book 1. *Belwin-Mills. £0.40* JFEZDW/PP/AY (B74-50454)
Book 2. *Belwin-Mills. £0.40* JFEZDW/PP/AY (B74-50455)
Keyboard allegro. (Arne, Thomas Augustine). *Oxford University Press. £0.50* PWPJ (B74-51121) ISBN 0-19-372151-1
Keys, Ivor. Brahms chamber music. *British Broadcasting Corporation. £0.45* BBTAN (B74-14311) ISBN 0-563-10168-7
Kimball, Robert. The Gershwins. *Cape. £9.50* BGH(N) (B74-24209) ISBN 0-224-01014-x
Kinderorgel : leichte Volkslieder aus aller Welt, für elektronische Orgel (1 Manuel). (Draths, Willi). *Schott. £1.45* RPVK/DW/G/AY (B74-50634)
Kindertotenlieder : für eine Singstimme und Orchester auf Gedichte von Friedrich Rückert. (Mahler, Gustav). *Peters. Unpriced* KE/MDW (B74-51060)
Kindling fire : twelve Burns songs, arranged for high voice using the airs to which Burns set his verses. (Liddell, Claire). *Roberton. £1.00* KFTDW/AY (B74-51072)
King Arthur. *Selections: arr.* Music from 'King Arthur'. (Purcell, Henry). *Paxton. £0.40* RK/JM (B74-50628)
King's College, *Cambridge. Library. MSS. (Rowe 2).* The Turpyn book of lute songs : King's College, Cambridge, Rowe MS 2. *5 Albert Grove, Leeds 6 : Boethius Press. £8.70* AKE/TWDW(YD/XDZS14) (B74-03504) ISBN 0-904263-00-2
King's daughter : SA and piano. (Nelson, Havelock). *Lengnick. £0.12* FDW (B74-50420)
Kinney, Phyllis. Canenon llafar gwlad = Songs from oral tradition
Vol.1. (Saer, D Roy). *National Museum of Wales, Welsh Folk Museum. Unpriced* JEZDW/G/AYDK (B74-51033) ISBN 0-85485-026-0
Kirkby-Mason, Barbara.
For children : piano solos
Book 1. *Keith Prowse Music. Unpriced* QPJ (B74-51174)
Book 2. *Keith Prowse Music. Unpriced* QPJ (B74-51175)
Kirkpatrick, John.
Easter carol : solo quartet, SATB and organ. (Ives, Charles). *Associated Music. Unpriced* DP/LL (B74-50355)
Memos. (Ives, Charles). *Calder and Boyars. £5.00* BIV(N) (B74-01379) ISBN 0-7145-0953-1
Kirkup, James. Ghosts, fire, water : for alto solo and unaccompanied mixed voices. (Mews, Douglas). *Oxford University Press. £0.30* EZDE (B74-50036) ISBN 0-19-343670-1
Kishida, Eriko. P.I. Tchaikovsky's 'Swan Lake'. (Hatsuyama, Shigeru). *F. Warne. £1.75* BTDAM/HMBN (B74-26150) ISBN 0-7232-1759-9
Klagende Lied, no.1. Waldmärchen. Vocal score. Waldmärchen = A forest legend (Das klagende Lied: 1). (Mahler, Gustav). *Belwin-Mills. Unpriced* DX (B74-50371)
Klassik : elektronische Orgel. (Sommer, Jürgen). *Nagel Bärenreiter. £1.80* RPVK/AAY (B74-50632)
Klavierschule für den Elementarunterricht. (Holzweissig, Erika). *Peters. Unpriced* Q/AC (B74-51123)
Klebe, Giselher. Sonata for violin & piano. Op.66. Sonate für Violine und Klavier. Op 66. *Bärenreiter. £3.60* SPE (B74-50663)
Klein, Maynard.
Adoramus te = We adore thee : motet for four-part chorus of mixed voices a cappella. (Perti, Giacomo Antonio). *Schirmer. Unpriced* EZDJ (B74-50951)
Alma redemptoris mater = Loving Mother of our Saviour : motet for four-part chorus of mixed voices a cappella. (Palestrina, Giovanni Pierluigi da). *Schirmer. Unpriced* EZDJ (B74-50950)
Cantiones sacrae. Deus misereatur nostri. Deus misereatur nostri = God be merciful unto us : for four-part chorus of mixed voices a cappella. (Schütz, Heinrich). *Schirmer. Unpriced* EZDR (B74-50407)
Cantiones sacrae. In te Domine, speravi. In te Domine, speravi = Lord in thee do I put my trust : motet for four-part chorus of mixed voices a cappella. (Schütz, Heinrich). *Schirmer. Unpriced* EZDJ (B74-50398)
Cantiones sacrae. Quoniam ad te clamabo, Domine. Quoniam ad te clamabo, Domine = Now behold to thee I cry, O Lord : motet for four-part chorus of mixed voices a cappella. (Schütz, Heinrich). *Chappell. Unpriced* EZDJ (B74-50399)
Cantiones sacrae. Verbum caro factum est. Verbum caro factum est = And the Word became flesh : motet for six-part chorus of mixed voices a cappella. (Hassler, Hans Leo). *Schirmer. Unpriced* EZDJ (B74-50949)
Deutsche Liturgie. Heilig. Heilig = Holy holy holy : for double chorus of mixed voices a cappella. (Mendelssohn, Felix). *Schirmer. Unpriced* EZDH (B74-50944)
Exaudi Deus = Oh hear me Lord God : general motet, for four-part chorus of mixed voices a cappella. (Croce, Giovanni). *Schirmer. Unpriced* EZDJ (B74-50043)
Geistliche Chormusik. Verleih uns Frieden genadiglich. Verleih uns Frieden genadiglich = Lord grant us peace : for five-part chorus of mixed voices a cappella. (Schutz, Heinrich). *Schirmer. Unpriced* EZDH (B74-50946)
Heute ist Christus der Herr geboren = Jesus our Lord on this day was born : motet for Christmas, for three-part chorus of women's voices with continuo (or piano) accompaniment. (Schütz, Heinrich). *Schirmer. Unpriced* FDH/LF (B74-50413)
Hodie Christus natus est. S.W.V.456. *Vocal score.* Hodie Christus natus est = On this day Christ the Lord is born : motet for six-part chorus of mixed voices. (Schütz, Heinrich). *Schirmer. Unpriced* DH/LF (B74-50351)
Libro de villanelle. *S'io fusse ciaul.* S'io fusse ciaul = Were I a tiny bird : canzonetta, for four-part chorus of mixed voices a cappella. (Lasso, Orlando di). *Schirmer. Unpriced* EZDU (B74-50052)
Libro de villanelle. *Tutto lo di mi dici 'Canta'.* Tutto lo di mi dici 'Canta' = Day after day they all say 'Sing' : canzonetta, for four-part chorus of mixed voices a cappella. (Lasso, Orlando di). *Schirmer. Unpriced* EZDU (B74-50053)
Motecta. Ne timeas, Maria. In venisti enim gratiam = You have been acclaimed the chosen one. The Annunciation : for four-part chorus of mixed voices a cappella. (Victoria, Tomàs Luis de). *Schirmer. Unpriced* EZDJ (B74-50400)
Motecta. Quem vidistis pastores? Quem vidistis, pastores = Whom did you see, kind shepherds? : Motet for Christmas time, for six-part chorus of mixed voices a cappella. (Victoria, Tomàs Luis de). *Chappell. Unpriced* EZDJ/LF (B74-50402)
Motecta. Vere languores nostres. Vere languores nostres = Truly our Saviour suffered : motet for four-part chorus of mixed voices a cappella. (Victoria, Tomás Luis de). *Schirmer. Unpriced* EZDJ/LK (B74-50953)
Newe teutsche Lieder mit vier Stimmen. *Ich waiss mir en Meidlein.* Ich waiss mir Meidlein = I know a fair maiden : madrigal, for four-part chorus of mixed voices a cappella. (Lasso, Orlando di). *Schirmer. Unpriced* EZDU (B74-50054)
Officium hebdomadie sanctae. Tenebrae factae sunt. Tenebrae factae sunt = Darkness was o'er the earth : Passion motet for four-part chorus of women's voices a

cappella. (Victoria, Tomas Luis de). *Chappell. Unpriced* FEZDGKH/LHL (B74-50428)
Responsoria hebdomadae sanctae. Caligaverunt oculi mei. Caligaverunt oculi mei = My eyes are blinded by my weeping : Lenten motet for four-part chorus of mixed voices a cappella. (Ingegneri, Marco Antonio). *Schirmer. Unpriced* FEZDGKH/LHL (B74-50073)
Sacrae cantiones quatuor vocum. Jubilate Deo. Jubilate Deo = Sing to God : motet for four-part chorus of mixed voices a cappella. (Lasso, Orlando di). *Schirmer. Unpriced* EZDJ (B74-50044)
Ziguenerlieder = Gypsy songs. Op.103 : for four-part chorus of mixed voices with soprano and tenor solos and piano accompaniment. (Brahms, Johannes). *Schirmer. Unpriced* DW (B74-50357)
Kleine deutsche Messe = Missa brevissima (1969) : für Chor und Orgel (Gemeinde und Schlagzeug ad libitum) oder für Chor a cappella (Schlagzeug ad libitum) oder Originalfassung, für Chor, Orgel, Streichtrio und Harfe (Gemeinde und Schlagzeng ad libitum). (Huber, Klaus). *Bärenreiter. £1.80* DG (B74-50335)
Kleine deutsche Messe (1969). *Vocal score.* Kleine deutsche Messe = Missa brevissima (1969) : für Chor und Orgel (Gemeinde und Schlagzeug ad libitum) oder für Chor a cappella (Schlagzeug ad libitum) oder Originalfassung, für Chor, Orgel, Streichtrio und Harfe (Gemeinde und Schlagzeng ad libitum). (Huber, Klaus). *Bärenreiter. £1.80* DG (B74-50335)
Kleine Marchensuite : für Klavier. (Pick, Karl-Heinz). *Peters. Unpriced* QPG (B74-51150)
Kleine Spielereien : für Akkordeon mit 2. Stimme und Schlagwerk ad lib. (Ebing, Hans). *Schott. £1.44* RSPMJ (B74-50213)
Kleine Suite für Viola. (Uhl, Alfred). *Schott. £0.96* SQPMG (B74-50241)
Klemm, Eberhardt. Kindertotenlieder : für eine Singstimme und Orchester auf Gedichte von Friedrich Rückert. (Mahler, Gustav). *Peters. Unpriced* KE/MDW (B74-51060)
Kliewer, Vernon Lee. Aural training : a comprehensive approach. *Prentice-Hall. £4.15* A/EF (B74-24904) ISBN 0-13-053231-2
Klopčič, Rok. Havanaise for violin and piano. Op.83. (Saint-Saens, Camille). *Schirmer. Unpriced* SPHMV (B74-50669)
Kneller Hall : concert march for military band. (Walters, Harold L). *Rubank : Novello. Unpriced* UMMGM (B74-50726)
Knight, Vernon. Suite for brass and percussion. *Schirmer. Unpriced* WMG (B74-50303)
Knitl, Irmengard.
Geistliche Sonate : für Sopran, Trompete und Orgel. Op.38. (Einem, Gottfried von). *Boosey and Hawkes. Unpriced* KFLE/WSPLRDE (B74-51070)
Koanga : opera in three acts with prologue and epilogue. (Delius, Frederick). *Boosey and Hawkes. Unpriced* CC (B74-50866)
Koanga. Vocal score. Koanga : opera in three acts with prologue and epilogue. (Delius, Frederick). *Boosey and Hawkes. Unpriced* CC (B74-50866)
Koch, Johnnes Hermann Ernst. Volksmusik für Bläser. *Bärenreiter. £1.10* UMK/DW/G/AY (B74-50722)
Kodály, Zoltán. The selected writings of Zoltán Kodály. *Boosey and Hawkes. £3.95* A(D) (B74-21534) ISBN 0-85162-021-3
Kodály method : comprehensive music education from infant to adult. (Choksy, Lois). *Prentice-Hall. £2.60* A(VC) (B74-23950) ISBN 0-13-516757-4
Kokoscha, Oskar. Die träumenden Knaben, Op.41 : Cantata für vierstimmigen gemischten Chor, Klarinette und Fagott. (Einem, Gottfried von). *Boosey and Hawkes. Unpriced* EVVPLVWDX (B74-50383)
Kolneder, Walter. L'Estro armonico, Op.3, no.11: arr. Concerto, d-Moll : für 2 Violinen, Streicher und Basso continuo. (Vivaldi, Antonio). *Schott. £2.32* SNTQK/LF (B74-51239)
Komlos, Katalin. 150 American folk songs to sing, read and play. (Erdei, Peter). *Boosey and Hawkes. £3.75* JEZDW/G/AYT (B74-50088)
Kommt her ihr Gesegneten meines Vaters = Come ye blessed ones of my Father : dialogue for five voices (SATTB) and continuo. (Scheidt, Samuel). *Novello. £1.00* JNBDH (B74-51043)
Kontakion. Opus 69 : for cello and piano. (Joubert, John). *Novello. Unpriced* SRPJ (B74-50682)
Korn, Peter Jona. Gloria. Opus 49 : rhapsodische Fantasie für Orgel. *Litolff : Peters. £4.20* RJ (B74-51193)
Kostelanetz, Richard. John Cage. *Allen Lane. £2.00* BCBG (B74-11048) ISBN 0-7139-0762-2
Krance, John.
Bachianas brasileiras, no.5. Aria (Cantilena). (Villa-Lobos, Heitor). *Associated Music. Unpriced* MMK/DW (B74-50508)
Bachianas brasileiras, no.5. Aria (Cantilena). (Villa-Lobos, Heitor). *Associated Music. Unpriced* RXMK/DW (B74-50645)
Bachianas brasileiras, no.5. Aria (Cantilena). (Villa-Lobos, Heitor). *Associated Music. Unpriced* VNK/DW (B74-50743)
Bachianas brasileiras, no.5. Aria (Cantilena). (Villa-Lobos, Heitor). *Associated Music. Unpriced* VVNK/DW (B74-50794)
Krapf, Gerhard. Concerts royaux I-IV : for flute, oboe, violin, viola da gamba and basso continuo
No.I. (Couperin, François). *Musica rara. Unpriced* VRPG (B74-50754)
Kreider, J Evan. Fantasias. Three fantasias. (Ferrabosco, Alfonso, *b.1575*). *Associated Music. Unpriced* VSNS (B74-50277)
Kroeger, Karl.
Die Frucht des Geistes ist Liebe. The fruit of the spirit is love = Die Frucht des Geistes ist Liebe : SATB chorus, flute and organ. (Geisler, Johann Christian). Moramus ed. *Boosey and Hawkes. Unpriced* EVRPLRDH (B74-50382)
Fürwahr, Er trug uns're Krankheit: arr. Surely he has borne our sorrows = Fürwahr, Er trug uns're Krankheit : S.A.T.B. with accompaniment. (Herbst, Johannes). Moramus ed. *Boosey and Hawkes. Unpriced* DH (B74-50346)
Höret alle die ihr von Hause: arr. Listen all who enter these portals = Höret alle die ihr von Hause : S.A.T.B. with accompaniment. (Herbst, Johannes). Moramus ed. *Boosey and Hawkes. Unpriced* DH (B74-50347)
Lobe den Herrn meine Seele: arr. Praise the Lord, O my soul = Lobe den Herrn meine Seele : S.A.T.B. with accompaniment. (Peter, Johann Friedrich). Moramus ed. *Boosey and Hawkes. Unpriced* DH (B74-50349)
Krol, Bernhard. Esslinger Sankt Pauls-Messe nach Texten aus den Briefen des Apostels Paulus : für vierstimmigen gemischten Chor, Gemeinde, Orgel und (ad libitum) Rhythmusgruppe, Orgel (oder Klavier). *Simrock. Unpriced* DG (B74-50336)
Kuhlau, Friedrich.
Concertino for two horns in F major. Op.45: arr. Concertino for 2 horns and orchestra. Op.45. *Musica rara. Unpriced* WTNTQK/LFL (B74-50845)
Quintet for flute & strings in A major. Op.51, no.3. Quintet in A for flute and strings. Op.51, no.3. *Musica rara. Unpriced* NVRNR (B74-50542)
Kumiuta and Danmono traditions of Japanese koto music. (Adriaansz, Willem). *University of California Press. £9.50* BZHPAL (B74-14313) ISBN 0-520-01785-4
Kümmerling, Harald. Biblische Motetten : für das Kirchenjahr
Band 2: Darstellung des Herrn bis Trinitas. (Ameln, Konrad). *Bärenreiter. Unpriced* EZDH/AYE (B74-50392)
Kyrie and Gloria for the Saturday Lady Mass : two-part (male voices). (Stapert, Calvin R). *Oxford University Press. £0.20* GEZDGB (B74-51014) ISBN 0-19-341217-9
Kyrie in D minor and Gloria in A major : unison. (Senator, Ronald). *Lengnick. £0.12* JDGB (B74-50439)
La Fontaine, Jean de. *See* Fontaine, Jean de la.
La Grange, Henry-Louis de. Mahler
Vol.1. *Gollancz. £7.50* BME(N) (B74-11049) ISBN 0-575-01672-8
La Messe de Nostre Dame : SATB, strings and two trombones. (Machaut, Guillaume de). *Oxford University Press. £0.75* ENVXUDG (B74-50031) ISBN 0-19-337395-5
Labor : meta-music for chamber orchestra. (Morthenson, Jan W). *Universal. Unpriced* MRJ (B74-51115)
Lacerda, Oswaldo. Three Brazilian miniatures for percussion. *Schott. £2.40* XN (B74-50324)
Laderman, Ezra.
Concerto for orchestra. *Oxford University Press. Unpriced* MMF (B74-50496) ISBN 0-19-385533-x
Duet for flute and dancers. *Oxford University Press. Unpriced* VRPMJ (B74-50761)
From the psalms : for soprano and piano. *Oxford University Press. Unpriced* KFLDH (B74-50483)
Octet for winds. *Oxford University Press. Unpriced* UNN (B74-50736)
Theme, variations and finale : for four winds and four strings. *Oxford University Press. Unpriced* NVNN/T (B74-50538)
Ladies only. Op.58 : five songs for SSA unaccompanied. (Blyton, Carey). *Novello. Unpriced* FEZDW (B74-51006)
Lady Glencora's waltz : from 'The Pallisers' BBC television series. (Josephs, Wilfred). *Weinberger. £0.25* QPK/AHW/JS (B74-50191)
Lai, Francis. Love story. Theme : arr. Theme from the film 'Love story'. *Famous Music : Chappell. Unpriced* UMJ (B74-51298)
Lake, Ian. Classics for the young pianist. *Chappell. Unpriced* QP/AY (B74-51142)
Lala and la : SSA. (Kennedy, John Brodbin). *Boosey and Hawkes. Unpriced* FEZDW (B74-51007)
Lam, Basil. The collected lute music of John Dowland. (Dowland, John). *Faber Music in association with Faber and Faber. Unpriced* TW/AZ (B74-51286) ISBN 0-571-10010-4
Lamb, Peter.
Concertante music: arr. Concertante music : for double bass, wind and strings; piano reduction. *Yorke. Unpriced* SSPK/LF (B74-51256)
Sonatina for flute and piano. *Boosey and Hawkes. £0.85* VRPEM (B74-50753)
Lamb of God = Agnus dei. (Monteverdi, Claudio). *Schirmer. Unpriced* DGF (B74-50878)
Lamb : SATB. (Binkerd, Gordon). *Boosey and Hawkes. Unpriced* EZDW (B74-50974)
Lambert, Constant. The Rio Grande. *Oxford University Press. £1.30* EMDX (B74-50376) ISBN 0-19-337303-3
Lambeth Libraries. Arnold Schoenberg, 1874 to 1951 - books, records and scores. *Central Library, Brixton Oval, S.W.2 : Lambeth Libraries. Free* BSET(T) (B74-25103) ISBN 0-9501893-6-7
Lámhleabhar ginearálta don cheoltóir. (Cecily, *Sister, OP*). *Folens. £0.48* A (B74-11047) ISBN 0-902592-58-0
Lancen, Serge. Fantasie concertante, no.1 : pour hautbois et piano. *Chappell. Unpriced* VTPJ (B74-50785)
Lanchberry, John. Three girls for five brass : a suite for brass quintet. *Novello. £0.75* WNRG (B74-50828)
Landon, Howard Chandler Robbins.
Mass in C major. K.337. Vocal score. Missa for Archibishop Colloredo, (Mass in C) : for four-part chorus of mixed voices. (Mozart, Wolfgang Amadeus). *Schirmer. Unpriced* DG (B74-50337)
Mass, no.1, in B flat major, 'Heiligmesse'. Vocal score. Missa Sancti Bernardi de Offida, 'Heiligmesse' : for four-part chorus of mixed voices. (Haydn, Joseph). *Schirmer. Unpriced* DG (B74-50007)
Mass, no.8, in B flat major, 'Sancti Joannis de Deo'. Vocal score. Missa brevis Sancti Joannis de Deo, 'Small organ mass' : for four-part chorus of mixed voices. (Haydn, Joseph). *Schirmer. Unpriced* DG (B74-50008)
Mass, no.15, in C major, 'Mariazellermesse'. Vocal score. Missa Cellensis in C, 'Mariazellermesse' : for four-part chorus of mixed voices. (Haydn, Joseph). *Schirmer. Unpriced* DG (B74-50009)
Láng, István. Duo for trumpets in C. *Boosey and Hawkes. £0.60* WSNU (B74-50316)
Lang, Istvan. In memoriam N.N : cantata. *Boosey and Hawkes. £2.50* EMDX (B74-50030)
Larcom, January Lucy. We pause beside this door : anthem for the New Year, for four-part chorus of mixed voices with organ accompaniment. (Ferguson, Edwin Earle). *Roberton. £0.10* DH/LFM (B74-50017)
Lasocki, David.
Concerto for flute & string orchestra in D minor. Concerto in D minor for flute, strings and continuo. (Quantz, Johann Joachim). *Musica rara. Unpriced* RXMPVRF (B74-50649)
Concerto for flute & string orchestra in D minor: arr. Concerto in D minor for flute, strings and continuo. (Quantz, Johann Joachim). *Musica rara. Unpriced* VRPK/LF (B74-50760)
Concerto for flute & string orchestra in G major. Wq.169. Concerto in G major : for flute, strings and basso continuo. Wq.169. (Bach, Carl Philipp Emanuel). *Musica rara. Unpriced* RXMPVRF (B74-50648)
Concerto for flute & string orchestra in G major. Wq.169: arr. Concerto in G major : for flute, strings and basso continuo. Wq.169. (Bach, Carl Philipp Emanuel). *Musica rara. Unpriced* VRPK/LF (B74-50759)
Concerto for oboe, violin & string orchestra in C minor 'Lund'. Concerto in C minor for oboe, violin and strings (Lund). (Vivaldi, Antonio). *Musica rara. Unpriced* RXMPVTPLSF (B74-50651)
Concerto for oboe, violin & string orchestra in C minor, 'Lund': arr. Concerto in C minor for oboe, violin and strings (Lund). (Vivaldi, Antonio). *Musica rara. Unpriced* NUTNTK/LF (B74-50530)
Concerto for treble recorder, oboe, violin, bassoon and basso continuo in G major. P.105. Concerto in G major : for treble recorder (flute), oboe, violin, bassoon and basso continuo. P.105. (Vivaldi, Antonio). *Musica rara. Unpriced* NUPNRF (B74-50525)
Concerto for treble recorder, oboe, violin, bassoon & basso continuo in G minor. P.403. Concerto in G minor : for treble recorder (flute), oboe, violin, bassoon and basso continuo. P.403. (Vivaldi, Antonio). *Musica rara. Unpriced* NUPNRF (B74-50526)
Concerto for two oboes & string orchestra in D minor. P.302. Concerto in D minor for 2 oboes, strings and basso continuo. (Vivaldi, Antonio). *Musica rara. Unpriced* RXMPVTNUF (B74-50650)
Concerto for two oboes & string orchestra in D minor. P.302: arr. Concerto in D minor for 2 oboes, strings and basso continuo. (Vivaldi, Antonio). *Musica rara. Unpriced* VTPK/LF (B74-50787)
Concerto for woodwind & string quartet & basso continuo in B flat major. Op.8, no.3. Concerto in B flat for 2 oboes or violins, 2 violins or oboes and basso continuo. Opus 8, no.3. (Pepusch, Johann Christoph). *Musica rara. Unpriced* NUTNRF (B74-50528)
Concerto for woodwind quartet & basso continuo in G major. Op.8, no.2. Concerto in G for 2 flutes, 2 oboes, violins and basso continuo. Op.8, no.2. (Pepusch, Johann Christoph). *Musica rara. Unpriced* NWPNRF (B74-50546)
Concertos for woodwind quartet & basso continuo. Op.8, nos. 1, 4-6. 4 concerti for 2 treble recorders, 2 flutes, tenor recorders, oboes, violins & basso continuo. Op.8, nos. 1, 4, 5, 6
Opus 8, no.4 in F major. (Pepusch, Johann Christoph). *Musica rara. Unpriced* NWPNRF (B74-50549)
Concertos for woodwind quartet & basso continuo. Op.8, nos. 1, 4-6. 4 concerti for 2 treble recorders, 2 flutes, tenor recorders, oboes, violins & basso continuo. Op.8, nos. 1, 4, 5, 6
Opus 8, no.6: in F major. (Pepusch, Johann Christoph). *Musica rara. Unpriced* NWPNRF (B74-50548)
Concertos for woodwind quartet & basso continuo. Op.8, nos. 1, 4-6. 4 concerti for 2 treble recorders, 2 flutes, tenor recorders, oboes, violins & basso continuo. Op.8, nos. 1,4,5,6
Opus 8, no.1: in B flat major. (Pepusch, Johann Christoph). *Musica rara. Unpriced* NWPNRF (B74-50547)
Concertos for woodwind quartet & basso continuo. Op.8, nos. 1, 4-6. 4 concerti for 2 treble recorders, 2 flutes, tenor recorders, oboes, violins & basso continuo. Op.8, nos. 1,4,5,6
Opus 8, no.5 in C major. (Pepusch, Johann Christoph). *Musica rara. Unpriced* NWPNRF (B74-50550)
Concerts royaux I-IV : for flute, oboe, violin, viola da gamba and basso continuo
No.I. (Couperin, François). *Musica rara. Unpriced* VRPG (B74-50754)

No.II. (Couperin, François). *Musica rara. Unpriced* VRPG (B74-50755)
No.III. (Couperin, François). *Musica rara. Unpriced* VRPG (B74-50756)
No.IV. (Couperin, François). *Musica rara. Unpriced* VRPG (B74-50757)
Sinfonia concertante for flute, oboe, horn, bassoon, no.5, in F major: arr. Symphonie concertante no.5 in F major : for flute, oboe (clarinet), horn, bassoon and orchestra. (Pleyel, Ignaz). *Musica rara. Unpriced* MPUNSE (B74-50516)
Sonata for flute & basso continuo in E minor, 'Stockholm'. Sonata in E minor : for flute and basso continuo. (Vivaldi, Antonio). *Musica rara. Unpriced* VRPE (B74-50752)
Sonata for two oboes & basso continuo in G minor, 'Lund'. Trio sonata in G minor (Lund) : for 2 oboes and basso continuo. (Vivaldi, Antonio). *Musica rara. Unpriced* VTNTPWE (B74-50780)
Sonata for violin & basso continuo in C minor. Op.5, no.3: arr. Sonata in C minor. Opus 5, no.3 : for treble (alto) recorder and basso continuo. (Corelli, Arcangelo). *Musica rara. Unpriced* VSSPK/AE (B74-50778)
Lasso, Orlando di.
Libro de villanelle. *S'io fusse ciaul.* S'io fusse ciaul = Were I a tiny bird : canzonetta, for four-part chorus of mixed voices a cappella. *Schirmer. Unpriced* EZDU (B74-50052)
Libro de villanelle. *Tutto lo di mi dici 'Canta'.* Tutto lo di mi dici 'Canta' = Day after day they all say 'Sing' : canzonetta, for four-part chorus of mixed voices a cappella. *Schirmer. Unpriced* EZDU (B74-50053)
Newe teutsche Lieder mit vier Stimmen. *Ich waiss mir en Meidlein.* Ich waiss mir Meidlein = I know a fair maiden : madrigal, for four-part chorus of mixed voices a cappella. *Schirmer. Unpriced* EZDU (B74-50054)
Sacrae cantiones quatuor vocum. Jubilate Deo. Jubilate Deo = Sing to God : motet for four-part chorus of mixed voices a cappella. *Schirmer. Unpriced* EZDJ (B74-50044)
Last, Joan.
Black and white : eight tunes for young pianists. *Oxford University Press. £0.45* QPJ (B74-50178) ISBN 0-19-373104-5
The day's play. *Forsyth. Unpriced* QPJ (B74-51176)
Notes and notions : eight short pieces for piano. *Oxford University Press. £0.45* QPJ (B74-50179) ISBN 0-19-373135-5
Last poems of Wallace Stevens : for voice, cello and piano. (Rorem, Ned). *Boosey and Hawkes. £3.00* KE/SRPDW (B74-50478)
Law, Leslie G. Two preparatory accordion solos. *Charnwood Music. Unpriced* RSPMJ (B74-51208)
Laxton, Alwyn. Elegy and Le Motif : organ. *Paxton. £0.35* RJ (B74-50202)
Lazan, Albert. Sonatas for violin & basso continuo. Op.1, nos. 1, 4, 8. 3 sonatas for violin and piano. (Veracini, Francesco Maria). *Associated Music. Unpriced* SPE (B74-50233)
Lazarof, Henri.
Asymtotes : for flute and vibraphone. *Associated Music. £7.50* VRPLXTRT (B74-50860)
Concerto for cello & orchestra. Selections. Cadence I : for solo cello. *Associated Music. £2.00* SRPMFM (B74-50684)
Espaces : for chamber ensemble. *Associated Music. Unpriced* MRJ (B74-50151)
Intonazione : for two piano. *Associated Music. £12.00* QNU (B74-50561)
Partita for brass quintet and tape. *Associated Music. £1.40* WNRG (B74-50829)
Rhapsody for violin and piano. *Associated Music. £7.50* SPJ (B74-50670)
Textures : for piano and 5 instrumental groups. *Associated Music. Unpriced* MPQ (B74-50144)
Three pieces for harpsichord. *Associated Music. £3.50* QRPJ (B74-50609)
Le Fleming, Christopher.
3 Motets for Christmas. I sing of a maiden. I sing of a maiden. *Roberton. Unpriced* EZDH/LF (B74-50948)
Three motets for Christmas, nos.2,3. Two motets for Christmas : SSATBB unaccompanied. *Roberton. £0.16* EZDH/LF (B74-50393)
Le Huray, Peter. Concerto for keyboard & string orchestra. Op.10, no.6: arr. Concerto in C major. (Stanley, John). *Oxford University Press. £0.90* RK/LF (B74-51204) ISBN 0-19-367705-9
Leach, John. Trio for 2 flutes & cello or bassoon in D major. (Wiseman, Charles). *Roberton. £0.50* NVPNT (B74-50541)
Leaf, Munro. Ferdinand : for speaker and solo violin. (Ridout, Alan). *Chappell. Unpriced* KHYE/SPM (B74-51080)
Lear, Edward. How pleasant to know Mr. Lear : for narrator and orchestra. (Roxburgh, Edwin). *United Music. Unpriced* KHYE/M (B74-50120)
Lebermann, Walter.
Concerto for cello & string orchestra in C major. Gérard 481: arr. Konzert No.4 für Violoncello und Klavier, C-dur. (Boccherini, Luigi). *Schott. £2.90* SRPK/LF (B74-51253)
Concerto for cello & string orchestra, no.2, in D major. Konzert No.2, D Dur für Violoncello und Streichorchester. (Boccherini, Luigi). *Schott. £2.40* RXMPSRF (B74-50221)
Concerto for cello & string orchestra, no.2, in D major: arr. Konzert No.2, D Dur, für Violoncello und Streichorchester. (Boccherini, Luigi). *Schott. £2.04* SRPK/LF (B74-50250)
Concerto for string orchestra & basso continuo in C major. P. 27. Concerto ripieno, C-Dur für Streichorchester und Basso continuo. PV27. (Vivaldi, Antonio). *Schott. £1.92* RXMF (B74-50216)
Concerto for viola & string orchestra, no.4, in D major: arr. Concerto no.4 in D major for viola and strings. (Stamitz, Anton). *Breitkopf and Härtel : Bärenreiter. £2.90* SQPK/LF (B74-50678)
Concerto for violin & string orchestra, no.2, in E major: arr. Konzert No.2: E-Dur für Violine und Streichorchester, zwei Oboen und zwei Hörner ad lib. (Viotti, Giovanni Battista). *Schott. £2.90* SPK/LF (B74-50676)
Madrigali et ricercari a quattro voci, nos 6. 7. Ricercari a quattro, nos.6 & 7. (Gabrieli, Andrea). *Schott. £1.92* RXMJ (B74-50219)
Ledbetter, Steven. Musice active micrologus. A compendium of musical practice. (Ornithoparchus, Andreas). *Dover Publications : Constable. £7.00* A/M(XDS) (B74-11735) ISBN 0-486-20912-1
Ledger, Philip.
Anthems for choirs
2: Twenty-four anthems for sopranos & altos (unison and two-part). *Oxford University Press. Unpriced* FDH/AY (B74-50068) ISBN 0-19-353240-9
3: Twenty-four anthems for sopranos & altos (three or more parts). *Oxford University Press. Unpriced* FDH/AY (B74-50069) ISBN 0-19-353242-5
Warlike Musick for flute, violin or harpsichord. Warlike Musick (1760) : marches and trumpet tunes, for flute or oboe or violin and basso continuo. (Warlike Musick). *Oxford University Press. £1.50* VRP/AY (B74-51317) ISBN 0-19-357552-3
Lees, Benjamin.
Fanfare for a centennial : for brass timpani and percussion. *Boosey and Hawkes. £1.75* WMGN (B74-50304)
Two miniatures for wind quintet : flute, oboe, clarinet, horn and bassoon. *Boosey and Hawkes. £1.75* UNR (B74-50737)
Lees, Heath. Deep river : spiritual for full female voice choir unaccompanied, S.S.A.. *Roberton. £0.08* FEZDW/LC (B74-51009)
Lefanu, Nicola. Quintet for clarinet and string quartet. *Novello. £1.50* NVVNR (B74-50154)
Lefevre, Jean Xavier. Sonata for clarinet & basso continuo in B flat. Op.12, no.1. Sonata in B flat. Opus 12, no.1 : for clarinet and piano. *Oxford University Press. £0.75* VVPE (B74-50292) ISBN 0-19-357548-5
Legende von der heiligen Elisabeth : Oratorium / von F. Liszt ; with, Die heilige Cäcilia : Legende gedichtet von Madame Emilie de Giradin, für ein Mezzo-Sopran-Stimme mit Chor (ad libitum) und Orchester oder Pianoforte, (Harmonium und Harfe) Begleitung / componirt von F. Liszt. (Liszt, Franz). *Gregg. £8.40* EMDD (B74-50931) ISBN 0-576-28231-6
Lehmann, Hans Ulrich. Monodie : für ein Blasinstrument (1970). *Ars Viva. £1.44* WPMJ (B74-50314)
Lehrstuch (1929). Vocal score. Lehrstuck (1929). (Hindemith, Paul). *Schott. £4.35* DX (B74-50929)
Lehrstuck (1929). (Hindemith, Paul). *Schott. £4.35* DX (B74-50929)
Leicester sketches : a suite for five miniatures for solo guitar. (Romani, G). *Charnwood Music. Unpriced* TSPMJ (B74-51275)
Leichte Stücke für Violoncello mit Begleitung durch 2 Violoncello
Heft 1. (Breval, Jean Baptiste). *Schott. £1.44* SRNU (B74-50245)
Heft 2. (Breval, Jean Baptiste). *Schott. £1.44* (B74-50096)
Leighton, Kenneth. Three psalms. Op.54 : for T.T. Bar. B.B., unaccompanied, by Kenneth Leighton. *Novello. £0.44* GEZDK (B74-50435)
Lengyel, Endre.
Violoncello music (intermediate) : easy concert pieces in the first position. (Pejtsik, Arpád). *Boosey and Hawkes : Editio Musica. £1.00* SRPK/AAY (B74-51251)
Lenkei, Gabriella. Music for violin (intermediate). *Boosey and Hawkes : Editio Musica. £1.00* SPK/AAY (B74-51245)
Leonard, William Ellery. Songs and epilogues : for bass voice and piano. (Travis, Roy). *Oxford University Press. Unpriced* KGXDW (B74-51078)
Leroi, Jean. Claire de lune: arr. Claire de lune. (Veneux, Thierry). *Chappell. Unpriced* TMK (B74-50690)
Lester, Bryan.
Explorations in guitar playing for beginners
Vol.1. *Ricordi. Unpriced* TS/AF (B74-50697)
Vol.2. *Ricordi. Unpriced* TS/AF (B74-50698)
L'Estro armonico, Op.3, no.11: arr. Concerto, d-Moll : für 2 Violinen, Streicher und Basso continuo. (Vivaldi, Antonio). *Schott. £2.32* SNTQK/LF (B74-51239)
Let it be forgotten : for mixed chorus (SSAATB) or treble chorus (SSAA) and piano. (Merrill, Marlin). *Oxford University Press. Unpriced* DW (B74-50361)
Let joybells ring. (Hitchcock, Gordon). *David and Charles. £2.95* JDP/LF/AY (B74-51024) ISBN 0-7153-6712-9
Lethbridge, Lionel.
Le Carnival des animaux. Selections: arr. Two pieces. (Saint-Saëns, Camille). *Oxford University Press. £0.60* VVPK (B74-51345) ISBN 0-19-358701-7
Le Carnival des animaux. Selections: arr. Two pieces. (Saint-Saëns, Camille). *Oxford University Press. £0.45* VWPK (B74-51348) ISBN 0-19-358703-3
Rinaldo. Lascia ch'io panga: arr. Evening hymn. (Handel, George Frideric). *Oxford University Press. Unpriced* DH (B74-50012) ISBN 0-19-351119-3
Let's play clarinet. (Couf, Herb). *Chappell. Unpriced* VV/AC (B74-51340)
Let's play harmonica. (Chimes, Michael). *Experience Music : Chappell. Unpriced* VX/AC (B74-50816)
Let's play piano. (Zayde, Jascha). *Experience Music : Chappell. Unpriced* Q/AC (B74-51124)
Let's play trumpet. (Kaderabek, Frank). *Experience Music : Chappell. Unpriced* WS/AC (B74-51365)
Letters from composers : for high voice and guitar. (Argento, Dominick). *Boosey and Hawkes. Unpriced* KFTE/TSDW (B74-51073)
Letting down my hair. (Davis, Lorrie). *Elek. £3.50* BMBDACM (B74-28314) ISBN 0-236-31072-0
Levitt, Rod. Woodmen of the world : jazz fantasy on a rock theme for woodwind quintet (with finger cymbals and tambourine). *Associated Music. Unpriced* NYHNPHX (B74-50552)
Lewin, Olive. Brown gal in de ring : 12 Jamaican folk-songs. *Oxford University Press. £0.40* JFDW/GS/AYULD (B74-51039) ISBN 0-19-330544-5
Lewis, Esme. Deg o ganenon gwerin i blant. *See* Lewis, Esme. Ten Welsh folk-songs for juniors.
Lewis, Esme. Ten Welsh folk-songs for juniors. *University of Wales Press. £0.50* JFE/NYJDW/G/AYDK (B74-50092)
Lewitus, Hans. Geistliche Lieder und Schmelli's Gesangbuch und dem Notenbuch der Anna Magdalena Bach. S. 439-567. *Selections: arr.* Geistliche Lieder. (Bach, Johann Sebastian). *Schott. £1.45* VSNSK/DM (B74-51332)
Liadov, Anatoly.
Eight Russian folksongs. Op. 58, nos. 1, 2, 4: arr. Russian folksongs, set 1. *Boosey and Hawkes. Score £1.50, Piano conductor £0.50, Set £2.50* MK (B74-51090)
Eight Russian folksongs. Op.58, nos. 6-8: arr. Russian folksongs. Set 2. *Boosey and Hawkes. £4.50* MH (B74-51088)
Liber primus sacrarum cantionum. Vigilate. Vigilate = Be ye watchful : motet for five voices S.A.T.Ba.B. (Byrd, William). *Oxford University Press. £0.20* EZDJ (B74-50395) ISBN 0-19-352056-7
Library Association. Research publications. Long, Maureen W. Music in British libraries : a directory of resources. 2nd ed. *Library Association. £3.00 (£2.40 to members)* A(U/BC/YC) (B74-19811) ISBN 0-85365-287-2
Libro de villanelle. *S'io fusse ciaul.* S'io fusse ciaul = Were I a tiny bird : canzonetta, for four-part chorus of mixed voices a cappella. (Lasso, Orlando di). *Schirmer. Unpriced* EZDU (B74-50052)
Libro de villanelle. *Tutto lo di mi dici 'Canta'.* Tutto lo di mi dici 'Canta' = Day after day they all say 'Sing' : canzonetta, for four-part chorus of mixed voices a cappella. (Lasso, Orlando di). *Schirmer. Unpriced* EZDU (B74-50053)
Lichfield Cathedral. The organs of Lichfield Cathedral. (Greening, Richard). *c/o 28 Walsall Rd, Lichfield, Staffs. WS13 8AB : Dean and Chapter of Lichfield. £0.45* AR/B(YDHNLB) (B74-13712) ISBN 0-9503008-1-0
Liddell, Claire. The kindling fire : twelve Burns songs, arranged for high voice using the airs to which Burns set his verses. *Roberton. £1.00* KFTDW/AY (B74-51072)
Lied über die Grenze : Folklore fremder Länder für drei gleiche Stimmen mit Begleitung
Heft II. (Cammin, Heinz). *Schott. £2.61* FDW/G/AY (B74-50996)
Lied über die Grenze : Folklore fremder Länder
Heft II. (Cammin, Heinz). *Schott. £1.74* TSPMK/DW/G/AY (B74-51284)
Life is like a mountain dulcimer : songs. (Hellman, Neal). *Ludlow Music : Essex Music. Unpriced* KE/TWTTDW/AY (B74-51065)
Ligeti, György. Chamber concerto for 13 instrumentalists. *Schott. £8.12* MRF (B74-51113)
Lindeman, Ludvig Matthias. Melodien til Landstads Salmebog. Kirken den er et. Built on the rock : anthem for unison choir or solo voice and organ. *Oxford University Press. Unpriced* JDH (B74-51017)
Lion, the witch and the wardrobe. Selections. Suite, The lion, the witch and the wardrobe : for orchestra. (McCabe, John). *Novello. £3.50* MMG (B74-50499)
Lions and martlets : fantasia for brass band. (Spurgin, Anthony). *British and Continental. Unpriced* WMJ (B74-50310)
Lipkin, Malcolm. The white crane : for voices, descant, recorders, percussion and piano, violins and guitar ad lib. *Chester. Unpriced* CQN (B74-50334)
List, Eugene.
L'Union. Op. 48: arr. L'Union. Op.48 : paraphrase de concert sur les airs nationaux. (Gottschalk, Louis Moreau). *Schirmer. £1.40* QNUK (B74-50562)
L'Union. Op. 48 : paraphrase de concert sur les airs nationaux. (Gottschalk, Louis Moreau). *Schirmer. Unpriced* UMPQ (B74-50734)
Listen all who enter these portals = Höret alle die ihr von Hause : S.A.T.B. with accompaniment. (Herbst, Johannes). Moramus ed. *Boosey and Hawkes. Unpriced* DH (B74-50347)
Listen to the lambs : negro spiritual. (Dexter, Harry). *Ashdown. £0.12* FDW/LC (B74-50072)
Liszt, Franz.
Christus : Oratorium nach Texten aus der heligen Schrift und der katholischen Liturgie : Soli, Chor, Orgel und grosses Orchester. *Gregg. £7.80* EMDE (B74-50932) ISBN 0-576-28232-4
Csardas. Selections. Two csardas for piano. *Schirmer. Unpriced* QPHJP (B74-50171)
Piano works
Vol.4: Hungarian rhapsodies II, nos 10-19. *Bärenreiter.*

£2.90 QP/AZ (B74-50571)

Technische Studien. *Selections.* The Liszt studies : essential selections from the technical studies for the piano, including the first English edition of the legendary Liszt Pedagogue, a lesson-diary of the master as teacher as kept by Mme August Boisser, 1831-2. *Associated Music. Unpriced* Q/AF (B74-50558)

Works, piano. Selections. Miniatures for piano. *Schirmer. Unpriced* QPJ (B74-50180)

Works, psalms. Collections. Six psalms (1864-81). *Gregg. £6.60* CB/DR/AZ (B74-50865) ISBN 0-576-28230-8

Works, selections. Die Legende von der heiligen Elisabeth : Oratorium / von F. Liszt ; with, Die heilige Cäcilia : Legende gedichtet von Madame Emilie de Giradin, für ein Mezzo-Sopran-Stimme mit Chor (ad libitum) und Orchester oder Pianoforte, (Harmonium und Harfe) Begleitung / componirt von F. Liszt. *Gregg. £8.40* EMDD (B74-50931) ISBN 0-576-28231-6

Liszt studies : essential selections from the technical studies for the piano, including the first English edition of the legendary Liszt Pedagogue, a lesson-diary of the master as teacher as kept by Mme August Boisser, 1831-2. (Liszt, Franz). *Associated Music. Unpriced* Q/AF (B74-50558)

Literature of the piano : a guide for amateur and student. (Hutcheson, Ernest). 3rd ed., revised. *Hutchinson. £4.75* AQ (B74-17389) ISBN 0-09-119120-3

Little camel boy : a carol for treble voices with audience (or choral) participation. (Walters, Edmund). *Boosey and Hawkes. £0.15* FLDP/LF (B74-51012)

Little carols of the saints : for organ. (Williamson, Malcolm). *Weinberger. Unpriced* RJ (B74-50625)

Little suite : for piano. (Jong, Conrad de). *Schroeder and Gunther. Unpriced* QPG (B74-50169)

Little symphony. (Stoker, Richard). *Boosey and Hawkes. £3.30* ME (B74-50130)

Livingston, Jerry. The twelth of never. *Frank Music. Unpriced* UMMK/DW (B74-51310)

Lobe den Herrn meine Seele: arr. Praise the Lord, O my soul = Lobe den Herrn meine Seele : S.A.T.B. with accompaniment. (Peter, Johann Friedrich). Moramus ed. *Boosey and Hawkes. Unpriced* DH (B74-50349)

Loboda, Samuel. Stand up for America! : for mixed chorus, SATB. (Peet, Richard). *Chappell. Unpriced* DW (B74-50362)

Lobos, Heitor Villa-. *See* Villa-Lobos, Heitor.

Locke, Matthew. Suite for strings, no.3, from Musick's Handmaid. Third suite for strings, from Musick's Handmaid. (Cruft, Adrian). *Chappell. Unpriced* RXMG (B74-50217)

Loesser, Frank.

Hans Christian Andersen. The inch worm: arr. The inch worm. *Frank Music. Unpriced* UMMK/DW/JR (B74-51311)

Where's Charley?. The New Ashmolean Marching Society and Students Conservatory Band: arr. The New Ashmolean Marching Society and Students Conservatory Band. *Frank Music. Unpriced* UMMK (B74-51309)

Lomax, Alan. Mister Jelly Roll : the fortunes of Jelly Roll Morton, New Orleans Creole and 'inventor of jazz'. 2nd ed. *University of California Press. £5.20* AMT(P) (B74-14971) ISBN 0-520-02402-8

Lomax books of American folk song. Lomax, Alan. Mister Jelly Roll : the fortunes of Jelly Roll Morton, New Orleans Creole and 'inventor of jazz'. 2nd ed. *University of California Press. £5.20* AMT(P) (B74-14971) ISBN 0-520-02402-8

Lombardi, Nilson. Cantilena no.1 : piano. *Arthur Napoleão : Essex Music. Unpriced* QPJ (B74-51177)

London College of Music. Examination in pianoforte playing and singing sight reading tests as set throughout 1973. Grades I-VIII and diplomas. *Ashdown. £0.35* Q/EG/AL (B74-50159)

Long, Maureen W. Music in British libraries : a directory of resources. 2nd ed. *Library Association. £3.00 (£2.40 to members)* A(U/BC/YC) (B74-19811) ISBN 0-85365-287-2

Longest cocktail party. (DiLello, Richard). *37 Soho Sq., W.1 : Charisma Books. £1.90* A/GB(Q/YC) (B74-18700) ISBN 0-85947-006-7

Lord, David. Nonsongs : six songs about nothing in particular for voices, descant recorders, pitched and unpitched percussion and piano. *Universal. Unpriced* JE/NYFSRDW (B74-51025)

Lord have mercy : for four-part chorus of mixed voices a cappella. (O'Neal, Barry). *Associated Music. Unpriced* EZDH (B74-50039)

Loth to depart : eleven songs for mixed voices. (Hughes, Donald Jefferson). *Oxford University Press. £0.35* EZDW/AY (B74-50411) ISBN 0-19-330492-9

Loubie, Patrick. Quand la chance est là. This old world = Quand la chance est là : for SATB chorus accompanied. (Brejean, Philippe). *Chappell. Unpriced* DW (B74-50358)

Louisiana story. *Boy fights alligator.* Boy fights alligator : fugue, for orchestra. (Thomson, Virgil). *Schirmer. Unpriced* MM/Y/JR (B74-50132)

Love is pleasing : songs of courtship and marriage. (Palmer, Roy). *Cambridge University Press. £0.50* JE/TSDW/AYD (B74-51030) ISBN 0-521-20445-3

Love story. Theme : arr. Theme from the film 'Love story'. (Lai, Francis). *Famous Music : Chappell. Unpriced* UMJ (B74-51298)

Love will find out the way : English folk song. (Sutcliffe, James H). *Roberton. £0.10* EZDW (B74-50063)

LSO at 70 : a history of the orchestra. (Pearton, Maurice). *Gollancz. £3.50* AMM/E(QB/X) (B74-24906) ISBN 0-575-01763-5

Luchese, Francesco Guami. *See* Guami, Francesco.

Lucrezia Borgia. (Donizetti, Gaetano). *93 Chancery La., W.C.2 : Egret House. Unpriced* CC (B74-50868)

Lucrezia Borgia. Vocal score. Lucrezia Borgia. (Donizetti, Gaetano). *93 Chancery La., W.C.2 : Egret House. Unpriced* CC (B74-50868)

Luening, Otto.

Fantasia brevis : for flute and piano. *Highgate Press : Galaxy : Galliard. Unpriced* VRPJ (B74-51319)

Trio for flute, violin and piano (cello or bassoon ad lib.). *Highgate Press : Galaxy : Galliard. Unpriced* NURNT (B74-51116)

Lully, Jean Baptiste. Adieu Madras, adieu foulards. *Chappell. Unpriced* TMK/DW (B74-50695)

Lutoslawski, Witold.

Musique funèbre : for string orchestra. *Chester. Unpriced* RXMJ (B74-50642)

Preludes and fugue for 13 solo strings. *Chester : Hansen. Unpriced* RXM/Y (B74-50640)

Lyra songbook : hymns and songs

Volume 1. (Mossman, Sheila). *Rahter. Unpriced* CB/AY (B74-50004)

Volume 2. (Mossman, Sheila). *Rahter. Unpriced* CB/AY (B74-50005)

McCabe, John.

Basse danse : for two pianos. *Novello. £5.00* QNUH (B74-50161)

The lion, the witch and the wardrobe. Selections. Suite, The lion, the witch and the wardrobe : for orchestra. *Novello. £3.50* MMG (B74-50499)

Rachmaninov. *Novello. £0.20* BRC(N) (B74-25491) ISBN 0-85360-059-7

Upon the high midnight : three nativity carols for SATB soli and chorus (unaccompanied). *Novello. Unpriced* EZDP/LF (B74-50964)

McCaldin, Denis. Te Deum. (Berlioz, Hector). *Breitkopf and Härtel : Bärenreiter. £13.20* EMDGKHB (B74-50374)

McCarthy, Albert.

Big band jazz. *Barrie and Jenkins. £5.00* AMT(XMT56) (B74-17388) ISBN 0-214-66894-0

The dance band era : the dancing decades from ragtime to swing, 1910-1950. *Spring Books. £1.95* AMT(M/XMK41) (B74-30607) ISBN 0-600-32907-0

MacDonald, Donald. A collection of the ancient martial music of Caledonia called piobaireache. 1st ed., reprinted. *EP Publishing. £4.00* VY/T (B74-50817) ISBN 0-7158-1031-6

MacDonald, Malcolm, *b.1948.* The symphonies of Havergal Brian

Vol.1: Symphonies 1-12. *25 Thurloe St., S.W.7 : Kahn and Averill. £3.50* BBTNAME (B74-14310) ISBN 0-900707-28-3

McDowall, Robert. Exultate Deo. Sing aloud with gladness = Exultate Deo : SATB a cappella. (Scarlatti, Alessandro). *Royal School of Church Music. £0.32* EZDJ (B74-50952)

MacEwan, Sydney. On the high C's : (a light-hearted journey): an autobiography. *J. Burns. £1.60* AKGH/E(P) (B74-03194) ISBN 0-900243-38-4

McGregor, Craig. Bob Dylan : a retrospective. *Angus and Robertson. £0.75* AKDW/GB/E(P) (B74-17386) ISBN 0-207-12675-5

Mach, Elyse. Technische Studien. *Selections.* The Liszt studies : essential selections from the technical studies for the piano, including the first English edition of the legendary Liszt Pedagogue, a lesson-diary of the master as teacher as kept by Mme August Boisser, 1831-2. (Liszt, Franz). *Associated Music. Unpriced* Q/AF (B74-50558)

Machaut, Guillaume de. La Messe de Nostre Dame : SATB, strings and two trombones. *Oxford University Press. £0.75* ENVXUDG (B74-50031) ISBN 0-19-337395-5

Mackenzie, Anne. Amhrain Anna Sheumais. *Ann Mackenzie. Unpriced* JFEZDW/G/AYDLZL (B74-50094)

McLain, Margaret Starr. Class piano. *Indiana University Press. £2.80* AQ/E(VC) (B74-22162) ISBN 0-253-31357-0

MacMillan, Keith. The Penguin book of Canadian folk songs. (Fowke, Edith). *Penguin. £0.75* JEZDW/G/AYSX (B74-50452) ISBN 0-14-070842-1

MacNeice, Louis. Christopher Columbus. Beatriz's song: arr. Beatriz's song. (Walton, *Sir* William). *Oxford University Press. £0.35* KE/TSDW/JM (B74-50481) ISBN 0-19-345866-7

Macnicol, Fred. The selected writings of Zoltán Kodály. (Kodály, Zoltán). *Boosey and Hawkes. £3.95* A(D) (B74-21534) ISBN 0-85162-021-3

Maconchy, Elizabeth.

The birds : extravaganza in one act after Aristophanes. *Boosey and Hawkes. Unpriced* CQC (B74-50873)

The birds. Vocal score. The birds : extravaganza in one act after Aristophanes. *Boosey and Hawkes. £2.75* CC (B74-50870)

Three bagatelles : for oboe and harpsichord (or piano). *Oxford University Press. £1.00* VTPJ (B74-50289) ISBN 0-19-357720-8

Macpherson's rant : for flute and double bass. (Dalby, Martin). *Yorke. Unpriced* VRPLSSHVHR (B74-51325)

Madrigali a cinque voci, libro sesto. Moro lasso : arr. Moro lasso. (Gesualdo, Carlo, *Prince of Venosa*). *Oxford University Press. Unpriced* UMK/DU (B74-51302)

Madrigali et ricercari a quattro voci, nos 6. 7. Ricercari a quattro, nos.6 & 7. (Gabrieli, Andrea). *Schott. £1.92* RXMJ (B74-50219)

Magnificat and Nunc dimittis : SSAATB. (Weelkes, Thomas). *Oxford University Press. £0.30* DGPP (B74-50342) ISBN 0-19-351646-2

Magnificat du 3e et 4e ton : for organ. (Corrette, Michel). *Novello. Unpriced* RDFF (B74-50617)

Magoichi, Kushida. P.I. Tchaikovsky's 'The nutcracker'. (Hori, Fumiko). *F. Warne. £1.75* BTDAM/HMBN (B74-26151) ISBN 0-7232-1760-2

Mahler, Alma. *See* Werfel, Alma Mahler.

Mahler, Gustav.

Kindertotenlieder : für eine Singstimme und Orchester auf Gedichte von Friedrich Rückert. *Peters. Unpriced* KE/MDW (B74-51060)

Das klagende Lied, no.1. Waldmärchen. Vocal score. Waldmärchen = A forest legend (Das klagende Lied: 1). *Belwin-Mills. Unpriced* DX (B74-50371)

Mahler. (Kennedy, Michael, *b.1926*). *Dent. £2.75* BME(N) (B74-16725) ISBN 0-460-03141-4

Mahler

Vol.1. (La Grange, Henry-Louis de). *Gollancz. £7.50* BME(N) (B74-11049) ISBN 0-575-01672-8

Maid of Bunclody : traditional Irish song. (Nelson, Havelock). *Roberton. £0.10* GEZDW (B74-50437)

Mainly under the fingers : easy accordion solos. (Parnell, Frederick). *Charnwood Music. Unpriced* RSPMJ (B74-51211)

Mairants, Ivor. Sonata for piano in D major: arr. Sonata in D. (Albeniz, Mateo). *British and Continental Music. Unpriced* TSPMK/AE (B74-50260)

Maitland, Alison I. Litaniae de S.S. Nomine Jesu. Litany in B flat (In nomine Jesu) for four-part chorus of mixed voices, soprano, alto, tenor and bass soli. (Haydn, Michael). *Schirmer. Unpriced* DS/LDB (B74-50916)

Make it happen : for concert band. (Cacavas, John). *Athenaeum : Chappell. Unpriced* UMJ (B74-51297)

Makers of the harpsichord and clavichord, 1440-1840. (Boalch, Donald Howard). 2nd ed. *Clarendon Press. £9.75* APW/BC(XCS401/C) (B74-21541) ISBN 0-19-816123-9

Makrokosmos

Volume 1 : for amplified piano. (Crumb, George). *Peters. £6.00* QPJ (B74-51170)

Mallet for classic : compositions by old masters. (Fink, Siegfried). *Simrock. Unpriced* XTQSPLXTRTK/AAY (B74-50328)

Man is for the woman made. (Purcell, Henry). *Boosey and Hawkes. Unpriced* DW (B74-50365)

Manchicourt, Pierre de. Nine chansons : for four voices or instruments. *London Pro musica. Unpriced* EZDU (B74-50972)

Mancini, Francesco.

Idaspe. Sinfonia. Sinfonia to 'Hydaspes' : for trumpet, strings and basso continuo. *Musica rara. Unpriced* RXMPWSE (B74-50653)

Idaspe. Sinfonia: arr. Sinfonia to 'Hydaspes' : for trumpet, strings and basso continuo. *Musica rara. Unpriced* WSPK/LE (B74-50842)

Manén, Lucie. The art of singing : a manual. *38 Russell Sq., WC1B 5DA : Faber Music Ltd. £2.20* AB/EBE (B74-21538) ISBN 0-571-10009-0

Mann, Manfred. The planets. Jupiter. *Selections: arr.* Joybringer : song based on 'Jupiter' by Gustav Holst. (Holst, Gustav). *Feldman. £0.25* KDW (B74-50459)

Mantra : for piano solo. (Camilleri, Charles). *Fairfield, Distributed by Novello. £1.00* QPJ (B74-50177)

Marais, Marin. Pièces de violes, liv. 4. Suite for viola da gamba, no.1, in D minor. Suite no.1 in D minor for viola da gamba and basso continuo. *Associated Music. Unpriced* STUPG (B74-51258)

Marble threshing floor : a collection of Greek folksongs. (Frye, Ellen). *University of Texas Press for the American Folklore Society. £5.85* JEZDW/G/AYPE (B74-50451) ISBN 0-292-75005-6

Marcello, Benedetto. Sonatas for cello and basso continuo. Op.2. Six sonatas : for cello or double bass and piano. *Schirmer. £1.85* SRPE (B74-50681)

March of the magnificants : for concert band. (Cacavas, John). *Chappell. Unpriced* UMGM (B74-51293)

March winds : military band. (Grundman, Clare). *Boosey and Hawkes. Unpriced* UMMJ (B74-51307)

Marenzio, Luca. Motectorum quarternis vocibus liber primus. O rex gloriae. O rex gloriae : motet for Ascension Day, SATB unacc. *Oxford University Press. £0.08* EZDJ/LM (B74-50404) ISBN 0-19-350343-3

Maria of the Cross, *Sister.* Mass for peace : for choir in two parts and organ. *Oxford University Press. Unpriced* FDG (B74-50986)

Maria Stuarda. (Donizetti, Gaetano). *93 Chancery La., W.C.2 : Egret House. Unpriced* CC (B74-50869)

Maria Stuarda. Vocal score. Maria Stuarda. (Donizetti, Gaetano). *93 Chancery La., W.C.2 : Egret House. Unpriced* CC (B74-50869)

Máriássy, István. Chamber music for beginners : for two melodic instruments and bass, with continuo. *Boosey and Hawkes : Editio Musica. £1.25* LNTQ/AY (B74-51084)

Marr, Peter. Three organists of St. Dionis Backchurch, London. *Hinrichsen. Unpriced* R/AY (B74-50612)

Married beau. *Selections: arr.* Wedding march. (Purcell, Henry). *Paxton. £0.35* RK/KDD (B74-51203)

Marsh, John. Two motets. (Wesley, Samuel). *Novello. £0.16* EZDJ (B74-50401)

Marshall, Philip. Fantasy and fugue on 'Edward Cuthbert Bairstow' : for organ. *Ashdown. £0.40* R/Y (B74-50616)

Martin, David Stone. Mister Jelly Roll : the fortunes of Jelly Roll Morton, New Orleans Creole and 'inventor of jazz'. (Lomax, Alan). 2nd ed. *University of California Press. £5.20* AMT(P) (B74-14971) ISBN 0-520-02402-8

Martín, Juan. The exciting sound of flamenco : guitar. *United Music. Unpriced* TSPMH (B74-50700)

Martini, Giovanni. Plaisir d'amour: arr. Plaisir d'amour. *Boosey and Hawkes. Unpriced* DW (B74-50359)

Martinu, Bohuslav. Concerto for piano, no.4, 'Incantation': arr. Incantation : 4th piano concerto. *Supraphon :*

Bärenreiter. £3.60 QNUK/LF (B74-50563)
Marvell, Andrew. Musick's empire. Op.9. Vocal score. Musick's empire. Opus 9 : for SATB, piano and optional strings. (Platts, Kenneth). *Ashdown. £0.15* DW (B74-50926)
Marwood, Desmond. A trip to the concert. (Blackwood, Alan, *b.1932*). *36 Park St., W1Y 4DE : Nelson Young World. £0.45* AM (B74-13709) ISBN 0-7238-0946-1
Mary Ann - Jamaica farewell : a quodlibet for two-part singing with piano accompaniment and optional parts for percussion with or without descant recorder. (Hudson, Hazel). *Ashdown. £0.10* FDW (B74-50070)
Mason, Barbara Kirkby-. *See* Kirkby-Mason, Barbara.
Mass. Almighty Father: arr. Almighty Father : chorale. (Bernstein, Leonard). *Amberson : Schirmer. Unpriced* GEZDH (B74-50434)
Mass. Almighty Father: arr. Almighty Father : chorale from 'Mass'. (Bernstein, Leonard). *Amberson : Schirmer. £5.60(full score and parts)(extra score £0.95, extra parts £0.30 each)* UMK (B74-50716)
Mass. *Gloria tibi: arr.* Gloria tibi : for two-part chorus of treble voices with tenor solo and piano and bongo accompaniment. (Bernstein, Leonard). *Amberson : Schirmer. Unpriced* ENYLDH (B74-50033)
Mass. Mediatation no.2 (on a sequence by Beethoven): arr. Meditation no.2 (on a sequence by Beethoven). (Bernstein, Leonard). *Amberson : Schirmer. Unpriced* UMK (B74-50717)
Mass, no.8, in B flat major, 'Sancti Joannis de Deo'. Vocal score. Missa brevis Sancti Joannis de Deo, 'Small organ mass' : for four-part chorus of mixed voices. (Haydn, Joseph). *Schirmer. Unpriced* DG (B74-50008)
Mass. Selections: arr. Two meditations. (Bernstein, Leonard). *Amberson : Schirmer. Unpriced* SRPK (B74-50249)
Massenet, Jules. Duo for double bass and cello. *Yorke. Unpriced* SRPLSS (B74-50683)
Master music makers : an anthology of music by the great composers. (Romani, G). *Charnwood Music. Unpriced* RSPM/AY (B74-51205)
Master musicians series.
Calvocoressi, Michael Dimitri. Mussorgsky. Revised ed. *Dent. £2.75* BMU (B74-13105) ISBN 0-460-03152-x
Hedley, Arthur. Chopin. Revised ed. *Dent. £2.50* BCE (B74-13109) ISBN 0-460-03154-6
Horton, John. Grieg. *Dent. £2.95* BGT (B74-13104) ISBN 0-460-03135-x
Hussey, Dyneley. Verdi. Revised ed.. *Dent. £2.50* BVE(N) (B74-17892) ISBN 0-460-03151-1
Jacobs, Robert Louis. Wagner. Revised ed.. *Dent. £2.75* BWC(N) (B74-25494) ISBN 0-460-03153-8
Kennedy, Michael, *b.1926*. Mahler. *Dent. £2.75* BME(N) (B74-16725) ISBN 0-460-03141-4
Robertson, Alec. Dvořák. Revised ed. *Dent. £3.00* BDX(N) (B74-27797) ISBN 0-460-03116-3
Scott, Marion Margareta. Beethoven. Revised ed.. *Dent. £2.95* BBJ (B74-22161) ISBN 0-460-03149-x
Mathew, A G. Works, organ. Selections. Selected organ works. (Walmisley, Thomas Attwood). *Peters. Unpriced* RJ (B74-50624)
Mathias, William.
Alleluya psallat = Sing alleluya. Op. 58 : SATB. *Oxford University Press. £0.15* DH (B74-50013) ISBN 0-19-350339-5
Celtic dances. Opus 60 : for orchestra. *Oxford University Press. £3.50* MMH (B74-51100) ISBN 0-19-365572-1
Missa brevis. Op.64 : for mixed voices and organ. *Oxford University Press. Unpriced* DGS (B74-50883) ISBN 0-19-351647-0
A vision of time and eternity. Op.61 : song. *Oxford University Press. £1.10* KDW (B74-50461) ISBN 0-19-345570-6
Matthews, Denis.
Sonata for piano no.13 in B flat major. K.333. Sonata in B flat, K. 333. (Mozart, Wolfgang Amadeus). *Associated Board of the Royal Schools of Music. Unpriced* QPE (B74-50167)
Sonata for piano, no.15, in C major. K.545. Sonata in C, K.545. (Mozart, Wolfgang Amadeus). *Associated Board of the Royal Schools of Music. £0.35* QPE (B74-51144)
Matthews, Jean. Callers' choice : a selection of recently composed dances
Book 1. (Matthews, Nibs). *English Folk Dance and Song Society. Unpriced* LH/H/AY (B74-50121) ISBN 0-85418-035-4
Matthews, Nibs. Callers' choice : a selection of recently composed dances
Book 1. *English Folk Dance and Song Society. Unpriced* LH/H/AY (B74-50121) ISBN 0-85418-035-4
Maxwell-Timmins, Donald. Morning has broken : hymns to play and sing. *Schofield and Sims. Unpriced* DM/AY (B74-50352) ISBN 0-7217-2524-4
May, Helmut.
Concerto for violin & string orchestra in A major: arr. Konzert, A-Dur für Violine, Streichorchester und Basso continuo. (Albinoni, Tommaso). *Schott. £2.03* SPK/LF (B74-51247)
Concerto for violin and string orchestra in A major. Giazotto 116. Konzert, A-Dur, für Violine, Streichorchester und Basso continuo. (Albinoni, Tommaso). *Schott. £4.35* RXMPSF (B74-51219)
L'Estro armonico. Op.3, no.11. Concerto d-Moll : für 2 Violinen, Streicher und Basso continuo. (Vivaldi, Antonio). *Schott. £4.35* RXMPRXNTF (B74-50647)
Mayes, Jerry. 12 simple studies for guitar. *Charnwood Music. Unpriced* TS/AF (B74-51271)
Mechem, Kirke.
The children of David. Op.37 : five modern psalms, for mixed chorus and organ
1: Psalm. *Boosey and Hawkes. Unpriced* DH (B74-50898)
2: Joy. *Boosey and Hawkes. Unpriced* DH (B74-50899)
3: The song of David. *Boosey and Hawkes. Unpriced* DH (B74-50900)
4: Man of my own people. *Boosey and Hawkes. Unpriced* DH (B74-50901)
5: Pied beauty. *Boosey and Hawkes. Unpriced* DH (B74-50902)
Medieval motet book : a collection of 13th century motets in various vocal and instrumental combinations. (Tischler, Hans). *Associated Music. Unpriced* DW/AY (B74-50366)
Medinger, Gregor. Beggar's opera. Selections: arr. Four songs from the Beggar's Opera. (Gay, John). *Oxford University Press. Unpriced* EZDW (B74-50978)
Medio, Alonso. Spanish guitar tutor . exercises, scales. *Clifford Essex. £0.75* TS/AC (B74-50254)
Meditation : for marimba and organ. (Creston, Paul). *Schirmer. Unpriced* XTQSPLRK (B74-50327)
Meditation no.2 (on a sequence by Beethoven). (Bernstein, Leonard). *Amberson : Schirmer. Unpriced* UMK (B74-50717)
Meditation on a folk tune : organ solo. (Turvey, A W). *Cramer. Unpriced* RJ (B74-51197)
Meditation on the Passion chorale. Op.72 : for organ. (Cruft, Adrian). *Chappell. Unpriced* RJ (B74-50198)
Meditation on the syllable Om : for men's voices. (Nelson, Ron). *Boosey and Hawkes. Unpriced* GEZDW (B74-50436)
Medway, Carol. Twelve famous marches. *Cramer. £0.36* QPK/AGM/AY (B74-51184)
Meerwein, Georg.
Concertino for trumpet, two oboes & bassoon in D major. MWV VIII, 5. Concertino à 4, no.1 : for solo trumpet (clarino), 2 oboes and bassoon. MWV VIII, 5. (Molter, Johann Melchior). *Musica rara. Unpriced* UNSFL (B74-50739)
Concertino for trumpet, two oboes & bassoon in D major. MWV VIII, 6. Concertino à 4, no.2 : for solo trumpet (clarino), 2 oboes and bassoon. MWV VIII, 6. (Molter, Johann Melchior). *Musica rara. Unpriced* UNSFL (B74-50740)
Concertino for trumpet, two oboes & bassoon in D major. MWV VIII, 7. Concertino à 4, no.3 : for solo trumpet (clarino), 2 oboes and bassoon. MWV VIII, 7. (Molter, Johann Melchior). *Musica rara. Unpriced* UNSFL (B74-50741)
Introduction and rondo for horn & piano in E flat major. Op.113, no.2. Introduction and rondo for horn and piano. Opus 113, no.2. (Ries, Ferdinand). *Musica rara. Unpriced* WTP/W (B74-50846)
Melita romantica : accordion solo. (Micallef, John). *Charnwood Music. Unpriced* RSPMJ (B74-51209)
Melly, George. Owning-up. *Penguin. £0.35* AKDW/HHW/E(P) (B74-07434) ISBN 0-14-002936-2
Melodien til Landstads Salmebog. Kirken den er et. Built on the rock : anthem for unison choir or solo voice and organ. (Lindeman, Ludvig Matthias). *Oxford University Press. Unpriced* JDH (B74-51017)
Memos. (Ives, Charles). *Calder and Boyars. £5.00* BIV(N) (B74-01379) ISBN 0-7145-0953-1
Menashe, Samuel. Two reflections : SSA unaccompanied. (Kennedy, John Brodbin). *Boosey and Hawkes. Unpriced* FEZDW (B74-51008)
Mendelssohn, Felix.
Deutsche Liturgie. Heilig. Heilig = Holy holy holy : for double chorus of mixed voices a cappella. *Schirmer. Unpriced* EZDH (B74-50944)
A midsummer night's dream. Op 61. Selections. Five orchestral pieces, Op.61. *Eulenburg. Unpriced* MM/JM (B74-51093)
Selections: arr. Mendelssohn's greatest hits; arranged for all organ. *Chappell. Unpriced* QPK (B74-50190)
Mendelssohn's greatest hits; arranged for all organ. (Mendelssohn, Felix). *Chappell. Unpriced* QPK (B74-50190)
Menon, Raghava Raghava. Discovering Indian music. *Abacus Press. £2.40* BZF (B74-02979) ISBN 0-85626-033-9
Menotti, Gian Carlo.
Amahl and the night visitors. *Selections: arr.* Introduction, march and shepherd's dance. *Schirmer. Unpriced* UMK (B74-50718)
Triplo concerto a tre. *Schirmer. Unpriced* MMF (B74-50137)
Menten, Dale. America sings: arr. America sings. *Unichappell : Chappell. Unpriced* DW (B74-50360)
Mercer, Johnny.
The good companions. Good companions: arr. Good companions : song. (Previn, André). *Chappell. Unpriced* KDW (B74-50462)
The good companions. *Selections: arr.* The good companions. (Previn, André). *Chappell. Unpriced* KDW (B74-51052)
Good companions. Slippin' around the corner. Slippin' around the corner. (Previn, André). *Chappell. Unpriced* DW (B74-50363)
Good companions. Stage struck. Stage struck : song. (Previn, André). *Chappell. Unpriced* DW (B74-50364)
The good companions. Ta luv: arr. Ta luv : song. (Previn, André). *Chappell. Unpriced* KDW (B74-50463)
The good companions. The dance of life: arr. The dance of life : song. (Previn, André). *Chappell. Unpriced* KDW (B74-50464)
The good companions. The pleasure of your company: arr. The pleasure of your company : song. (Previn, André). *Chappell. Unpriced* KDW (B74-50465)
Mercer Island suite. Op.1 : for recorder quartet (descant, treble, tenor, bass). (Bamforth, Dennis Anthony). *Carne House, Parsons Lane, Bury : Tomus. Unpriced* VSNSG (B74-50768)
Merrill, Marlin.
Let it be forgotten : for mixed chorus (SSAATB) or treble chorus (SSAA) and piano. *Oxford University Press. Unpriced* DW (B74-50361)
Recopilacion de sonetos y villancicos. *En la fuente del rosel.* En la fuente del rosel = 'Neath the rosebush in the stream : for four-part chorus of mixed voices a cappella. (Vasquez, Juan). *Roberton. £0.10* EZDU (B74-50055)
Messiah. Handel's conducting score of 'Messiah' : reproduced in facsimile from the manuscript in the library of St Michael's College, Tenbury Wells. (Handel, George Frideric). *Scolar Press for the Royal Musical Association. £37.50* BHCADD (B74-24210) ISBN 0-85967-158-5
Messiah. The trumpet shall sound: arr. The trumpet shall sound. (Handel, George Frideric). *Associated Board of the Royal Schools of Music. £0.15* WSPK/DH (B74-51368)
Metalepsis Z : cantata for mezzo-soprano solo, SATB and orchestral accompaniment. (Rands, Bernard). *Universal. Unpriced* EMDX (B74-50377)
Méthode de violoncelle. Op.4. Leçons et exercises, nos.10-18. Nine studies : for two cellos. (Raoul, Jean Marie). *Oxford University Press. £0.55* SRNU (B74-50680) ISBN 0-19-358480-8
Metropolitan Museum fanfare : for brass ensemble and percussion. (Thomson, Virgil). *Schirmer. Unpriced* WMGN (B74-50305)
Mettrick, Tony. Jesus is alive today : unison hymn. (Mills, Betty Lou). *32a Fore St., St Austell, Cornwell : Good News Crusade. £0.20* JDM (B74-50443)
Metyelitsa : SATB unaccompanied Russian folk song. (Hopkins, Ewart). *Roberton. £0.07* EZDW (B74-50410)
Mews, Donald. Gigue de Pan : organ with optional drums. *Oxford University Press. £0.60* RHP (B74-51190) ISBN 0-19-375565-3
Mews, Douglas. Ghosts, fire, water : for alto solo and unaccompanied mixed voices. *Oxford University Press. £0.30* EZDE (B74-50036) ISBN 0-19-343670-1
Mexicana. (Bolton, Cecil). *Affiliated Music. £1.00* WMJ (B74-50307)
Miall, Antony. The parlour song book : a casquet of vocal gems. (Turner, Michael R). *Pan Books. £1.75* KDW/GB/AY(XH564) (B74-51058) ISBN 0-330-24113-3
Micallef, John. Melita romantica : accordion solo. *Charnwood Music. Unpriced* RSPMJ (B74-51209)
Michael, row the boat ashore : Georgia sea island chant for four-part chorus of men's voices a cappella. (Russell, Wilbur F). *Roberton. £0.07* GEZDW/LC (B74-50082)
Michel, Joseph. Weihnachten : elektronische Orgel. *Nagel Bärenreiter. £1.80* RPVK/AAY (B74-50629)
Mick Jagger. (Scaduto, Anthony). *W.H. Allen. £3.50* AKDW/GB/E(P) (B74-23497) ISBN 0-491-01122-9
Middleton, Richard.
Music and society today. (Bray, Trevor). *Open University Press. Unpriced* A(Z) (B74-24207) ISBN 0-335-00869-0
The rise of the symphony
2. *Open University Press. £1.70* AMME(X) (B74-18934) ISBN 0-335-00859-3
Midsummer night's dream. Op 61. Selections. Five orchestral pieces, Op.61. (Mendelssohn, Felix). *Eulenburg. Unpriced* MM/JM (B74-51093)
Midwinter, Eric. Preschool priorities. *Ward Lock. £0.85* BREAQ (B74-12162) ISBN 0-7062-3383-2
Miguez, Leopoldo. Bluetes, 1, a serie
album no.1. Op.31 (de 1 a 10) : piano. *Arthur Napoleão Essex Music. Unpriced* QPJ (B74-51178)
Mikhail Glinka : a biographical and critical study. (Brown, David, *b.1929*). *Oxford University Press. £7.00* BGL(N) (B74-03503) ISBN 0-19-315311-4
Miles, Bernard. Treasure island. Vocal score. Treasure island : a musical adventure. (Ornadel, Cyril). *Sparta Florida Music : Aviva Music. £0.99* CM (B74-50006)
Miliband, Ralph. The Socialist Register
1973. *Merlin Press. £4.00* 335.005 (B74-18687) ISBN 0-85036-178-8
Milich, Boris Evseyevich.
Easy Russian piano music
Book 1. (Aldridge, Maisie). *Oxford University Press. £0.50* QP/AYM (B74-50569) ISBN 0-19-372131-7
Book 2. (Aldridge, Maisie). *Oxford University Press. £0.60* QP/AYM (B74-50570) ISBN 0-19-372132-5
Millard, Daryl. Mass. Almighty Father: arr. Almighty Father : chorale. (Bernstein, Leonard). *Amberson : Schirmer. Unpriced* GEZDH (B74-50434)
Millay, Edna St. Vincent. Pity me not : SATB a cappella. (Calder, Robert). *Associated Music. Unpriced* EZDW (B74-50058)
Millet, Kadish. Stained glass windows (and simple wood benches). *Chappell. Unpriced* DW (B74-50925)
Mills, Betty Lou. Jesus is alive today : unison hymn. *32a Fore St., St Austell, Cornwall : Good News Crusade. £0.20* JDM (B74-50443)
Miniature scores:.
Adler, Samuel. Quartet for strings, no.5. String quartet, no.5. *Boosey and Hawkes. £2.50* RXNS (B74-51225)
Arnold, Malcolm. Symphony no.6. Op.95. *Faber Music. Unpriced* MME (B74-50493)
Bach, Johann Christian. Sinfonia concertante for oboe, cello & orchestra in F major. Sinfonia concertante, F major for oboe, violoncello and orchestra. *Eulenburg. Unpriced* MPVTPLSRE (B74-50145)
Bach, Johann Christian. Symphony in G minor. Opus 6, no.6. Symphony, G minor. Op. 6, no.6. *Eulenburg. £0.80*

MRE (B74-50147)
Bach, Johann Sebastian. Concerto for violin & string orchestra in A minor. S. 1041. Konzert, A-moll, für Violine und Streichorchester. BWV 1041. *Peters. Unpriced* RXMPSF (B74-51220)
Bach, Johann Sebastian. Siehe zu dass deine Gottesfurcht nicht Heuchelei sei : Kantate 179 (auf den 11 Sonntag nach Trinitis). *Eulenburg. £1.00* EMDE (B74-50028)
Berkeley, Lennox. Antiphon : for string orchestra. *Chester. Unpriced* RXMJ (B74-51217)
Berlioz, Hector. Waverley. Op.1 : overture. *Eulenberg. Unpriced* MMJ (B74-50502)
Bizet, Georges. Symphony in C major. Symphony, C major. *Eulenburg. Unpriced* MME (B74-51097)
Butting, Max. Quartet for strings, no.8. Op.96. VIII. Streichquartett. Opus 96. *Peters. Unpriced* RXNS (B74-51226)
Chavez, Carlos. Discovery = Descubrimiento : for orchestra. *Schirmer. £2.35* MMJ (B74-50503)
Einem, Gottfried von. Rosa mystica. Op. 40 : acht Gesänge für mittlere Singstimme und Orchester. *Boosey and Hawkes. Unpriced* KFVE/MDW (B74-50118)
Einem, Gottfried von. Die träumenden Knaben, Op.41 : Cantata für vierstimmigen gemischten Chor, Klarinette und Fagott. *Boosey and Hawkes. Unpriced* EVVPLVWDX (B74-50383)
Franck, César. Le Chasseur maudit. *Eulenburg. Unpriced* MMJ (B74-50505)
Handel, George Frideric. Concertos for organ. Op.7. Organ concertos. Op.7
No.1: B flat major. *Eulenburg. £0.80* MPRF (B74-50509)
Handel, George Frideric. Concertos for organ. Op.7. Organ concertos. Op.7
No.2: A major. *Eulenburg. £0.80* MPRF (B74-50510)
Handel, George Frideric. Concertos for organ. Op.7. Organ concertos. Op.7
No.3: B flat major. *Eulenburg. £0.80* MPRF (B74-50511)
Handel, George Frideric. Concertos for organ. Op.7. Organ concertos. Op.7
No.4: D minor. *Eulenburg. £0.80* MPRF (B74-50512)
Handel, George Frideric. Concertos for organ. Op.7. Organ concertos. Op.7
No.5: G minor. *Eulenburg. £0.80* MPRF (B74-50513)
Handel, George Frideric. Concertos for organ. Op.7. Organ concertos. Op.7
No.6: B flat major. *Eulenburg. £0.80* MPRF (B74-50514)
Handel, George Frideric. Water music. *Eulenburg. £0.70* MRG (B74-50148)
Lambert, Constant. The Rio Grande. *Oxford University Press. £1.30* EMDX (B74-50376) ISBN 0-19-337303-3
Mahler, Gustav. Kindertotenlieder : für eine Singstimme und Orchester auf Gedichte von Friedrich Rückert. *Peters. Unpriced* KE/MDW (B74-51060)
Mendelssohn, Felix. A midsummer night's dream. Op 61. Selections. Five orchestral pieces, Op.61. *Eulenburg. Unpriced* MM/JM (B74-51093)
Mozart, Wolfgang Amadeus. Concerto for clarinet in A major. K.622. Concerto, A major, for clarinet and orchestra. K.622. *Eulenburg. £0.85* MPVVF (B74-51112)
Mozart, Wolfgang Amadeus. Concerto for piano, no.25, in C major. K.503. Piano concerto, C major. K.503. *Eulenburg. Unpriced* MPQF (B74-51106)
Penderecki, Krzysztof. Ecloga VIII (Vergili 'Bucolica') : for 6 male voices (1972). *Schott. £2.40* JNGEZAZDX (B74-50095)
Rachmaninoff, Sergei. The isle of the dead. Op. 29 : symphonic poem. *Boosey and Hawkes. £1.25* MMJ (B74-50141)
Saint-Saëns, Camille. Le Carnival des animaux : grande fantasie zoologique. *Peters. Unpriced* MMJ (B74-51104)
Schubert, Franz. Quintet for strings in C major. D.956. Quintet, C major, for 2 violins, viola and 2 cellos. D.956. *Eulenburg. Unpriced* RXNR (B74-51224)
Shostakovich, Dmitry. Quartet for strings, no.13. Op.138. String quartet no.13. Op.138. *Boosey and Hawkes. £1.25* RXNS (B74-50657)
Skriabin, Aleksandr Nikolaevich. Symphony no.2 in C minor. Op. 29. *Eulenburg. Unpriced* MME (B74-50135)
Smetana, Bedřich. My country. Vltava. My fatherland = Ma vlast : a cycle of symphonic poems
No.2: Vltava. *Eulenburg. Unpriced* MMJ (B74-50507)
Strauss, Richard. Till Eulenspiegel. Op.28. Till Eulenspiegels Lustige Streiche : nach alter Schelmenweise in Rondeauforme. *Eulenburg. Unpriced* MMJ (B74-51105)
Tchaikowsky, André. Quartet for strings in A major. Op.3. String quartet in A. Op.3. *Weinberger. Unpriced* RXNS (B74-50658)
Williamson, Malcolm. Concerto grosso. *Weinberger. Unpriced* MMF (B74-50497)
Zoephel, Klaus. Quintet for wind instruments. Quintett für Flöte, Oboe, Klarinette in B, Horn in F und Fagott. *Peters. Unpriced* VNR (B74-51312)
Miniature suite for piano. (Wilson, Robert Barclay). *Freeman. Unpriced* QPG (B74-50170)
Miniatures for piano. (Liszt, Franz). *Schirmer. Unpriced* QPJ (B74-50180)
Minstrels : medieval music to sing and play. (Sargent, Brian). *Cambridge University Press. Unpriced* DW/AY (B74-50367) ISBN 0-521-20166-7
Minter, Robert L.
Idaspe. Sinfonia. Sinfonia to 'Hydaspes' : for trumpet, strings and basso continuo. (Mancini, Francesco). *Musica rara. Unpriced* RXMPWSE (B74-50653)
Idaspe. Sinfonia: arr. Sinfonia to 'Hydaspes' : for trumpet, strings and basso continuo. (Mancini, Francesco). *Musica rara. Unpriced* WSPK/LE (B74-50842)
Sonata for eight trumpets, timpani & basso continuo in C major, 'Scti Polycarpi'. Sonata 'Scti Polycarpi' : for 8 trumpets, timpani and basso continuo. (Biber, Heinrich Ignaz Franz). *Musica rara. Unpriced* WSME (B74-50832)
Sonata for trumpet, violin, trombone, bassoon & basso continuo in G major, 'La Carioletta'. Sonata in G, 'La Carioletta' : for cornetto (trumpet), violin, trombone, bassoon and basso continuo. (Schmelzer, Johann Heinrich). *Musica rara. Unpriced* NUNRE (B74-50522)
Sonata for two trumpets, two violins & basso continuo. Sonata for 2 cornetti (trumpets), 2 violins and basso continuo. (Brückner, H). *Musica rara. Unpriced* NUXSNRE (B74-50537)
Sonata for violin, trombone, bassoon & basso continuo in A minor. Sonata à 3 : for violin, trombone, bassoon & basso continuo. (Schmelzer, Johann Heinrich). *Musica rara. Unpriced* NUNSE (B74-50523)
Mirages : a song cycle for baritone and piano. (Alwyn, William). *Lengnick. £1.25* KGNDW (B74-50489)
Missa brevis Sancti Joannis de Deo, 'Small organ mass' : for four-part chorus of mixed voices. (Haydn, Joseph). *Schirmer. Unpriced* DG (B74-50008)
Missa Cellensis in C, 'Mariazellermesse' : for four-part chorus of mixed voices. (Haydn, Joseph). *Schirmer. Unpriced* DG (B74-50009)
Missa festiva : for two-part choir, (upper voices), and orchestra. (Pert, Morris). *Oxford University Press. £0.60* FDE (B74-50066) ISBN 0-19-337830-2
Missa festiva. Vocal score. Missa festiva : for two-part choir, (upper voices), and orchestra. (Pert, Morris). *Oxford University Press. £0.60* FDE (B74-50066) ISBN 0-19-337830-2
Missa for Archibishop Colloredo, (Mass in C) : for four-part chorus of mixed voices. (Mozart, Wolfgang Amadeus). *Schirmer. Unpriced* DG (B74-50337)
Missa Sancti Bernardi de Offida, 'Heiligmesse' : for four-part chorus of mixed voices. (Haydn, Joseph). *Schirmer. Unpriced* DG (B74-50007)
Mister Jelly Roll : the fortunes of Jelly Roll Morton, New Orleans Creole and 'inventor of jazz'. (Lomax, Alan). 2nd ed. *University of California Press. £5.20* AMT(P) (B74-14971) ISBN 0-520-02402-8
Mitchell, Anne G. Philosophy of modern music. (Adorno, Theodor Wiesengrund). *Sheed and Ward. £4.50* BSET (B74-09866) ISBN 0-7220-7339-9
Mitchell, Donald. Gustav Mahler : memories and letters. (Werfel, Alma Mahler). 3rd ed. *J. Murray. £5.00* BME(N) (B74-00161) ISBN 0-7195-2944-1
Mock marriage. Man is for the woman made: arr. Man is for the woman made. (Purcell, Henry). *Boosey and Hawkes. Unpriced* DW (B74-50365)
Modern organ music
Book 3: Five pieces by contemporary composers. *Oxford University Press. £0.95* R/AY (B74-50196) ISBN 0-19-375143-7
Mogill, Leonard. Etudes for violin. Op.45, 54, 74. Selections: arr. Forty selected studies in first position for the viola. (Wohlfahrt, Franz). *Schirmer. Unpriced* SQK/AF (B74-50239)
Moisy, Heinz von. Advanced technique for the drumset. *Simrock. Unpriced* XQ/AF (B74-50854)
Molter, Johann Melchior.
Concertino for trumpet, two oboes & bassoon in D major. MWV VIII, 5. Concertino à 4, no.1 : for solo trumpet (clarino), 2 oboes and bassoon. MWV VIII, 5. *Musica rara. Unpriced* UNSFL (B74-50739)
Concertino for trumpet, two oboes & bassoon in D major. MWV VIII, 6. Concertino à 4, no.2 : for solo trumpet (clarino), 2 oboes and bassoon. MWV VIII, 6. *Musica rara. Unpriced* UNSFL (B74-50740)
Concertino for trumpet, two oboes & bassoon in D major. MWV VIII, 7. Concertino à 4, no.3 : for solo trumpet (clarino), 2 oboes and bassoon. MWV VIII, 7. *Musica rara. Unpriced* UNSFL (B74-50741)
Mon mary m'a diffamée : chanson, S.T.T. (Brown, Howard Mayer). *Oxford University Press. Unpriced* ETWDU (B74-50035) ISBN 0-19-341203-9
Monodie : für ein Blasinstrument (1970). (Lehmann, Hans Ulrich). *Ars Viva. £1.44* WPMJ (B74-50314)
Monsieur Butterfly : the story of Puccini. (Jackson, Stanley, *b.1910*). *W.H. Allen. £3.50* BPU(N) (B74-05267) ISBN 0-491-01162-8
Monteverdi, Claudio.
Paraphrase on the dramatic madrigal Il Combattimento de Tancredi e Clorinda by Claudio Monteverdi. Op.28: for clarinet solo. (Goehr, Alexander). *Schott. £.25* VVPMJ (B74-50294)
Selva morale e spirituale. Messa a 4 da capella. Agnus Dei. Vocal score. Lamb of God = Agnus dei. *Schirmer. Unpriced* DGF (B74-50878)
Selva morale e spirituale. Messa a 4 da capella. Sanctus. Vocal score. Holy holy holy = Sanctus. *Schirmer. Unpriced* DGE (B74-50877)
Moody horn : for horn and piano. (Hardy, Mabel). *Imperial Music. £0.40* WTPJ (B74-50847)
Moore, Gerald, *b.1899.* Am I too loud? : memoirs of an accompanist. *Penguin. £0.60* AQ/ED(P) (B74-21540) ISBN 0-14-002480-8
Moore, Marianne. Fables. Fables : five very short operas. (Rorem, Ned). *Boosey and Hawkes. £3.25* CC (B74-50871)
More classic to contemporary piano music in its original form. (Grant, Lawrence). *Ashley : Phoenix. Unpriced* QP/AY (B74-50568)
Morehen, John.
Alleluya psallat = Sing alleluya. Op. 58 : SATB. (Mathias, William). *Oxford University Press. £0.15* DH (B74-50013) ISBN 0-19-350339-5
Gradualia, lib.1. Sacerdotes Domini. Sacerdotes Domini = Then did priests make offering : SATB. (Byrd, William). Revised ed. *Oxford University Press. Unpriced* EZDGKAF (B74-50038) ISBN 0-19-352008-7
Gradulia, lib 2. Victimae paschali. Victimae paschali = Unto Christ the victim : motet for five voices, SSAT unacc. (Byrd, William). *Oxford University Press. £0.30* DGKADD/LL (B74-50879) ISBN 0-19-352010-9
Liber primus sacrarum cantionum. Vigilate. Vigilate = Be ye watchful : motet for five voices S.A.T.Ba.B. (Byrd, William). *Oxford University Press. £0.20* EZDJ (B74-50395) ISBN 0-19-352056-7
Works, viols. Selections. Three consort pieces : for treble, tenor and bass viols. (Parsley, Osbert). *Oxford University Press. £0.16* STNS (B74-50689) ISBN 0-19-358105-1
Morgan, Thomas. Suite, Love and honour : for strings and continuo. *Oxford University Press. £1.75* RXMG (B74-50641) ISBN 0-19-357824-7
Morning has broken : hymns to play and sing. (Maxwell-Timmins, Donald). *Schofield and Sims. Unpriced* DM/AY (B74-50352) ISBN 0-7217-2524-4
Moro lasso. (Gesualdo, Carlo, *Prince of Venosa*). *Oxford University Press. Unpriced* UMK/DU (B74-51302)
Morrish, Donald James.
Basic goals in music
1. New ed.. *McGraw-Hill. £1.10* A(VK) (B74-22799) ISBN 0-07-094430-x
2. New ed.. *McGraw-Hill. £1.20* A(VK) (B74-22800) ISBN 0-07-094431-8
Book 3. *McGraw-Hill. Unpriced* C/AC (B74-50862) ISBN 0-07-094432-6
Book 4. *McGraw-Hill. Unpriced* C/AC (B74-50863) ISBN 0-07-094433-4
Book 5. *McGraw-Hill. Unpriced* C/AC (B74-50864) ISBN 0-07-094434-2
Morrow, Michael. Five pieces for four viols from 'Musica teutsch' and 'Musica und Tabulatur'. (Gerle, Hans). *Oxford University Press. £0.16* STNSK/DW/AYE (B74-51257) ISBN 0-19-341214-4
Mors janua vitae : for male-voice choir (TTBB) and piano or organ or strings. (Wilson, Robert Barclay). *Cramer. £0.12* GDH (B74-51013)
Mors janua vitae. Vocal score. Mors janua vitae : for male-voice choir (TTBB) and piano or organ or strings. (Wilson, Robert Barclay). *Cramer. £0.12* GDH (B74-51013)
Morthenson, Jan W. Labor : meta-music for chamber orchestra. *Universal. Unpriced* MRJ (B74-51115)
Mossman, Sheila.
Lyra songbook : hymns and songs
Volume 1. *Rahter. Unpriced* CB/AY (B74-50004)
Volume 2. *Rahter. Unpriced* CB/AY (B74-50005)
Motecta. Ne timeas, Maria. In venisti enim gratiam = You have been acclaimed the chosen one. The Annunciation : for four-part chorus of mixed voices a cappella. (Victoria, Tomàs Luis de). *Schirmer. Unpriced* EZDJ (B74-50400)
Motecta. Quem vidistis pastores? Quem vidistis, pastores = Whom did you see, kind shepherds? : Motet for Christmas time, for six-part chorus of mixed voices a cappella. (Victoria, Tomàs Luis de). *Chappell. Unpriced* EZDJ/LF (B74-50402)
Motecta. Vere languores nostres. Vere languores nostres = Truly our Saviour suffered : motet for four-part chorus of mixed voices a cappella. (Victoria, Tomás Luis de). *Schirmer. Unpriced* EZDJ/LK (B74-50953)
Motectorum quarternis vocibus liber primus. O rex gloriae. O rex gloriae : motet for Ascension Day, SATB unacc. (Marenzio, Luca). *Oxford University Press. £0.08* EZDJ/LM (B74-50404) ISBN 0-19-350343-3
Mountains of Mourne : variations for euphonium and piano on the theme by Houston Collison (sic). (Newsome, Roy). *Keith Prowse. £0.75* WWP/T (B74-50853)
Mouravieff, Leon. Tanz-Metamorphosen : für Streicher. *Litolff : Peters. Unpriced* RXMJ (B74-51218)
Moyse, Louis.
Sonata for flute in A minor. Wq.132. Sonata in A minor for flute alone. (Bach, Carl Philipp Emanuel). *Schirmer. £0.70* VRPME (B74-51326)
Sonatas for violin & piano. K.10-15: arr. Six sonatas for flute and piano. (Mozart, Wolfgang Amadeus). *Schirmer. Unpriced* VRPK/AE (B74-51323)
Suite for orchestra, no.2, in B minor. S. 1067: arr. Suite in B minor. (Bach, Johann Sebastian). *Schirmer. Unpriced* VRPK/AG (B74-51324)
Mozart, Wolfgang Amadeus.
Adagio and fugue for string quartet in C minor. K.546: arr. Adagio and fugue in C minor. K.546 and 426. *Schirmer. Unpriced* QNUK/Y (B74-50564)
Concerto for clarinet in A. K.622. Adagio; arr. Adagio. *Rubank : Novello. Unpriced* VVTRPK (B74-50809)
Concerto for clarinet in A major. K.622. Concerto, A major, for clarinet and orchestra. K.622. *Eulenburg. £0.85* MPVVF (B74-51112)
Concerto for clarinet in A major. K.622: arr. Concerto for clarinet and orchestra. K.622. *Schott. £2.00* VVPK/LF (B74-50804)
Concerto for piano, no.21, in C major. K.467. Andante: arr. Theme from Elvira Madigan. *Chappell. Unpriced* QPK (B74-50595)
Concerto for piano, no.25, in C major. K.503. Piano concerto, C major. K.503. *Eulenburg. Unpriced* MPQF (B74-51106)
Duets for two horns. K.487: arr. 12 easy duets for winds
Volume 3: For trombones, baritones, tubas (and cellos and basses ad lib). *Schirmer. Unpriced* UNUK (B74-50742)
Mass in C major. K.337. Vocal score. Missa for Archibishop Colloredo, (Mass in C) : for four-part chorus of mixed voices. *Schirmer. Unpriced* DG

(B74-50337)
Sonata for piano no.13 in B flat major. K.333. Sonata in B flat, K. 333. *Associated Board of the Royal Schools of Music. Unpriced* QPE (B74-50167)
Sonata for piano, no.15, in C major. K.545. Sonata in C, K.545. *Associated Board of the Royal Schools of Music. £0.35* QPE (B74-51144)
Sonatas for violin & piano. K.10-15: arr. Six sonatas for flute and piano. *Schirmer. Unpriced* VRPK/AE (B74-51323)
Muczynski, Robert.
Charade. Op.28 : for orchestra. *Schirmer. Unpriced* MMJ (B74-51103)
Impromptus. Op.32 : for solo tuba. *Schirmer. £0.95* WVPMJ (B74-50852)
Muczynsky, Robert. Synonyms for life. Op. 33 : for four-part chorus of mixed voices with piano accompaniment. *Schirmer. Unpriced* DW (B74-50023)
Muffat, Georg. Exquisitioris harmoniae instrumentalis gravijucundae selectus primus. *Concerto no.9 for two violins & string orchestra, 'Victoria maesta'.* Concerto 9, 'Victoria maesta'. *Schott. £1.92* RXMPSNUF (B74-50220)
Mulgan, Denis. Quartets for oboe & strings, nos.1,2. Quartet for oboe (flute), violin, viola and cello. Op.7, nos.1 and 2. (Vanhal, Jan). *Musica rara. Unpriced* NVTNS (B74-50543)
Murder on the Orient Express : theme. (Bennett, Richard Rodney). *EMI. £0.25* QPK/JR (B74-51186)
Murder on the Orient Express. Theme: arr. Murder on the Orient Express : theme. (Bennett, Richard Rodney). *EMI. £0.25* QPK/JR (B74-51186)
Murray, Gregory. Herz und Mund und That und Leben. S.147. Wohl mir dass ich Jesum habe: arr. Jesu, joy of man's desiring. (Bach, Johann Sebastian). *Oxford University Press. Unpriced* VSNQK/DM (B74-51330) ISBN 0-19-355290-6
Murray, Margaret. Elementaria : first acquaintance with Orff-Schulwerk. (Keetman, Gunild). *48 Great Marlborough St., W1V 2BN : Schott and Co. Ltd. £4.50* A(VG) (B74-13706) ISBN 0-901938-04-1
Musgrave, Thea.
Concerto for horn. Horn concerto. *Chester. Unpriced* MPWTF (B74-50517)
Impromptu for flute, oboe and clarinet, no.2. Impromptu no.2 for flute, oboe and clarinet. *Chester : Wilhelm Hansen. Unpriced* VNT (B74-51314)
Music. (Glynne-Jones, Marjorie Lilian). *Macmillan. £2.60* A(VJ) (B74-21533) ISBN 0-333-12252-6
Music. (Hart, Muriel). *Heinemann Educational. £0.80* A(VG) (B74-15369) ISBN 0-435-80606-8
Music & Man : an interdisciplinary journal of studies on music
Vol.1, no.1- ; 1973-. *Gordon and Breach. £3.50 (yearly) (£10.15 yearly to libraries and institutions)* A(B) (B74-14306)
Music and society : the later writings of Paul Honigsheim. (Honigsheim, Paul). *Wiley-Interscience. £8.50* A(Z) (B74-07432) ISBN 0-471-24680-8
Music and society today. (Bray, Trevor). *Open University Press. Unpriced* A(Z) (B74-24207) ISBN 0-335-00869-0
Music by Vivaldi. (Vivaldi, Antonio). *Schirmer. £1.05* TSNTK (B74-50256)
Music for piano (intermediate). (Szávai, Magda). *Boosey and Hawkes. £1.00* QP/AY (B74-50166)
Music for radio (1937). Prairie journal : for orchestra. (Copland, Aaron). *Boosey and Hawkes. £15.00* MMJ (B74-51101)
Music for the movies. (Thomas, Tony). *A.S. Barnes : Tantivy Press. £4.50* A/JR(YT/XNJ43) (B74-02980) ISBN 0-900730-63-3
Music from 'King Arthur'. (Purcell, Henry). *Paxton. £0.40* RK/JM (B74-50628)
Music in British libraries : a directory of resources. (Long, Maureen W). 2nd ed. *Library Association. £3.00 (£2.40 to members)* A(U/BC/YC) (B74-19811) ISBN 0-85365-287-2
Music in the United States : a historical introduction. (Hitchcock, Hugh Wiley). 2nd ed. *Prentice-Hall. £3.65* A(YT/X) (B74-28313) ISBN 0-13-608398-6
Music is my mistress. (Ellington, Duke). *W.H. Allen. £5.50* AMT(P) (B74-20925) ISBN 0-491-01720-0
Music Library Association. Music Library Association catalog of cards for printed music, 1953-1972 : a supplement to the Library of Congress catalogs. (Olmsted, Elizabeth H). *2 Rugby St., WC1N 3QU : Rowman and Littlefield. £33.35* A(T) (B74-13898) ISBN 0-87471-474-5
Music Library Association. Reprint series. Ornithoparchus, Andreas. Musice active micrologus. A compendium of musical practice. *Dover Publications : Constable. £7.00* A/M(XDS) (B74-11735) ISBN 0-486-20912-1
Music man. Goodnight, my someone. *Vocal score: arr.* Goodnight, my someone. (Willson, Meredith). *Frank Music. Unpriced* FDW (B74-50995)
Music notation : a manual of modern practice. (Read, Gardner). 2nd ed. *Gollancz. £3.50* A(QU) (B74-08076) ISBN 0-575-01758-9
Music of William Walton. (Howes, Frank). 2nd ed. *Oxford University Press. £3.00* BWJ (B74-00528) ISBN 0-19-315431-5
Music on stamps
Part 3: G-L. (Peat, Sylvester). *Citadel Works, Bath Rd, Chippenham, Wilts. SN15 2AA : Picton Publishing. £0.60* A(ZE) (B74-17382) ISBN 0-902633-20-1
Music outside : contemporary jazz in Britain. (Carr, Ian, *b.1933*). *Latimer New Dimensions. £3.00* AMT(M) (B74-01930) ISBN 0-901539-25-2
Music theory. (Jones, George Thaddeus). *28 Tavistock St., WC2E 7PN : Barnes and Noble. £1.95* A/AM (B74-25492) ISBN 0-06-460137-4
Musica Deo sacra III. (Tomkins, Thomas). *Stainer and Bell for the British Academy. Unpriced* EZDK (B74-50047)
Musica Deo sacra. O praise the Lord: arr. O praise the Lord. (Tomkins, Thomas). *Carne House, Parsons Lane, Bury, Lancs. : Tomus. £0.75* VSNK/DK (B74-51329)
Musical instruments from the Renaissance to the 19th century. (Paganelli, Sergio). *Hamlyn. £0.50* AL/B(XD401) (B74-20189) ISBN 0-600-31853-2
Musical reading and writing
Vol.1. (Szönyi, Erzsébet). *Boosey and Hawkes. £2.95* A(VC/QU) (B74-25493) ISBN 0-85162-011-6
Musical season : an English critic in New York. (Porter, Andrew). *Gollancz. £4.00* A/E(YTF/XQM2) (B74-30189) ISBN 0-575-01950-6
Musice active micrologus. A compendium of musical practice. (Ornithoparchus, Andreas). *Dover Publications : Constable. £7.00* A/M(XDS) (B74-11735) ISBN 0-486-20912-1
Musicks delight on the dulcimer, or, The New Elizabethan, wherein are contained a collection of ten pieces in tablature for the Appalachian dulcimer. (Nicholson, Roger). *Scratchwood Music : EMI Music. Unpriced* TWTTPMK (B74-51288)
Musick's empire. Op.9. Vocal score. Musick's empire. Opus 9 : for SATB, piano and optional strings. (Platts, Kenneth). *Ashdown. £0.15* DW (B74-50926)
Musick's empire. Opus 9 : for SATB, piano and optional strings. (Platts, Kenneth). *Ashdown. £0.15* DW (B74-50926)
Musique funèbre : for string orchestra. (Lutoslawski, Witold). *Chester. Unpriced* RXMJ (B74-50642)
Mussorgsky. (Calvocoressi, Michael Dimitri). Revised ed. *Dent. £2.75* BMU (B74-13105) ISBN 0-460-03152-x
Must I now = Muss i denn : German folk song. (Boyd, Jack). *Warner : Blossom. Unpriced* ESSPLRSDW (B74-50379)
Muston, Jeff. Journey to the centre of the earth: arr. Journey to the centre of the earth. (Wakeman, Rick). *Rondor : Music Sales. Unpriced* QPK/DW (B74-50603)
My country. Vltava. My fatherland = Ma vlast : a cycle of symphonic poems
No.2: Vltava. (Smetana, Bedřich). *Eulenburg. Unpriced* MMJ (B74-50507)
My fatherland = Ma vlast : a cycle of symphonic poems
No.2: Vltava. (Smetana, Bedřich). *Eulenburg. Unpriced* MMJ (B74-50507)
My favourite intermissions. My favourite intervals. (Borge, Victor). *Woburn Press. £2.25* A/D(YB/M) (B74-09227) ISBN 0-7130-0126-7
My favourite intervals. (Borge, Victor). *Woburn Press. £2.25* A/D(YB/M) (B74-09227) ISBN 0-7130-0126-7
My Lord is hence removed : SSATTB with tenor solo and viol accompaniment. (Amner, John). *Oxford University Press. Unpriced* DH (B74-50343) ISBN 0-19-350326-3
My soul, there is a country : SATB. (Drayton, Paul). *Oxford University Press. £0.12* DH (B74-50896) ISBN 0-19-350348-4
My top pop book. (Gray, Andy). *Hamlyn. £0.85* AKDW/GB/E(M) (B74-30606) ISBN 0-600-37073-9
My viola and I : a complete autobiography, with, Beauty of tone in string playing, and other essays. (Tertis, Lionel). *Elek. £4.00* ASQ/E(P) (B74-23500) ISBN 0-236-31040-2
Myatt, William Dean-. *See* Dean-Myatt, William.
Myrow, Gerald. The music man. Goodnight, my someone. *Vocal score: arr.* Goodnight, my someone. (Willson, Meredith). *Frank Music. Unpriced* FDW (B74-50995)
Nabokov, Nicolas. Twentieth century composers
Vol.4: France, Italy and Spain. *Weidenfeld and Nicolson. £4.50* AD(YB/M/XM) (B74-29004) ISBN 0-297-76793-3
Nagel, Frank.
Duo for flute and guitar in D major. Op. 109, no.6. Serenade für Flöte (Violine) und Gitarre. (Carulli, Ferdinando). *Schott. £1.32* VRPLTS (B74-50273)
Sonata for treble recorder & basso continuo in D minor. Sonate d-Moll, für Altblockflöte und Basso continuo. (Vivaldi, Antonio). *Schott. £1.08* VSSPE (B74-50288)
Narholz, Gerhard. Ricochet: arr. Ricochet. Fasten seat belts : original theme music, arranged for piano from the BBC Radio Two series. *Berry Music. Unpriced* QPK/JS (B74-51187)
National Council of Social Service. Report of Joint Study Conference on Music and the Physically Handicapped, held on April 6th, 1970, at the Goldsmiths' Hall, London, E.C.2 ... (Joint Study Conference on Music and the Physically Handicapped, *London, 1970*). *346 Kensington High St., W.14 : Disabled Living Foundation. £0.50* A(Z/D) (B74-16560) ISBN 0-901908-02-9
National Federation of Women's Institutes. Sound in the round. *National Federation of Women's Institutes. £0.15* FE/XNDW/XC (B74-50426) ISBN 0-900556-42-0
National Operatic and Dramatic Association. Year book 1974. *1 Crestfield St., WC1H 8AU : The Association. Unpriced* AC/E(YC/Q) (B74-29672) ISBN 0-901318-06-x
Nativitie : SATB a cappella. (O'Neal, Barry). *Associated Music. Unpriced* EZDH/LF (B74-50041)
Naylor, Bernard. Deus misereatur : two-part trebles. *Oxford University Press : Roberton. £0.10* FLDGNQD (B74-50078)
Naylor, Frank. The entertainer: arr. The entertainer : piano solo. (Joplin, Scott). *Bosworth. Unpriced* QPHX (B74-51152)
Neale, John Mason.
Canticle of fire : for chorus (SATB) and organ. (Williamson, Malcolm). *Weinberger. Unpriced* DE (B74-50875)
O wondrous type! : anthem for the Feast of the Transfiguration, SATB choir unaccompanied. (Petrich, Roger). *Oxford University Press. Unpriced* EZDH (B74-50945)
Neander, Joachim. Praise to the Lord : hymn-anthem for four-part chorus of mixed voices with organ or piano accompaniment, melody 'Lobe den Herrn' from Stralsund Gesangbuch. (Newbury, Kent A). *Schirmer. Unpriced* DH (B74-50014)
Nelson, Havelock.
Come down, O love divine : anthem for SSA (unaccompanied) suitable for Whitsun or general use. *Elkin. £0.07* FEZDH (B74-50074)
The girl with the buckles on her shoes : Irish traditional melody, unison song with piano. *Roberton. £0.07* JDW (B74-50085)
The king's daughter : SA and piano. *Lengnick. £0.12* FDW (B74-50420)
The maid of Bunclody : traditional Irish song. *Roberton. £0.10* GEZDW (B74-50437)
Nelson, Ron. Meditation on the syllable Om : for men's voices. *Boosey and Hawkes. Unpriced* GEZDW (B74-50436)
Nelson, Sheila M. Right from the start : twenty tunes for young violinists for violin and piano. *Boosey and Hawkes. £2.25* SPJ (B74-50671)
Nettl, Bruno. Folk and traditional music of the Western continents. 2nd ed. *Prentice-Hall. £4.70* A/G (B74-16181) ISBN 0-13-322941-6
Never weather-beaten sail. (Campion, Thomas). *Studio Music. Unpriced* WMK/DW (B74-51360)
New Ashmolean Marching Society and Students Conservatory Band. (Loesser, Frank). *Frank Music. Unpriced* UMMK (B74-51309)
New dance. Op. 18c : for concert band. (Riegger, Wallingford). *Associated Music. Unpriced* UMH (B74-51295)
New instrumentation.
Howell, Thomas. The avant-garde flute : a handbook for composers and flutists. *University of California Press. £5.50* AVR/E/CY (B74-21542) ISBN 0-520-02305-6
Turetzky, Bertram. The contemporary contrabass. *University of California Press. £4.40* ASS/E/CY (B74-28317) ISBN 0-520-02291-2
New music : an introduction and general survey for the non-specialist. (Hellewell, David). *57 Lansdowne Rd, Bournemouth, Hants. BH1 1RN : Apollo Contemporary Music. £0.50* A(XM73) (B74-06501) ISBN 0-9503225-0-4
New Oxford history of music
Vol.10: The modern age, 1890-1960. *Oxford University Press. £9.50* A(X) (B74-22160) ISBN 0-19-316310-1
Newbolt, *Sir* Henry. The fighting Téméraire : TTBB. (Bantock, *Sir* Granville). *Roberton. £0.16* GEZDW (B74-51016)
Newbury, Kent A.
Praise to the Lord : hymn-anthem for four-part chorus of mixed voices with organ or piano accompaniment, melody 'Lobe den Herrn' from Stralsund Gesangbuch. *Schirmer. Unpriced* DH (B74-50014)
Send forth thy spirit, O Lord : Ascension or general anthem, for four-part chorus of mixed voices a cappella (or optional piano). *Schirmer. Unpriced* EZDK/LM (B74-50957)
Newe teutsche Lieder mit vier Stimmen. *Ich waiss mir en Meidlein.* Ich waiss mir Meidlein = I know a fair maiden : madrigal, for four-part chorus of mixed voices a cappella. (Lasso, Orlando di). *Schirmer. Unpriced* EZDU (B74-50054)
Newman, Anthony.
Barricades (after Couperin) : for voice, guitar and keyboard. *Schirmer. Unpriced* KE/TSPDW (B74-51064)
Bhajeb : for organ. *Schirmer. Unpriced* RJ (B74-51194)
Newman, Mary Jane. Barricades (after Couperin) : for voice, guitar and keyboard. (Newman, Anthony). *Schirmer. Unpriced* KE/TSPDW (B74-51064)
Newsome, Roy.
Concorde : cornet solo and brass band. *Studio Music. Unpriced* WMPWR (B74-51362)
Investiture antiphonal fanfares for three brass choirs: arr. Investiture antiphonal fanfares for three brass choirs. (Bliss, *Sir* Arthur). *Novello. £0.50* WMK/AGN (B74-51357)
Variations for euphonium & piano, 'The mountains of Mourne'. The mountains of Mourne : variations for euphonium and piano on the theme by Houston Collison (sic). *Keith Prowse. £0.75* WWP/T (B74-50853)
Newton, John.
Amazin' grace : old negro hymn tune. (Whalum, Wendell). *Roberton. £0.13* DM (B74-50019)
Amazing grace. (Davis, Katherine Kennicott). *Galaxy : Galliard. Unpriced* DM (B74-50907)
Nicholson, Roger. Musicks delight on the dulcimer, or, The New Elizabethan, wherein are contained a collection of ten pieces in tablature for the Appalachian dulcimer. *Scratchwood Music : EMI Music. Unpriced* TWTTPMK (B74-51288)
Night music : for solo flute and small orchestra. (Dorati, Antal). *Chester : Hansen. Unpriced* MPVR (B74-51111)
Nina. (Pallandt, Nina, *barones van*). *Hale. £2.80* AKDW/GB/E(P) (B74-17384) ISBN 0-7091-4586-1
Nine chansons : for four voices or instruments. (Manchicourt, Pierre de). *London Pro musica. Unpriced* EZDU (B74-50972)

Nine studies : for two cellos. (Raoul, Jean Marie). *Oxford University Press. £0.55* SRNU (B74-50680) ISBN 0-19-358480-8
Nisi Dominus. Psalm 127 : motet for SSATB and organ continuo. (Carissimi, Giacomo). *Novello. £0.20* DR (B74-50913)
Nocturne, Op.54 : song for medium voice and piano. (Rubbra, Edmund). *Lengnick. £0.30* KFVDW (B74-50487)
Nocturnes pour un sax : saxophone and piano. (Gallois, Olivier). *Chappell. Unpriced* VUPJ (B74-51339)
Nocturnos für Violoncello und Harfe (1965). (Reimann, Aribert). *Schott. £1.92* SRPLTQ (B74-50251)
Nolan, Sidney. Children's crusade = Kinderkreuzzug. Op.82 : a ballad for children's voices and orchestra. (Britten, Benjamin). *Faber Music : Faber. £15.00* BBUADX (B74-21537) ISBN 0-571-10370-7
Nonsongs : six songs about nothing in particular for voices, descant recorders, pitched and unpitched percussion and piano. (Lord, David). *Universal. Unpriced* JE/NYFSRDW (B74-51025)
Norman, Theodore. Selections: arr. Music by Vivaldi. (Vivaldi, Antonio). *Schirmer. £1.05* TSNTK (B74-50256)
North West Regional Curriculum Development Project. Creative music making and the young school leaver. *Blackie. £1.40* A(VK/YDJC/XQG4) (B74-20922) ISBN 0-216-89673-8
Notes and notions : eight short pieces for piano. (Last, Joan). *Oxford University Press. £0.45* QPJ (B74-50179) ISBN 0-19-373135-5
Novello, Ivor. Works, songs. Selections. Ivor Novello song album. *Chappell. Unpriced* KDW (B74-51050)
Novello short biographies. McCabe, John. Rachmaninov. *Novello. £0.20* BRC(N) (B74-25491) ISBN 0-85360-059-7
Now glad of heart be every one : Easter carol, for SATB and organ. (Drayton, Paul). *Novello. £0.10* DP/LL (B74-50021)
Nutcracker. *See* Hori, Fumiko.
Nyman, Michael. Experimental music : Cage and beyond. *Studio Vista. £3.75* A(XPK24) (B74-23495) ISBN 0-289-70182-1
Nystedt, Knut.
  Entrata festiva. Op. 60 : for concert band. *Associated Music. Unpriced* UMJ (B74-50263)
  Pia memoria : requiem for nine brass instruments and optional chimes. Op.65. *Associated Music Publishers. £4.20* WNM (B74-50827)
  Suoni. Op.62 : for flute, marimba and full chorus of women's voices. *Associated Music. Unpriced* FE/VRPLXTQSDX (B74-50425)
O come, O come Emmanuel = Veni Emmanuel : Advent anthem for unison or 2-part mixed chorus and organ. (Hilty, Everett Jay). *Oxford University Press. Unpriced* JDP/LEZ (B74-50444)
O Lord arise : anthem for seven voices, S.S.A.A.T.B.B. (Weelkes, Thomas). *Oxford University Press. £0.20* EZDK (B74-50955) ISBN 0-19-352126-1
O Lord, of whom I do depend : the humble suit of a sinner, SATB. (Amner, John). *Royal School of Church Music. Unpriced* EZDK (B74-50046)
O Musica, thou noble art : for five-part chorus of mixed voices a cappella. (Peuerl, Paul). *Roberton. £0.10* EZDW (B74-50060)
O my lord : negro spiritual. (Dinham, Kenneth J). *Banks. Unpriced* EZDP/LF (B74-50962)
O praise the Lord. (Tomkins, Thomas). *Carne House, Parsons Lane, Bury, Lancs. : Tomus. £0.75* VSNK/DK (B74-51329)
O rex gloriae : motet for Ascension Day, SATB unacc. (Marenzio, Luca). *Oxford University Press. £0.08* EZDJ/LM (B74-50404) ISBN 0-19-350343-3
O wondrous type! : anthem for the Feast of the Transfiguration, SATB choir unaccompanied. (Petrich, Roger). *Oxford University Press. Unpriced* EZDH (B74-50945)
Octet for winds. (Laderman, Ezra). *Oxford University Press. Unpriced* UNN (B74-50736)
Ode to freedom : mixed chorus, SATB accompanied by band and/or orchestra. (Washburn, Robert). *Oxford University Press. Unpriced* DX (B74-50930)
Ode to freedom. Vocal score. Ode to freedom : mixed chorus, SATB accompanied by band and/or orchestra. (Washburn, Robert). *Oxford University Press. Unpriced* DX (B74-50930)
Oekumenische Beatmesse : Liebe ist nicht nur ein Wort. (Blarr, Oskar Gottlieb). *Bosse : Bärenreiter. £1.60* ELDE (B74-50372)
Offenbach, Jacques. La Périchole. Vocal score. La Périchole : operetta in three acts: music. *Weinberger. Unpriced* CF (B74-50332)
Officium hebdomadie sanctae. Tenebrae factae sunt. Tenebrae factae sunt = Darkness was o'er the earth : Passion motet for four-part chorus of women's voices a cappella. (Victoria, Tomas Luis de). *Chappell. Unpriced* FEZDGKH/LHL (B74-50428)
O'Gorman, Denis. The wild rover : the story of the Prodigal Son: a musical play for children. *Grail Publications. £0.50* BOFGACN (B74-11053) ISBN 0-901829-22-6
Ohrlin, Glenn. The hell-bound train : a cowboy songbook. *University of Illinois Press. £4.30* JEZDW/GNF/AY (B74-50453) ISBN 0-252-00190-7
Oiseau de feu = Der Feuervogel. (Stravinsky, Igor). *Schott. £1.44* QPK/HM (B74-50194)
Oishi, Makoto. E.H. Grieg's 'Peer Gynt'. (Suzuki, Yoshiharu). *F. Warne. £1.75* BGTAM/JMBN (B74-26152) ISBN 0-7232-1784-x
Okeghem, Jean. Salve regina : for four-part chorus of mixed voices a cappella. *Associated Music. Unpriced* EZDJ (B74-50397)
Old comrades : quick march. (Teike, Carl). *Boosey and Hawkes. £0.95* UMMK/AGM (B74-50732)
Old Hundreth Psalm tune ('All people that on earth do dwell') : anthem for unison or mixed (SATB) choir accompanied by organ with band and/or orchestra. (Vaughan Williams, Ralph). *Oxford University Press. Unpriced* EUMDM (B74-50381)
Old musical instruments. (Clemenicic, René). *Octopus Books. £0.99* AL/B(XD351) (B74-07433) ISBN 0-7064-0057-7
Old Time Music booklets. Atkins, John. The Carter family. *33 Brunswick Gardens, W8 4AW : Old Time Music. £0.60* ADW/G(YT/P) (B74-12389) ISBN 0-904395-00-6
Olleson, Philip. The rise of the string quartet. *Open University Press. Unpriced* ARXNS(X) (B74-18935) ISBN 0-335-00862-3
Olmsted, Elizabeth H. Music Library Association catalog of cards for printed music, 1953-1972 : a supplement to the Library of Congress catalogs. *2 Rugby St., WC1N 3QU : Rowman and Littlefield. £33.35* A(T) (B74-13898) ISBN 0-87471-474-5
Omnes de Saba venient : motet for Epiphany, SATTB unacc. (Handl, Jacob). *Oxford University Press. £0.08* EZDJ/LFP (B74-50403) ISBN 0-19-350342-5
On the go : six sketches for piano. (Price, Beryl). *Oxford University Press. £0.40* QPJ (B74-50181) ISBN 0-19-373534-2
On the high C's : (a light-hearted journey): an autobiography. (MacEwan, Sydney). *J. Burns. £1.60* AKGH/E(P) (B74-03194) ISBN 0-900243-38-4
On wings of song : a biography of Felix Mendelssohn. (Blunt, Wilfrid). *Hamilton. £5.50* BMJ(N) (B74-14969) ISBN 0-241-02455-2
One hundred songs of toil : with guitar chords. (Dallas, Karl). *Wolfe. £1.75* KE/TSDW/GM/AYC (B74-50112) ISBN 0-7234-0525-5
O'Neal, Barry.
  Lord have mercy : for four-part chorus of mixed voices a cappella. *Associated Music. Unpriced* EZDH (B74-50039)
  Nativitie : SATB a cappella. *Associated Music. Unpriced* EZDH/LF (B74-50041)
O'Neal, Hank. The Eddie Condon scrapbook of jazz. (Condon, Eddie). *Hale. £4.80* AMT(P) (B74-13108) ISBN 0-7091-4476-8
O'Neill, Francis. Irish folk music : a fascinating hobby, with some account of allied subjects including O'Farrell's treatise on the Irish or Union pipes and Touhey's hints to amateur pipers. 1st ed. reprinted. *EP Publishing. £3.00* A/G(YDM/XA1909) (B74-12387) ISBN 0-85409-910-7
Open University.
  Baroque instrumental music
  1: People, instruments and the continuo. (Edwards, Owain). *Open University Press. £2.20* AL(XE151) (B74-08077) ISBN 0-335-00852-6
  2: Suite, sonata and concerto. (Edwards, Owain). *Open University Press. Unpriced* AL(XE151) (B74-08078) ISBN 0-335-00853-4
  The Baroque organ (containing an introduction to units 1-2); and, Bach organ music. (Hendrie, Gerald). *Open University Press. £2.00* AR/B(XE151) (B74-07435) ISBN 0-335-00850-x
  From classical to romantic keyboard music. (Ratcliffe, Ronald V). *Open University Press. Unpriced* AQ/B/E(XA1849) (B74-23499) ISBN 0-335-00864-x
  Music and society today. (Bray, Trevor). *Open University Press. Unpriced* A(Z) (B74-24207) ISBN 0-335-00869-0
  The rise of the string quartet. (Olleson, Philip). *Open University Press. Unpriced* ARXNS(X) (B74-18935) ISBN 0-335-00862-3
  The rise of the symphony
  2. (Middleton, Richard). *Open University Press. £1.70* AMME(X) (B74-18934) ISBN 0-335-00859-3
  Twentieth century music, 1900-1945. (Bray, Trevor). *Open University Press. Unpriced* A(XM46) (B74-21535) ISBN 0-335-00866-6
Oper : elektronische Orgel. (Sommer, Jürgen). *Nagel Bärenreiter. £1.80* RPVK/AAY (B74-50633)
'Opera nights' : an album of operatic favourites. (Romani, G). *Ricordi. Unpriced* RSPMK/AAY (B74-51215)
Opera nova de balli, 1553 : for four instruments. (Bendusi, Francesco). *London Pro Musica. Unpriced* LNSH (B74-51082)
Opera recordings : a critical guide. (Harris, Kenn). *David and Charles. £3.95* AC/FD (B74-00871) ISBN 0-7153-6362-x
Opernmelodien : für elektronische Orgel. (Parker, John). *Schott. £2.40* RPVK/DW/AY (B74-50208)
Orff, Carl. De temporum fine comoedia = Das Spiel vom Ende der Zeiten Vigilia. *Schott. Unpriced* EMDX (B74-50933)
Orga, Ateş. The Proms. *David and Charles. £3.95* A(YDB/W) (B74-24907) ISBN 0-7153-6679-3
Organ : its evolution, principles of construction and use. (Sumner, William Leslie). 4th ed. revised and enlarged. *Macdonald and Co. £5.00* AR/B(X) (B74-01931) ISBN 0-356-04162-x
Organ music for today
  Vol.1. *Chappell. Unpriced* RJ (B74-50620)
Organ parade. (Fair Organ Preservation Society). *c/o K. Redfern, 3 Bentley Rd, Denton, Manchester M34 3AZ : Fair Organ Preservation Society. £1.50 (Free to members)* A/FM(EM) (B74-07436) ISBN 0-9502701-1-3
Organ works. (Hart, Philip). *Hinrichsen. Unpriced* R/AZ (B74-50613)
Organism : for organ solo. (Bamert, Matthias). *Schirmer. Unpriced* RJ (B74-51192)
Organists and Masters of the Choristers of St George's Chapel in Windsor Castle. (Fellowes, Edmund Horace). *S.P.C.K. House, Northumberland Ave., W.C.2 : Society for the Promotion of Christian Knowledge for the Dean and Canons of St George's Chapel in Windsor Castle. Unpriced* AR/E(YDEUW) (B74-23496)
Organs of Lichfield Cathedral. (Greening, Richard). *c/o 28 Walsall Rd, Lichfield, Staffs. WS13 8AB : Dean and Chapter of Lichfield. £0.45* AR/B(YDHNLB) (B74-13712) ISBN 0-9503008-1-0
Orgelstücke alter Meister : elektronische Orgel. (Schweizer, Rolf). *Nagel : Bärenreiter. £1.80* RPVK/AAY (B74-50630)
Ornadel, Cyril.
  The Strauss family. (Bailey, Andrew). *Wise : Distributed by Music Sales Ltd. £1.50* QPK/AH (B74-50602)
  Treasure island. Vocal score. Treasure island : a musical adventure. *Sparta Florida Music : Aviva Music. £0.99* CM (B74-50006)
Ornithoparchus, Andreas. Musice active micrologus. A compendium of musical practice. *Dover Publications : Constable. £7.00* A/M(XDS) (B74-11735) ISBN 0-486-20912-1
Osborne, Charles, *b.1927.* The concert song companion : a guide to the classical repertoire. *Gollancz. £4.00* AKDW(XEXK301) (B74-24211) ISBN 0-575-01825-9
Osterling, Eric.
  Adventurous night suite : military band. *Warner Blossom. Unpriced* UMMG (B74-50723)
  Samaria : for concert band. *Chappell. Unpriced* UMJ (B74-51299)
Osterpsalm für gemischten Chor. (Kameke, Ernst Ulrich von). *Bärenreiter. £0.75* EZDR/LL (B74-50408)
Our town : music from the film score. (Copland, Aaron). *Boosey and Hawkes. £6.75* MM/JR (B74-51094)
Out of the depths, based on Psalm 129 (130) : (SATB). (Hughes, Edward). *Campbell, Connelly. Unpriced* DH (B74-50348)
Overture to 'The school for scandal'. (Barber, Samuel). *Schirmer. Unpriced* UMK (B74-50715)
Owen, David. Welcome Yule : SATB unacc. *Oxford University Press. Unpriced* EZDP/LF (B74-50049) ISBN 0-19-343044-4
Owen, Don. Circus overture. (Schuman, William). *Schirmer. Unpriced* UMK (B74-50267)
Owning-up. (Melly, George). *Penguin. £0.35* AKDW/HHW/E(P) (B74-07434) ISBN 0-14-002936-2
Oxford studies of composers. Brown, David, *b.1929.* Wilbye. *Oxford University Press. £1.65* BWNRB (B74-13708) ISBN 0-19-315220-7
Paganelli, Sergio. Musical instruments from the Renaissance to the 19th century. *Hamlyn. £0.50* AL/B(XD401) (B74-20189) ISBN 0-600-31853-2
Page, Andrew. Koanga. Vocal score. Koanga : opera in three acts with prologue and epilogue. (Delius, Frederick). *Boosey and Hawkes. Unpriced* CC (B74-50866)
Paggi, Giovanni. Rimembranze napoletane : for flute with pianoforte accompaniment. *Wye Music : Emerson. Unpriced* VRPJ (B74-51320)
Pahlen, Kurt. Great singers from the seventeenth century to the present day. *W.H. Allen. £4.75* AK/E(M/XM71) (B74-00870) ISBN 0-491-01361-2
Palestrina, Giovanni Pierluigi da.
  Alma redemptoris mater = Loving Mother of our Saviour : motet for four-part chorus of women's voices a cappella. *Schirmer. Unpriced* EZDJ (B74-50950)
  Stabat mater dolorosa : for eight voices. *Chester. Unpriced* EZDGKADD/LK (B74-50942)
Pallandt, Nina, *barones van.* Nina. *Hale. £2.80* AKDW/GB/E(P) (B74-17384) ISBN 0-7091-4586-1
Palmer, Peggy Spencer. This is the day which the Lord hath made: arr. This is the day which the Lord hath made : festival anthem. *Cramer. £0.15* DK (B74-50905)
Palmer, Roy.
  Love is pleasing : songs of courtship and marriage. *Cambridge University Press. £0.50* JE/TSDW/AYD (B74-51030) ISBN 0-521-20445-3
  Poverty knock : a picture of industrial life in the nineteenth century through songs, ballads and contemporary accounts. *Cambridge University Press. £0.80(non-net)* AKDW/K/G(YD/XFZ155) (B74-30366) ISBN 0-521-20443-7
  A touch of the times : songs of social change, 1770 to 1914. *Penguin. £0.80* KE/TSDW/K/G/AYD(XFYK145) (B74-51063) ISBN 0-14-081182-6
Palmieri, Robert. Twenty piano exercises. *Oxford University Press. Unpriced* Q/AF (B74-50559)
Panther rock series. Rock file
  2. *Panther. £0.50* ADW/GB (B74-18933) ISBN 0-586-04087-0
Panufnik, Andrzej.
  Thames pageant : a cantata for young players and singers. *Boosey and Hawkes. £1.50* FE/MDX (B74-50424)
  Universal prayer : for 4 solo voices, 3 harps, organ and mixed chorus. *Boosey and Hawkes. £4.50* ETQNSRDE (B74-50034)
Paraphrase on the dramatic madrigal Il Combattimento de Tancredi e Clorinda by Claudio Monteverdi. Op.28: for clarinet solo. (Goehr, Alexander). *Schott. £.25* VVPMJ (B74-50294)
Parc aux fees. Idylle: arr. Idylle. (Veneux, Thierry). *Chappell. Unpriced* TMK (B74-50693)
Parfrey, Raymond. Trio for oboe, clarinet, bassoon. *Emerson*

Edition. £0.50 VNT (B74-50744)
Park, Phil. La Périchole. Vocal score. La Périchole : operetta in three acts: music. (Offenbach, Jacques). *Weinberger. Unpriced* CF (B74-50332)
Parker, Andrew.
Motectorum quarternis vocibus liber primus. O rex gloriae. O rex gloriae : motet for Ascension Day, SATB unacc. (Marenzio, Luca). *Oxford University Press. £0.08* EZDJ/LM (B74-50404) ISBN 0-19-350343-3
Tomus primus operis musici. Omnes de Saba venient. Omnes de Saba venient : motet for Epiphany, SATTB unacc. (Handl, Jacob). *Oxford University Press. £0.08* EZDJ/LFP (B74-50403) ISBN 0-19-350342-5
Parker, John.
American folk songs : für elektronische Orgel. *Schott. £2.40* RPVK/DW/G/AYT (B74-50209)
Opernmelodien : für elektronische Orgel. *Schott. £2.40* RPVK/DW/AY (B74-50208)
Pop hits 1 : for all electronic organs. *Schott. £2.90* RPVK/DW/GB/AY (B74-50636)
Spirituals für elektronische Orgel. *Schott. £2.40* RPVK/DW/LC/AY (B74-50210)
Die Welt der Orgel : eine Sammlung für alle elektronischen Orgeln. *Schott. £2.40* RPVK/AAY (B74-50207)
Parkinson, John Alfred. Why this haste, O shepherd, say : old French noël. *Oxford University Press. £0.08* EZDP/LF (B74-50965) ISBN 0-19-343047-9
Parlour song book : a casquet of vocal gems. (Turner, Michael R). *Pan Books. £1.75* KDW/GB/AY(XH564) (B74-51058) ISBN 0-330-24113-3
Parnell, Frederick.
Gondoliera : accordion solo. *Charnwood Music. Unpriced* RSPMJ (B74-51210)
Mainly under the fingers : easy accordion solos. *Charnwood Music. Unpriced* RSPMJ (B74-51211)
Tarantelle : accordion solo. *Charnwood Music. Unpriced* RSPMHVS (B74-51206)
Parrott, Ian. Soliloquy and dance : for harp. *Thames. Unpriced* TQPMH (B74-51265)
Parry, William Howard. St Jerome and the lion : a legend for voices, piano and optional recorders and percussion. *Keith Prowse Music. £0.75* JFDE (B74-50089)
Parsley, Osbert. Works, viols. Selections. Three consort pieces : for treble, tenor and bass viols. *Oxford University Press. £0.16* STNS (B74-50689) ISBN 0-19-358105-1
Partita for brass quintet and tape. (Lazarof, Henri). *Associated Music. £1.40* WNRG (B74-50829)
Paseo grande = The big walk : military band. (Sosnik, Harry). *Warner : Blossom. Unpriced* UMMJ (B74-50731)
Past the evening sun : orchestra. (Johnson, Hunter). *Galaxy : Galliard. Unpriced* MMJ (B74-50506)
Pastoral and fugue for two flutes. (Hovhaness, Alan). *Associated Music. Unpriced* VRNU/Y (B74-51316)
Pastorale and allegro : B flat cornet duet. (Heath, Reginald). *R. Smith. Unpriced* WRNTQ (B74-50315)
Pastorale and allegro : B flat cornet duet and brass band. (Heath, Reginald). *R. Smith. Unpriced* WMPWRNU (B74-50313)
Pastorale : for oboe (or B flat clarinet) and piano. (Johnson, Thomas Arnold). *British and Continental Music Agencies. Unpriced* VTPJ (B74-50784)
Patrick Hadley : a memoir. (Todds, Walter). *10e Prior Bolton St., N.1 : Triad Press. £1.75* BHBD(N) (B74-11050) ISBN 0-902070-10-x
Patterns for brass band. (Gregson, Edward). *210 Strand, WC2R 1AP : R. Smith and Co. Ltd. Unpriced* WMJ (B74-50822)
Patterns : for percussion instruments (four or more). (Stahmer, Klaus). *Schott. £2.90* XNS (B74-51374)
Patterson, Paul.
Concerto for horn: arr. Horn concerto. *Weinberger. Unpriced* WTPK/LF (B74-50849)
Gloria : for choir, SATB and piano, with two players, one at the keyboard and the other manipulating the strings. *Weinberger. Unpriced* DE (B74-50874)
Payne, Anthony. Phoenix mass : for mixed chorus, 3 trumpets and 3 trombones. *Chester : Hansen. Unpriced* EWNQDE (B74-50940)
Payne, Mary Monroe. In Bethlehem, that fair city : Christmas carol for mixed chorus unaccompanied. *Oxford University Press. Unpriced* EZDP/LF (B74-50406)
Peanut song : an adaptation of a popular American folksong. (Dexter, Harry). *Ashdown. £0.12* FDW (B74-50418)
Pearton, Maurice. The LSO at 70 : a history of the orchestra. *Gollancz. £3.50* AMM/E(QB/X) (B74-24906) ISBN 0-575-01763-5
Peat, Sylvester. Music on stamps
Part 3: G-L. *Citadel Works, Bath Rd, Chippenham, Wilts. SN15 2AA : Picton Publishing. £0.60* A(ZE) (B74-17382) ISBN 0-902633-20-1
Peellaert, Guy. Rock dreams. *Pan Books. £1.95* ADW/GB/E(M/XPM22/EM) (B74-07429) ISBN 0-330-24008-0
Peer Gynt. *See* Suzuki, Yoshiharu.
Peet, Richard. Stand up for America! : for mixed chorus, SATB. *Chappell. Unpriced* DW (B74-50362)
Pehkonen, Elis. Fafnir and the knights, and other settings of poems by Stevie Smith : for treble voices and piano duet. *Lengnick. £2.00* FLDX (B74-50079)
Pejtsik, Arpád.
Violoncello music (intermediate) : easy concert pieces in the first position. *Boosey and Hawkes : Editio Musica. £1.00* SRPK/AAY (B74-51251)
Pelican books. Kostelanetz, Richard. John Cage. *Allen Lane. £2.00* BCBG (B74-11048) ISBN 0-7139-0762-2
Penderecki, Krzysztof.
Canon for string orchestra. Kanon für Streichorchester. *Schott. £4.06* RXM/X (B74-50639)
Ecloga VIII (Vergili 'Bucolica') : for 6 male voices (1972). *Schott. £2.40* JNGEZAZDX (B74-50095)
Penguin book of Canadian folk songs. (Fowke, Edith). *Penguin. £0.75* JEZDW/G/AYSX (B74-50452) ISBN 0-14-070842-1
Pepusch, Johann Christoph.
Concerto for woodwind & string quartet & basso continuo in B flat major. Op.8, no.3. Concerto in B flat for 2 oboes or violins, 2 violins or oboes and basso continuo. Opus 8, no.3. *Musica rara. Unpriced* NUTNRF (B74-50528)
Concerto for woodwind quartet & basso continuo in G major. Op.8, no.2. Concerto in G for 2 flutes, 2 oboes, violins and basso continuo. Op.8, no.2. *Musica rara. Unpriced* NWPNRF (B74-50546)
Concertos for woodwind quartet & basso continuo. Op.8, nos. 1, 4-6. 4 concerti for 2 treble recorders, 2 flutes, tenor recorders, oboes, violins & basso continuo. Op.8, nos. 1, 4, 5, 6
Opus 8, no.6: in F major. *Musica rara. Unpriced* NWPNRF (B74-50548)
Concertos for woodwind quartet & basso continuo. Op.8, nos. 1, 4-6. 4 concerti for 2 treble recorders, 2 flutes, tenor recorders, oboes, violins & basso continuo. Op.8, nos. 1, 4, 5, 6
Opus 8, no.4 in F major. *Musica rara. Unpriced* NWPNRF (B74-50549)
Concertos for woodwind quartet & basso continuo. Op.8, nos. 1, 4-6. 4 concerti for 2 treble recorders, 2 flutes, tenor recorders, oboes, violins & basso continuo. Op.8, nos. 1,4,5,6
Opus 8, no.1: in B flat major. *Musica rara. Unpriced* NWPNRF (B74-50547)
Concertos for woodwind quartet & basso continuo. Op.8, nos. 1, 4-6. 4 concerti for 2 treble recorders, 2 flutes, tenor recorders, oboes, violins & basso continuo. Op.8, nos. 1,4,5,6
Opus 8, no.5 in C major. *Musica rara. Unpriced* NWPNRF (B74-50550)
Périchole : operetta in three acts: music. (Offenbach, Jacques). *Weinberger. Unpriced* CF (B74-50332)
Periodical overture, no.17, in E flat major. Symphony in E flat major, Periodical overture 17 : for flutes, clarinets/oboes, bassoon, horns, strings and continuo. (Erskine, Thomas, *Earl of Kelly*). *Oxford University Press. £2.75* MRE (B74-50518) ISBN 0-19-365170-x
Periodicals:, *New periodicals and those issued with changed titles.*
Donizetti Society. The Journal of the Donizetti Society
Issue no.1-. *The Secretary, 56 Harbut Rd, SW11 2RB : The Society. £2.50* BDR(B) (B74-13107) ISBN 0-9503333-0-1
The English Harpsichord Magazine, and early keyboard instrument review
Vol.1, no.2- ; Apr. 1974-. *Rose Cottage, Bois La., Chesham Bois, Amersham, Bucks. HP6 6BP : Edgar Hunt. £0.55* APW(B) (B74-12390)
The Harpsichord Magazine, and early keyboard instrument review
Vol.1, no.1; Oct. 1973. *Rose Cottage, Bois La., Chesham Bois, Amersham, Bucks. HP6 6BP : Edgar Hunt. £0.50* APW(B) (B74-12391)
Music & Man : an interdisciplinary journal of studies on music
Vol.1, no.1- ; 1973-. *Gordon and Breach. £3.50 (yearly) (£10.15 yearly to libraries and institutions)* A(B) (B74-14306)
Sandy Bell's Broadsheet
Issue no.1- ; Aug. 20, 1973-. *Forrest Hill Bar, Forrest Rd, Edinburgh : John Barrow. £0.03* A/G(YDL/B) (B74-16726)
Pert, Morris. Missa festiva. Vocal score. Missa festiva : for two-part choir, (upper voices), and orchestra. *Oxford University Press. £0.60* FDE (B74-50066) ISBN 0-19-337830-2
Perti, Giacomo Antonio. Adoramus te = We adore thee : motet for four-part chorus of mixed voices a cappella. *Schirmer. Unpriced* EZDJ (B74-50951)
Peter, Johann Friedrich. Lobe den Herrn meine Seele: arr. Praise the Lord, O my soul = Lobe den Herrn meine Seele : S.A.T.B. with accompaniment. Moramus ed. *Boosey and Hawkes. Unpriced* DH (B74-50349)
Peter Warlock handbook
Vol.1. (Tomlinson, Fred). *10e Prior Bolton St., N.1 : Triad Press. £2.75* BWKH(TC) (B74-21168) ISBN 0-902070-11-8
Petit prelude. Aria : organ. (Jongen, Joseph). *Oxford University Press. £0.35* RJ (B74-50619) ISBN 0-19-375495-9
Petite musique de chambre. Partita 1. *selections.* Suite no.2. (Telemann, Georg Philipp). *Boosey and Hawkes. £0.65* WSPJ (B74-50835)
Petite musique de chambre. Partitas 4, 5. *selections.* Suite no.1 : arranged for trumpet in B flat and piano from the music of G.P. Telemann. (Telemann, Georg Philipp). *Boosey and Hawkes. £0.65* WSPJ (B74-50836)
Petrich, Roger. O wondrous type! : anthem for the Feast of the Transfiguration, SATB choir unaccompanied. *Oxford University Press. Unpriced* EZDH (B74-50945)
Petrucci, Ottaviano dei. Harmonice musices odhecaton. Selections. Ten pieces from 'Harmonice musices odhecaton'. *Associated Music. Unpriced* VSNSK/DU/AY (B74-50280)
Petzoldt, Richard. Georg Philipp Telemann. *E. Benn. £3.25* BTE (B74-26608) ISBN 0-510-35905-1
Peuerl, Paul. Weltspiegel. *O Musika du edle Kunst.* O Musica, thou noble art : for five-part chorus of mixed voices a cappella. *Roberton. £0.10* EZDW (B74-50060)
Philipp, Gunter. Studies for piano. Op.8. 12 studies for piano. Op.8. (Skriabin, Aleksandr Nikolaevich). *Peters. Unpriced* QPJ (B74-51180)
Phillips, Gordon. Works, organ. Selections. Selected organ works. (Walmisley, Thomas Attwood). *Peters. Unpriced* RJ (B74-50624)
Phillips, Peter.
Madrigali a cinque voci, libro sesto. Moro lasso : arr. Moro lasso. (Gesualdo, Carlo, *Prince of Venosa*). *Oxford University Press. Unpriced* UMK/DU (B74-51302)
Sonata for harpsichord in C major. L.164: arr. Sonata. (Scarlatti, Domenico). *Oxford University Press. Unpriced* UMK/AE (B74-50720)
Philosophy of modern music. (Adorno, Theodor Wiesengrund). *Sheed and Ward. £4.50* BSET (B74-09866) ISBN 0-7220-7339-9
Phoenix mass : for mixed chorus, 3 trumpets and 3 trombones. (Payne, Anthony). *Chester : Hansen. Unpriced* EWNQDE (B74-50940)
Phonogram Limited. Phonogram complete alphabetical and numerical catalogue
1974 : containing full details of all long playing 33 1/3 rpm records, musicassettes, and 8-track cartridges issued up to and including December 1973. *Stanhope House, Stanhope Place, W2 2HH : Phonogram Ltd. £5.00* A/FD(WM) (B74-12650) ISBN 0-904400-00-x
P.I. Tchaikovsky's 'Swan Lake'. (Hatsuyama, Shigeru). *F. Warne. £1.75* BTDAM/HMBN (B74-26150) ISBN 0-7232-1759-9
P.I. Tchaikovsky's 'The nutcracker'. (Hori, Fumiko). *F. Warne. £1.75* BTDAM/HMBN (B74-26151) ISBN 0-7232-1760-2
Pia memoria : requiem for nine brass instruments and optional chimes. Op.65. (Nystedt, Knut). *Associated Music Publishers. £4.20* WNM (B74-50827)
Piano Panel. The concert piano in Scotland : a report to the Scottish Arts Council. *19 Charlotte Sq., Edinburgh EH2 4DF : Scottish Arts Council. £0.25* AQ(W/YDL) (B74-09233) ISBN 0-902989-13-8
Piano pieces. (Skempton, Howard). *Faber Music. Unpriced* QPJ (B74-50184)
Piano rags. (Joplin, Scott). *Novello. £0.55* QPHXJ (B74-50580)
Picador. Cott, Jonathan. Stockhausen : conversations with the composer. *Pan Books. £0.95* BSNK (B74-27248) ISBN 0-330-24165-6
Picht-Axenfeld, Edith.
Das wohltemperirte Clavier, Tl.1. Prelude and fugue, no.5. S.850. Praeludium V und Fuga V : Klavier (Cembalo). (Bach, Johann Sebastian). *Schott. £0.60* PWP/Y (B74-50554)
Das wohltemperirte Clavier, Tl.1. Prelude and fugue, no.6. S.851. Praeludium VI und Fuga VI : Klavier (Cembalo). (Bach, Johann Sebastian). *Schott. £0.60* PWP/Y (B74-50555)
Das wohltemperirte Clavier, Tl.1. Prelude and fugue, no.16. S.861. Praeludium XVI and Fuga XVI : Klavier (Cembalo). (Bach, Johann Sebastian). *Schott. £0.60* PWP/Y (B74-50556)
Das wohltemperirte Clavier, Tl.2. Prelude and fugue, no.2. S.871. Praeludium II and Fuga II : Klavier (Cembalo). (Bach, Johann Sebastian). *Schott. £0.60* PWP/Y (B74-50557)
Pick, Karl-Heinz. Kleine Marchensuite : für Klavier. *Peters. Unpriced* QPG (B74-51150)
Picket, Frederick. Aleynu l'shabench : a new Friday evening service, cantor solo with mixed chorus, SATB and organ, commissioned by the Anshe Emet Synagogue, Chicago, Illinois, on the occasion of the hundredth jubilee year (1873-1973)
9: Shiru ladonai shir chadash. *Ethnic Music : Phoenix. Unpriced* DGU (B74-50892)
Pierpont, J. Jingle bells : traditional. *Keith Prowse. Unpriced* WMK/DW/LF (B74-51361)
Piggott, Patrick. Rachmaninov orchestral music. *British Broadcasting Corporation. £0.45* BRCAM (B74-14309) ISBN 0-563-12468-7
Pigs : a present for Gordon Jacob, for four bassoons. (Ridout, Alan). *Emerson. Unpriced* VWNS (B74-50296)
Pilinszky, Janos. In memoriam N.N : cantata. (Lang, Istvan). *Boosey and Hawkes. £2.50* EMDX (B74-50030)
Pine apple rag : piano. (Joplin, Scott). *Chappell. Unpriced* QPHXJ (B74-50581)
Pinturas negras : concierto para organo y orquesta (1972). (Halffter, Cristóbal). *Universal. Unpriced* MPRF (B74-51108)
Piston, Walter.
Quartet for violin, viola, cello and piano. *Associated Music. Unpriced* NXNS (B74-51119)
Trio for violin, cello and piano. *Associated Music. Unpriced* NXNT (B74-51120)
Pitfield, Thomas Baron. Sonatina for double bass and piano. *Yorke. Unpriced* SSPE (B74-50686)
Pity me not : SATB a cappella. (Calder, Robert). *Associated Music. Unpriced* EZDW (B74-50058)
Plain man's guide to jazz. (Postgate, John). *61 Berners St., W1P 3AE : Hanover Books Ltd. £1.50* AMT(X) (B74-13710) ISBN 0-900994-05-3
Plaisir d'amour. (Martini, Giovanni). *Boosey and Hawkes. Unpriced* DW (B74-50359)
Plaisir d'amour: arr. Plaisir d'amour. (Martini, Giovanni). *Boosey and Hawkes. Unpriced* DW (B74-50359)
Planets. Jupiter. *Selections: arr.* Joybringer : song based on 'Jupiter' by Gustav Holst. (Holst, Gustav). *Feldman.*

£0.25 KDW (B74-50459)

Plath, Sylvia. Ariel : five poems of Sylvia Plath, for soprano clarinet and piano. (Rorem, Ned). *Boosey and Hawkes. £3.00* KFLE/VVPDW (B74-50115)

Plath, Wolfgang.

Divertimenti for violin & keyboard, nos 1-6. 6 divertimenti da camera for harpsichord (piano) and violin 1: Divertimenti I and II. (Schuster, Joseph). *Nagel : Bärenreiter. £3.45* SPJ (B74-50672)

Divertimenti for violin & keyboard, nos 1-6. 6 divertimenti da camera for harpsichord (piano) and violin 2: Divertimenti III and IV. (Schuster, Joseph). *Nagel : Bärenreiter. £2.55* SPJ (B74-50673)

Divertimenti for violin & keyboard, nos 1-6. 6 divertimenti da camera for harpsichord (piano) and violin 3: Divertimenti V and VI. (Schuster, Joseph). *Nagel : Bärenreiter. £2.55* SPJ (B74-50674)

Platt, Richard.

Overture no.5 in D major. (Greene, Maurice). *Eulenburg. £1.50* MRJ (B74-50149)

Overture no.6 in E flat major. (Greene, Maurice). *Eulenburg. £1.50* MRJ (B74-50150)

Suite, Love and honour : for strings and continuo. (Morgan, Thomas). *Oxford University Press. £1.75* RXMG (B74-50641) ISBN 0-19-357824-7

Symphony in G minor. Opus 6, no.6. Symphony, G minor. Op. 6, no.6. (Bach, Johann Christian). *Eulenburg. £0.80* MRE (B74-50147)

Symphony no.5 in A major. Symphony 5 in A major : for horns and strings. (Wesley, Samuel). *Oxford University Press. Score £3.50, parts unpriced* MRE (B74-50519) ISBN 0-19-368650-3

Platts, Kenneth.

Musick's empire. Op.9. Vocal score. Musick's empire. Opus 9 : for SATB, piano and optional strings. *Ashdown. £0.15* DW (B74-50909)

Prelude and scherzo for small orchestra. Op.7. *Keith Prowse. £0.50* MJ (B74-50131)

Three bird songs : for treble voices, piano and percussion. *Ashdown. £0.30* JFLE/NYLDW (B74-51042)

Play time : Longman first recorder course. (Fagan, Margo). *Longman. £0.70* VS/AC (B74-51327) ISBN 0-582-18539-4

Play time : Longman first recorder course Stage 3. (Fagan, Margo). *Longman. £0.30* VS/AC (B74-50274) ISBN 0-582-18538-6

Play together : for voice and guitar. (Ashlund, Ulf Goran). *Oxford University Press. £0.65* KE/TSNDW/AY (B74-50482) ISBN 0-19-322212-4

Pleasants, Henry. The great American popular singers. *Gollancz. £3.75* AKDW/GB/E(M/YT/XN54) (B74-28316) ISBN 0-575-01774-0

Pleasure it is : for unaccompanied mixed chorus. (Kechley, Gerald). *Galaxy : Galliard. Unpriced* EZDP (B74-50958)

Pleasure of your company : song. (Previn, André). *Chappell. Unpriced* KDW (B74-50465)

Pleyel, Ignaz.

Concerto for bassoon in B flat: arr. Concerto in B flat for bassoon and orchestra. *Musica rara. Unpriced* VWPK/LF (B74-50813)

Sinfonia concertante for flute, oboe, horn, bassoon, no.5, in F major: arr. Symphonie concertante no.5 in F major : for flute, oboe (clarinet), horn, bassoon and orchestra. *Musica rara. Unpriced* MPUNSE (B74-50516)

Plumes of time : 4 songs for medium voice and piano. (Hamilton, Alasdair). *Roberton. £0.50* KFVDW (B74-50117)

Plumstead, Mary. Slowly : three-part women's voices and piano. *Boosey and Hawkes. Unpriced* FDW (B74-50421)

Pocohontas : orchestral suite from the ballet. (Carter, Elliott). *Associated Music. Unpriced* MMG/HM (B74-50138)

Poem in October : for voice and orchestra. (Corigliano, John). *Schirmer. Unpriced* KDX (B74-51059)

Poem in October. Vocal score. Poem in October : for voice and orchestra. (Corigliano, John). *Schirmer. Unpriced* KDX (B74-51059)

Pommer, Max. Le Carnival des animaux : grande fantasie zoologique. (Saint-Saëns, Camille). *Peters. Unpriced* MMJ (B74-51104)

Pop generation : to-day's singers and their songs for to-day's people. *EMI. Unpriced* KDW/GB/AY (B74-51057)

Pop hits 1 : for all electronic organs. (Parker, John). *Schott. £2.90* RPVK/DW/GB/AY (B74-50636)

Pop-pourri : for soprano, rock group, chorus (SATB) and orchestra. (Tredici, David del). *Boosey and Hawkes. Unpriced* EMDX (B74-50934)

Pope, Alexander. Universal prayer : for 4 solo voices, 3 harps, organ and mixed chorus. (Panufnik, Andrzej). *Boosey and Hawkes. £4.50* ETQNSRDE (B74-50034)

Pope, Roger Hugh. Impressions : piano solos. *196 Grays Inn Rd WC1X 8EW : Warren and Phillips. Unpriced* QPJ (B74-51179)

Popinella : arr. Popinella. (Astor, Bob). *Chappell. Unpriced* TMK (B74-51259)

Popinella. (Astor, Bob). *Chappell. Unpriced* TMK (B74-51259)

Popplewell, Richard.

Suite for organ. *Oxford University Press. £1.10* RG (B74-50618) ISBN 0-19-375658-7

There is no rose : solo voice and SSAATTBB unacc. *Banks. Unpriced* EZDP/LF (B74-50966)

Pops Foster - the autobiography of a New Orleans jazzman. (Foster, Pops). *University of California Press. £1.65* AMT(P) (B74-03506) ISBN 0-520-02355-2

Porter, Andrew. A musical season : an English critic in New York. *Gollancz. £4.00* A/E(YTF/XQM2) (B74-30189) ISBN 0-575-01950-6

Porter, Cole. Songs from Cole : an entertainment. *Chappell. Unpriced* KDW (B74-51051)

Portrait of Hitch : a musical portrait of Alfred Hitchcock, for orchestra. (Herrmann, Bernard). *Novello. Unpriced* MMJ (B74-51102)

Postgate, John. A plain man's guide to jazz. *61 Berners St., W1P 3AE : Hanover Books Ltd. £1.50* AMT(X) (B74-13710) ISBN 0-900994-05-3

Potpourri for clarinet & piano. Op.80. (Spohr, Louis). *Musica rara. Unpriced* VVPJ (B74-50802)

Poulton, Diana. The collected lute music of John Dowland. (Dowland, John). *Faber Music in association with Faber and Faber. Unpriced* TW/AZ (B74-51286) ISBN 0-571-10010-4

Poverty knock : a picture of industrial life in the nineteenth century through songs, ballads and contemporary accounts. (Palmer, Roy). *Cambridge University Press. £0.80(non-net)* AKDW/K/G(YD/XFZ155) (B74-30366) ISBN 0-521-20443-7

Powell, Maurice F. Potpourri for clarinet & piano. Op.80. (Spohr, Louis). *Musica rara. Unpriced* VVPJ (B74-50802)

Power, Leonel. Gloria : TTTBB. *Oxford University Press. Unpriced* GEZDGC (B74-50080) ISBN 0-19-341209-8

Praeludium, Basso ostinato. Op.7, and Doppelfuge zum Choral. Op.76. (Busoni, Ferruccio Benvenuto). *Cranz. £0.60* R/Y (B74-50614)

Praeludium II and Fuga II : Klavier (Cembalo). (Bach, Johann Sebastian). *Schott. £0.60* PWP/Y (B74-50557)

Praeludium V und Fuga V : Klavier (Cembalo). (Bach, Johann Sebastian). *Schott. £0.60* PWP/Y (B74-50554)

Praeludium VI und Fuga VI : Klavier (Cembalo). (Bach, Johann Sebastian). *Schott. £0.60* PWP/Y (B74-50555)

Praeludium XVI and Fuga XVI : Klavier (Cembalo). (Bach, Johann Sebastian). *Schott. £0.60* PWP/Y (B74-50556)

Prairie journal : for orchestra. (Copland, Aaron). *Boosey and Hawkes. £15.00* MMJ (B74-51101)

Praise the Lord, O my soul = Lobe den Herrn meine Seele : S.A.T.B. with accompaniment. (Peter, Johann Friedrich). Moramus ed. *Boosey and Hawkes. Unpriced* DH (B74-50349)

Praise to the Lord : hymn-anthem for four-part chorus of mixed voices with organ or piano accompaniment, melody 'Lobe den Herrn' from Stralsund Gesangbuch. (Newbury, Kent A). *Schirmer. Unpriced* DH (B74-50014)

Praise with instruments

Volume 1. (Reynolds, Gordon). *Novello. £0.75* LN/L (B74-50122)

Pratt, George. Four anthems : unison. *Royal School of Church Music. £0.32* JDH (B74-51018)

Prayer : anthem for SATB and organ. (Wills, Arthur). *Novello. £0.12* DH (B74-50903)

Prayers : for voice and guitar. (Surinach, Carlos). *Associated Music Publishers. £0.70* KE/TSDW (B74-50480)

Prediger Salomo 12, 1-9 : Solokantate für tiefe Singstimme, Flöte und Klavier (oder Orgel). (Reitter, Hermann). *Schott. £2.32* KFXE/VRPDE (B74-50488)

Preliminary band book. (Johnson, Stuart). *210 Strand, WC2R 1AP : R. Smith and Co. Ltd. Unpriced* WMJ (B74-50823)

Prelude and scherzo for small orchestra. Op.7. (Platts, Kenneth). *Keith Prowse. £0.50* MJ (B74-50131)

Prelude et final : pour deux clarinettes (en si bemol). (Vallier, Jacques). *Chappell. Unpriced* VVNU (B74-51341)

Prelude, fugue & allegro for organ in D major. S.998: arr. Prelude, fugue and allegro. BWV 998. (Bach, Johann Sebastian). *Oxford University Press. £0.60* TSPMK (B74-50708) ISBN 0-19-355303-1

Premier livre d'orgue. *Selections.* Magnificat du 3e et 4e ton : for organ. (Corrette, Michel). *Novello. Unpriced* RDFF (B74-50617)

Premiere film music : piano - vocal

Vol.1. *Chappell. Unpriced* QPK/DW/JR/AY (B74-50192)

Vol.2. *Chappell. Unpriced* QPK/DW/JR/AY (B74-50193)

Prentice-Hall history of music series.

Hitchcock, Hugh Wiley. Music in the United States : a historical introduction. 2nd ed. *Prentice-Hall. £3.65* A(YT/X) (B74-28313) ISBN 0-13-608398-6

Nettl, Bruno. Folk and traditional music of the Western continents. 2nd ed. *Prentice-Hall. £4.70* A/G (B74-16181) ISBN 0-13-322941-6

Salzman, Eric. Twentieth-century music : an introduction. 2nd ed. *Prentice-Hall. £4.70* A(XM71) (B74-24208) ISBN 0-13-935015-2

Preschool priorities. (Midwinter, Eric). *Ward Lock. £0.85* BREAQ (B74-12162) ISBN 0-7062-3383-2

Prevaux, Blandine Ollivier de. Technische Studien. *Selections.* The Liszt studies : essential selections from the technical studies for the piano, including the first English edition of the legendary Liszt Pedagogue, a lesson-diary of the master as teacher as kept by Mme August Boisser, 1831-2. (Liszt, Franz). *Associated Music. Unpriced* Q/AF (B74-50558)

Previn, André.

Concerto for guitar: arr. Concerto for guitar and orchestra. *Schirmer. Unpriced* TSPMK/LF (B74-51285)

The good companions. Good companions: arr. Good companions : song. *Chappell. Unpriced* KDW (B74-50462)

The good companions. *Selections: arr.* The good companions. *Chappell. Unpriced* KDW (B74-51052)

Good companions. Slippin' around the corner. Slippin' around the corner. *Chappell. Unpriced* DW (B74-50363)

Good companions. Stage struck. Stage struck : song. *Chappell. Unpriced* DW (B74-50364)

The good companions. Ta luv: arr. Ta luv : song. *Chappell. Unpriced* KDW (B74-50463)

The good companions. The dance of life: arr. The dance of life : song. *Chappell. Unpriced* KDW (B74-50464)

The good companions. The pleasure of your company: arr. The pleasure of your company : song. *Chappell. Unpriced* KDW (B74-50465)

The invisible drummer : five preludes for piano. *Boosey and Hawkes. £1.50* QPHX (B74-51151)

Price, Beryl. On the go : six sketches for piano. *Oxford University Press. £0.40* QPJ (B74-50181) ISBN 0-19-373534-2

Price, Milburn. I sing of a Maiden : arr. I sing of a Maiden. (Shaw, Martin). *Oxford University Press. Unpriced* EZDP/LF (B74-50967)

Procesional : para dos pianos solistas y orquesta. (Halffter, Cristóbal). *Universal. Unpriced* MPQNU (B74-51107)

Procter-Gregg, Humphrey. Sir Thomas Beecham, conductor and impresario, as remembered by his friends and colleagues. *3 Oakland, Windermere, Cumbria : H. Procter-Gregg. £3.50* A/EC(P) (B74-23498) ISBN 0-9503649-0-8

Prologue and dance : for orchestra. (Washburn, Robert). *Oxford University Press. Unpriced* MMH (B74-50500)

Proms. (Orga, Ateş). *David and Charles. £3.95* A(YDB/W) (B74-24907) ISBN 0-7153-6679-3

Proof of Plain Bob Major. (Chant, Harold). *c/o 'Monsal', Bredon, Tewkesbury, Glos. GL20 7LY : Central Council of Church Bell Ringers, Education Committee. Unpriced* XSR (B74-50859)

Prostakoff, Joseph.

Csardas. Selections. Two csardas for piano. (Liszt, Franz). *Schirmer. Unpriced* QPHJP (B74-50171)

Works, piano. Selections. Miniatures for piano. (Liszt, Franz). *Schirmer. Unpriced* QPJ (B74-50180)

Proverbs : for SATB and organ. (Stoker, Richard). *Ashdown. £0.15* DK (B74-50906)

Proverbs. Vocal score. Proverbs : for SATB and organ. (Stoker, Richard). *Ashdown. £0.15* DK (B74-50906)

Psalm 31 : for four-part chorus of mixed voices a cappella. (Waters, James). *Schirmer. Unpriced* EZDR (B74-50971)

Psalm 143 : full chorus of mixed voices a cappella, SAATTB. (Wyner, Yehudi). *Associated Music. Unpriced* EZDR (B74-50051)

Psalms and early songs. (Wyner, Yehudi). *Associated Music. Unpriced* KDH (B74-50097)

Psalms for today. (Chappell, Herbert). *Chappell. Unpriced* JDR (B74-50445)

Publius Vergilius Maro. *See* Virgil.

Pulkingham, Betty. Sound of living waters : songs of revival. *Hodder and Stoughton. Unpriced* DM/AY (B74-50908) ISBN 0-340-18893-6

Pulkingham, Betty Carr. Songs of fellowship. *The Fishermen Inc., by arrangement with the Fountanin Trust. Unpriced* JE/TSDM/AY (B74-50087)

Purcell, Henry.

King Arthur. *Selections: arr.* Music from 'King Arthur'. *Paxton. £0.40* RK/JM (B74-50628)

The married beau. *Selections: arr.* Wedding march. *Paxton. £0.35* RK/KDD (B74-51203)

The mock marriage. Man is for the woman made: arr. Man is for the woman made. *Boosey and Hawkes. Unpriced* DW (B74-50365)

Suite for strings, no.3, from Musick's Handmaid. Third suite for strings, from Musick's Handmaid. (Cruft, Adrian). *Chappell. Unpriced* RXMG (B74-50217)

Purslow, Frank. The foggy dew : more English folk songs from the Hammond Gardiner Mss. *E.F.D.S. £0.90* KEZDW/G/AYD (B74-50113)

Quand la chance est là. This old world = Quand la chance est là : for SATB chorus accompanied. (Brejean, Philippe). *Chappell. Unpriced* DW (B74-50358)

Quantz, Johann Joachim.

Concerto for flute & string orchestra in D minor. Concerto in D minor for flute, strings and continuo. *Musica rara. Unpriced* RXMPVRF (B74-50649)

Concerto for flute & string orchestra in D minor: arr. Concerto in D minor for flute, strings and continuo. *Musica rara. Unpriced* VRPK/LF (B74-50760)

Concerto for two flutes, no.1, in G minor: arr. Concerto no.1 in G minor for 2 flutes and orchestra. *Musica rara. Unpriced* VRNTQK/LF (B74-50746)

Quem vidistis, pastores = Whom did you see, kind shepherds? : Motet for Christmas time, for six-part chorus of mixed voices a cappella. (Victoria, Tomàs Luis de). *Chappell. Unpriced* EZDJ/LF (B74-50402)

Quine, Hector.

Christopher Columbus. Beatriz's song: arr. Beatriz's song. (Walton, *Sir* William). *Oxford University Press. £0.35* KE/TSDW/JM (B74-50481) ISBN 0-19-345866-7

Divertimento for guitar, no.1. Op.1. First set of divertimenti. Op.1. (Sor, Fernando). *Oxford University Press. £0.50* TSPMJ (B74-50702) ISBN 0-19-358863-3

Divertimento for guitar, no.2. Op.2. Second set of divertimenti. Op.2. (Sor, Fernando). *Oxford University Press. £0.50* TSPMJ (B74-50703) ISBN 0-19-358864-1

Divertimento for guitar, no.3. Op.8. Third set of divertimenti. Op.8. (Sor, Fernando). *Oxford Universtion Press. £0.50* TSPMJ (B74-50704) ISBN 0-19-358865-x

Fantasia for guitar, no.1, in C major. Op.7. Fantasia no.1, Op.7. (Sor, Fernando). *Oxford University Press. £0.50* TSPMJ (B74-50705) ISBN 0-19-358860-9

Fantasia for guitar, no.2, in A major. Op.4. Fantasia no.2. Op.4. (Sor, Fernando). *Oxford University Press. £0.40* TSPMJ (B74-50706) ISBN 0-19-358861-7

Fantasia for guitar, no.3, in F major. Op.10. Fantasia no.3,

Op.10. (Sor, Fernando). *Oxford University Press. Unpriced* TSPMJ (B74-50707) ISBN 0-19-358862-5
Prelude, fugue & allegro for organ in D major. S.998: arr. Prelude, fugue and allegro. BWV 998. (Bach, Johann Sebastian). *Oxford University Press. £0.60* TSPMK (B74-50708) ISBN 0-19-355303-1
Selections: arr. Two pieces for solo guitar : by C.P.E. Bach. (Bach, Carl Philipp Emanuel). *Oxford University Press. Unpriced* TSPMK (B74-51277) ISBN 0-19-355299-x
Quintet for clarinet and string quartet. (Lefanu, Nicola). *Novello. £1.50* NVVNR (B74-50154)
Quoist, Michel. Prayers : for voice and guitar. (Surinach, Carlos). *Associated Music Publishers. £0.70* KE/TSDW (B74-50480)
Quoniam ad te clamabo, Domine = Now behold to thee I cry, O Lord : motet for four-part chorus of mixed voices a cappella. (Schütz, Heinrich). *Chappell. Unpriced* EZDJ (B74-50399)
Rachmaninoff, Sergei.
The isle of the dead. Op. 29 : symphonic poem. *Boosey and Hawkes. £1.25* MMJ (B74-50141)
Songs. Collections. Songs with piano accompaniment Volume 1. *Boosey and Hawkes. £4.00* KDW/AZ (B74-50100)
Songs. Collections. Songs with piano accompaniment Volume 2. *Boosey and Hawkes. £4.00* KDW/AZ (B74-50101)
Rachmaninov. (McCabe, John). *Novello. £0.20* BRC(N) (B74-25491) ISBN 0-85360-059-7
Rachmaninov orchestral music. (Piggott, Patrick). *British Broadcasting Corporation. £0.45* BRCAM (B74-14309) ISBN 0-563-12468-7
Radecke, Winfried. Sonata for treble recorder & basso continuo in D minor. Sonate d-Moll, für Altblockflöte und Basso continuo. (Vivaldi, Antonio). *Schott. £1.08* VSSPE (B74-50288)
Ragossnig, Konrad.
Suite espagnole. Sevilla. Granada Serenata : für Gitarre. (Albeniz, Isaac). *Schott. £0.72* TSPMK (B74-50257)
Suite espagnole. *Sevilla.* Sevilla a Sevillanas. (Albeniz, Isaac). *Schott. £0.96* TSPMK (B74-50258)
Rakhmaninov, Sergei. *See* Rachmaninoff, Sergei.
Rakhmaniov, Sergei. *See* Rachmaninoff, Sergei.
Ramsbotham, A. Liber primus sacrarum cantionum. Vigilate. Vigilate = Be ye watchful : motet for five voices S.A.T.Ba.B. (Byrd, William). *Oxford University Press. £0.20* EZDJ (B74-50395) ISBN 0-19-352056-7
Randall, Alan. George Formby complete. (Formby, George). *Wise. Unpriced* KDW/AY (B74-50099)
Rands, Bernard. Metalepsis Z : cantata for mezzo-soprano solo, SATB and orchestral accompaniment. *Universal. Unpriced* EMDX (B74-50377)
Rankine, Andrew. Two Scottish country dances. *42 Whinfell Rd, Darras Hall, Ponteland, Newcastle : Royal Scottish Country Dance Society (Newcastle and District Branch). £0.125* QPH/H/AYDL (B74-50578)
Raoul, Jean Marie. Méthode de violoncelle. Op.4. Leçons et exercises, nos.10-18. Nine studies : for two cellos. *Oxford University Press. £0.55* SRNU (B74-50680) ISBN 0-19-358480-8
Ratcliffe, Desmond.
Eight for Christmas : French carols with English words. *Novello. Unpriced* EZDP/LF/AYH (B74-50970)
King Arthur. *Selections: arr.* Music from 'King Arthur'. (Purcell, Henry). *Paxton. £0.40* RK/JM (B74-50628)
Ratcliffe, Ronald V. From classical to romantic keyboard music. *Open University Press. Unpriced* AQ/B/E(XA1849) (B74-23499) ISBN 0-335-00864-x
Raven, Jon. Turpin hero : 30 folk songs for voices and guitar. *Oxford University Press. £1.60* JFDW/G/AY (B74-51037) ISBN 0-19-330626-3
Read, Gardner. Music notation : a manual of modern practice. 2nd ed. *Gollancz. £3.50* A(QU) (B74-08076) ISBN 0-575-01758-9
Real sailor songs. (Ashton, John, *b.1834*). 1st ed. reprinted. *15 Mortimer Terrace, N.W.5 : Broadsheet King. Unpriced* ADW/KC(YD) (B74-02415) ISBN 0-902617-10-9
Recitativarie : für singende Cembalistin, 1971/72. (Kagel, Mauricio). *Universal. Unpriced* KHYE/QRP (B74-51079)
Recopilacion de sonetos y villancicos. *En la fuente del rosel.* En la fuente del rosel = 'Neath the rosebush in the stream : for four-part chorus of mixed voices a cappella. (Vasquez, Juan). *Roberton. £0.10* EZDU (B74-50055)
Recorder for the first school. (Dedicott, W). *Stockwell. £0.33* VSR/AC (B74-50769) ISBN 0-7223-0560-5
Red Arrows march. (Banks, Eric). *Affiliated Music. £1.00* WMK/AGM (B74-50311)
Red clouds : 12 folk songs from Austria, Switzerland and Tirol, for violin (or recorder or flute) and piano, with optional cello. (Alt, Hansi). *Oxford University Press. Unpriced* SPK/DW/G/AYEM (B74-51246)
Rees, Ifor. Ten Welsh folk-songs for juniors. (Lewis, Esme). *University of Wales Press. £0.50* JFE/NYJDW/G/AYDK (B74-50092)
Reese, Gustave. Musice active micrologus. A compendium of musical practice. (Ornithoparchus, Andreas). *Dover Publications : Constable. £7.00* A/M(XDS) (B74-11735) ISBN 0-486-20912-1
Reeves, James. Slowly : three-part women's voices and piano. (Plumstead, Mary). *Boosey and Hawkes. Unpriced* FDW (B74-50421)
Reger, Max. Suite for violin & piano in F major. Op.93, 'in olden style'. Suite im alten Stil für Violine und Klavier. Opus 93,. *Peters. Unpriced* SPG (B74-51242)
Regimental quick march, The Queen's Lancashire Regiment, 'The attack', 'The red rose'. (Gibson, John). *Boosey and Hawkes. £1.00* UMMGM/KH (B74-51306)
Regimental quick march, 'The Royal Highland Fusiliers'. (Brush, J A). *Boosey and Hawkes. £0.65* UMMGM/KH (B74-50727)
Regimental quick march 'The Royal Irish Rangers'. (Clark, M E). *Boosey and Hawkes. £0.65* UMMGM/KH (B74-50728)
Reid, Ron. Tomorrow's people. (Sandford, Jeremy). *47 Catherine Place, S.W.1 : Jerome Publishing Co. Ltd. £1.95* A/GB(WE/YC) (B74-14305) ISBN 0-904125-05-x
Reifliches Divertimento. Op. 35a : Variationen über Thema aus dem 3. Bild der Oper 'Der Besuch der alten dame'. (Einem, Gottfried von). *Boosey and Hawkes. £1.50* NUXTNS/T (B74-50152)
Reimann, Aribert.
Nocturnos für Violoncello und Harfe (1965). *Schott. £1.92* SRPLTQ (B74-50251)
Spektren für Klavier (1967). *Ars Viva. £1.92* QPJ (B74-50182)
Reimer, Bennett. The experience of music. *Prentice-Hall. £6.00* A/C (B74-16180) ISBN 0-13-294553-3
Reisner, Robert George. Bird - the legend of Charlie Parker. *Quartet Books. £3.95* AMT(P) (B74-27252) ISBN 0-7043-2063-0
Reitter, Hermann. Prediger Salomo 12, 1-9 : Solokantate für tiefe Singstimme, Flöte und Klavier (oder Orgel). *Schott. £2.32* KFXE/VRPDE (B74-50488)
Remembering Bix : a memoir of the jazz age. (Berton, Ralph). *W.H. Allen. £4.95* 788.10924 (B74-27250) ISBN 0-491-01951-3
Renard, J. C'est ça la France: arr. C'est ça la France. *Chappell. Unpriced* UMK (B74-50719)
Resources of music. Palmer, Roy. Poverty knock : a picture of industrial life in the nineteenth century through songs, ballads and contemporary accounts. *Cambridge University Press. £0.80(non-net)* AKDW/K/G(YD/XFZ155) (B74-30366) ISBN 0-521-20443-7
Responsoria hebdomadae sanctae. Caligaverunt oculi mei. Caligaverunt oculi mei = My eyes are blinded by my weeping : Lenten motet for four-part chorus of mixed voices a cappella. (Ingegneri, Marco Antonio). *Schirmer. Unpriced* FEZDGKH/LHL (B74-50073)
Reutter, Hermann. Sonata monotematica : für Violoncello (oder Fagott) und Klavier. *Schott. £1.92* SRPE (B74-50247)
Rêverie. (Debussy, Claude). *Ashdown. £0.30* VRPK (B74-50272)
Reynolds, Gordon. Praise with instruments
Volume 1. *Novello. £0.75* LN/L (B74-50122)
Rhapsody for violin and piano. (Lazarof, Henri). *Associated Music. £7.50* SPJ (B74-50670)
Rhodes, Anthony. Musical instruments from the Renaissance to the 19th century. (Paganelli, Sergio). *Hamlyn. £0.50* AL/B(XD401) (B74-20189) ISBN 0-600-31853-2
Ricercari a quattro, nos.6 & 7. (Gabrieli, Andrea). *Schott. £1.92* RXMJ (B74-50219)
Richards, Goff. The entertainer: arr. The entertainer. (Joplin, Scott). *Chappell. Unpriced* WMK/AHXJ (B74-51359)
Richardson, M K. The white crane : for voices, descant, recorders, percussion and piano, violins and guitar ad lib. (Lipkin, Malcolm). *Chester. Unpriced* CQN (B74-50334)
Richardson, Norman.
Six classical solos. *Boosey and Hawkes. Unpriced* WUPK/AAY (B74-51371)
Sonatina for clarinet and piano. *Boosey and Hawkes. £0.75* VVPEM (B74-50293)
Ricochet: arr. Ricochet. Fasten seat belts : original theme music, arranged for piano from the BBC Radio Two series. (Narholz, Gerhard). *Berry Music. Unpriced* QPK/JS (B74-51187)
Ricochet. Fasten seat belts : original theme music, arranged for piano from the BBC Radio Two series. (Narholz, Gerhard). *Berry Music. Unpriced* QPK/JS (B74-51187)
Riddle song : a folk-song from Kentucky, SSA (S.solo) unacc. (Trant, Brian). *Oxford University Press. Unpriced* FEZDW (B74-50429) ISBN 0-19-342595-5
Ridout, Alan.
2 organ pieces. *Chappell. Unpriced* RJ (B74-51195)
Caliban and Ariel : for solo bassoon. *Chappell. Unpriced* VWPMJ (B74-50814)
Ferdinand : for speaker and solo violin. *Chappell. Unpriced* KHYE/SPM (B74-51080)
Pigs : a present for Gordon Jacob, for four bassoons. *Emerson. Unpriced* VWNS (B74-50296)
Three nocturnes : for flute and piano. *Chappell. Unpriced* VRPJ (B74-51321)
Riegger, Wallingford. New dance. Op. 18c : for concert band. *Associated Music. Unpriced* UMH (B74-51295)
Ries, Ferdinand. Introduction and rondo for horn & piano in E flat major. Op.113, no.2. Introduction and rondo for horn and piano. Opus 113, no.2. *Musica rara. Unpriced* WTP/W (B74-50846)
Right from the start : twenty tunes for young violinists for violin and piano. (Nelson, Sheila M). *Boosey and Hawkes. £2.25* SPJ (B74-50671)
Rimembranze napoletane : for flute with pianoforte accompaniment. (Paggi, Giovanni). *Wye Music : Emerson. Unpriced* VRPJ (B74-51320)
Rinaldo. Lascia ch'io panga: arr. Evening hymn. (Handel, George Frideric). *Oxford University Press. Unpriced* DH (B74-50012) ISBN 0-19-351119-3
Rio Grande. (Lambert, Constant). *Oxford University Press. £1.30* EMDX (B74-50376) ISBN 0-19-337303-3
Rise eagle rise. (Schäfer, Karl-Heinz). *Maneges, Chappell : Chappell. Unpriced* KDW (B74-50466)
Rise of the string quartet. (Olleson, Philip). *Open University Press. Unpriced* ARXNS(X) (B74-18935) ISBN 0-335-00862-3
Rise of the symphony
2. (Middleton, Richard). *Open University Press. £1.70* AMME(X) (B74-18934) ISBN 0-335-00859-3
Rising again : a calypso for voices and piano. (Ager, Laurence). *Ashdown. £0.12* JFDH/LL (B74-50090)
Rizzo, Jacques. Quand la chance est là. This old world = Quand la chance est là : for SATB chorus accompanied. (Brejean, Philippe). *Chappell. Unpriced* DW (B74-50358)
Rizzo, Jacques C.
America sings: arr. America sings. (Menten, Dale). *Unichappell : Chappell. Unpriced* DW (B74-50360)
Stained glass windows (and simple wood benches). (Millet, Kadish). *Chappell. Unpriced* DW (B74-50925)
Roberts, Don. Introduction to the 12 string guitar : 12 string guitar techniques. *Robbins Music : E M I. Unpriced* TS/AC (B74-51269)
Robertson, Alec. Dvořák. Revised ed. *Dent. £3.00* BDX(N) (B74-27797) ISBN 0-460-03116-3
Robinson Crusoe : a pantomime. (Crocker, John, *b.1925*). *Evans Plays. £0.50* BCQRACPP (B74-12388) ISBN 0-237-74975-0
Rocherolle, Eugenie R. Christmas child : for unison, SA or SAB chorus and piano. *Warner : Blossom. Unpriced* JDW/LF (B74-50448)
Rock dreams. (Peellaert, Guy). *Pan Books. £1.95* ADW/GB/E(M/XPM22/EM) (B74-07429) ISBN 0-330-24008-0
Rock file
2. *Panther. £0.50* ADW/GB (B74-18933) ISBN 0-586-04087-0
Rode, Pierre.
24 Capricen in Etüdenform für Bratsche allein in den 24 Tonarten. *Schott. £2.40* SQPMK (B74-50242)
24 Caprices in Etüdenform für Violine allein in den 24 Tonarten. *Schott. £2.40* SPMJ (B74-50238)
Roe, Betty. Sonatina dolorosa : for solo guitar. *Thames. Unpriced* TSPMEM (B74-51273)
Roethke, Theodor. The serpent. (Rorem, Ned). *Boosey and Hawkes. Unpriced* KDW (B74-51053)
Roger, Roger. Gavotina. *Chappell. Unpriced* TMK/AHM (B74-50694)
Rogers, Douglas. The entertainer: arr. The entertainer : a ragtime two step. (Joplin, Scott). *221a Kensington High St., W.8 : Aura Music. Unpriced* TSPMK/AHXJ (B74-51282)
Roget, Peter Mark. Synonyms for life. Op. 33 : for four-part chorus of mixed voices with piano accompaniment. (Muczynsky, Robert). *Schirmer. Unpriced* DW (B74-50023)
Roisman, Leonid. Piano pieces by Soviet composers for children
Vol.3. *Peters. Unpriced* QP/AYM (B74-51143)
Rollin, Robert Leon. Two pieces for solo flute. *Galaxy Music : Galliard. Unpriced* VRPMJ (B74-50762)
'Rolling Stone' rock 'n' roll reader. (Fong-Torres, Ben). *Bantam. £0.75* A/GB(XQG4) (B74-15523) ISBN 0-552-67483-4
Rolling Stones story. (Tremlett, George). *49 Poland St., W1A 2LG : Futura Publications Ltd. £0.40* AKDW/GB/E(P) (B74-25496) ISBN 0-86007-128-6
Romani, Felice. Lucrezia Borgia. Vocal score. Lucrezia Borgia. (Donizetti, Gaetano). *93 Chancery La., W.C.2 : Egret House. Unpriced* CC (B74-50868)
Romani, G.
Leicester sketches : a suite for five miniatures for solo guitar. *Charnwood Music. Unpriced* TSPMJ (B74-51275)
Master music makers : an anthology of music by the great composers. *Charnwood Music. Unpriced* RSPM/AY (B74-51205)
'Opera nights' : an album of operatic favourites. *Ricordi. Unpriced* RSPMK/AAY (B74-51215)
Useful tunes for guitar
No.4: Rigadoon, from 'Musick's hand-maid' 1689 and Jig from 'Abdalazar'. *Charnwood Music. Unpriced* RSPMK (B74-51213)
Rondo concertante : for orchestra. (Diemer, Emma Lou). *Boosey and Hawkes. Unpriced* MMF/W (B74-51099)
Rooke, Pat. That's the Spirit : musical play. (Arch, Gwyn). *British and Continental. Unpriced* CN/L (B74-50333)
Rorem, Ned.
Ariel : five poems of Sylvia Plath, for soprano clarinet and piano. *Boosey and Hawkes. £3.00* KFLE/VVPDW (B74-50115)
Concerto in six movements for piano and orchestra: arr. Concerto in six movements for piano and orchestra. *Boosey and Hawkes. £5.00* QNUK/LF (B74-51140)
Fables. Fables : five very short operas. *Boosey and Hawkes. £3.25* CC (B74-50871)
Last poems of Wallace Stevens : for voice, cello and piano. *Boosey and Hawkes. £3.00* KE/SRPDW (B74-50478)
Missa brevis : for mixed chorus unaccompanied. *Boosey and Hawkes. Unpriced* EZDG (B74-50385)
The serpent. *Boosey and Hawkes. Unpriced* KDW (B74-51053)
Three motets : SATB and organ. *Boosey and Hawkes. Unpriced* DH (B74-50350)
Three sisters who are not sisters. *Vocal score.* Three sisters who are not sisters : an opera. *Boosey and Hawkes. £4.25* CC (B74-50872)
War scenes : for medium-low voice and piano. *Boosey and Hawkes. Unpriced* KFVDW (B74-51074)
Rosa mystica. Op. 40 : acht Gesänge für mittlere Singstimme und Orchester. (Einem, Gottfried von). *Boosey and Hawkes. Unpriced* KFVE/MDW

(B74-50118)
Rosa mystica. Op.40 : acht Gesänge für mittlere Singstimme und Orchester. (Einem, Gottfried von). *Boosey and Hawkes. £2.50* KFVDW (B74-50116)
Rosa mystica. Op.40. Vocal score. Rosa mystica. Op.40 : acht Gesänge für mittlere Singstimme und Orchester. (Einem, Gottfried von). *Boosey and Hawkes. £2.50* KFVDW (B74-50116)
Rose, Bernard. Musica Deo sacra III. (Tomkins, Thomas). *Stainer and Bell for the British Academy. Unpriced* EZDK (B74-50047)
Rose, Gregory. Animals etcetera : unaccompanied voices, 4-part. *Boosey and Hawkes. £0.05* EZDW (B74-50061)
Rose, Michael.
Easter day : anthem for female or boys' voices and organ. *Novello. £0.14* DH/LL (B74-50018)
Seven Welsh folk songs : voice and harp. *Adlais. Unpriced* KE/TQDW/G/AYDK (B74-51061)
Rosemary Brown piano album : 7 pieces inspired by Beethoven, Schubert, Chopin, Schumann, Brahms and Liszt. (Brown, Rosemary). *Paxton. £0.60* QPJ (B74-50585)
Rosetti, Antonio. *See* Rössler, Franz Anton.
Rossetti, Christina. Child of wonder. Alleluia and chorale. Alleluia and chorale : SATB with piano, four-hands. (Forcucci, Samuel L). *Schirmer. Unpriced* DH/LF (B74-50016)
Rossini, Gioacchino Antonio. Sonata for strings, no.2, in A major. Sonata per archi, A-Dur : 2 Violinen, Violoncello und Kontrabass (chorisch oder solistish). *Schott. £2.90* RXME (B74-51216)
Rossini, Gioachino Antonio. Duets for two cats : for 2-part chorus of female voices or SA duet with piano. *Roberton. £0.12* FDW (B74-50422)
Rössler, Franz Anton. Partita for wind band in F major (1785). Partita (1785) in F Major for two flutes, two oboes, two clarinets, three horns, and two bassoons, with double bass. *Oxford University Press. Score £3.00, Parts unpriced* UMG (B74-51290) ISBN 0-19-358650-9
Rostal, Max.
24 Capricen in Etüdenform für Bratsche allein in den 24 Tonarten. (Rode, Pierre). *Schott. £2.40* SQPMK (B74-50242)
24 Caprices in Etüdenform für Violine allein in den 24 Tonarten. (Rode, Pierre). *Schott. £2.40* SPMJ (B74-50238)
Concerto for violin in D major. Op. 35: arr. Konzert für Violine und Orchester. Opus 35. (Tchaikovsky, Peter). *Schott. £2.40* SPK/LF (B74-50236)
Round the star and back : for piano and a small number of other instruments capable of reasonable blend. (Harvey, Jonathan). *Novello. £1.50* QPJ (B74-50591)
Routley, Erik.
Hymns for celebration : a supplement for use at Holy Communion today. *Royal School of Church Music. Unpriced* DM/AY (B74-50353) ISBN 0-85402-055-1
Three antiphonal canticles : for SATB and congregation (or two groups of singers) and organ. *Novello. £0.10* DH (B74-50015)
Rowland-Entwistle, Theodore. Famous composers. *David and Charles. £2.50* A/D(YB/M) (B74-09226) ISBN 0-7153-6375-1
Rowlands, Richard. Songs of Ophelia, nos. 3, 4. Christmas cradle song. (Brahms, Johannes). *Novello. Unpriced* EZDP/LF (B74-50959)
Roxburgh, Edwin. How pleasant to know Mr. Lear : for narrator and orchestra. *United Music. Unpriced* KHYE/M (B74-50120)
Royal College of Organists. Year book
1973-1974. *Kensington Gore, SW7 2QS : The College. £0.75* AR(YC/VP/Q) (B74-14972) ISBN 0-902462-04-0
Royal Musical Association. Messiah. Handel's conducting score of 'Messiah' : reproduced in facsimile from the manuscript in the library of St Michael's College, Tenbury Wells. (Handel, George Frideric). *Scolar Press for the Royal Musical Association. £37.50* BHCADD (B74-24210) ISBN 0-85967-158-5
Royal School of Church Music.
English church music : a collection of essays
1974. *Addington Palace, Croydon CR9 5AD : Royal School of Church Music. £1.12* AD/LD(YD/D) (B74-20190) ISBN 0-85402-057-8
Festival service books
7: The journey: a meditation. *Royal School of Church Music. Unpriced* DGM (B74-50340)
Royal Scottish Country Dance Society. *Newcastle and District Branch.* Two Scottish country dances. (Rankine, Andrew). *42 Whinfell Rd, Darras Hall, Ponteland, Newcastle : Royal Scottish Country Dance Society (Newcastle and District Branch). £0.125* QPH/H/AYDL (B74-50578)
Rubbra, Edmund.
Blessed be he. Op. 147 : SATB. *Lengnick. £0.12* EZDH (B74-50040)
Nocturne, Op.54 : song for medium voice and piano. *Lengnick. £0.30* KFVDW (B74-50487)
Rudolph Johann Joseph Rainer, *Archduke of Austria Cardinal Archbishop of Olmutz.* Sonata for clarinet in A & piano in A major. Op.2. Sonata for clarinet and piano. Op.2. *Musica rara. Unpriced* VVQPE (B74-50808)
Ruf, Hugo.
Essercizii musici, trio 12. Sonata for instruments in E flat major. Sonata Es-Dur, für Oboe, obligates Cembalo und Basso continuo. (Telemann, Georg Philipp). *Schott. £2.61* NWNTE (B74-51118)
Trio sonatas by old English masters : for two treble recorders and basso continuo
1. *Bärenreiter. £2.55* VSSNTPWE/AYD (B74-50772)
2. *Bärenreiter. £2.18* VSSNTPWE/AYD (B74-50771)
Ruffo, Vincenzo. Capricci in musica a tre voci, nos. 4, 10, 1. Three pieces for three instruments. *Pro Musica. Unpriced* LNT (B74-50125)
Russell, Carlton T. Magnificat : for three-part chorus of women's voices a cappella. *Schirmer. Unpriced* FEZDGPQ (B74-51001)
Russell, Leslie. Blaydon races : variations for orchestra. *Boosey and Hawkes. £10.50* MM/T (B74-51095)
Russell, Wilbur F. Michael, row the boat ashore : Georgia sea island chant for four-part chorus of men's voices a cappella. *Roberton. £0.07* GEZDW/LC (B74-50082)
Russell-Smith, Geoffry.
A box of toys and entertainment for speech and percussion. *Novello. £1.02* FHYE/XMDX (B74-50077)
Musical reading and writing
Vol.1. (Szönyi, Erzsébet). *Boosey and Hawkes. £2.95* A(VC/QU) (B74-25493) ISBN 0-85162-011-6
Russell-Smith, Mollie. A box of toys and entertainment for speech and percussion. (Russell-Smith, Geoffry). *Novello. £1.02* FHYE/XMDX (B74-50077)
Russian folksongs, set 1. (Liadov, Anatoly). *Boosey and Hawkes. Score £1.50, Piano conductor £0.50, Set £2.50* MK (B74-51090)
Russian folksongs. Set 2. (Liadov, Anatoly). *Boosey and Hawkes. £4.50* MH (B74-51088)
Rutter, John.
Dancing day : a cycle of traditional Christmas carols. *Oxford University Press. £1.50* FE/TQDPDE/LF (B74-50999) ISBN 0-19-338065-x
Five childhood lyrics : for unaccompanied mixed voices. *Oxford University Press. £0.80* EZDW (B74-50980) ISBN 0-19-343716-3
Jesu child : SATB. *Oxford University Press. £0.20* DP/LF (B74-50910) ISBN 0-19-343045-2
Shepherd's pipe carol : for mixed voices and small orchestra. *Oxford University Press. £1.00* EMDP/LF (B74-50029) ISBN 0-19-344803-3
Two hymns of praise : with introductory fanfares
1: Now thank we all our God. *Oxford University Press. £1.00* EWMDM/AY (B74-50938) ISBN 0-19-367376-2
2: All creatures of our God and king : melody from Geistliche Kirchengesang (Köln 1623). *Oxford University Press. £1.10* EWMDM/AY (B74-50939) ISBN 0-19-367359-2
Sacerdotes Domini = Then did priests make offering : SATB. (Byrd, William). Revised ed. *Oxford University Press. Unpriced* EZDGKAF (B74-50038) ISBN 0-19-352008-7
Sacrae cantiones quatuor vocum. Jubilate Deo. Jubilate Deo = Sing to God : motet for four-part chorus of mixed voices a cappella. (Lasso, Orlando di). *Schirmer. Unpriced* EZDJ (B74-50044)
Sacred hymnes. My Lord is hence removed. *Vocal score.* My Lord is hence removed : SSATTB with tenor solo and viol accompaniment. (Amner, John). *Oxford University Press. Unpriced* DH (B74-50343) ISBN 0-19-350326-3
Sadie, Stanley.
Sonata for piano no.13 in B flat major. K.333. Sonata in B flat, K. 333. (Mozart, Wolfgang Amadeus). *Associated Board of the Royal Schools of Music. Unpriced* QPE (B74-50167)
Sonata for piano, no.15, in C major. K.545. Sonata in C, K.545. (Mozart, Wolfgang Amadeus). *Associated Board of the Royal Schools of Music. £0.35* QPE (B74-51144)
Sadleir, Dick.
Selections: arr. Gilbert and Sullivan for descant recorder with chord symbols for guitar, piano or tuned percussion. (Sullivan, *Sir* Arthur Seymour). *British and Continental. Unpriced* VSRPMK/DW (B74-51336)
Selections: arr. Waltz themes from Tchaikovsky : for descant recorder, treble or melodica or guitar. (Tchaikovsky, Peter). *British and Continental Music Agencies. Unpriced* VSRPMK/AHW (B74-50770)
Sadleir, Richard. Eight solos for guitar. *British and Continental. Unpriced* TSPMK/AAY (B74-51281)
Sadler's Wells Opera. *For later publications of this Company see* English National Opera Limited.
Saens, Camille Saint-. *See* Saint-Saens, Camille.
Saer, D Roy. Canenon llafar gwlad = Songs from oral tradition
Vol.1. *National Museum of Wales, Welsh Folk Museum. Unpriced* JEZDW/G/AYDK (B74-51033) ISBN 0-85485-026-0
St Jerome and the lion : a legend for voices, piano and optional recorders and percussion. (Parry, William Howard). *Keith Prowse Music. £0.75* JFDE (B74-50089)
St Katherine's Communion service, (series 3) : for congregational use, unaccompanied or with keyboard accompaniment. (Sharp, Ian). *Stainer and Bell. Unpriced* JDGS (B74-50440)
St Matthew Passion. *Aus Liebe will mein Heiland sterben: arr.* Aria. (Bach, Johann Sebastian). *Schirmer. Unpriced* VRNSK/DH/LH (B74-50271)
St Michael's College. *Library. MSS.(346-7).* Messiah. Handel's conducting score of 'Messiah' : reproduced in facsimile from the manuscript in the library of St Michael's College, Tenbury Wells. (Handel, George Frideric). *Scolar Press for the Royal Musical Association. £37.50* BHCADD (B74-24210) ISBN 0-85967-158-5
Saint-Saëns, Camille.
Le Carnival des animaux : grande fantasie zoologique. *Peters. Unpriced* MMJ (B74-51104)
Le Carnival des animaux. Selections: arr. Two pieces. *Oxford University Press. £0.60* VVPK (B74-51345) ISBN 0-19-358701-7
Le Carnival des animaux. Selections: arr. Two pieces. *Oxford University Press. £0.45* VWPK (B74-51348) ISBN 0-19-358703-3
Saint-Saens, Camille.
Havanaise for violin and piano. Op.83. *Schirmer. Unpriced* SPHMV (B74-50669)
Introduction and rondo capriccioso for violin & orchestra. Opus 28: arr. Introduktion und Rondo capriccioso. Opus 28 : für Violine und Orchester. *Peters. £2.40* SPK (B74-51244)
Salatino. Maria Stuarda. Vocal score. Maria Stuarda. (Donizetti, Gaetano). *93 Chancery La., W.C.2 : Egret House. Unpriced* CC (B74-50869)
Salvation Army Brass Band Journal (Festival series)
Nos.353-356: The Southern Cross: festival march, by Brian Bowen. Oh the blessed Lord: Toccata, by Wilfred Heaton. Notturno religioso, by Erik Leidzen. Songs of praise: suite, by James Curnow. *Salvationist Publishing and Supplies. Unpriced* WM/AY (B74-50301)
Salvation Army Brass Band Journal (General series)
Nos 1641-1644: There will be God: trombone solo, by Joy Webb; arr. Ray Steadman-Allen and, When the harvest is past: flugel horn solo, by Ray Steadman-Allen; Temple 85: march, by Norman Bearcroft. The seeking heart: selection, by Charles Dove. Hallelujah!: chorus setting, by Terry Camsey, and, Troyte: hymn tune arrangement, by Brindley Boon. *Salvationist Publishing and Supplies. Unpriced* WM/AY (B74-50818)
Nos. 1645-1648: The Irish Salvationist march, by Walter Fletcher. The joy of Christmas suite, by Robert Redhead. Sweet little Jesus boy, negro spiritual, arr. Joy Webb, trans. Christopher Cole with David of the White Rock: Welsh melody, arr. Ray Bowes. The secret place: selection, by Neville McFarlane. *Salvationist Publishing & Supplies. Unpriced* WM/AY (B74-50302)
Nos.1649-1652: A shrine of quietness : meditation / by Derek Jordan. Congregational tunes no.8 / arr. Ray Steadman-Allen. I reckon on you : trombone ensemble by Douglas Kiff ; arr. Eiliv Herikstad. Norwich citadel : march / by Albert Drury. *Salvationist Publishing and Supplies. Unpriced* WM/AY (B74-51350)
Nos.1653-1656: Away in a manger (Normandy carol) : song transcription / by Robert Redhead, and, The wonder of his grace : song arrangement / by Howard Davies. Selection from 'Hosea' / by Ray Steadman-Allen, (melodies John Larsson). Melcombe : hymn tune arrangement / by Ray Steadman-Allen. The battle cry : march / by Bjorn Garsegg; arr. Eric Ball. *Salvationist Publishing and Supplies. Unpriced* WM/AY (B74-51351)
Salvation Army Brass Band Journal (Triumph series)
Nos 757-760 : Bognor Regis: march, by Leslie Condon. Hosea: suite, by Robert Redhead. Jesus loves me: song setting, by James Anderson. The Kiwi: march, by Ray Cresswell. *Salvationist Publishing and Supplies. Unpriced* WM/AY (B74-50819)
Nos 761-764: Joy in Bethlehem: selection, by Leslie Condon. Stainer: prelude, by Barbara Steadman-Allen, and, Hold the fort! song arrangement, by Terry Camsey. Be strong! march, by Christopher Cole. Congregational tunes: no.7, arr. by Ray Steadman-Allen. *Salvationist Publishing and Supplies. Unpriced* WM/AY (B74-50820)
Nos.769-772: Rhapsody on Danish traditional airs / by Erik Silferberg. A call to prayer : selection / by E.A. Smith. Dandenony citadel : march / by Allen Pengilly. March from the 'Occasional' oratorio / by Handel ; arr. Richard Slater, and, Nearer to thee : coronet solo / by Ira D. Sankey ; arr. Howard Davies. *Salvationist Publishing and Supplies. Unpriced* WM/AY (B74-51352)
Nos.773-776: Jesus I come : meditation / by Ray Steadman-Allen. Prospects of joy : selection / by F.J. Dockerill. He came to give us life : song transcription / by John Larsson : trans. Robert Redhead. Caribbean congress : march / by David Wells. *Salvationist Publishing and Supplies. Unpriced* WM/AY (B74-51353)
Salve regina : for four-part chorus of mixed voices a cappella. (Okeghem, Jean). *Associated Music. Unpriced* EZDJ (B74-50397)
Salzman, Eric. Twentieth-century music : an introduction. 2nd ed. *Prentice-Hall. £4.70* A(XM71) (B74-24208) ISBN 0-13-935015-2
Samaria : for concert band. (Osterling, Eric). *Chappell. Unpriced* UMJ (B74-51299)
Sampson, Alistair. Horrortorio. Vocal score. Horrortorio : a choral extravaganza for SATB soli & chorus and orchestra. (Horovitz, Joseph). *Novello. £0.65* EMDX (B74-50375)
Samuel Renn : English organ builder. (Sayer, Michael). *Phillimore. £5.50* AR/BC(YD/P) (B74-18936) ISBN 0-85033-078-5
Sandford, Jeremy. Tomorrow's people. *47 Catherine Place, S.W.1 : Jerome Publishing Co. Ltd. £1.95* A/GB(WE/YC) (B74-14305) ISBN 0-904125-05-x
Sandy Bell's Broadsheet
Issue no.1- ; Aug. 20, 1973-. *Forrest Hill Bar, Forrest Rd, Edinburgh : John Barrow. £0.03* A/G(YDL/B) (B74-16726)
Sansom, Clive A. Cantate rag : for S.A.T.B., piano and percussion. *Paterson. Unpriced* ENYLDE (B74-50935)
Sappho. Songs and epilogues : for bass voice and piano. (Travis, Roy). *Oxford University Press. Unpriced* KGXDW (B74-51078)
Sargent, Brian.
Minstrels : medieval music to sing and play. *Cambridge University Press. Unpriced* DW/AY (B74-50367)

ISBN 0-521-20166-7
Troubadours : medieval music to sing and play. *Cambridge University Press. Unpriced* DW/AY (B74-50368) ISBN 0-521-20471-2
Satires of circumstance (1969) : song cycle, soprano, flute (piccola), clarinet, violin, violoncello, double bass and piano. (Shifrin, Seymour). *Peters. Unpriced* KFLE/NUPNQDW (B74-51067)
Saunders, Neil.
Benedic anima mea. Psalm 104 : for mixed voice choir, soprano and tenor soli and organ. *Roberton. £0.32* DR (B74-50914)
Jubilate Deo : for 5-part chorus of mixed voices S.S.A.T.B., soprano and baritone soli and brass ensemble. *Roberton. £0.20* EWNRDGNT (B74-50941)
Saville, John. The Socialist Register
1973. *Merlin Press. £4.00* 335.005 (B74-18687) ISBN 0-85036-178-8
Sayer, Michael. Samuel Renn : English organ builder. *Phillimore. £5.50* AR/BC(YD/P) (B74-18936) ISBN 0-85033-078-5
Scaduto, Anthony. Mick Jagger. *W.H. Allen. £3.50* AKDW/GB/E(P) (B74-23497) ISBN 0-491-01122-9
Scarlatti, Alessandro. Exultate Deo. Sing aloud with gladness = Exultate Deo : SATB a cappella. *Royal School of Church Music. £0.32* EZDJ (B74-50952)
Scarlatti, Domenico. Sonata for harpsichord in C major. L.164: arr. Sonata. *Oxford University Press. Unpriced* UMK/AE (B74-50720)
Schadewaldt, Wolfgang. De temporum fine comoedia = Das Spiel vom Ende der Zeiten Vigilia. (Orff, Carl). *Schott. Unpriced* EMDX (B74-50933)
Schäfer, Karl-Heinz. Rise eagle rise. *Maneges, Chappell : Chappell. Unpriced* KDW (B74-50466)
Schalit, Heinrich. Aleynu l'shabench : a new Friday evening service, cantor solo with mixed chorus, SATB and organ, commissioned by the Anshe Emet Synagogue, Chicago, Illinois, on the occasion of the hundredth jubilee year (1873-1973)
7: Psalm 150. *Ethnic Music : Phoenix. Unpriced* DGU (B74-50890)
Schedrin, Rodion. Concerto for piano, no.2(1966). Konzert Nr.2 für Klavier und Orchester (1966). *Peters. Unpriced* QNUK/LF (B74-51141)
Schehadé, Georges. L'Histoire de Vasco. *Adaptations.* The story of Vasco : opera in three acts. (Crosse, Gordon, *b.1937*). *Oxford University Press, Music Department. £0.70* BCRAC (B74-09228) ISBN 0-19-335702-x
Scheidt, Samuel. Geistliche Concerten, Tl.2. Dialogus. Kommt her ihr Gesegneten meines Vaters = Come ye blessed ones of my Father : dialogue for five voices (SATTB) and continuo. *Novello. £1.00* JNBDH (B74-51043)
Scherill, James. Meditation on the syllable Om : for men's voices. (Nelson, Ron). *Boosey and Hawkes. Unpriced* GEZDW (B74-50436)
Scherzo : for horn or bassoon (or violoncello) and piano. (Head, Michael). *Boosey and Hawkes. £0.60* WTPJ (B74-50848)
Schmelzer, Johann Heinrich.
Sonata for trumpet, violin, trombone, bassoon & basso continuo in G major, 'La Carioletta'. Sonata in G, 'La Carioletta' : for cornetto (trumpet), violin, trombone, bassoon and basso continuo. *Musica rara. Unpriced* NUNRE (B74-50522)
Sonata for violin, trombone, bassoon & basso continuo in A minor. Sonata à 3 : for violin, trombone, bassoon & basso continuo. *Musica rara. Unpriced* NUNSE (B74-50523)
Schmitt, Daniel. Jardins de Paris : pour voix moyenne. (Berthomieu, Marc). *Chappell. Unpriced* KFVDW (B74-50485)
Schmitz, Hans Peter. Sonata for flute & piano in C major. Op.13. Sonata in C major for flute or violin and piano. (Hoffmeister, Franz Anton). *Nagel : Bärenreiter. £3.80* VRPE (B74-50751)
Schoenbach, Sol.
Concertos for bassoon. Selections: arr. 10 bassoon concerti Vol.1. (Vivaldi, Antonio). *Schirmer. Unpriced* VWPK/LF (B74-50299)
Concertos for bassoon. Selections: arr. 10 bassoon concerti Vol.2. (Vivaldi, Antonio). *Schirmer. Unpriced* VWPK/LF (B74-50300)
Schoenberg, Arnold. Letters of Arnold Schoenberg. *Faber. £2.95* BSET(N) (B74-04793) ISBN 0-571-10514-9
Schonzeler, Hans-Hubert. Symphony in C major. Symphony, C major. (Bizet, Georges). *Eulenburg. Unpriced* MME (B74-51097)
School for scandal, Op.5. Overture. Overture to 'The school for scandal'. (Barber, Samuel). *Schirmer. Unpriced* UMK (B74-50715)
School of English Church Music. *See* Royal School of Church Music.
School recorder assembly book : sixteen hymn tunes and nine pieces for descant and treble recorders with pianoforte accompaniment. (Appleby, Benjamin William). *Arnold. Unpriced* VSMK/AAY (B74-51328) ISBN 0-560-00382-x
Schooling in the middle years. *See* Basic books in education : schooling in the middle years.
Schostakowitsch, Dimitri. *See* Shostakovich, Dmitry.
Schreiner, Alexander. Improvisation on a Mormon hymn: arr. Improvisation on a Mormon hymn: Come, come ye saints. (Johannesen, Grant). *Oxford University Press. Unpriced* RK (B74-50626)
Schroeder, Hermann. Drei Dialoge für Oboe und Orgel. *Schott. £1.44* VTPLR (B74-50290)
Schubart, Christian Friedrich David. The shepherds' carol : old German Weihnachtslied. *Banks. Unpriced* FDP/LF (B74-50988)
Schubert, Franz.
Mass in G major. D.167. Vocal score. Mass in G D.167. *Schirmer. Unpriced* DG (B74-50338)
Quintet for strings in C major. D.956. Quintet, C major, for 2 violins, viola and 2 cellos. D.956. *Eulenburg. Unpriced* RXNR (B74-51224)
Schubert's songs. (Capell, Richard). 3rd ed. *Duckworth. £4.95* BSFAKDW (B74-05269) ISBN 0-7156-0735-9
Schuller, Gunther.
Diptych : for brass quintet and concert band. *Associated Music. Unpriced* UMPWNR (B74-50735)
The entertainer: arr. The entertainer : piano solo. (Joplin, Scott). *Belwin-Mills. £0.30* QPHXJ (B74-50579)
Schulze, Hans-Joachim. Concerto for violin & string orchestra in A minor. S. 1041. Konzert, A-moll, für Violine und Streichorchester. BWV 1041. (Bach, Johann Sebastian). *Peters. Unpriced* RXMPSF (B74-51220)
Schuman, William. Circus overture. *Schirmer. Unpriced* UMK (B74-50267)
Schuster, Joseph.
Divertimenti for violin & keyboard, nos 1-6. 6 divertimenti da camera for harpsichord (piano) and violin
1: Divertimenti I and II. *Nagel : Bärenreiter. £3.45* SPJ (B74-50672)
Divertimenti for violin & keyboard, nos 1-6. 6 divertimenti da camera for harpsichord (piano) and violin
2: Divertimenti III and IV. *Nagel : Bärenreiter. £2.55* SPJ (B74-50673)
Divertimenti for violin & keyboard, nos 1-6. 6 divertimenti da camera for harpsichord (piano) and violin
3: Divertimenti V and VI. *Nagel : Bärenreiter. £2.55* SPJ (B74-50674)
Schütz, Heinrich.
Cantiones sacrae. Deus misereatur nostri. Deus misereatur nostri = God be merciful unto us : for four-part chorus of mixed voices a cappella. *Schirmer. Unpriced* EZDR (B74-50407)
Cantiones sacrae. In te Domine, speravi. In te Domine, speravi = Lord in thee do I put my trust : motet for four-part chorus of mixed voices a cappella. *Schirmer. Unpriced* EZDJ (B74-50398)
Cantiones sacrae. Quoniam ad te clamabo, Domine. Quoniam ad te clamabo, Domine = Now behold to thee I cry, O Lord : motet for four-part chorus of mixed voices a cappella. *Chappell. Unpriced* EZDJ (B74-50399)
Schutz, Heinrich. Geistliche Chormusik. Verleih uns Frieden genadiglich. Verleih uns Frieden genadiglich = Lord grant us peace : for five-part chorus of mixed voices a cappella. *Schirmer. Unpriced* EZDH (B74-50946)
Schütz, Heinrich.
Heute ist Christus der Herr geboren = Jesus our Lord on this day was born : motet for Christmas, for three-part chorus of women's voices with continuo (or piano) accompaniment. *Schirmer. Unpriced* FDH/LF (B74-50413)
Hodie Christus natus est. S.W.V.456. *Vocal score.* Hodie Christus natus est = On this day Christ the Lord is born : motet for six-part chorus of mixed voices. *Schirmer. Unpriced* DH/LF (B74-50351)
Schwartz, Charles. Gershwin : his life and music. *Abelard-Schuman. £4.90* BGH(N) (B74-20923) ISBN 0-200-72129-1
Schwartz, Stephen. Mass. Almighty Father: arr. Almighty Father : chorale. (Bernstein, Leonard). *Amberson : Schirmer. Unpriced* GEZDH (B74-50434)
Schwarze Spinne, Op.80a : Suite für Orchester. (Burkhard, Willy). *Bärenreiter. £3.25* MMG (B74-50498)
Schweizer, Rolf. Orgelstücke alter Meister : elektronische Orgel. *Nagel : Bärenreiter. £1.80* RPVK/AAY (B74-50630)
Schwieger, Hans. Der Zigeunerbaron. Selections: arr. The gypsy baron suite. (Strauss, Johann, *b.1825*). *Boosey and Hawkes. £15.00* MMK (B74-50143)
Scipio : march. (Handel, George Frideric). *Chappell. Unpriced* UMK/AGM (B74-51301)
Scipione. March : arr. Il Scipio : march. (Handel, George Frideric). *Chappell. Unpriced* UMK/AGM (B74-51301)
Scott, Marion Margareta. Beethoven. Revised ed.. *Dent. £2.95* BBJ (B74-22161) ISBN 0-460-03149-x
Scott Joplin : the king of ragtime writers: easy piano. (Joplin, Scott). *Lewis Music : Ashley-Fields. Unpriced* QPHXJ (B74-51159)
Scottish Arts Council. The concert piano in Scotland : a report to the Scottish Arts Council. (Piano Panel). *19 Charlotte Sq., Edinburgh EH2 4DF : Scottish Arts Council. £0.25* AQ(W/YDL) (B74-09233) ISBN 0-902989-13-8
Scrapbook of jazz. *See* Condon, Eddie.
Sculthorpe, Peter. Sun music IV : for orchestra. *Faber Music. Unpriced* MMJ (B74-50142)
Sea of life : SATB. (Habash, John Mitri). *Robbins. Unpriced* DW (B74-50920)
Sea of life : SSA. (Habash, John Mitri). *Robbins. Unpriced* FDW (B74-50992)
Searle, Humphrey. Cat variations : for clarinet in A and piano on a theme from Prokofiev's 'Peter and the wolf'. *Faber Music. Unpriced* VVQP/T (B74-50807)
Seasons : unison. (Sturman, Paul). *Ashdown. £0.40* JDW (B74-50086)
Sechak, Steve. The best dulcimer method yet. (Gamse, Albert). *Lewis : Ashley-Fields. Unpriced* TWT/AC (B74-51287)
Second set of divertimenti. Op.2. (Sor, Fernando). *Oxford University Press. £0.50* TSPMJ (B74-50703) ISBN 0-19-358864-1
Secunda, Sholom. Aleynu l'shabench : a new Friday evening service, cantor solo with mixed chorus, SATB and organ, commissioned by the Anshe Emet Synagogue, Chicago, Illinois, on the occasion of the hundredth jubilee year (1873-1973)
3: Hashkivenu. *Ethnic Music : Phoenix. Unpriced* DGU (B74-50886)
Segovia technique. (Bobri, Vladimir). *Macmillan : Collier Macmillan. £5.45* ATS/E/CY (B74-13713) ISBN 0-02-511990-7
Sehring, Rudi. Anleitung zur Improvisation für Schlagzeug. (Combe, Stuff). *Schott. £1.56* XHX/DZ/AF (B74-50322)
Seidel, Uwe. Oekumenische Beatmesse : Liebe ist nicht nur ein Wort. (Blarr, Oskar Gottlieb). *Bosse : Bärenreiter. £1.60* ELDE (B74-50372)
Selections. The flute solos from the Bach cantatas, passions and oratorios. (Bach, Johann Sebastian). *Schirmer. £2.35* VR (B74-50745)
Selva morale e spirituale. Messa a 4 da capella. Agnus Dei. Vocal score. Lamb of God = Agnus dei. (Monteverdi, Claudio). *Schirmer. Unpriced* DGF (B74-50878)
Selva morale e spirituale. Messa a 4 da capella. Sanctus. Vocal score. Holy holy holy = Sanctus. (Monteverdi, Claudio). *Schirmer. Unpriced* DGE (B74-50877)
Senator, Ronald. Kyrie in D minor and Gloria in A major : unison. *Lengnick. £0.12* JDGB (B74-50439)
Send forth thy spirit, O Lord : Ascension or general anthem, for four-part chorus of mixed voices a cappella (or optional piano). (Newbury, Kent A). *Schirmer. Unpriced* EZDK/LM (B74-50957)
Serenade : for two strings and two winds. (Boatwright, Howard). *Oxford University Press. Unpriced* NVNS (B74-50540) ISBN 0-19-385008-7
Serenade für Flöte (Violine) und Gitarre. (Carulli, Ferdinando). *Schott. £1.32* VRPLTS (B74-50273)
Serpent. (Rorem, Ned). *Boosey and Hawkes. Unpriced* KDW (B74-51053)
Servicing electronic organs. (Applebaum, Max H). *Foulsham-Tab. £1.80* ARPV/BT (B74-27249) ISBN 0-7042-0108-9
Seven lessons for beginners. (Griffiths, Ann). *Adlais. Unpriced* TQ/AF (B74-51261)
Sevilla a Sevillanas. (Albeniz, Isaac). *Schott. £0.96* TSPMK (B74-50258)
Shakelford, Rudy. Concert set for piano : arr. Concert set for organ. (Binkerd, Gordon). *Boosey and Hawkes. £3.75* RK (B74-51198)
Shakespeare, William. Tell me where is fancy bred : for voice and guitar. (Carter, Elliott). *Associated Music. Unpriced* KE/TSDW (B74-50110)
Shanty sequence : for 4-part chorus of mixed voices unaccompanied. (Bailey, Leon). *Roberton. £0.26* EZDW (B74-50056)
Shaper, Hal. Treasure island. Vocal score. Treasure island : a musical adventure. (Ornadel, Cyril). *Sparta Florida Music : Aviva Music. £0.99* CM (B74-50006)
Sharp, Cecil. Cecil Sharp's collection of English folk songs. (Karpeles, Maud). *Oxford University Press. £44 for set* JEZDW/G/AYD (B74-51032) ISBN 0-19-313125-0
Sharp, Ian. St Katherine's Communion service, (series 3) : for congregational use, unaccompanied or with keyboard accompaniment. *Stainer and Bell. Unpriced* JDGS (B74-50440)
Sharpe, Frederick. The church bells of Berkshire : their inscriptions and founders, arranged alphabetically by parishes ... 2nd ed. *Kingsmead Reprints. £4.00* AXSR/B(YDEU) (B74-05271) ISBN 0-901571-46-6
Sharpley, Neil. Music from Ireland
Vol.1. (Bulmer, Dave). *154 Bamburgh Ave, South Shields : Dave Bulmer. Unpriced* LPM/AYDM (B74-51087)
Shaw, Francis. Four little pieces : for piano. *Ashdown. Unpriced* QPJ (B74-50183)
Shaw, Martin. I sing of a Maiden : arr. I sing of a Maiden. *Oxford University Press. Unpriced* EZDP/LF (B74-50967)
Shead, Richard. Constant Lambert. *c/o Lutterworth Press, Luke House, Farnham Rd, Guildford, Surrey : Simon Publications. £2.95* BLBP(N) (B74-05266) ISBN 0-903620-01-4
Shealy, Alexander.
The entertainer : a rag time two step. (Joplin, Scott). *Lewis Music : Ashley Fields. Unpriced* QPHXJ (B74-51153)
The entertainer: arr. The entertainer : ragtime two step. (Joplin, Scott). *Lewis Music : Ashley Fields. Unpriced* QPHXJ (B74-51156)
The entertainer: arr. The entertainer : ragtime two step. (Joplin, Scott). *Lewis Music : Ashley Fields. Unpriced* QPHXJ (B74-51157)
Five string banjo : picture chords, songs, exercises, diagrams and instructions. *Lewis Music : Ashley-Fields. Unpriced* TT/AC (B74-50710)
World's favourite best known Debussy piano music. (Debussy, Claude). *Ashley : Phoenix. Unpriced* QPJ (B74-50587)
Shepherd, Audrey. Quintet for strings in C major. D.956. Eight studies for the beginner guitarist. *Charnwood Music. Unpriced* TS/AF (B74-51272)
Shepherd, Burt. Here's Jupiter : SATB a capella (or improvised rock accompaniment ad lib.). (Kent, Richard). *Warner : Blossom. Unpriced* EZDW (B74-50979)
Shepherds : a Spanish Christmas carol sequence for voices with optional parts for guitar, tuned and untuned percussion and piano. (Hudson, Hazel). *Ashdown. £0.40* FDP/LF/AYK (B74-50415)
Shepherds' carol : old German Weihnachtslied. (Schubart, Christian Friedrich David). *Banks. Unpriced* FDP/LF (B74-50988)
Shepherd's pipe carol : for mixed voices and small orchestra. (Rutter, John). *Oxford University Press. £1.00*

EMDP/LF (B74-50029) ISBN 0-19-344803-3
Sherman, Robert. My favourite intervals. (Borge, Victor). *Woburn Press. £2.25* A/D(YB/M) (B74-09227) ISBN 0-7130-0126-7
Shield of faith : anthem for unison voices with accompaniment for organ or piano. (Eldridge, Guy). *Cramer. £0.09* JDK (B74-51019)
Shifrin, Seymour. Satires of circumstance (1969) : song cycle, soprano, flute (piccola), clarinet, violin, violoncello, double bass and piano. *Peters. Unpriced* KFLE/NUPNQDW (B74-51067)
Shinohara, Makoto. Fragment : for tenor recorder. *Schott. £0.65* VSTPMJ (B74-50779)
Shirley, Nancy. Infant holy : Polish carol. *Roberton. £0.07* FEZDP/LF (B74-50075)
Shirtcliff, J. Stanley. The married beau. *Selections: arr.* Wedding march. (Purcell, Henry). *Paxton. £0.35* RK/KDD (B74-51203)
Short, Michael. Gustav Holst - letters to W.G. Whittaker. (Holst, Gustav). *The University, Glasgow G12 8QG : University of Glasgow Press. £4.00* BHP(N) (B74-26028) ISBN 0-85261-106-4
Short history of Surrey bells and ringing customs. (Jennings, Trevor Stanley). *'Marchants', 53 Latchmere La., Kingston-upon-Thames, Surrey KT2 5SF : The author. £1.00* AXSR/E(YDCH) (B74-18432) ISBN 0-9500076-3-3
Shostakovich, Dmitry.
Quartet for strings, no.7. Op.108. Streichquartett Nr.7. Opus 108. *Peters. £3.50* RXNS (B74-51227)
Quartet for strings, no.13. Op.138. String quartet no.13. Op.138. *Boosey and Hawkes. £1.25* RXNS (B74-50657)
Shot heard round the world : for SATB chorus, organ and optional B flat trumpets. (Davis, Katherine Kennicott). *Warner : Blossom. Unpriced* DH (B74-50345)
Siebert, Edrich.
Dr Zhivago. *Somewhere my love: arr.* Somewhere by love. (Jarre, Maurice). *Francis, Day and Hunter. £0.25* WUNS (B74-50320)
Jingle bells : traditional. (Pierpont, J). *Keith Prowse. Unpriced* WMK/DW/LF (B74-51361)
Siehe zu dass deine Gottesfurcht nicht Heuchelei sei : Kantate 179 (auf den 11 Sonntag nach Trinitis). (Bach, Johann Sebastian). *Eulenburg. £1.00* EMDE (B74-50028)
Siena, Bianco da. *See* Da Siena, Bianco.
Sigman, Carl. Quand la chance est là. This old world = Quand la chance est là : for SATB chorus accompanied. (Brejean, Philippe). *Chappell. Unpriced* DW (B74-50358)
Silent spring : SATB. (Habash, John Mitri). *Robbins. Unpriced* DW (B74-50921)
Silent spring : SSA. (Habash, John Mitri). *Robbins. Unpriced* FDW (B74-50993)
Silver swan : for full chorus of mixed voices a cappella. (Chorbajian, John). *Schirmer. Unpriced* EZDW (B74-50976)
Silverman, Jerry.
Beginning the five-string banjo. *Macmillan : Collier Macmillan. Unpriced (hard cover), £1.95 (paperback)* TT/AC (B74-50711)
How to play the guitar : folk, blues, calypso. *Nelson. £1.95* TS/AC (B74-51270) ISBN 0-17-141039-4
Silverman, Stanley. Tell me where is fancy bred : for voice and guitar. (Carter, Elliott). *Associated Music. Unpriced* KE/TSDW (B74-50110)
Simon, Alfred. The Gershwins. (Kimball, Robert). *Cape. £9.50* BGH(N) (B74-24209) ISBN 0-224-01014-x
Simon, Frank.
Zillertal : for B flat cornet or trumpet with piano accompaniment. *Rubank : Novello. Unpriced* WRPJ (B74-51364)
Zillertal : for baritone with piano accompaniment. *Rubank : Novello. Unpriced* WTZPJ (B74-51370)
Zillertal : for E flat or BB flat bass with piano accompaniment. *Rubank : Novello. Unpriced* WXPJ (B74-51372)
Simpson, Dudley. Great TV themes : piano arrangements. *Affiliated Music. £0.75* QPK/JS/AY (B74-50195)
Simpson, Robert.
Symphony no.3. *Lengnick. £6.50* MME (B74-50134)
Symphony no.3 (1962). Revised ed. *Lengnick. Unpriced* MME (B74-50495)
Sinfonia to 'Hydaspes' : for trumpet, strings and basso continuo. (Mancini, Francesco). *Musica rara. Unpriced* RXMPWSE (B74-50653)
Sinfonia to 'Hydaspes' : for trumpet, strings and basso continuo. (Mancini, Francesco). *Musica rara. Unpriced* WSPK/LE (B74-50842)
Sinfonia to the serenata 'Il Barcheggio' : for trumpet, strings and basso continuo
Part 1. (Stradella, Alessandro). *Musica rara. Unpriced* RXMPWSE (B74-50654)
Part 1. (Stradella, Alessandro). *Musica rara. Unpriced* WSPK/LE (B74-50843)
Sing a new song to the Lord. Op.36, no.4 : anthem for soprano solo, SATB with divisions and organ. (Jackson, Francis). *Novello. Unpriced* DR (B74-50356)
Sing aloud unto God our strength : SATB chorus with three trumpets, three trombones and timpani. (Webb, Evelyn). *Schott. £2.00* ENYHXPNPDK (B74-50032)
Sing aloud with gladness = Exultate Deo : SATB a cappella. (Scarlatti, Alessandro). *Royal School of Church Music. £0.32* EZDJ (B74-50952)
Singing joyfully, God's power proclaim : unison voices and piano or organ. (Wills, Arthur). *Boosey and Hawkes. Unpriced* JDR (B74-50446)
S'io fusse ciaul = Were I a tiny bird : canzonetta, for four-part chorus of mixed voices a cappella. (Lasso, Orlando di). *Schirmer. Unpriced* EZDU (B74-50052)
Sir Patrick Spens : chorus and orchestra, SATB. (Young, Douglas). *Faber Music. Unpriced* DW (B74-50024)
Sir Patrick Spens. Vocal score. Sir Patrick Spens : chorus and orchestra, SATB. (Young, Douglas). *Faber Music. Unpriced* DW (B74-50024)
Sir Thomas Beecham, conductor and impresario, as remembered by his friends and colleagues. (Procter-Gregg, Humphrey). *3 Oakland, Windermere, Cumbria : H. Procter-Gregg. £3.50* A/EC(P) (B74-23498) ISBN 0-9503649-0-8
Sitwell, *Sir* Sacheverell, *bart.* The Rio Grande. (Lambert, Constant). *Oxford University Press. £1.30* EMDX (B74-50376) ISBN 0-19-337303-3
Six classical solos. (Richardson, Norman). *Boosey and Hawkes. Unpriced* WUPK/AAY (B74-51371)
Six inventions for harpsichord
Set 1. (Dodgson, Stephen). *Chappell. Unpriced* QRPJ (B74-50606)
Set 2. (Dodgson, Stephen). *Chappell. Unpriced* QRPJ (B74-50607)
Set 3. (Dodgson, Stephen). *Chappell. Unpriced* QRPJ (B74-50608)
Six low solos : bassoon and piano. (Hughes, Eric). *Emerson. Unpriced* VWPJ (B74-50297)
Six pieces for bassoon and piano. (Srebotnjak, Alojz). *Schirmer. £1.15* VWPJ (B74-50812)
Six pieces from the Fitzwilliam Virginal Book. *Oxford University Press. £0.45* VSNUK (B74-51334) ISBN 0-19-355550-6
Six voluntaries for trumpet and organ. (Cooper, Barry). *Musica rara. Unpriced* WSPLRK/AAY (B74-50844)
Skelton, Geoffrey. Lehrstuch (1929). Vocal score. Lehrstuck (1929). (Hindemith, Paul). *Schott. £4.35* DX (B74-50929)
Skempton, Howard. Piano pieces. *Faber Music. Unpriced* QPJ (B74-50184)
Skoda, Paul Badura-. *See* Badura-Skoda, Paul.
Skriabin, Aleksandr Nikolaevich.
Studies for piano. Op.8. 12 studies for piano. Op.8. *Peters. Unpriced* QPJ (B74-51180)
Symphony no.2 in C minor. Op. 29. *Eulenburg. Unpriced* MME (B74-50135)
Skrjabin, Alexander. *See* Skriabin, Aleksandr Nikolaevich.
Slack, Roy. Too many clarinets : mini-suite for clarinets and strings. *Keith Prowse. £0.65* NVVG (B74-50153)
Slatford, Rodney. Duo for double bass and cello. (Massenet, Jules). *Yorke. Unpriced* SRPLSS (B74-50683)
Slind, Lloyd H.
Basic goals in music
Book 3. (Morrish, D L). *McGraw-Hill. Unpriced* C/AC (B74-50862) ISBN 0-07-094432-6
Book 4. (Morrish, D L). *McGraw-Hill. Unpriced* C/AC (B74-50863) ISBN 0-07-094433-4
Book 5. (Morrish, D L). *McGraw-Hill. Unpriced* C/AC (B74-50864) ISBN 0-07-094434-2
Slippin' around the corner. (Previn, André). *Chappell. Unpriced* DW (B74-50363)
Sloane, Irving. Guitar repair : a manual of repair for guitars and fretted instruments. *Nelson. £2.50* ATR/BT (B74-28318) ISBN 0-17-149062-2
Slonimski, Sergei. Chromatic poem : for organ (1969). *Peters. Unpriced* RJ (B74-51196)
Slowly : three-part women's voices and piano. (Plumstead, Mary). *Boosey and Hawkes. Unpriced* FDW (B74-50421)
Small, Winifred. Rondo for oboe or violin and piano. (Head, Michael). *Boosey and Hawkes. £0.60* VTP/W (B74-50781)
Smart, Christopher.
The children of David. Op.37 : five modern psalms, for mixed chorus and organ
3: The song of David. (Mechem, Kirke). *Boosey and Hawkes. Unpriced* DH (B74-50900)
Easter day : anthem for female or boys' voices and organ. (Rose, Michael). *Novello. £0.14* DH/LL (B74-50018)
Smetana, Bedřich. My country. Vltava. My fatherland = Ma vlast : a cycle of symphonic poems
No.2: Vltava. *Eulenburg. Unpriced* MMJ (B74-50507)
Smith, Geoffry Russell-. *See*
Russell-Smith, Geoffrey.
Russell-Smith, Geoffry.
Smith, Henry Charles. Duets for two horns. K.487: arr. 12 easy duets for winds
Volume 3: For trombones, baritones, tubas (and cellos and basses ad lib). (Mozart, Wolfgang Amadeus). *Schirmer. Unpriced* UNUK (B74-50742)
Smith, Mollie Russell-. *See* Russell-Smith, Mollie.
Smith, Peter.
Jesus folk : a new collection of folk songs. *Galliard : Stainer and Bell. Unpriced* JE/TSDM/AY (B74-51026) ISBN 0-85249-304-5
Sonata for strings & basso continuo in G minor. Op.35, 'La Sampiera'. Sonata 'La Sampiera' : for strings and continuo. (Cazzati, Mauritio). *Schott. £1.50* NXNRE (B74-50155)
Stabat mater : for SATB soli and chorus, string orchestra and organ continuo. (Bononcini, Antonio). *Novello. £1.25* EMDGKADD/LK (B74-50373)
Smith, Peter Melville. Joy to the world : treble voices. *Banks. Unpriced* FLDP/LF (B74-51010)
Smith, Stevie. Fafnir and the knights, and other settings of poems by Stevie Smith : for treble voices and piano duet. (Pehkonen, Elis). *Lengnick. £2.00* FLDX (B74-50079)
Smokey smokestack : SATB. (Habash, John Mitri). *Robbins. Unpriced* DW (B74-50922)
Smokey smokestack : SSA. (Habash, John Mitri). *Robbins. Unpriced* FDW (B74-50994)
Snyder, Randall. Variations for wind ensemble. *Schirmer. Unpriced* UMM/T (B74-51303)
Soft shoe dance : for double bass and piano. (Hoag, Charles Kelso). *Schirmer. Unpriced* SSPHVPS (B74-50252)
Softly and gently. Op.4, no.3 : for voice and piano. (Holst, Gustav). *Bosworth. Unpriced* KDW (B74-51048)
Solace : a Mexican serenade, for piano. (Joplin, Scott). *Chappell. Unpriced* QPHXJ (B74-50582)
Šolc, Karel. Concerto for piano, no.4, 'Incantation': arr. Incantation : 4th piano concerto. (Martinu, Bohuslav). *Supraphon : Bärenreiter. £3.60* QNUK/LF (B74-50563)
Soler, Antonio. Soleriana for concert band. (Surinach, Carlos). *Associated Music. Unpriced* UMHK/T (B74-50261)
Soleriana for concert band. (Surinach, Carlos). *Associated Music. Unpriced* UMHK/T (B74-50261)
Soliloquy and dance : for harp. (Parrott, Ian). *Thames. Unpriced* TQPMH (B74-51265)
Soliloquy : for solo flute. (Stoker, Richard). *Ashdown. £0.30* VRPMJ (B74-50763)
Soliloquy : for solo violin. (Butt, James). *Thames. Unpriced* SPMG (B74-51249)
Soliloquys sic. Opus 39 : solo cello. (Barrell, Bernard). *Thames. Unpriced* SRPMJ (B74-51255)
Solo for alto saxophone and piano. (Heiden, Bernhard). *Associated Music Publishers. £1.15* VUSPJ (B74-50793)
Solo oboe piece. Opus 84. (Josephs, Wilfred). *Novello. £0.50* VTPMJ (B74-50789)
Solos for a German flute. Op.1, 4. Complete works for flute and basso continuo
Set 1: Solo 1 in D minor, Solo 2 in G minor (from Eight solos, opus 1). (Stanley, John). *Oxford University Press. £2.50* VRP/AZ (B74-50747) ISBN 0-19-358896-x
Solos for a German flute. Op.1, 4. Complete works for flute and basso continuo
Set 2: Solo 3 in G major, Solo 4 in D major (from Eight solos, opus 1). (Stanley, John). *Oxford University Press. £2.50* VRP/AZ (B74-50748) ISBN 0-19-358897-8
Solos for a German flute. Op.1, 4. Complete works for flute and basso continuo
Set 3: Solo 5 in C major, Solo 6 in D major (from Eight solos, opus 1). (Stanley, John). *Oxford University Press. £2.50* VRP/AZ (B74-50749) ISBN 0-19-358898-6
Solos for a German flute. Op.1, 4. Complete works for flute and basso continuo
Set 4: Solo 7 in D minor, Solo 8 in E minor (from Eight solos, opus 1). (Stanley, John). *Oxford University Press. £2.50* VRP/AZ (B74-50750) ISBN 0-19-358899-4
Solos for the vibraphone player. (Finkel, Ian). *Schirmer. Unpriced* XTQTPMK/AAY (B74-50861)
Solymos, Peter. French piano music : for the young musician. *Boosey and Hawkes. £1.00* PWP/AYH (B74-50157)

Some of Noah's ark, Op.55 : six sketches for guitar. (Duarte, John William). *Ricordi. Unpriced* TSPMJ (B74-50701)
Somewhere by love. (Jarre, Maurice). *Francis, Day and Hunter. £0.25* WUNS (B74-50320)
Sommer, Jürgen.
Barock : elektronische Orgel. *Nagel : Bärenreiter. £1.80* RPVK/AAY (B74-50631)
Klassik : elektronische Orgel. *Nagel : Bärenreiter. £1.80* RPVK/AAY (B74-50632)
Oper : elektronische Orgel. *Nagel : Bärenreiter. £1.80* RPVK/AAY (B74-50633)
Volkslieder : elektronische Orgel. *Nagel : Bärenreiter. £1.80* RPVK/DW/G/AYE (B74-50635)
Sonata. (Scarlatti, Domenico). *Oxford University Press. Unpriced* UMK/AE (B74-50720)
Sonata à 3 : for violin, trombone, bassoon & basso continuo. (Schmelzer, Johann Heinrich). *Musica rara. Unpriced* NUNSE (B74-50523)
Sonata for piano, no.6. Op.78, no.3. Sonata no.6. Opus 78, no.3. (Hoddinott, Alun). *Oxford University Press. £1.25* QPE (B74-50572) ISBN 0-19-372840-0
Sonata for strings & basso continuo in G minor. Op.35, 'La Sampiera'. Sonata 'La Sampiera' : for strings and continuo. (Cazzati, Mauritio). *Schott. £1.50* NXNRE (B74-50155)
Sonata giocosa per la renascita di una cattedrale. Opus 42 organ. (Jackson, Francis). *Oxford University Press. £1.80* RE (B74-51189)
Sonata monotematica : für Violoncello (oder Fagott) und Klavier. (Reutter, Hermann). *Schott. £1.92* SRPE (B74-50247)
Sonatina classica : piano. (Camilleri, Charles). *Roberton. £0.50* QPEM (B74-51146)
Sonatina dolorosa : for solo guitar. (Roe, Betty). *Thames. Unpriced* TSPMEM (B74-51273)
Songs and ballads of northern England. (Stokoe, John). 1st ed., reprinted. *Graham. £5.00* KDW/K/G/AYDJJ (B74-50109) ISBN 0-85983-040-3
Songs and epilogues : for bass voice and piano. (Travis, Roy). *Oxford University Press. Unpriced* KGXDW (B74-51078)
Songs for 'Singing Together' : fifty songs from around the world taken from the BBC's music programme Singing Together. (Coombes, Douglas). *British Broadcasting Corporation. £1.25* JFDW/G/AY (B74-51036) ISBN 0-563-13189-6
Songs from Cole : an entertainment. (Porter, Cole). *Chappell. Unpriced* KDW (B74-51051)
Songs of fellowship. (Pulkingham, Betty Carr). *The Fishermen Inc., by arrangement with the Fountanin Trust. Unpriced* JE/TSDM/AY (B74-50087)
Songs of Ophelia, nos. 3, 4. Christmas cradle song. (Brahms, Johannes). *Novello. Unpriced* EZDP/LF (B74-50959)
Songs of protest, war and peace : a bibliography &

discography. (Denisoff, R Serge). Revised ed. *30 Cornmarket St., Oxford OX1 3EY : ABC-Clio Inc. £1.45* ADW/KJWX(T) (B74-16447) ISBN 0-87436-121-4
Sor, Fernando.
Divertimento for guitar, no.1. Op.1. First set of divertimenti. Op.1. *Oxford University Press. £0.50* TSPMJ (B74-50702) ISBN 0-19-358863-3
Divertimento for guitar, no.2. Op.2. Second set of divertimenti. Op.2. *Oxford University Press. £0.50* TSPMJ (B74-50703) ISBN 0-19-358864-1
Divertimento for guitar, no.3. Op.8. Third set of divertimenti. Op.8. *Oxford Universtion Press. £0.50* TSPMJ (B74-50704) ISBN 0-19-358865-x
Fantasia for guitar, no.1, in C major. Op.7. Fantasia no.1, Op.7. *Oxford University Press. £0.50* TSPMJ (B74-50705) ISBN 0-19-358860-9
Fantasia for guitar, no.2, in A major. Op.4. Fantasia no.2. Op.4. *Oxford University Press. £0.40* TSPMJ (B74-50706) ISBN 0-19-358861-7
Fantasia for guitar, no.3, in F major. Op.10. Fantasia no.3, Op.10. *Oxford University Press. Unpriced* TSPMJ (B74-50707) ISBN 0-19-358862-5
Sosnik, Harry. El Paseo grande = The big walk : military band. *Warner : Blossom. Unpriced* UMMJ (B74-50731)
Soul, pop, rock, stars, superstars. *Octopus Books. £3.95* AKDW/GB/E(M/XPK19) (B74-29003) ISBN 0-7064-0409-2
Sound in the round. *National Federation of Women's Institutes. £0.15* FE/XNDW/XC (B74-50426) ISBN 0-900556-42-0
Sound of living waters : songs of revival. (Pulkingham, Betty). *Hodder and Stoughton. Unpriced* DM/AY (B74-50908) ISBN 0-340-18893-6
Sound world : a collection of new keyboard experiences for the intermediate pianist and the advanced beginner. (Applebaum, Stan). *Schroeder and Gunther. Unpriced* Q/AF (B74-51127)
Sounds and signs : aspects of musical notation. (Cole, Hugo). *Oxford University Press. £1.50* A(QU) (B74-02414) ISBN 0-19-317105-8
Southworth, Mary. How to make musical sounds. *Studio Vista. £1.25* AL/BC (B74-05792) ISBN 0-289-70405-7
Spanish dances for piano, vol.2. Andaluza: arr. Andaluza. (Granados, Enrique). *Schott. £1.00* VSNRQK/AH (B74-51331)
Spartans of tomorrow : march, for wind band. (Balent, Andrew). *Warner : Blossom. Unpriced* UMGM (B74-51292)
Spektren für Klavier (1967). (Reimann, Aribert). *Ars Viva. £1.92* QPJ (B74-50182)
Spence, Lewis. The plumes of time : 4 songs for medium voice and piano. (Hamilton, Alasdair). *Roberton. £0.50* KFVDW (B74-50117)
Speth, Johann. Ars magna consoni et dissoni : for organ. *Bärenreiter. £3.80* RJ (B74-50621)
Spinacino, Francesco. Mon mary m'a diffamée : chanson, S.T.T. (Brown, Howard Mayer). *Oxford University Press. Unpriced* ETWDU (B74-50035) ISBN 0-19-341203-9
Spink, Ian. English song, Dowland to Purcell. *Batsford. £5.50* ADW(YD/XE101) (B74-06503) ISBN 0-7134-0756-5
Spiritual songs, with music. *The Horton Trust. Unpriced* DM/AY (B74-50020)
Spiritual songs with music. *1 Sherbourne Rd., Great Horton, Bradford : Horton Trust. Unpriced* DM/AY (B74-50909)
Spohr, Louis. Potpourri for clarinet & piano. Op.80. *Musica rara. Unpriced* VVPJ (B74-50802)
Spring cantata : SATB
I: The succession of the four sweet months. (Washburn, Robert). *Boosey and Hawkes. Unpriced* EZDX (B74-50981)
II: April. (Washburn, Robert). *Boosey and Hawkes. Unpriced* EZDX (B74-50982)
III: May. (Washburn, Robert). *Boosey and Hawkes. Unpriced* EZDX (B74-50983)
IV: Lazy June. (Washburn, Robert). *Boosey and Hawkes. Unpriced* EZDX (B74-50984)
V: July. (Washburn, Robert). *Boosey and Hawkes. Unpriced* EZDX (B74-50985)
Spurgin, Anthony. Lions and martlets : fantasia for brass band. *British and Continental. Unpriced* WMJ (B74-50310)
Square set : for two pianos. (Haufrecht, Herbert). *Associated Music. Unpriced* QNUHG (B74-50162)
Srebotnjak, Alojz. Six pieces for bassoon and piano. *Schirmer. £1.15* VWPJ (B74-50812)
Stage fright : its causes and cures, with special reference to violin playing. (Havas, Kato). *Bosworth. £2.50* AS/E/CS (B74-12392) ISBN 0-900180-69-2
Stage struck : song. (Previn, André). *Chappell. Unpriced* DW (B74-50364)
Stahmer, Klaus. Patterns : for percussion instruments (four or more). *Schott. £2.90* XNS (B74-51374)
Stained glass windows (and simple wood benches). (Millet, Kadish). *Chappell. Unpriced* DW (B74-50925)
Stamitz, Anton. Concerto for viola & string orchestra, no.4, in D major: arr. Concerto no.4 in D major for viola and strings. *Breitkopf and Härtel : Bärenreiter. £2.90* SQPK/LF (B74-50678)
Stand up for America! : for mixed chorus, SATB. (Peet, Richard). *Chappell. Unpriced* DW (B74-50362)
Standford, Patric.
Siciliano : for violin and piano. *Lengnick. £0.25* SPHVQ (B74-50234)
Sonata for violin solo. Op.36. *Novello. £0.75* SPME (B74-50237)
Trio for violin, cello & piano. *Novello. £1.50* NXNT (B74-50156)
Stanfield, Milly Bernardine. The intermediate cellist. *Oxford University Press. £2.00* ASR/E (B74-03505) ISBN 0-19-318508-3
Stanley, John.
Concerto for keyboard & string orchestra. Op.10, no.6: arr. Concerto in C major. *Oxford University Press. £0.90* RK/LF (B74-51204) ISBN 0-19-367705-9
Solos for a German flute. Op.1, 4. Complete works for flute and basso continuo
Set 1: Solo 1 in D minor, Solo 2 in G minor (from Eight solos, opus 1). *Oxford University Press. £2.50* VRP/AZ (B74-50747) ISBN 0-19-358896-x
Solos for a German flute. Op.1, 4. Complete works for flute and basso continuo
Set 2: Solo 3 in G major, Solo 4 in D major (from Eight solos, opus 1). *Oxford University Press. £2.50* VRP/AZ (B74-50748) ISBN 0-19-358897-8
Solos for a German flute. Op.1, 4. Complete works for flute and basso continuo
Set 3: Solo 5 in C major, Solo 6 in D major (from Eight solos, opus 1). *Oxford University Press. £2.50* VRP/AZ (B74-50749) ISBN 0-19-358898-6
Solos for a German flute. Op.1, 4. Complete works for flute and basso continuo
Set 4: Solo 7 in D minor, Solo 8 in E minor (from Eight solos, opus 1). *Oxford University Press. £2.50* VRP/AZ (B74-50750) ISBN 0-19-358899-4
Stapert, Calvin R.
Kyrie and Gloria for the Saturday Lady Mass : two-part (male voices). *Oxford University Press. £0.20* GEZDGB (B74-51014) ISBN 0-19-341217-9
Kyrie and Gloria for the Saturday Lady Mass : two-part (male voices). (Stapert, Calvin R). *Oxford University Press. £0.20* GEZDGB (B74-51014) ISBN 0-19-341217-9
Star of Erin : quick march for military band. (Horabin, E G). *Boosey and Hawkes. £0.65* UMMGM (B74-50725)
Steane, John Barry. The grand tradition : seventy years of singing on record. *Duckworth. £10.00* AB/FD (B74-15525) ISBN 0-7156-0661-1
Stein, Erwin. Letters of Arnold Schoenberg. (Schoenberg, Arnold). *Faber. £2.95* BSET(N) (B74-04793) ISBN 0-571-10514-9
Stein, Gertrude. Three sisters who are not sisters. *Vocal score.* Three sisters who are not sisters : an opera. (Rorem, Ned). *Boosey and Hawkes. £4.25* CC (B74-50872)
Steinitz, Paul. Geistliche Concerten, Tl.2. Dialogus. Kommt her ihr Gesegneten meines Vaters = Come ye blessed ones of my Father : dialogue for five voices (SATTB) and continuo. (Scheidt, Samuel). *Novello. £1.00* JNBDH (B74-51043)
Steinman, David Ward-. *See* Ward-Steinman, David.
Stent, Keith. Two carols for the Caribbean. *Novello. £0.24* ENYLDP/LF (B74-50936)
Stephan, Wolfgang. Trio concertante for two clarinets & bassoon in C major. Op.1. Trio, C-Dur. Op.1 : für zwei Klarinetten und Fagott. (Carulli, Benedetto). *Schott. £5.22* VNTF (B74-51315)
Stephens, Hugh. Humming bird : waltz song. *Hambly Music. £0.20* KDW (B74-50467)
Stephens, Norris L. Mass in G major. D.167. Vocal score. Mass in G D.167. (Schubert, Franz). *Schirmer. Unpriced* DG (B74-50338)
Sterne, Colin. Canzoni da sonare, lib. 1. *Romanesca.* Canzona on 'Romanesca'. (Frescobaldi, Girolamo). *Associated Music. Unpriced* VSNRPW (B74-50275)
Stevens, Denis. La Messe de Nostre Dame : SATB, strings and two trombones. (Machaut, Guillaume de). *Oxford University Press. £0.75* ENVXUDG (B74-50031) ISBN 0-19-337395-5
Stevens, Gillian. This endris night : SATB unacc. *Banks. Unpriced* EZDP/LF (B74-50968)
Stevens, John. Two songs for Christmas. (Bent, Margaret). *Oxford University Press. Unpriced* EZDP/LF (B74-50405) ISBN 0-19-341208-x
Stevens, Wallace. Last poems of Wallace Stevens : for voice, cello and piano. (Rorem, Ned). *Boosey and Hawkes. £3.00* KE/SRPDW (B74-50478)
Stevenson, Robert Louis. Beach of Falesá. *Adaptations.* The beach of Falesá : opera in three acts. (Jones, Glyn, *b.1905*). *Oxford University Press, Music Department. £0.70* BHNDAC (B74-09229) ISBN 0-19-336833-1
Stewart, Lawrence Delbert. The Gershwin years. (Jablonski, Edward). *Robson Books. £6.95* BGH(N) (B74-27798) ISBN 0-903895-19-6
Stockhausen, Karlheinz.
Stockhausen : conversations with the composer. (Cott, Jonathan). *Pan Books. £0.95* BSNK (B74-27248) ISBN 0-330-24165-6
Stockhausen : conversations with the composer. (Cott, Jonathan). *28 Poland St., W1V 3DB : Robson Books Ltd. £3.50* BSNK (B74-10399) ISBN 0-903895-12-9
Stockhausen : conversations with the composer. (Cott, Jonathan). *28 Poland St., W1V 3DB : Robson Books Ltd. £3.50* BSNK (B74-10399) ISBN 0-903895-12-9
Stoddard, Tom. Pops Foster - the autobiography of a New Orleans jazzman. (Foster, Pops). *University of California Press. £1.65* AMT(P) (B74-03506) ISBN 0-520-02355-2
Stoker, Richard.
Benedictus. Vocal score. Benedictus : for SATB and organ, or for SATB, organ and orchestra. *Ashdown. Unpriced* DGNS (B74-50882)
Chorale for strings. *Fenette Music : Breitkopf and Härtel. Unpriced* RXMJ (B74-50643)
The glory of the dove : for S.A., T.B., or SATB (unaccompanied). *Ashdown. Unpriced* EZDW (B74-50409)
Little symphony. *Boosey and Hawkes. £3.30* ME (B74-50130)
Proverbs. Vocal score. Proverbs : for SATB and organ. *Ashdown. £0.15* DK (B74-50906)
Soliloquy : for solo flute. *Ashdown. £0.30* VRPMJ (B74-50763)
Sonata for piano, no.1. Opus 26. Piano sonata, no.1. Opus 26. *Peters. Unpriced* QPE (B74-50573)
A supplication : for SAB unaccompanied. *Ashdown. £0.12* EZDW (B74-50062)
Three pieces for oboe solo or cor anglais. Opus 29. *Peters. Unpriced* VTPMJ (B74-50790)
Triptych : for clarinet in B flat or bass clarinet. *Ashdown. £0.30* VVPMJ (B74-50806)
Stokoe, John. Songs and ballads of northern England. 1st ed., reprinted. *Graham. £5.00* KDW/K/G/AYDJJ (B74-50109) ISBN 0-85983-040-3
Stone, David.
L'Arlesienne, 1st suite. Carillon: arr. Carillon. (Bizet, Georges). *Boosey and Hawkes. Score £1.50, Piano conductor £0.50, Set £2.50* MK/JM (B74-51091)
Eight Russian folksongs. Op. 58, nos. 1, 2, 4: arr. Russian folksongs, set 1. (Liadov, Anatoly). *Boosey and Hawkes. Score £1.50, Piano conductor £0.50, Set £2.50* MK (B74-51090)
Eight Russian folksongs. Op.58, nos. 6-8: arr. Russian folksongs. Set 2. (Liadov, Anatoly). *Boosey and Hawkes. £4.50* MH (B74-51088)
Stone, David C.
Sonata for violin & basso continuo, no.3, in G major. Violin sonata no.3 in G major. (Gibbs, Joseph). *Schott. Unpriced* SPE (B74-51240)
Sonata for violin & basso continuo, no.5, in E major. Violin sonata no.5 in E major. (Gibbs, Joseph). *Schott. Unpriced* SPE (B74-51241)
Stones Touring Party : a journey through America with the Rolling Stones. (Greenfield, Robert). *Joseph. £3.00* AKDW/GB/E(P) (B74-25497) ISBN 0-7181-1249-0
Story of pop. *Adaptations.* Soul, pop, rock, stars, superstars. *Octopus Books. £3.95* AKDW/GB/E(M/XPK19) (B74-29003) ISBN 0-7064-0409-2
Story of Vasco : opera in three acts. (Crosse, Gordon, *b.1937*). *Oxford University Press, Music Department. £0.70* BCRAC (B74-09228) ISBN 0-19-335702-x
STP. Stones Touring Party : a journey through America with the Rolling Stones. (Greenfield, Robert). *Joseph. £3.00* AKDW/GB/E(P) (B74-25497) ISBN 0-7181-1249-0
Stradella, Alessandro.
Il Barcheggio. Sinfonia. Sinfonia to the serenata 'Il Barcheggio' : for trumpet, strings and basso continuo Part 1. *Musica rara. Unpriced* RXMPWSE (B74-50654)
Il Barcheggio. Sinfonia: arr. Sinfonia to the serenata 'Il Barcheggio' : for trumpet, strings and basso continuo Part 1. *Musica rara. Unpriced* WSPK/LE (B74-50843)
Strangeways, A H Fox-. *See* Fox-Strangeways, A H.
Strauss, Johann, *b.1825.* Der Zigeunerbaron. Selections: arr. The gypsy baron suite. *Boosey and Hawkes. £15.00* MMK (B74-50143)
Strauss, Richard.
Andante for horn & piano in C major. Op. posth. Andante für Horn und Klavier. Op. posth. *Boosey and Hawkes. £0.65* WTPJ (B74-50318)
Till Eulenspiegel. Op.28. Till Eulenspiegels Lustige Streiche : nach alter Schelmenweise in Rondeauforme. *Eulenburg. Unpriced* MMJ (B74-51105)
Strauss family. (Bailey, Andrew). *Wise : Distributed by Music Sales Ltd. £1.50* QPK/AH (B74-50602)
Stravinsky, Igor. Firebird. Selections: arr. L'Oiseau de feu = Der Feuervogel. *Schott. £1.44* QPK/HM (B74-50194)
Stravinsky, Soulima. Firebird. Selections: arr. L'Oiseau de feu = Der Feuervogel. (Stravinsky, Igor). *Schott. £1.44* QPK/HM (B74-50194)
Strawberry fair : two-part. (Brown, Christopher). *Oxford University Press. £0.08* FDW (B74-50990) ISBN 0-19-341509-7
Strawinsky, Igor. *See* Stravinsky, Igor.
Street, Tison. Quartet for strings (1972). String quartet (1972). *Schirmer. Unpriced* RXNS (B74-51228)
Streetman, David. Geistlicher Harmonien, erster Teil. *Wie der Hirsch schreiet.* As the deer cries for flowing water : for four-part chorus of mixed voices with organ accompaniment. (Bernhard, Christoph). *Roberton. £0.26* DH (B74-50011)
Structure of atonal music. (Forte, Allen). *Yale University Press. £4.95* A/PN/PF (B74-11052) ISBN 0-300-01610-7
Stschedrin, Rodion. *See* Schedrin, Rodion.
Studies for two equal clarinets. (Harvey, Jonathan). *Novello. £0.75* VVNU (B74-50800)
Study piece : portrait of a lady, for band. (Thomson, Virgil). *Schirmer. Unpriced* UMJ (B74-50265)
Sturman, Paul. Seasons : unison. *Ashdown. £0.40* JDW (B74-50086)
Sudhalter, Richard M. Bix - man & legend. *Quartet Books. £4.95* AMT(P) (B74-27251) ISBN 0-7043-2070-3
Sugár, Rezsö. Hungarian children's songs : for piano. *Boosey and Hawkes. £0.85* QPJ (B74-50185)
Sugár, Rezso. Hungarian children's songs : for piano duet. *Boosey and Hawkes. £0.85* QNV (B74-50566)
Suite de pièces. Op.24. (Bennett, *Sir* William Sterndale). *Stainer and Bell. Unpriced* QPG (B74-50576)
Suite espagnole. Sevilla. Granada Serenata : für Gitarre. (Albeniz, Isaac). *Schott. £0.72* TSPMK (B74-50257)
Suite espagnole. *Sevilla.* Sevilla a Sevillanas. (Albeniz, Isaac). *Schott. £0.96* TSPMK (B74-50258)
Suite for strings, no.3, from Musick's Handmaid. Third suite for strings, from Musick's Handmaid. (Cruft, Adrian). *Chappell. Unpriced* RXMG (B74-50217)

Suite im alten Stil für Violine und Klavier. Opus 93,. (Reger, Max). *Peters. Unpriced* SPG (B74-51242)

Suite in D : for oboe and harpsichord (piano). (Dodgson, Stephen). *Oxford University Press. £1.10* VTPJ (B74-50783) ISBN 0-19-356268-5

Suite, Love and honour : for strings and continuo. (Morgan, Thomas). *Oxford University Press. £1.75* RXMG (B74-50641) ISBN 0-19-357824-7

Suite no.1 : arranged for trumpet in B flat and piano from the music of G.P. Telemann. (Telemann, Georg Philipp). *Boosey and Hawkes. £0.65* WSPJ (B74-50836)

Suite no.2. (Telemann, Georg Philipp). *Boosey and Hawkes. £0.65* WSPJ (B74-50835)

Suite, The lion, the witch and the wardrobe : for orchestra. (McCabe, John). *Novello. £3.50* MMG (B74-50499)

Sullivan, *Sir* Arthur Seymour.

Selections: arr. Gilbert and Sullivan for descant recorder with chord symbols for guitar, piano or tuned percussion. *British and Continental. Unpriced* VSRPMK/DW (B74-51336)

Works, operettas. Selections: arr. The best of Gilbert and Sullivan : songs from operettas arranged with piano accompaniment. *Chappell. Unpriced* KDW (B74-50468)

Summer rhapsody : for piano. (Ashburnham, George). *Ashburnham School of Music. Unpriced* QPJ (B74-51162)

Sumner, William Leslie. The organ : its evolution, principles of construction and use. 4th ed. revised and enlarged. *Macdonald and Co. £5.00* AR/B(X) (B74-01931) ISBN 0-356-04162-x

Sumsion, Herbert. Magnificat and Nunc dimittis in D : for boys' voices. *Royal School of Church Music. Unpriced* FDGPP (B74-50067)

Sun music IV : for orchestra. (Sculthorpe, Peter). *Faber Music. Unpriced* MMJ (B74-50142)

Suoni. Op.62 : for flute, marimba and full chorus of women's voices. (Nystedt, Knut). *Associated Music. Unpriced* FE/VRPLXTQSDX (B74-50425)

Supplication : for SAB unaccompanied. (Stoker, Richard). *Ashdown. £0.12* EZDW (B74-50062)

Surely he has borne our sorrows = Fürwahr, Er trug uns're Krankheit : S.A.T.B. with accompaniment. (Herbst, Johannes). Moramus ed. *Boosey and Hawkes. Unpriced* DH (B74-50346)

Surinach, Carlos.

Prayers : for voice and guitar. *Associated Music Publishers. £0.70* KE/TSDW (B74-50480)

Soleriana for concert band. *Associated Music. Unpriced* UMHK/T (B74-50261)

Via crucis : a cycle of fifteen saetas, for four-part chorus of mixed voices and Spanish guitar. *Associated Music. Unpriced* ETSDE (B74-50380)

Survey of musical activities in Cornwall. (Combellack, Myrna May). *Trevenson House, Pool, Redruth, Cornwall : Institute of Cornish Studies. £0.30* A(YDFR) (B74-22803) ISBN 0-903686-05-8

Sutcliffe, James H. Love will find out the way : English folk song. *Roberton. £0.10* EZDW (B74-50063)

Sutermeister, Heinrich. Concerto for cello, no.2: arr. 2. Konzert für Violoncello und Orchester (1971). *Schott. £8.70* SRPK/LF (B74-51254)

Sutherland, Douglas. Twilight of the swans. *New English Library. £3.00* A(P) (B74-11051) ISBN 0-450-01876-8

Suzuki, Yoshiharu. E.H. Grieg's 'Peer Gynt'. *F. Warne. £1.75* BGTAM/JMBN (B74-26152) ISBN 0-7232-1784-x

Swan Lake. *See* Hatsuyama, Shigeru.

Swenson, Warren. Feed us now, O Son of God: arr. Feed us now, O Son of God. (Allen, Peter). *Galaxy : Galliard. Unpriced* EZDH (B74-50386)

Swift, Basil. Das klagende Lied, no.1. Waldmärchen. Vocal score. Waldmärchen = A forest legend (Das klagende Lied: 1). (Mahler, Gustav). *Belwin-Mills. Unpriced* DX (B74-50371)

Sylvester, Joshua. Joy to the world : treble voices. (Smith, Peter Melville). *Banks. Unpriced* FLDP/LF (B74-51010)

Symons, Mary. Fingers and thumbs : a project of preliminary exercises at the pianoforte. *60 Muswell Rd, N.10 : C.W. Daniel. Unpriced* Q/ELM/AF (B74-50560) ISBN 0-85207-112-4

Symphonie fantastique. (Berlioz, Hector). *Breitkopf and Härtel : Bärenreiter. £13.20* MME (B74-50494)

Symphonies of Havergal Brian

Vol.1: Symphonies 1-12. (MacDonald, Malcolm, *b.1948*). *25 Thurloe St., S.W.7 : Kahn and Averill. £3.50* BBTNAME (B74-14310) ISBN 0-900707-28-3

Symphony no.3. (Tippett, *Sir* Michael). *Schott. Unpriced* KFLE/MDX (B74-50114)

Synonyms for life. Op. 33 : for four-part chorus of mixed voices with piano accompaniment. (Muczynsky, Robert). *Schirmer. Unpriced* DW (B74-50023)

Systematic discography. (Foreman, Lewis). *Bingley. £3.00* A/FD(U) (B74-25104) ISBN 0-85157-161-1

Szávai, Magda. Music for piano (intermediate). *Boosey and Hawkes. £1.00* QP/AY (B74-50166)

Szelényi, István. Piano works

Vol.4: Hungarian rhapsodies II, nos 10-19. (Liszt, Franz). *Bärenreiter. £2.90* QP/AZ (B74-50571)

Szönyi, Erzsébet. Musical reading and writing

Vol.1. *Boosey and Hawkes. £2.95* A(VC/QU) (B74-25493) ISBN 0-85162-011-6

Ta luv : song. (Previn, André). *Chappell. Unpriced* KDW (B74-50463)

Ta, ta, ta. G.205. To Maelzel : for 4-part chorus of mixed voices unaccompanied or with wood-block. (Beethoven, Ludwig van). *Roberton. £0.12* EZDW/X (B74-50412)

Ta, ta, ta. K.-H 162. To Maelzel : for 4-part chorus of female voices unaccompanied or with wood-block. (Beethoven, Ludwig van). *Roberton. £0.10* FEZDW/X (B74-50432)

Table for starting courses of Stedman Cinques in the Tittums. (Burton, Shirley). *c/o 'Monsal', Bredon, Tewkesbury, Glos. GL20 7LY : Central Council of Church Bell Ringers, Education Committee. Unpriced* XSR (B74-50855)

Tagore, Rabindranath. Drei Lieder : für Bariton und Klavier. (Hohensee, Wolfgang). *Peters. Unpriced* KGNDW (B74-51077)

Take me high : song album. (Cole, Tony). *Coronado Music. £0.75* KDW/JR (B74-50108)

Take your partners : easy arrangements of English country dance tunes (from the English Dancing Master) for descant recorder and guitar. (Duarte, John William). *Novello. £0.50* VSRPLTSK/AH/G/AYD (B74-50284)

Tallis, Thomas.

English sacred music

1: Anthems. *Stainer and Bell. Unpriced* CB/LD (B74-50329)

2: Service music. *Stainer and Bell. Unpriced* CB/LD (B74-50330)

Tamblyn, William. You are Peter : brass accompaniment, 3 trumpets and trombone. *Boosey and Hawkes. £0.40* EWNSDK (B74-50384)

Tango brasileiro. 30 de maio : guitar. (Anderaos, Nelson). *Fermata de Brasil : Essex Music. Unpriced* TSPMHVR (B74-51274)

Tanz-Metamorphosen : für Streicher. (Mouravieff, Leon). *Litolff : Peters. Unpriced* RXMJ (B74-51218)

Tanzstücke für zwei Altblockflöten

Heft 2. (Genzmer, Harald). *Schott. £1.08* VSSNU (B74-50287)

Tarr, Edward H.

Sonata for trumpet, string trio & basso continuo in D major. G.1. Sonata for trumpet, strings and continuo in D. G. I. (Torelli, Giuseppe). *Musica rara. Unpriced* NUXSNRE (B74-50536)

Sonata for trumpet, string trio & basso continuo in D major. G.1: arr. Sonata for trumpet, strings and continuo in D. G.1. (Torelli, Giuseppe). *Musica rara. Unpriced* WSPK/LE (B74-50840)

Sonata for trumpet, string trio & basso continuo in D major. G.2. Sonata for trumpet, strings and continuo in D. G.2. (Torelli, Giuseppe). *Musica rara. Unpriced* NUXSNRE (B74-50535)

Sonata for trumpet, string trio & basso continuo in D major. G.2: arr. Sonata for trumpet, strings and continuo in D. G.2. (Torelli, Giuseppe). *Musica rara. Unpriced* WSPK/LE (B74-50841)

Taylor, Colin. Three fables. 3 fables : piano solo. Revised ed. *Boosey and Hawkes. £0.45* QPJ (B74-50186)

Taylor, Derek. As time goes by. *30 Gray's Inn Rd, WC1X 8JL : Abacus. £0.75* A/GB (B74-27796) ISBN 0-349-13381-6

Taylor, Samuel Coleridge-. *See* Coleridge-Taylor, Samuel.

Tchaikovsky, Peter.

'1812' overture: arr. '1812' overture : for school orchestra. *Bosworth. £2.10* MK (B74-50491)

Concerto for violin in D major. Op. 35: arr. Konzert für Violine und Orchester. Opus 35. *Schott. £2.40* SPK/LF (B74-50236)

Selections: arr. Two Russian marches. *Chappell. Unpriced* UMK/AGM (B74-50721)

Selections: arr. Waltz themes from Tchaikovsky : for descant recorder, treble or melodica or guitar. *British and Continental Music Agencies. Unpriced* VSRPMK/AHW (B74-50770)

Tchaikowsky, André. Quartet for strings in A major. Op.3. String quartet in A. Op.3. *Weinberger. Unpriced* RXNS (B74-50658)

Tcherepnin, Alexander.

Canzona for piano. Op.28. New ed. *Simrock. Unpriced* QPJ (B74-50187)

Toccata for piano, no.2. Op.20. Toccata no.2 for piano. Op.20. New ed. *Simrock. Unpriced* QPJ (B74-50188)

Teacher's guide to the guitar. (Winters). *Schoolmaster Publishing Co. Unpriced* TS/AC (B74-50255)

Teasdale, Sara. Let it be forgotten : for mixed chorus (SSAATB) or treble chorus (SSAA) and piano. (Merrill, Marlin). *Oxford University Press. Unpriced* DW (B74-50361)

Technische Studien. *Selections.* The Liszt studies : essential selections from the technical studies for the piano, including the first English edition of the legendary Liszt Pedagogue, a lesson-diary of the master as teacher as kept by Mme August Boisser, 1831-2. (Liszt, Franz). *Associated Music. Unpriced* Q/AF (B74-50558)

Teike, Carl. Alte Kameraden: arr. Old comrades : quick march. *Boosey and Hawkes. £0.95* UMMK/AGM (B74-50732)

Telemann, Georg Philipp.

Concerto for oboe, strings & basso continuo in C minor. Concerto a 5 für Oboe, Streicher und Basso continuo C-moll. *Litolff : Peters. £2.80* NUTNRF (B74-51117)

Concerto for two clarinets & string orchestra in D minor. Concerto for 2 clarinets (chalumeaux) and strings. *Musica rara. Unpriced* RXMPVVNUF (B74-50652)

Concerto for two clarinets & string orchestra in D minor: arr. Concerto for 2 clarinets (chalumeaux) and strings. *Musica rara. Unpriced* VVNTQK/LF (B74-50799)

Concerto for violin in E minor. Konzert, E-moll, für Violine, zwei Oboen, Streicher und Basso continuo, (Fagott ad libitum). *Peters. Unpriced* MPSF (B74-51109)

Essercizii musici, trio 12. Sonata for instruments in E flat major. Sonata Es-Dur, für Oboe, obligates Cembalo und Basso continuo. *Schott. £2.61* NWNTE (B74-51118)

Der getreue Music-Meister. Sonata for treble recorder & basso continuo in C major. Sonata no.4 in C major : for treble recorder and continuo. *Schott. £0.75* VSSPE (B74-50773)

Der getreue Music-Meister. Sonata for treble recorder & basso continuo in C major (in canon). Sonata no.2 in C major (in canon) : for treble recorder and continuo. *Schott. £0.75* VSSPE/X (B74-50777)

Der getreue Music-Meister. Sonata for treble recorder & basso continuo in F major. Sonata no.1 in F major : for treble recorder and continuo. *Schott. £0.75* VSSPE (B74-50774)

Der getreue Music-Meister. Sonata for treble recorder & basso continuo in F minor. Sonata no.3 in F minor : for treble recorder and continuo. *Schott. £0.75* VSSPE (B74-50775)

Petite musique de chambre. Partita 1. *selections.* Suite no.2. *Boosey and Hawkes. £0.65* WSPJ (B74-50835)

Petite musique de chambre. Partitas 4, 5. *selections.* Suite no.1 : arranged for trumpet in B flat and piano from the music of G.P. Telemann. *Boosey and Hawkes. £0.65* WSPJ (B74-50836)

Sonata for oboe, violin & basso continuo in G major. Sonata in Gmajor for oboe, violin and basso continuo. *Bärenreiter. £1.80* NUTNTE (B74-50529)

Twelve fantasias for violin. Zwolf Fantasien für Violine ohne Bass. *Peters. Unpriced* SPMJ (B74-51250)

Telemann, George Philipp. Der getreue Music-Meister. Sonatas for treble recorders & basso continuo. Sonatas 1-4 : for treble recorder and continuo. *Schott. £2.50* VSSPE (B74-50776)

Tell me where is fancy bred : for voice and guitar. (Carter, Elliott). *Associated Music. Unpriced* KE/TSDW (B74-50110)

Temperley, Nicholas. Symphonie fantastique. (Berlioz, Hector). *Breitkopf and Härtel : Bärenreiter. £13.20* MME (B74-50494)

Ten & twelve bell compositions. (Central Council of Church Bell Ringers). *c/o 'Monsal', Bredon, Tewkesbury, Glos. GL20 7LY : The Council. Unpriced* XSR (B74-50856)

Ten pieces from 'Harmonice musices odhecaton'. (Petrucci, Ottaviano dei). *Associated Music. Unpriced* VSNSK/DU/AY (B74-50280)

Ten Welsh folk-songs for juniors. (Lewis, Esme). *University of Wales Press. £0.50* JFE/NYJDW/G/AYDK (B74-50092)

Tenebrae factae sunt = Darkness was o'er the earth : Passion motet for four-part chorus of women's voices a cappella. (Victoria, Tomas Luis de). *Chappell. Unpriced* FEZDGKH/LHL (B74-50428)

Tennyson, Alfred, *Baron Tennyson.* Dark house : for full chorus of mixed voices a cappella. (Chorbajian, John). *Schirmer. Unpriced* EZDW (B74-50975)

Terry, Earle.

Basic goals in music

1. (Morrish, Donald James). New ed.. *McGraw-Hill. £1.10* A(VK) (B74-22799) ISBN 0-07-094430-x

2. (Morrish, Donald James). New ed.. *McGraw-Hill. £1.20* A(VK) (B74-22800) ISBN 0-07-094431-8

Terry, Richard Runciman. Gradualia, lib.1. Sacerdotes Domini. Sacerdotes Domini = Then did priests make offering : SATB. (Byrd, William). Revised ed. *Oxford University Press. Unpriced* EZDGKAF (B74-50038) ISBN 0-19-352008-7

Terry, *Sir* Richard Runciman. Gradulia, lib 2. Victimae paschali. Victimae paschali = Unto Christ the victim : motet for five voices, SSATB unacc. (Byrd, William). *Oxford University Press. £0.30* DGKADD/LL (B74-50879) ISBN 0-19-352010-9

Tertis, Lionel. My viola and I : a complete autobiography, with, Beauty of tone in string playing, and other essays. *Elek. £4.00* ASQ/E(P) (B74-23500) ISBN 0-236-31040-2

Textures : for piano and 5 instrumental groups. (Lazarof, Henri). *Associated Music. Unpriced* MPQ (B74-50144)

Thames pageant : a cantata for young players and singers. (Panufnik, Andrzej). *Boosey and Hawkes. £1.50* FE/MDX (B74-50424)

That's the Spirit : musical play. (Arch, Gwyn). *British and Continental. Unpriced* CN/L (B74-50333)

Thematic catalogue of Gustav Holst's music. (Holst, Imogen). *38 Russell Sq., WC1B 5DA : Faber Music Ltd : G. and I. Holst Ltd. £15.00* BHP(TD) (B74-21167) ISBN 0-571-10004-x

Theme from Elvira Madigan. (Mozart, Wolfgang Amadeus). *Chappell. Unpriced* QPK (B74-50595)

Theme, variations and finale : for four winds and four strings. (Laderman, Ezra). *Oxford University Press. Unpriced* NVNN/T (B74-50538)

There is no rose : solo voice and SSAATTBB unacc. (Popplewell, Richard). *Banks. Unpriced* EZDP/LF (B74-50966)

There was an old lady who swallowed a fly. (Adams, Pamela). *Restrop Manor, Purton, Wilts. : Child's Play (International) Ltd. £1.00* A/G(YSW) (B74-05270) ISBN 0-85953-021-3

They don't write songs like these any more : 50 songs from the golden age of song writing

1. *Wise. £1.50* KDW/GB/AY (B74-50103)

2. *Wise. £1.50* KDW/GB/AY (B74-50104)

3. *Wise. £1.50* KDW/GB/AY (B74-50105)

4. *Wise. £1.50* KDW/GB/AY (B74-50106)

5. *Wise. £1.50* KDW/GB/AY (B74-50107)

They're playing our song : from Jerome Kern to Stephen Sondheim - the stories behind the words and music of two generations. (Wilk, Max). *W.H. Allen. £3.50* ADW/GB(YT/M) (B74-11736) ISBN 0-491-01530-5

Thiemann, Ulfert.

Introduction and rondo capriccioso for violin & orchestra. Opus 28: arr. Introduktion und Rondo capriccioso. Opus

28 : für Violine und Orchester. (Saint-Saens, Camille). *Peters. £2.40* SPK (B74-51244)
Suite for violin & piano in F major. Op.93, 'in olden style'. Suite im alten Stil für Violine und Klavier. Opus 93,. (Reger, Max). *Peters. Unpriced* SPG (B74-51242)
Twelve fantasias for violin. Zwolf Fantasien für Violine ohne Bass. (Telemann, Georg Philipp). *Peters. Unpriced* SPMJ (B74-51250)
Thiman, Eric Harding. Works, organ. Selections. A collection of organ music. *Novello. £1.50* RJ (B74-50622)
Things heard and seen in summer : for piano, violin and cello. (Weingarden, Louis). *Oxford University Press. Unpriced* NXNT (B74-50551)
Third set of divertimenti. Op.8. (Sor, Fernando). *Oxford Universtion Press. £0.50* TSPMJ (B74-50704) ISBN 0-19-358865-x
Third suite for strings, from Musick's Handmaid. (Cruft, Adrian). *Chappell. Unpriced* RXMG (B74-50217)
This endris night : SATB unacc. (Stevens, Gillian). *Banks. Unpriced* EZDP/LF (B74-50968)
This is show business : songs
Vol.1. *Chappell. Unpriced* KDW/AY (B74-50470)
Vol.3. *Chappell. Unpriced* KDW/AY (B74-51055)
Vol.4. *Chappell. Unpriced* KDW/AY (B74-51056)
This is show business
Vol.2. *Chappell. Unpriced* KDW/AY (B74-50471)
This is the day which the Lord hath made: arr. This is the day which the Lord hath made : festival anthem. (Palmer, Peggy Spencer). *Cramer. £0.15* DK (B74-50905)
This is the day which the Lord hath made : festival anthem. (Palmer, Peggy Spencer). *Cramer. £0.15* DK (B74-50905)
This old world = Quand la chance est là : for SATB chorus accompanied. (Brejean, Philippe). *Chappell. Unpriced* DW (B74-50358)
Thomas, Bernard.
77 newe ausserlesne liebliche zierliche Polnischer und Teutscher Art Tantze. Selections. Fifteen German and Polish dances, 1601 : for five instruments. (Demantius, Johann Christoph). *London Pro Musica. Unpriced* LNRH (B74-51081)
Capricci in musica a tre voci, nos. 4, 10, 1. Three pieces for three instruments. (Ruffo, Vincenzo). *Pro Musica. Unpriced* LNT (B74-50125)
Four pieces of the late fifteenth century : for four instruments ATTB. *Pro Musica. Unpriced* LNS (B74-50123)
Nine chansons : for four voices or instruments. (Manchicourt, Pierre de). *London Pro musica. Unpriced* EZDU (B74-50972)
Opera nova de balli, 1553 : for four instruments. (Bendusi, Francesco). *London Pro Musica. Unpriced* LNSH (B74-51082)
Ricercari a due voci, nos. 1-3, 6-10, 16-23. Ten ricercari, 1588 : for two instruments, A.T. (Guami, Francesco). *Pro Musica. Unpriced* LNU (B74-50126)
Ricercari for two instruments. *Selections.* Seven ricercari, 1588 : for two instruments, S.A. (Guami, Francesco). *London Pro Musica. Unpriced* LNU (B74-51085)
Twelve chansons (c.1530) : for four instruments or voices. *Pro Musica. Unpriced* LNS (B74-50124)
Twenty-one masque dances of the early seventeenth century for one instrument and continuo. (Walls, Peter). *London Pro musica. Unpriced* LPH/AYD(XEJ10) (B74-51086)
Thomas, Dylan.
Mors janua vitae. Vocal score. Mors janua vitae : for male-voice choir (TTBB) and piano or organ or strings. (Wilson, Robert Barclay). *Cramer. £0.12* GDH (B74-51013)
Poem in October. Vocal score. Poem in October : for voice and orchestra. (Corigliano, John). *Schirmer. Unpriced* KDX (B74-51059)
Thomas, Tony. Music for the movies. *A.S. Barnes : Tantivy Press. £4.50* A/JR(YT/XNJ43) (B74-02980) ISBN 0-900730-63-3
Thomas, Werner. De temporum fine comoedia = Das Spiel vom Ende der Zeiten Vigilia. (Orff, Carl). *Schott. Unpriced* EMDX (B74-50933)
Thomson, Virgil.
Edges : a portrait of Robert Indiana, for band. *Schirmer. Unpriced* UMJ (B74-50264)
Edges : a portrait of Robert Indiana for piano. *Schirmer. Unpriced* QPJ (B74-50592)
Louisiana story. *Boy fights alligator.* Boy fights alligator : fugue, for orchestra. *Schirmer. Unpriced* MM/Y/JR (B74-50132)
Metropolitan Museum fanfare : for brass ensemble and percussion. *Schirmer. Unpriced* WMGN (B74-50305)
Passacaglia for organ. *Schirmer. Unpriced* RHT (B74-51191)
Sonata da chiesa for wind & string quintet (Revised version). Sonata da chiesa (Revised version) : for clarinet in E flat, trumpet in C, viola, horn in F and trombone. *Boosey and Hawkes. Unpriced* NVNRE (B74-50539)
Study piece : portrait of a lady, for band. *Schirmer. Unpriced* UMJ (B74-50265)
Thorn, Eric A. The world belongs to Jesus : nine contemporary songs of worship. (Hodson, Keith). *the Baptist Church, Rochdale Rd, Heywood, Lancs. OL10 1LG : Wigwam Publications for Songcrafts. Unpriced* JDM (B74-50442) ISBN 0-904434-00-1
Three African sketches : piano. (Camilleri, Charles). *Roberton. £0.40* QPJ (B74-51167)
Three almanack verses : SATB. (Allcock, Stephen). *Boosey and Hawkes. Unpriced* EZDW (B74-50973)
Three antiphonal canticles : for SATB and congregation (or two groups of singers) and organ. (Routley, Erik). *Novello. £0.10* DH (B74-50015)
Three arguments. Opus 59 : for bassoon and cello. (Fricker, Peter Racine). *Fenette Music : Breitkopf and Härtel. Unpriced* VWPLSR (B74-51349)
Three bagatelles : for oboe and harpsichord (or piano). (Maconchy, Elizabeth). *Oxford University Press. £1.00* VTPJ (B74-50289) ISBN 0-19-357720-8
Three bird songs : for treble voices, piano and percussion. (Platts, Kenneth). *Ashdown. £0.30* JFLE/NYLDW (B74-51042)
Three Brazilian miniatures for percussion. (Lacerda, Oswaldo). *Schott. £2.40* XN (B74-50324)
Three Chinese folksongs : for oboe and piano. (Wen, Chi Chung). *Schott. £1.00* VTPJ (B74-51338)
Three consort pieces : for treble, tenor and bass viols. (Parsley, Osbert). *Oxford University Press. £0.16* STNS (B74-50689) ISBN 0-19-358105-1
Three contrasts : piano. (Wilson, Robert Barclay). *Cramer. £0.15* QPJ (B74-51182)
Three early English lyrics : for SSAA unaccompanied chorus. (Walker, Robert). *Weinberger. £0.15* FEZDW (B74-50430)
Three French songs from the late 14th century : for voice and 2 or 3 instruments. (Wilkin, Nigel). *Antico. Unpriced* KE/LNTDW/AYH (XCTQ26) (B74-50477)
Three girls for five brass : a suite for brass quintet. (Lanchberry, John). *Novello. £0.75* WNRG (B74-50828)

Three kings came to Bethlehem Town : solo, unison or two-part (or mixed voices), with accompaniment for guitar or piano ad lib. (Dinham, Kenneth J). *Banks. Unpriced* KE/TSDP/LF (B74-51062)
Three Latin motets : for five voices. (Berkeley, Lennox). *Chester. Unpriced* EZDJ (B74-50394)
Three motets : SATB and organ. (Rorem, Ned). *Boosey and Hawkes. Unpriced* DH (B74-50350)
Three organists of St. Dionis Backchurch, London. (Marr, Peter). *Hinrichsen. Unpriced* R/AY (B74-50612)
Three pieces for harpsichord. (Lazarof, Henri). *Associated Music. £3.50* QRPJ (B74-50609)
Three pieces for oboe solo or cor anglais. Opus 29. (Stoker, Richard). *Peters. Unpriced* VTPMJ (B74-50790)
Three psalms. Op.54 : for T.T. Bar. B.B., unaccompanied by Kenneth Leighton. (Leighton, Kenneth). *Novello. £0.44* GEZDK (B74-50435)
Three settings of E.E. Cummings
1: Buffalo Bill's: TTBB a cappella. (Yannatos, James). *Associated Music. Unpriced* GEZDW (B74-50081)
2: The rose: SSAA a capella. (Yannatos, James). *Associated Music. Unpriced* FEZDW (B74-50076)
3: In just- : SSATB a cappella. (Yannatos, James). *Associated Music. Unpriced* EZDW (B74-50065)
Three short fantasias : for piano. (Wyner, Yehudi). *Associated Music. Unpriced* QPJ (B74-50593)
Three short meditations : for string trio and harp (1969). (Huber, Klaus). *Bärenreiter. £2.70* RWNS (B74-50638)
Three singing duets. (Kasschau, Howard). *Schirmer. Unpriced* QNVK/DW/AY (B74-50164)
Three sisters who are not sisters : an opera. (Rorem, Ned). *Boosey and Hawkes. £4.25* CC (B74-50872)
Three sisters who are not sisters. *Vocal score.* Three sisters who are not sisters : an opera. (Rorem, Ned). *Boosey and Hawkes. £4.25* CC (B74-50872)
Three sketches : for trumpet or cornet and piano. (Hanmer, Ronald). *Emerson Edition. £0.50* WSPJ (B74-50833)
Three sonatas for violin (flute, treble recorder) and basso continuo. (Veracini, Francesco Maria). *Bärenreiter. £3.60* SPE (B74-50664)
Three songs from eastern Canada : for mixed voice S.A.T.B. and piano
1: Les trois canes (Cheticamp, N.S.). (Churchill, John). *Lengnick. £0.12* DW/G/AYSXC (B74-50025)
2: Ave maris stella (Acadian 17th cent.). (Churchill, John). *Lengnick. £0.12* DW/G/AYSXC (B74-50026)
3: I'se the b'y (Newfoundland). (Churchill, John). *Lengnick. £0.12* DW/G/AYSXC (B74-50027)
Thurston, Richard E. Sonata for piano, no.2: arr. The Alcotts. (Ives, Charles). *Associated Music. Unpriced* UMK (B74-50266)
Thwaites, Anthony. Autumn cicada : ko-uta on four Japanese texts, for SSA, harp and 4 handbells. (Cole, Bruce). *Boosey and Hawkes. £0.10* FE/NYJNRDW (B74-50427)
Till Eulenspiegel. Op.28. Till Eulenspiegels Lustige Streiche : nach alter Schelmenweise in Rondeauforme. (Strauss, Richard). *Eulenburg. Unpriced* MMJ (B74-51105)
Till Eulenspiegels Lustige Streiche : nach alter Schelmenweise in Rondeauforme. (Strauss, Richard). *Eulenburg. Unpriced* MMJ (B74-51105)
Tilney, Colin.
Sonata for violin & basso continuo, no.3, in G major. Violin sonata no.3 in G major. (Gibbs, Joseph). *Schott. Unpriced* SPE (B74-51240)
Sonata for violin & basso continuo, no.5, in E major. Violin sonata no.5 in E major. (Gibbs, Joseph). *Schott. Unpriced* SPE (B74-51241)
Times of day : five Southern impressions, piano. (Camilleri, Charles). *Roberton. £0.60* QPJ (B74-51168)
Time's passing : SATB a cappella. (Woolf, Gregory). *Associated Music. Unpriced* EZDW (B74-50064)
Timmins, Donald Maxwell-. *See* Maxwell-Timmins, Donald.
Tiomkin, Dimitri. High noon: arr. Highnoon. *Affiliated Music. £1.00* WMK/DW (B74-50312)
Tippett, *Sir* Michael. Symphony no.3. *Schott. Unpriced* KFLE/MDX (B74-50114)
Tischler, Hans. A medieval motet book : a collection of 13th century motets in various vocal and instrumental combinations. *Associated Music. Unpriced* DW/AY (B74-50366)
To be sung upon the water : barcarolles and nocturnes for high voice, piano and clarinet (also bass clarinet). (Argento, Dominick). *Boosey and Hawkes. Unpriced* KFTE/VVDW (B74-50484)
To Maelzel : for 4-part chorus of female voices unaccompanied or with wood-block. (Beethoven, Ludwig van). *Roberton. £0.10* FEZDW/X (B74-50432)
To Maelzel : for 4-part chorus of mixed voices unaccompanied or with wood-block. (Beethoven, Ludwig van). *Roberton. £0.12* EZDW/X (B74-50412)
To music : for tenor solo, SATB and orchestra. (Hedges, Anthony). *Chappell. Unpriced* DX (B74-50370)
To music. *Vocal score.* To music : for tenor solo, SATB and orchestra. (Hedges, Anthony). *Chappell. Unpriced* DX (B74-50370)
To you, my love : four part SATB. (Habash, John Mitri). *Robbins. Unpriced* DW (B74-50923)
Toccata for piano, no.2. Op.20. Toccata no.2 for piano. Op.20. (Tcherepnin, Alexander). New ed. *Simrock. Unpriced* QPJ (B74-50188)
Toccata no.2 for piano. Op.20. (Tcherepnin, Alexander). New ed. *Simrock. Unpriced* QPJ (B74-50188)
Todds, Walter. Patrick Hadley : a memoir. *10e Prior Bolton St., N.1 : Triad Press. £1.75* BHBD(N) (B74-11050) ISBN 0-902070-10-x
Tomblings, Philip. Behold now praise the Lord : anthem for SATB. *St Gregory Publications. £0.15* DR (B74-50915)
Tomkins, Thomas.
Musica Deo sacra III. *Stainer and Bell for the British Academy. Unpriced* EZDK (B74-50047)
Musica Deo sacra. O praise the Lord: arr. O praise the Lord. *Carne House, Parsons Lane, Bury, Lancs. : Tomus. £0.75* VSNK/DK (B74-51329)
Tomlin, Peter. Woodwind for schools. *Dryad Press. £2.25* AV/E(VK) (B74-14973) ISBN 0-85219-089-1
Tomlinson, Fred. A Peter Warlock handbook
Vol.1. *10e Prior Bolton St., N.1 : Triad Press. £2.75* BWKH(TC) (B74-21168) ISBN 0-902070-11-8
Tomlinson, Geoffrey. Concourse : for percussion and other instruments. *Boosey and Hawkes. £1.20* XMJ (B74-50323)
Tomorrow's people. (Sandford, Jeremy). *47 Catherine Place, S.W.1 : Jerome Publishing Co. Ltd. £1.95* A/GB(WE/YC) (B74-14305) ISBN 0-904125-05-x
Tomus primis operis musici. *Hodie Christus natus est.* Hodie Christus natus est = Christ was born today : song, for full chorus of mixed voices a cappella. (Handl, Jacob). *Roberton. £0.10* EZDJ/LF (B74-50045)
Tomus primus operis musici. Omnes de Saba venient. Omnes de Saba venient : motet for Epiphany, SATTB unacc. (Handl, Jacob). *Oxford University Press. £0.08* EZDJ/LFP (B74-50403) ISBN 0-19-350342-5
Tonal harmony in concept and practice. (Forte, Allen). 2nd ed. *Holt, Rinehart and Winston. £6.95* A/R (B74-14970) ISBN 0-03-077495-0
Too many clarinets : mini-suite for clarinets and strings. (Slack, Roy). *Keith Prowse. £0.65* NVVG (B74-50153)
Top pop scene
1974. *Purnell. £0.70* A/GB (B74-22801) ISBN 0-361-02840-7
Torch of freedom : march for brass band. (Ball, Eric). *R. Smith. Unpriced* WMGM (B74-50821)
Torelli, Giuseppe.
Sonata for trumpet, string trio & basso continuo in D major. G.1. Sonata for trumpet, strings and continuo in D. G. I. *Musica rara. Unpriced* NUXSNRE (B74-50536)
Sonata for trumpet, string trio & basso continuo in D major. G.1: arr. Sonata for trumpet, strings and continuo in D. G.1. *Musica rara. Unpriced* WSPK/LE (B74-50840)
Sonata for trumpet, string trio & basso continuo in D major. G.2. Sonata for trumpet, strings and continuo in D. G.2. *Musica rara. Unpriced* NUXSNRE (B74-50535)

Sonata for trumpet, string trio & basso continuo in D major. G.2: arr. Sonata for trumpet, strings and continuo in D. G.2. *Musica rara. Unpriced* WSPK/LE (B74-50841)
Torres, Ben Fong-. *See* Fong-Torres, Ben.
Touch of the times : songs of social change, 1770 to 1914. (Palmer, Roy). *Penguin. £0.80* KE/TSDW/K/G/AYD(XFYK145) (B74-51063) ISBN 0-14-081182-6
Touchin, Colin M. Fanfare, intermezzo and scherzo. Op.1 : for recorder trio, (descant, treble, tenor). *Tomus. Unpriced* VSNT (B74-50281)
Tradition of western music. (Abraham, Gerald). *Oxford University Press. £1.00* A (B74-22802) ISBN 0-19-316324-1
Traite du violoncello. Selections. Leichte Stücke für Violoncello mit Begleitung durch 2 Violoncello
Heft 1. (Breval, Jean Baptiste). *Schott. £1.44* SRNU (B74-50245)
Traite du violoncello. Selections. Leichte Stücke für Violoncello mit Begleitung durch 2 Violoncello
Heft 2. (Breval, Jean Baptiste). *Schott. £1.44* (B74-50096)
Trant, Brian.
The riddle song : a folk-song from Kentucky, SSA (S.solo) unacc. *Oxford University Press. Unpriced* FEZDW (B74-50429) ISBN 0-19-342595-5
The shepherds' carol : old German Weihnachtslied. (Schubart, Christian Friedrich David). *Banks. Unpriced* FDP/LF (B74-50988)
Träumenden Knaben, Op.41 : Cantata für vierstimmigen gemischten Chor, Klarinette und Fagott. (Einem, Gottfried von). *Boosey and Hawkes. Unpriced*

EVVPLVWDX (B74-50383)
Travelling the northern road. (Donald, Mike). *EFDS. Unpriced* JE/TSDW (B74-51027)
Travis, Roy. Songs and epilogues : for bass voice and piano. *Oxford University Press. Unpriced* KGXDW (B74-51078)
Treasure island : a musical adventure. (Ornadel, Cyril). *Sparta Florida Music : Aviva Music. £0.99* CM (B74-50006)
Treasure island. Vocal score. Treasure island : a musical adventure. (Ornadel, Cyril). *Sparta Florida Music : Aviva Music. £0.99* CM (B74-50006)
Tredici, David Del. Four songs on poems of James Joyce : for voice and piano. *Boosey and Hawkes. £2.25* KDW (B74-50469)
Tredici, David del.
I hear an army : for soprano and string quartet. *Boosey and Hawkes. £2.00* KFLE/RXNSDX (B74-51069)
Pop-pourri : for soprano, rock group, chorus (SATB) and orchestra. *Boosey and Hawkes. Unpriced* EMDX (B74-50934)
Tremlett, George.
The David Essex story. *49 Poland St., W1A 2LG : Futura Publications Ltd. £0.40* AKDW/GB/E(P) (B74-26609) ISBN 0-86007-092-1
The Rolling Stones story. *49 Poland St., W1A 2LG : Futura Publications Ltd. £0.40* AKDW/GB/E(P) (B74-25496) ISBN 0-86007-128-6
Tria carmina paschalia : for women's voices (SSA) harp and guitar (or harpsichord. (Argento, Dominick). *Boosey and Hawkes. Unpriced* FE/TQPLTSDH (B74-51000)
Triad Press bibliographical series. Foreman, Ronald Lewis Edmund. Discographies : a bibliography of catalogues of recordings, mainly relating to specific musical subjects, composers and performers. *10e Prior Bolton St., N.1 : Triad Press. £1.60* A/FD(T/WT) (B74-03642) ISBN 0-902070-08-8
Trilogy of praise : for four-part chorus of mixed voices a cappella. (Wetzler, Robert). *Schirmer. Unpriced* EZDE (B74-50037)
Trio sonata : organ. (Wills, Arthur). *Boosey and Hawkes. £1.00* RJ (B74-50204)
Trip to the concert. (Blackwood, Alan, *b.1932*). *36 Park St., W1Y 4DE : Nelson Young World. £0.45* AM (B74-13709) ISBN 0-7238-0946-1
Triphtongas 1 : for organ. (Károlyi, Pál). *Boosey and Hawkes. £0.75* RJ (B74-50201)
Triptych : for clarinet in B flat or bass clarinet. (Stoker, Richard). *Ashdown. £0.30* VVPMJ (B74-50806)
Triptych : three pieces for piano. (Weingarden, Louis). *Boosey and Hawkes. £2.25* QPJ (B74-51181)
Trog. Owning-up. (Melly, George). *Penguin. £0.35* AKDW/HHW/E(P) (B74-07434) ISBN 0-14-002936-2
Trombonioso : for trombones and band. (Binge, Ronald). *R. Smith. Unpriced* WMPWUN (B74-51363)
Troubadours : medieval music to sing and play. (Sargent, Brian). *Cambridge University Press. Unpriced* DW/AY (B74-50368) ISBN 0-521-20471-2
Trumpet shall sound. (Handel, George Frideric). *Associated Board of the Royal Schools of Music. £0.15* WSPK/DH (B74-51368)
Trumpets triumphant : pageantry for antiphonal trumpets. (Grundman, Clare). *Boosey and Hawkes. Unpriced* UMMJ (B74-50730)
Truscott, Harold. Fantasia for viola, two clarinets & string orchestra: arr. Fantasia for viola and string orchestra with two clarinets. (Hummel, Johann Nepomuk). *Musica rara. Unpriced* RXMPNVVNT (B74-50646)
Tschaikowsky, Peter. *See* Tchaikovsky, Petr.
Tsutsui, Keisuke. D.B. Kabalevsky's 'Joey the clown' ('The comedians'). (Watanabe, Saburo). *F. Warne. £1.75* BKDBAM/HMBN (B74-26153) ISBN 0-7232-1783-1
Tu solus, qui facis mirabilia : for four-part chorus of mixed voices a cappella. (Josquin Des Prés). *Associated Music. Unpriced* EZDJ (B74-50396)
Tunley, David. The eighteenth-century French cantata. *Dobson. £6.00* ADX(YH/XF71) (B74-25495) ISBN 0-234-77070-8
Turetzky, Bertram. The contemporary contrabass. *University of California Press. £4.40* ASS/E/CY (B74-28317) ISBN 0-520-02291-2
Turnbull, Harvey. The guitar : from the Renaissance to the present day. *Batsford. £4.00* ATS(X) (B74-14312) ISBN 0-7134-2784-1
Turner, Michael R. The parlour song book : a casquet of vocal gems. *Pan Books. £1.75* KDW/GB/AY(XH564) (B74-51058) ISBN 0-330-24113-3
Turner, Roy. Glory choruses
No.3; arranged by Walter Eden and Norman Wicker. *112a Beacon Hill Rd, Newark : Henri's Evangelical Revival Association. Unpriced* JDM (B74-51021)
Turpin hero : 30 folk songs for voices and guitar. (Raven, Jon). *Oxford University Press. £1.60* JFDW/G/AY (B74-51037) ISBN 0-19-330626-3
Turpyn book of lute songs : King's College, Cambridge, Rowe MS 2. *5 Albert Grove, Leeds 6 : Boethius Press. £8.70* AKE/TWDW(YD/XDZS14) (B74-03504) ISBN 0-904263-00-2
Turvey, A W.
Epilogue to evensong : organ solo. *Cramer. Unpriced* RJ (B74-50623)
Meditation on a folk tune : organ solo. *Cramer. Unpriced* RJ (B74-51197)
Tutto lo di mi dici 'Canta' = Day after day they all say 'Sing' : canzonetta, for four-part chorus of mixed voices a cappella. (Lasso, Orlando di). *Schirmer. Unpriced* EZDU (B74-50053)
Twelth of never. (Livingston, Jerry). *Frank Music. Unpriced* UMMK/DW (B74-51310)
Twelve famous marches. (Medway, Carol). *Cramer. £0.36* QPK/AGM/AY (B74-51184)
Twelve preludes for all seasons : piano solo. (Allanbrook, Douglas). *Boosey and Hawkes. £2.50* QPJ (B74-51160)
Twelve studies for violin : for technical problems in contemporary music. (Zámečnik, Evžen). *Bärenreiter. £3.25* S/AF (B74-50659)
Twentieth century composers
Vol.4: France, Italy and Spain. *Weidenfeld and Nicolson. £4.50* AD(YB/M/XM) (B74-29004) ISBN 0-297-76793-3
Twentieth century music, 1900-1945. (Bray, Trevor). *Open University Press. Unpriced* A(XM46) (B74-21535) ISBN 0-335-00866-6
Twentieth-century music : an introduction. (Salzman, Eric). 2nd ed. *Prentice-Hall. £4.70* A(XM71) (B74-24208) ISBN 0-13-935015-2
Twilight of the swans. (Sutherland, Douglas). *New English Library. £3.00* A(P) (B74-11051) ISBN 0-450-01876-8
Two carols for the Caribbean. (Stent, Keith). *Novello. £0.24* ENYLDP/LF (B74-50936)
Two hymns of praise : with introductory fanfares
1: Now thank we all our God. (Rutter, John). *Oxford University Press. £1.00* EWMDM/AY (B74-50938) ISBN 0-19-367376-2
2: All creatures of our God and king : melody from Geistliche Kirchengesang (Köln 1623). (Rutter, John). *Oxford University Press. £1.10* EWMDM/AY (B74-50939) ISBN 0-19-367359-2
Two idylls : for unaccompanied women's chorus, (SSA). (Whitecotton, Shirley). *Galaxy : Galliard. Unpriced* FEZDW (B74-50431)
Two Irish songs : military band. (Grundman, Clare). *Boosey and Hawkes. £15.00* UMMJ (B74-51308)
Two meditations. (Bernstein, Leonard). *Amberson : Schirmer. Unpriced* SRPK (B74-50249)
Two miniatures for wind quintet : flute, oboe, clarinet, horn and bassoon. (Lees, Benjamin). *Boosey and Hawkes. £1.75* UNR (B74-50737)
Two motets. (Wesley, Samuel). *Novello. £0.16* EZDJ (B74-50401)
Two pieces for solo flute. (Rollin, Robert Leon). *Galaxy Music : Galliard. Unpriced* VRPMJ (B74-50762)
Two preparatory accordion solos. (Law, Leslie G). *Charnwood Music. Unpriced* RSPMJ (B74-51208)
Two reflections : SSA unaccompanied. (Kennedy, John Brodbin). *Boosey and Hawkes. Unpriced* FEZDW (B74-51008)
Two Russian marches. (Tchaikovsky, Peter). *Chappell. Unpriced* UMK/AGM (B74-50721)
Two Scottish country dances. (Rankine, Andrew). *42 Whinfell Rd, Darras Hall, Ponteland, Newcastle : Royal Scottish Country Dance Society (Newcastle and District Branch). £0.125* QPH/H/AYDL (B74-50578)
Two songs for Christmas. (Bent, Margaret). *Oxford University Press. Unpriced* EZDP/LF (B74-50405) ISBN 0-19-341208-x
Two songs for three years. (Adler, Samuel). *Boosey and Hawkes. Unpriced* KDW (B74-51045)
Tyree, Ronald. Six trios for 3 bassoons. Op.4. (Weissenborn, Julius). *Musica rara. Unpriced* VWNT (B74-50810)
Tyson, Alan. Beethoven : studies. *Oxford University Press. £4.50* BBJ(D) (B74-11734) ISBN 0-19-315312-2
UCLA. *See* University of California at Los Angeles.
Uhl, Alfred. Kleine Suite für Viola. *Schott. £0.96* SQPMG (B74-50241)
Unguis incarnatus est : für Klavier und ... (Kagel, Mauricio). *Universal. Unpriced* LPJ (B74-50127)
Union. Op. 48: arr. L'Union. Op.48 : paraphrase de concert sur les airs nationaux. (Gottschalk, Louis Moreau). *Schirmer. £1.40* QNUK (B74-50562)
Union. Op. 48 : paraphrase de concert sur les airs nationaux. (Gottschalk, Louis Moreau). *Schirmer. Unpriced* UMPQ (B74-50734)
Union. Op.48 : paraphrase de concert sur les airs nationaux. (Gottschalk, Louis Moreau). *Schirmer. £1.40* QNUK (B74-50562)
Universal prayer : for 4 solo voices, 3 harps, organ and mixed chorus. (Panufnik, Andrzej). *Boosey and Hawkes. £4.50* ETQNSRDE (B74-50034)
University of California. Ernest Bloch lectures. *See* Ernest Bloch lectures.
University of California at Los Angeles. *Center for the Study of Armament and Disarmament.* War-peace bibliography series. *See* War-peace bibliography series.
University of Cambridge. *Fitzwilliam Museum. See* Fitzwilliam Museum.
University of Cambridge. *King's College. See* King's College, *Cambridge.*
University of Cambridge. *Library. MSS.(Add.5943).*
A fifteenth century song book : Cambridge University Library Add.MS 5943. *5 Albert Grove, Leeds 6 : Boethius Press. £4.60* AELDW(YD/XCQ) (B74-04046) ISBN 0-904263-01-0
A fifteenth century song book : Cambridge University Library Add.MS 5943. *5 Albert Grove, Leeds 6 : Boethius Press. £4.60* 784.3063 (B74-04046) ISBN 0-904263-01-0
University of Washington. John Danz lectures. *See* John Danz lectures.
Unum ex illorum sabbatorum : piano. (Crump, Peter). *Thames. Unpriced* QPJ (B74-51171)
Upon the high midnight : three nativity carols for SATB soli and chorus (unaccompanied). (McCabe, John). *Novello. Unpriced* EZDP/LF (B74-50964)
Urakawa, Takaya. Concerto movement for violin in C major. G.148: arr. Concerto movement for violin and chamber orchestra, 1790/92. Wo05. (Beethoven, Ludwig van). *Breitkopf and Härtel : Bärenreiter. £3.25* SPK (B74-50675)
Useful tunes for guitar
No.1: Little brown jug : trad. and, Home on the range : trad. *Charnwood Music. Unpriced* TSPMK (B74-51278)
No.2: The national anthem and Jingle bells : trad. *Charnwood Music. Unpriced* TSPMK (B74-51279)
No.3: Minuet in G (from 'Notenbüchlein für Anna Magdelena Bach' 1725. *Charnwood Music. Unpriced* TSPMK (B74-51280)
No.4: Rigadoon, from 'Musick's hand-maid' 1689 and Jig from 'Abdalazar'. *Charnwood Music. Unpriced* RSPMK (B74-51213)
No.5: Hot cross buns : trad. and Auld lang syne : trad. *Charnwood Music. Unpriced* RSPMK (B74-51214)
Vallier, Jacques.
Improvisation pour clarinette (en si bemol) seule. *Chappell. Unpriced* VVPMJ (B74-51346)
Prelude et final : pour deux clarinettes (en si bemol). *Chappell. Unpriced* VVNU (B74-51341)
Sonatina for clarinet & piano, no.2. Op.72. Sonatine no.2 pour clarinette en si bemol et piano. Op.72. *Chappell. Unpriced* VVPEM (B74-51343)
Vámos, László. The selected writings of Zoltán Kodály. (Kodály, Zoltán). *Boosey and Hawkes. £3.95* A(D) (B74-21534) ISBN 0-85162-021-3
Van Beethoven, Ludwig. *See* Beethoven Ludwig van.
Van Camp, Leonard. *See* Camp, Leonard Van.
Van Pallandt, Nina, *barones. See* Pallandt, Nina, *barones van.*
Vanhal, Jan.
Quartets for oboe & strings, nos.1,2. Quartet for oboe (flute), violin, viola and cello. Op.7, nos.1 and 2. *Musica rara. Unpriced* NVTNS (B74-50543)
Sonata for clarinet & piano, no.2, in B flat major. Sonata in B flat for clarinet and piano. *Musica rara. £6.50* VVPE (B74-50801)
Variations for euphonium & piano, 'The mountains of Mourne'. The mountains of Mourne : variations for euphonium and piano on the theme by Houston Collison (sic). (Newsome, Roy). *Keith Prowse. £0.75* WWP/T (B74-50853)
Variations on a theme by Georg Friedrich Handel : for soprano recorder (flute) and harpsichord. (Walter, Heinz). *Schott. £1.74* VSSP/T (B74-51337)
Variety of guitar music. (Duarte, John William). *Faber Music. Unpriced* TSPMK/AAY (B74-50259)
Vasquez, Juan. Recopilacion de sonetos y villancicos. *En la fuente del rosel.* En la fuente del rosel = 'Neath the rosebush in the stream : for four-part chorus of mixed voices a cappella. *Roberton. £0.10* EZDU (B74-50055)
Vaughan, Henry.
My soul, there is a country : SATB. (Drayton, Paul). *Oxford University Press. £0.12* DH (B74-50896) ISBN 0-19-350348-4
A vision of time and eternity. Op.61 : song. (Mathias, William). *Oxford University Press. £1.10* KDW (B74-50461) ISBN 0-19-345570-6
Vaughan Williams, Ralph. The Old Hundreth Psalm tune ('All people that on earth do dwell') : anthem for unison or mixed (SATB) choir accompanied by organ with band and/or orchestra. *Oxford University Press. Unpriced* EUMDM (B74-50381)
Vaughan Williams Memorial Library. The Vaughan Williams Memorial Library catalogue of the English Folk Dance and Song Society : acquisitions to the library of books, pamphlets, periodicals, sheet music and manuscripts from its inception to 1971. *Mansell Information Publishing. £25.00* A/G(WJ) (B74-06945) ISBN 0-7201-0368-1
Veneux, Thierry.
Claire de lune: arr. Claire de lune. *Chappell. Unpriced* TMK (B74-50690)
Impressions et images, suite no.3. Letter J: arr. Impressions et images, 3e suite. Lettre J. *Chappell. Unpriced* TMK (B74-50691)
Impressions et images, suite no.3. Letter K: arr. Impressions et images, 3e suite. Lettre K. *Chappell. Unpriced* TMK (B74-50692)
Le Parc aux fees. Idylle: arr. Idylle. *Chappell. Unpriced* TMK (B74-50693)
Veracini, Francesco Maria.
Sonatas for violin & basso continuo. Op.1, nos. 1, 4, 8. 3 sonatas for violin and piano. *Associated Music. Unpriced* SPE (B74-50233)
Sonate a violino o flauto solo e basso, nos 1-3. Three sonatas for violin (flute, treble recorder) and basso continuo. *Bärenreiter. £3.60* SPE (B74-50664)
Verbum caro factum est = And the Word became flesh : motet for six-part chorus of mixed voices a cappella. (Hassler, Hans Leo). *Schirmer. Unpriced* EZDJ (B74-50949)
Verdi. (Hussey, Dyneley). Revised ed.. *Dent. £2.50* BVE(N) (B74-17892) ISBN 0-460-03151-1
Verdi. (Wechsberg, Joseph). *Weidenfeld and Nicolson. £4.50* BVE(N) (B74-22804) ISBN 0-297-76818-2
Vere languores nostres = Truly our Saviour suffered : motet for four-part chorus of mixed voices a cappella. (Victoria, Tomás Luis de). *Schirmer. Unpriced* EZDJ/LK (B74-50953)
Vergilius Maro, Publius. *See* Virgil.
Verleih uns Frieden genadiglich = Lord grant us peace : for five-part chorus of mixed voices a cappella. (Schutz, Heinrich). *Schirmer. Unpriced* EZDH (B74-50946)
Veszpremi, Lili. Music for piano (intermediate). (Szávai, Magda). *Boosey and Hawkes. £1.00* QP/AY (B74-50166)
Via crucis : a cycle of fifteen saetas, for four-part chorus of mixed voices and Spanish guitar. (Surinach, Carlos).

Associated Music. Unpriced ETSDE (B74-50380)
Victimae paschali = Unto Christ the victim : motet for five voices, SSATB unacc. (Byrd, William). *Oxford University Press. £0.30* DGKADD/LL (B74-50879) ISBN 0-19-352010-9
Victoria, Tomàs Luis de.
Motecta. Ne timeas, Maria. In venisti enim gratiam = You have been acclaimed the chosen one. The Annunciation : for four-part chorus of mixed voices a cappella. *Schirmer. Unpriced* EZDJ (B74-50400)
Motecta. Quem vidistis pastores? Quem vidistis, pastores = Whom did you see, kind shepherds? : Motet for Christmas time, for six-part chorus of mixed voices a cappella. *Chappell. Unpriced* EZDJ/LF (B74-50402)
Victoria, Tomás Luis de. Motecta. Vere languores nostres. Vere languores nostres = Truly our Saviour suffered : motet for four-part chorus of mixed voices a cappella. *Schirmer. Unpriced* EZDJ/LK (B74-50953)
Victoria, Tomas Luis de. Officium hebdomadie sanctae. Tenebrae factae sunt. Tenebrae factae sunt = Darkness was o'er the earth : Passion motet for four-part chorus of women's voices a cappella. *Chappell. Unpriced* FEZDGKH/LHL (B74-50428)
Vigilate = Be ye watchful : motet for five voices S.A.T.Ba.B. (Byrd, William). *Oxford University Press. £0.20* EZDJ (B74-50395) ISBN 0-19-352056-7
Villa-Lobos, Heitor.
Bachianas brasileiras, no.5. Aria (Cantilena). *Associated Music. Unpriced* MMK/DW (B74-50508)
Bachianas brasileiras, no.5. Aria (Cantilena). *Associated Music. Unpriced* RXMK/DW (B74-50645)
Bachianas brasileiras, no.5. Aria (Cantilena). *Associated Music. Unpriced* VNK/DW (B74-50743)
Bachianas brasileiras, no.5. Aria (Cantilena). *Associated Music. Unpriced* VVNK/DW (B74-50794)
Vintage musical comedy book. (Drinkrow, John). *Osprey Publishing. £1.95* ACMBN (B74-04045) ISBN 0-85045-103-5
Vinton, John. Dictionary of contemporary music. *See* Vinton, John. Dictionary of twentieth-century music.
Vinton, John. Dictionary of twentieth-century music. *Thames and Hudson. £9.50* A(C/XM71) (B74-24905) ISBN 0-500-01100-1
Violin-making as it was and is : being a historical, theoretical and practical treatise on the science and art of violin-making for the use of violin makers and players, amateur and professional. (Heron-Allen, Edward). 2nd ed. *Ward Lock. £4.50* AS/BC (B74-02416) ISBN 0-7063-1045-4
Viotti, Giovanni Battista. Concerto for violin & string orchestra, no.2, in E major: arr. Konzert No.2: E-Dur für Violine und Streichorchester, zwei Oboen und zwei Hörner ad lib. *Schott. £2.90* SPK/LF (B74-50676)
Virgil. Ecloga VIII (Vergili 'Bucolica') : for 6 male voices (1972). (Penderecki, Krzysztof). *Schott. £2.40* JNGEZAZDX (B74-50095)
Vision of time and eternity. Op.61 : song. (Mathias, William). *Oxford University Press. £1.10* KDW (B74-50461) ISBN 0-19-345570-6
Vivaldi, Antonio.
Concerto for oboe, violin & string orchestra in C minor 'Lund'. Concerto in C minor for oboe, violin and strings (Lund). *Musica rara. Unpriced* RXMPVTPLSF (B74-50651)
Concerto for oboe, violin & string orchestra in C minor, 'Lund': arr. Concerto in C minor for oboe, violin and strings (Lund). *Musica rara. Unpriced* NUTNTK/LF (B74-50530)
Concerto for string orchestra & basso continuo in C major. P. 27. Concerto ripieno, C-Dur für Streichorchester und Basso continuo. PV27. *Schott. £1.92* RXMF (B74-50216)
Concerto for treble recorder, oboe, violin, bassoon and basso continuo in G major. P.105. Concerto in G major : for treble recorder (flute), oboe, violin, bassoon and basso continuo. P.105. *Musica rara. Unpriced* NUPNRF (B74-50525)
Concerto for treble recorder, oboe, violin, bassoon & basso continuo in G minor. P.403. Concerto in G minor : for treble recorder (flute), oboe, violin, bassoon and basso continuo. P.403. *Musica rara. Unpriced* NUPNRF (B74-50526)
Concerto for two oboes & string orchestra in D minor. P.302. Concerto in D minor for 2 oboes, strings and basso continuo. *Musica rara. Unpriced* RXMPVTNUF (B74-50650)
Concerto for two oboes & string orchestra in D minor. P.302: arr. Concerto in D minor for 2 oboes, strings and basso continuo. *Musica rara. Unpriced* VTPK/LF (B74-50787)
Concertos for bassoon. Selections: arr. 10 bassoon concerti Vol.1. *Schirmer. Unpriced* VWPK/LF (B74-50299)
Concertos for bassoon. Selections: arr. 10 bassoon concerti Vol.2. *Schirmer. Unpriced* VWPK/LF (B74-50300)
L'Estro armonico. Op.3, no.11. Concerto d-Moll : für 2 Violinen, Streicher und Basso continuo. *Schott. £4.35* RXMPRXNTF (B74-50647)
Gloria: arr. Gloria : for four-part chorus of mixed voices, two solo sopranos and solo alto. *Schirmer. £0.95* DGC (B74-50339)
L'Estro armonico, Op.3, no.11: arr. Concerto, d-Moll : für 2 Violinen, Streicher und Basso continuo. *Schott. £2.32* SNTQK/LF (B74-51239)
Magnificat. Esurientes implevit. Vocal score. He hath filled the hungry = Esurientes implevit : for two-part chorus of treble voices, s.A.. *Roberton. £0.12* FDH (B74-50987)
Selections: arr. Music by Vivaldi. *Schirmer. £1.05* TSNTK (B74-50256)
Sonata for flute & basso continuo in E minor, 'Stockholm'. Sonata in E minor : for flute and basso continuo. *Musica rara. Unpriced* VRPE (B74-50752)
Sonata for treble recorder & basso continuo in D minor. Sonate d-Moll, für Altblockflöte und Basso continuo. *Schott. £1.08* VSSPE (B74-50288)
Sonata for two oboes & basso continuo in G minor, 'Lund'. Trio sonata in G minor (Lund) : for 2 oboes and basso continuo. *Musica rara. Unpriced* VTNTPWE (B74-50780)
Vokalisen für Kammerchor. (Blacher, Boris). *Boosey and Hawkes. £0.30* EZDW (B74-50057)
Volkslieder : elektronische Orgel. (Sommer, Jürgen). *Nagel Bärenreiter. £1.80* RPVK/DW/G/AYE (B74-50635)
Volksmusik für Bläser. (Koch, Johnnes Hermann Ernst). *Bärenreiter. £1.10* UMK/DW/G/AY (B74-50722)
Von Einem, Gottfried. *See* Einem, Gottfried von.
Von Kameke, Ernst Ulrich. *See* Kameke, Ernst Ulrich von.
Von Moisy, Heinz. *See* Moisy, Heinz von.
Voxman, H. Concerto for clarinet in A. K.622. Adagio; arr. Adagio. (Mozart, Wolfgang Amadeus). *Rubank : Novello. Unpriced* VVTRPK (B74-50809)
Voxman, Himie.
Concerto for two flutes, no.1, in G minor: arr. Concerto no.1 in G minor for 2 flutes and orchestra. (Quantz, Johann Joachim). *Musica rara. Unpriced* VRNTQK/LF (B74-50746)
Sonata for clarinet in A & piano in A major. Op.2. Sonata for clarinet and piano. Op.2. (Rudolph Johann Joseph Rainer, *Archduke of Austria Cardinal Archbishop of Olmutz*). *Musica rara. Unpriced* VVQPE (B74-50808)
Symphonie concertante for two clarinets in B flat major. Opus 25: arr. Symphonie concertante for two clarinets and orchestra. Opus 25. (Devienne, François). *Musica rara. Unpriced* VVNTQK/LE (B74-50798)
Trio for clarinet, cello & piano in E flat major, Op.36. Grand trio for piano, clarinet and violoncello. Op.36. (Eberl, Anton). *Musica rara. £2.85* NUVNT (B74-50531)
Voyage : for medium voice and piano. (Carter, Elliot). *Associated Music Publishers. £0.40* KFVDW (B74-50486)
Vries, Han de. Concertino for oboe in F major. Op.110: arr. Concertino for oboe and orchestra. Op.110. (Kalliwoda, Jan Vaclav). *Musica rara. Unpriced* VTPK/LFL (B74-50788)
Wade-Gery, H J. Nocturne, Op.54 : song for medium voice and piano. (Rubbra, Edmund). *Lengnick. £0.30* KFVDW (B74-50487)
Wagner. (Jacobs, Robert Louis). Revised ed.. *Dent. £2.75* BWC(N) (B74-25494) ISBN 0-460-03153-8
Wagner's 'Ring' and its symbols : the music and the myth. (Donington, Robert). 3rd ed. *Faber. £3.95* BWCAC (B74-09867) ISBN 0-571-04825-0
Wain, John. Metalepsis Z : cantata for mezzo-soprano solo, SATB and orchestral accompaniment. (Rands, Bernard). *Universal. Unpriced* EMDX (B74-50377)
Wakeman, Rick. Journey to the centre of the earth: arr. Journey to the centre of the earth. *Rondor : Music Sales. Unpriced* QPK/DW (B74-50603)
Waldis, Burkhard. Pleasure it is : for unaccompanied mixed chorus. (Kechley, Gerald). *Galaxy : Galliard. Unpriced* EZDP (B74-50958)
Waldmärchen = A forest legend (Das klagende Lied: 1). (Mahler, Gustav). *Belwin-Mills. Unpriced* DX (B74-50371)
Wales, Tony. Folk directory
1974. *The Society. £1.25 (£0.75 to members)* A/G(BC) (B74-13106) ISBN 0-85418-096-6
Walker, Eldon. Duologue : 2 clarinets. *Thames. Unpriced* VVNU (B74-51342)
Walker, Francis G. Hänsel und Gretel. *Abends will ich schlafen gehen: arr.* Angel scene. (Humperdinck, Engelbert). *Cramer. Unpriced* RK/DW (B74-50206)
Walker, Robert.
Communion service in E, series 3 : for congregational use. *Novello. £0.16* JDGS (B74-50441)
Three early English lyrics : for SSAA unaccompanied chorus. *Weinberger. £0.15* FEZDW (B74-50430)
Walley, John. George Formby complete. (Formby, George). *Wise. Unpriced* KDW/AY (B74-50099)
Walls, Peter. Twenty-one masque dances of the early seventeenth century for one instrument and continuo. *London Pro musica. Unpriced* LPH/AYD(XEJ10) (B74-51086)
Walmisley, Thomas Attwood. Works, organ. Selections. Selected organ works. *Peters. Unpriced* RJ (B74-50624)
Walter, Heinz. Variations on a theme by Georg Friedrich Handel : for soprano recorder (flute) and harpsichord. *Schott. £1.74* VSSP/T (B74-51337)
Walters, Edmund.
Babe of Bethlehem : a carol for treble voices (with audience or additional choral participation). *Boosey and Hawkes. £0.10* FLDP/LF (B74-51011)
Ding-dong-doh : a carol for unison treble voices (with optional second and third parts). *Boosey and Hawkes. £0.10* JFLDP/LF (B74-51041)
Little camel boy : a carol for treble voices with audience (or choral) participation. *Boosey and Hawkes. £0.15* FLDP/LF (B74-51012)
Walters, Harold L.
Japanese folk suite : for military band. *Rubank : Novello. Unpriced* UMMG (B74-50724)
Kneller Hall : concert march for military band. *Rubank : Novello. Unpriced* UMMGM (B74-50726)
Walton, *Sir* William.
Cantico del sole : for unaccompanied mixed voices. *Oxford University Press. £0.50* EZDH (B74-50947) ISBN 0-19-338490-6
Christopher Columbus. Beatriz's song: arr. Beatriz's song. *Oxford University Press. £0.35* KE/TSDW/JM (B74-50481) ISBN 0-19-345866-7
Five bagetelles for guitar. *Oxford University Press. £1.50* TSPMJ (B74-51276) ISBN 0-19-359407-2
Sonata for string orchestra. *Oxford University Press. £3.90* RXME (B74-50214) ISBN 0-19-368427-6
Waltz theme. (Bennett, Richard Rodney). *EMI. £0.25* QPK/AHW/JR (B74-51185)
Waltz themes from Tchaikovsky : for descant recorder, treble or melodica or guitar. (Tchaikovsky, Peter). *British and Continental Music Agencies. Unpriced* VSRPMK/AHW (B74-50770)
Wanek, Friedrich. Concerto for violin & string orchestra in A major: arr. Konzert, A-Dur für Violine, Streichorchester und Basso continuo. (Albinoni, Tommaso). *Schott. £2.03* SPK/LF (B74-51247)
Wanhal, Jan. *See* Vanhal, Jan.
War-peace bibliography series. Denisoff, R Serge. Songs of protest, war and peace : a bibliography & discography. Revised ed. *30 Cornmarket St., Oxford OX1 3EY : ABC-Clio Inc. £1.45* ADW/KJWX(T) (B74-16447) ISBN 0-87436-121-4
War scenes : for medium-low voice and piano. (Rorem, Ned). *Boosey and Hawkes. Unpriced* KFVDW (B74-51074)
Ward-Steinman, David. Child's play : for bassoon and piano. *Highgate Press : Galaxy : Galliard. Unpriced* VWPJ (B74-51347)
Warlike Musick. Warlike Musick for flute, violin or harpsichord. Warlike Musick (1760) : marches and trumpet tunes, for flute or oboe or violin and basso continuo. *Oxford University Press. £1.50* VRP/AY (B74-51317) ISBN 0-19-357552-3
Warlike Musick (1760) : marches and trumpet tunes, for flute or oboe or violin and basso continuo. (Warlike Musick). *Oxford University Press. £1.50* VRP/AY (B74-51317) ISBN 0-19-357552-3
Warlike Musick for flute, violin or harpsichord. Warlike Musick (1760) : marches and trumpet tunes, for flute or oboe or violin and basso continuo. (Warlike Musick). *Oxford University Press. £1.50* VRP/AY (B74-51317) ISBN 0-19-357552-3
Warlock, Peter. Candlelight : a cycle of nursery jingles. *Thames Music. Unpriced* KDW (B74-51054)
Warren, Raymond. Quartet for strings, no.1. String quartet no.1. *Novello. Unpriced* RXNS (B74-51229)
Washburn, Robert.
Chorale for band : wind band. *Oxford University Press. Unpriced* UMJ (B74-51300)
Ode to freedom. Vocal score. Ode to freedom : mixed chorus, SATB accompanied by band and/or orchestra. *Oxford University Press. Unpriced* DX (B74-50930)
The Old Hundreth Psalm tune ('All people that on earth do dwell') : anthem for unison or mixed (SATB) choir accompanied by organ with band and/or orchestra. (Vaughan Williams, Ralph). *Oxford University Press. Unpriced* EUMDM (B74-50381)
Prologue and dance : for orchestra. *Oxford University Press. Unpriced* MMH (B74-50500)
Quintet for winds. *Oxford University Press. Unpriced* UNR (B74-50738)
Spring cantata : SATB
I: The succession of the four sweet months. *Boosey and Hawkes. Unpriced* EZDX (B74-50981)
II: April. *Boosey and Hawkes. Unpriced* EZDX (B74-50982)
III: May. *Boosey and Hawkes. Unpriced* EZDX (B74-50983)
IV: Lazy June. *Boosey and Hawkes. Unpriced* EZDX (B74-50984)
V: July. *Boosey and Hawkes. Unpriced* EZDX (B74-50985)
Washington, Henry. Stabat mater dolorosa : for eight voices. (Palestrina, Giovanni Pierluigi da). *Chester. Unpriced* EZDGKADD/LK (B74-50942)
Washington University. *See* University of Washington.
Wastall, Peter.
Petite musique de chambre. Partita 1. *selections.* Suite no.2. (Telemann, Georg Philipp). *Boosey and Hawkes. £0.65* WSPJ (B74-50835)
Petite musique de chambre. Partitas 4, 5. *selections.* Suite no.1 : arranged for trumpet in B flat and piano from the music of G.P. Telemann. (Telemann, Georg Philipp). *Boosey and Hawkes. £0.65* WSPJ (B74-50836)
Watanabe, Saburo. D.B. Kabalevsky's 'Joey the clown' ('The comedians'). *F. Warne. £1.75* BKDBAM/HMBN (B74-26153) ISBN 0-7232-1783-1
Water music. (Handel, George Frideric). *Eulenburg. £0.70* MRG (B74-50148)
Water music. Selections: arr. Three pieces. (Handel, George Frideric). *Schirmer. Unpriced* QNTZNK (B74-50160)
Waters, Charles Frederick. Impromptu for the organ. *Cramer. £0.24* RJ (B74-50203)
Waters, James. Psalm 31 : for four-part chorus of mixed voices a cappella. *Schirmer. Unpriced* EZDR (B74-50971)
Waverley. Op.1 : overture. (Berlioz, Hector). *Eulenberg. Unpriced* MMJ (B74-50502)
Waxman, Donald. Selections : arr. Adagio for a musical clock and Rondo a capriccio 'Rage over the lost groschen'. (Beethoven, Ludwig van). *Galaxy : Galliard. Unpriced* QNUK (B74-51139)
We pause beside this door : anthem for the New Year, for four-part chorus of mixed voices with organ accompaniment. (Ferguson, Edwin Earle). *Roberton. £0.10* DH/LFM (B74-50017)
Webb, Evelyn. Sing aloud unto God our strength : SATB chorus with three trumpets, three trombones and

timpani. *Schott. £2.00* ENYHXPNPDK (B74-50032)
Wechsberg, Joseph. Verdi. *Weidenfeld and Nicolson. £4.50* BVE(N) (B74-22804) ISBN 0-297-76818-2
Wedderburn, James. Balulalow : unison voices (or solo) and piano (or organ). (Hughes-Jones, Llifon). *Thames. Unpriced* JDP/LF (B74-51023)
Wedderburn, John. Balulalow : unison voices (or solo) and piano (or organ). (Hughes-Jones, Llifon). *Thames. Unpriced* JDP/LF (B74-51023)
Wedderburn, Robert. Balulalow : unison voices (or solo) and piano (or organ). (Hughes-Jones, Llifon). *Thames. Unpriced* JDP/LF (B74-51023)
Wedding responses : SATB unacc. (Guest, Donald). *Oxford University Press. £0.06* DGMM/KDD (B74-50341) ISBN 0-19-351649-7
Weelkes, Thomas.
First evening service. Magnificat and Nunc dimittis : SSAATB. *Oxford University Press. £0.30* DGPP (B74-50342) ISBN 0-19-351646-2
O Lord arise : anthem for seven voices, S.S.A.A.T.B.B. *Oxford University Press. £0.20* EZDK (B74-50955) ISBN 0-19-352126-1
Weihnachten : elektronische Orgel. (Michel, Joseph). *Nagel : Bärenreiter. £1.80* RPVK/AAY (B74-50629)
Weiner, Lazar.
Aleynu l'shabench : a new Friday evening service, cantor solo with mixed chorus, SATB and organ, commissioned by the Anshe Emet Synagogue, Chicago, Illinois, on the occasion of the hundredth jubilee year (1873-1973)
6: May the words. *Ethnic Music : Phoenix. Unpriced* DGU (B74-50889)
10: Veshomru. *Ethnic Music : Phoenix. Unpriced* DGU (B74-50893)
Weingarden, Louis.
Things heard and seen in summer : for piano, violin and cello. *Oxford University Press. Unpriced* NXNT (B74-50551)
Triptych : three pieces for piano. *Boosey and Hawkes. £2.25* QPJ (B74-51181)
Weissenborn, Julius. Six trios for 3 bassoons. Op.4. *Musica rara. Unpriced* VWNT (B74-50810)
Wekselbaltt, Herbert. First solos for the tuba player. *Schirmer. £1.05* WVPK/AAY (B74-50321)
Welcome Yule : SATB unacc. (Owen, David). *Oxford University Press. Unpriced* EZDP/LF (B74-50049) ISBN 0-19-343044-4
Well, what do you know? : SATB with piano accompaniment and optional violins, string bass and guitar. (Artman, Ruth). *Warner : Blossom. Unpriced* DW (B74-50917)
Wels, Byron Gerald. How to repair musical instrument amplifiers. *Yeovil Rd, Slough, Bucks. SL1 4JH : Foulsham-Tab Ltd. £1.50* APV/BT (B74-05794) ISBN 0-7042-0050-3
Welsh flavour : a selection of Welsh hymn tunes set to English words
Vol.7. (Battye, Ken). *Ken Battye. Unpriced* DM/AYDK (B74-50354)
Welsh folksong fantasies : harp
No.1: Sweet but simple Gwennie. (Griffiths, Ann). *Adlais. Unpriced* TQPMJ (B74-51266)
No.2: What is summer to me? (Griffiths, Ann). *Adlais. Unpriced* TQPMJ (B74-51267)
Welt der Orgel : eine Sammlung für alle elektronischen Orgeln. (Parker, John). *Schott. £2.40* RPVK/AAY (B74-50207)
Weltspiegel. *O Musika du edle Kunst.* O Musica, thou noble art : for five-part chorus of mixed voices a cappella. (Peuerl, Paul). *Roberton. £0.10* EZDW (B74-50060)
Wen, Chi Chung. Three Chinese folksongs : for oboe and piano. *Schott. £1.00* VTPJ (B74-51338)
Wendt, Wolfgang. Studies for the piano
Book 2: Portato, legato and staccato in combinations, introduction to other kinds of touch. *Peters. Unpriced* Q/AF (B74-51128)
Wennerstrom, Mary. Sonatas for violin & basso continuo. Op.1, nos. 1, 4, 8. 3 sonatas for violin and piano. (Veracini, Francesco Maria). *Associated Music. Unpriced* SPE (B74-50233)
We're all in this together : arr. We're all in this together : for mixed chorus (SATB). (Hague, Albert). *Chappell. Unpriced* DW (B74-50924)
We're all in this together : for mixed chorus (SATB). (Hague, Albert). *Chappell. Unpriced* DW (B74-50924)
Werfel, Alma Mahler. Gustav Mahler : memories and letters. 3rd ed. *J. Murray. £5.00* BME(N) (B74-00161) ISBN 0-7195-2944-1
Wesley, Samuel.
Symphony no.5 in A major. Symphony 5 in A major : for horns and strings. *Oxford University Press. Score £3.50, parts unpriced* MRE (B74-50519) ISBN 0-19-368650-3
Two motets. *Novello. £0.16* EZDJ (B74-50401)
Westmore, Peter. Out of the depths, based on Psalm 129 (130) : (SATB). (Hughes, Edward). *Campbell, Connelly. Unpriced* DH (B74-50348)
Weston, Pamela. Quintet for clarinet & strings in B minor. Op. 115: arr. Clarinet quintet in B minor. (Brahms, Johannes). *Fenette Music : Breitkopf and Härtel. Unpriced* VVQPK (B74-50295)
Westrup, *Sir* Jack. Beethoven. (Scott, Marion Margareta). Revised ed.. *Dent. £2.95* BBJ (B74-22161) ISBN 0-460-03149-x
Westrup, *Sir* Jack Allan. An introduction to musical history. 2nd ed. *Hutchinson. £1.50* A(XB) (B74-04792) ISBN 0-09-031591-x
Wetzler, Robert. Trilogy of praise : for four-part chorus of mixed voices a cappella. *Schirmer. Unpriced* EZDE (B74-50037)
Whalum, Wendell. Amazin' grace : old negro hymn tune. *Roberton. £0.13* DM (B74-50019)
When David heard that his son was slain : for full chorus of mixed voices a cappella. (Chorbajian, John). *Schirmer. Unpriced* EZDK (B74-50954)
When I was one and twenty : for voice and piano. (Duke, John). *Schirmer. Unpriced* KDW (B74-50098)
Where's Charley?. The New Ashmolean Marching Society and Students Conservatory Band: arr. The New Ashmolean Marching Society and Students Conservatory Band. (Loesser, Frank). *Frank Music. Unpriced* UMMK (B74-51309)
Whitcomb, Robert. Great is the Lord : SATB a cappella. *Associated Music. Unpriced* EZDK (B74-50956)
White, William. Fantasies for five viols. Meyer 1,3, 'Diapente'. Diapente: two fantasies a 5. (Meyer nos. 1 and 3) : for viols or other stringed instruments. *Peters. Unpriced* STNQR (B74-50688)
White crane : for voices, descant, recorders, percussion and piano, violins and guitar ad lib. (Lipkin, Malcolm). *Chester. Unpriced* CQN (B74-50334)
Whitecotton, Shirley. Two idylls : for unaccompanied women's chorus, (SSA). *Galaxy : Galliard. Unpriced* FEZDW (B74-50431)
Whiteley, John Scott. Petit prelude. Aria : organ. (Jongen, Joseph). *Oxford University Press. £0.35* RJ (B74-50619) ISBN 0-19-375495-9
Whitman, Paul. Calamus. Op.104. Vocal score. Calamus. Op.104 : mixed chorus of brass-percussion ensemble or piano : music by Paul Creston. (Creston, Paul). *Schirmer. Unpriced* DX (B74-50927)
Whitman, Walt. War scenes : for medium-low voice and piano. (Rorem, Ned). *Boosey and Hawkes. Unpriced* KFVDW (B74-51074)
Whitter, Mark. A carol for Mary : SATB unacc. *Oxford University Press. £0.05* EZDP/LF (B74-50050) ISBN 0-19-343043-6
Whittier, John Greenleaf. Spring cantata : SATB
II: April. (Washburn, Robert). *Boosey and Hawkes. Unpriced* EZDX (B74-50982)
Whone, Herbert. The hidden face of music. *Gollancz. £3.00* A/CC (B74-12385) ISBN 0-575-01739-2
Why this haste, O shepherd, say : old French noël. (Parkinson, John Alfred). *Oxford University Press. £0.08* EZDP/LF (B74-50965) ISBN 0-19-343047-9
Whyton, Wally. Guitar song book
Book 1. *Durham Music. £1.25* JE/TSDW/AY (B74-51029)
Wicker, Norman. Glory choruses
No.3; arranged by Walter Eden and Norman Wicker. (Turner, Roy). *112a Beacon Hill Rd, Newark : Henri's Evangelical Revival Association. Unpriced* JDM (B74-51021)
Widerkehr, Jacob Christian Michael. Sonata for oboe & piano in E minor. Duo sonata for oboe and piano. *Musica rara. Unpriced* VTPE (B74-50782)
Wigwam tune book : 20 exciting modern tunes to your favourite hymns. (Hodson, Keith). *Wigwam Publications. Unpriced* JDM/AY (B74-50084)
Wilbur, Richard.
A black November turkey : for four-part chorus of mixed voices with soprano and alto solos a cappella. (Corigliano, John). *Schirmer. Unpriced* EZDW (B74-50059)
L'Invitation au voyage : for four-part chorus of mixed voices with soprano, alto, tenor, and bass solos a cappella. (Corigliano, John). *Schirmer. Unpriced* EZDW (B74-50977)
Wilbye. (Brown, David, *b.1929*). *Oxford University Press. £1.65* BWNRB (B74-13708) ISBN 0-19-315220-7
Wilcock, Anthea. Christus natus est : unison with descant. *Chappell. Unpriced* FDP/LF (B74-50989)
Wild, Stephen. E.J. Moeran. *10e Prior Bolton St., N.1 : Triad Press. £1.50* BMLE (B74-08075) ISBN 0-902070-09-6
Wild rover : the story of the Prodigal Son: a musical play for children. (O'Gorman, Denis). *Grail Publications. £0.50* BOFGACN (B74-11053) ISBN 0-901829-22-6
Wilk, Max. They're playing our song : from Jerome Kern to Stephen Sondheim - the stories behind the words and music of two generations. *W.H. Allen. £3.50* ADW/GB(YT/M) (B74-11736) ISBN 0-491-01530-5
Wilkin, Nigel. Three French songs from the late 14th century : for voice and 2 or 3 instruments. *Antico. Unpriced* KE/LNTDW/AYH (XCTQ26) (B74-50477)
Wilkins, Eithne. Letters of Arnold Schoenberg. (Schoenberg, Arnold). *Faber. £2.95* BSET(N) (B74-04793) ISBN 0-571-10514-9
Wilkinson, Philip George. 100 score-reading exercises. *Novello. £1.50* LNT (B74-51083)
Wilkinson, Stephen. Songs of Ophelia, nos. 3, 4. Christmas cradle song. (Brahms, Johannes). *Novello. Unpriced* EZDP/LF (B74-50959)
Williams, John. Concerto for guitar: arr. Concerto for guitar and orchestra. (Previn, André). *Schirmer. Unpriced* TSPMK/LF (B74-51285)
Williams, Pater. Concertos for organ. Op.7. Organ concertos. Op.7
No.3: B flat major. (Handel, George Frideric). *Eulenburg. £0.80* MPRF (B74-50511)
Williams, Patrick. Also hat Gott die Welt geliebt. S.68. Mein gläubiges Herz: arr. 'Air', My heart ever faithful. (Bach, Johann Sebastian). *Cramer. £0.21* RK/DH (B74-51202)
Williams, Peter.
Concertos for organ. Op.7. Organ concertos. Op.7
No.1: B flat major. (Handel, George Frideric). *Eulenburg. £0.80* MPRF (B74-50509)
Concertos for organ. Op.7. Organ concertos. Op.7
No.2: A major. (Handel, George Frideric). *Eulenburg. £0.80* MPRF (B74-50510)
Concertos for organ. Op.7. Organ concertos. Op.7
No.4: D minor. (Handel, George Frideric). *Eulenburg. £0.80* MPRF (B74-50512)
Concertos for organ. Op.7. Organ concertos. Op.7
No.5: G minor. (Handel, George Frideric). *Eulenburg. £0.80* MPRF (B74-50513)
Concertos for organ. Op.7. Organ concertos. Op.7
No.6: B flat major. (Handel, George Frideric). *Eulenburg. £0.80* MPRF (B74-50514)
Williams, Ralph Vaughan. *See* Vaughan Williams, Ralph.
Williamson, Malcolm.
Canticle of fire : for chorus (SATB) and organ. *Weinberger. Unpriced* DE (B74-50875)
Concerto grosso. *Weinberger. Unpriced* MMF (B74-50497)
Little carols of the saints : for organ. *Weinberger. Unpriced* RJ (B74-50625)
Wills, Arthur.
Prayer : anthem for SATB and organ. *Novello. £0.12* DH (B74-50903)
Singing joyfully, God's power proclaim : unison voices and piano or organ. *Boosey and Hawkes. Unpriced* JDR (B74-50446)
Trio sonata : organ. *Boosey and Hawkes. £1.00* RJ (B74-50204)
Willson, Meredith. The music man. Goodnight, my someone. *Vocal score: arr.* Goodnight, my someone. *Frank Music. Unpriced* FDW (B74-50995)
Wilson, John Whitridge. Hymns for celebration : a supplement for use at Holy Communion today. (Routley, Erik). *Royal School of Church Music. Unpriced* DM/AY (B74-50353) ISBN 0-85402-055-1
Wilson, Josephine. Treasure island. Vocal score. Treasure island : a musical adventure. (Ornadel, Cyril). *Sparta Florida Music : Aviva Music. £0.99* CM (B74-50006)
Wilson, Robert Barclay.
Caprice : piano solo. *Lengnick. £0.18* QPJ (B74-50189)
A miniature suite for piano. *Freeman. Unpriced* QPG (B74-50170)
Mors janua vitae. Vocal score. Mors janua vitae : for male-voice choir (TTBB) and piano or organ or strings. *Cramer. £0.12* GDH (B74-51013)
Three contrasts : piano. *Cramer. £0.15* QPJ (B74-51182)
Wilson, *Sir* Steuart. The bells do ring : based on a French tune for four-part chorus of mixed voices with optional handbells. (Glarum, Leonard Stanley). *Schirmer. Unpriced* EZDP/LF (B74-50963)
Wind encores : a collection of 12 short familiar pieces arranged for four-part clarinet ensemble (2 B flat clarinets, alto clarinet (or bassoon) and bass clarinet (or bassoon)). (Coursey, Ralph de). *Associated Music. Unpriced* VVNSK/AAY (B74-50796)
Winding, Thomas. My favourite intervals. (Borge, Victor). *Woburn Press. £2.25* A/D(YB/M) (B74-09227) ISBN 0-7130-0126-7
Winkworth, Catherine. Praise to the Lord : hymn-anthem for four-part chorus of mixed voices with organ or piano accompaniment, melody 'Lobe den Herrn' from Stralsund Gesangbuch. (Newbury, Kent A). *Schirmer. Unpriced* DH (B74-50014)
Winners got scars too. Johnny Cash - winners got scars too. (Wren, Christopher, *b.1936*). *Abacus. £0.60* AKDW/GCW(P) (B74-11737) ISBN 0-349-13740-4
Winstead, William.
Concertos for bassoon. Selections: arr. 10 bassoon concerti
Vol.1. (Vivaldi, Antonio). *Schirmer. Unpriced* VWPK/LF (B74-50299)
Concertos for bassoon. Selections: arr. 10 bassoon concerti
Vol.2. (Vivaldi, Antonio). *Schirmer. Unpriced* VWPK/LF (B74-50300)
Winter afternoons : cantata for six solo voices and double bass. (Dickinson, Peter). *Novello. £0.50* ESSDE (B74-50937)
Winters. A teacher's guide to the guitar. *Schoolmaster Publishing Co. Unpriced* TS/AC (B74-50255)
Wise, Oressa. Songs of fellowship. (Pulkingham, Betty Carr). *The Fishermen Inc., by arrangement with the Fountanin Trust. Unpriced* JE/TSDM/AY (B74-50087)
Wiseman, Charles. Trio for 2 flutes & cello or bassoon in D major. *Roberton. £0.50* NVPNT (B74-50541)
Withams, Eric L. The horse of wood : a pop-style cantata. *Universal. Unpriced* FDX (B74-50998)
Wohlfahrt, Franz. Etudes for violin. Op.45, 54, 74. Selections: arr. Forty selected studies in first position for the viola. *Schirmer. Unpriced* SQK/AF (B74-50239)
Wohltemperirte Clavier, Tl.1. Prelude and fugue, no.5. S.850. Praeludium V und Fuga V : Klavier (Cembalo). (Bach, Johann Sebastian). *Schott. £0.60* PWP/Y (B74-50554)
Wohltemperirte Clavier, Tl.1. Prelude and fugue, no.6. S.851. Praeludium VI und Fuga VI : Klavier (Cembalo). (Bach, Johann Sebastian). *Schott. £0.60* PWP/Y (B74-50555)
Wohltemperirte Clavier, Tl.1. Prelude and fugue, no.16. S.861. Praeludium XVI and Fuga XVI : Klavier (Cembalo). (Bach, Johann Sebastian). *Schott. £0.60* PWP/Y (B74-50556)
Wohltemperirte Clavier, Tl.2. Prelude and fugue, no.2. S.871. Praeludium II and Fuga II : Klavier (Cembalo). (Bach, Johann Sebastian). *Schott. £0.60* PWP/Y (B74-50557)
Wombling song : for recorders, descant, treble tenor and piano. (Batt, Mike). *Chappell. Unpriced* VSNTQ (B74-50282)
Women speaking : six songs for sopranos. *Thames. Unpriced* KFLDW/AY (B74-51066)
Wood, Barbara. Join the band : a selection of folk dance tunes for beginners, with second parts. *English Folk*

Dance and Song Society. *Unpriced* LNUH/G/AY
(B74-50490)   ISBN 0-85418-079-6
Wood, David, *b.1944.*
   Flibberty and the penguin : a musical play. *French. £0.50*
   BWPDACN (B74-22805)   ISBN 0-573-05033-3
   Hijack over Hygenia : a musical play for children. *French.*
   £0.75 BWPDACN (B74-28315)   ISBN 0-573-05034-1
Woodfield, Ian. Five pieces for four viols from 'Musica
   teutsch' and 'Musica und Tabulatur'. (Gerle, Hans).
   Oxford University Press. £0.16 STNSK/DW/AYE
   (B74-51257)   ISBN 0-19-341214-4
Wooding, Dan. I thought Terry Dene was dead. *Coverdale*
   House. £0.50 AKDW/GB/E(P) (B74-25498)
                                 ISBN 0-902088-55-6
Woodmen of the world : jazz fantasy on a rock theme for
   woodwind quintet (with finger cymbals and tambourine).
   (Levitt, Rod). *Associated Music. Unpriced* NYHNPHX
   (B74-50552)
Woodwind for schools. (Tomlin, Peter). *Dryad Press. £2.25*
   AV/E(VK) (B74-14973)   ISBN 0-85219-089-1
Wooldridge, David. Concerto for horn: arr. Concerto for
   horn and orchestra. (Heiden, Bernhard). *Associated*
   Music. Unpriced WTPK/LF (B74-50319)
Woolf, Gregory. A time's passing : SATB a cappella.
   Associated Music. Unpriced EZDW (B74-50064)
Wordsworth, William. To be sung upon the water :
   barcarolles and nocturnes for high voice, piano and
   clarinet (also bass clarinet). (Argento, Dominick). *Boosey*
   and Hawkes. Unpriced KFTE/VVDW (B74-50484)
World belongs to Jesus : nine contemporary songs of
   worship. (Hodson, Keith). *the Baptist Church, Rochdale*
   Rd, Heywood, Lancs. OL10 1LG : Wigwam Publications
   for Songcrafts. Unpriced JDM (B74-50442)
                                 ISBN 0-904434-00-1
World cup fanfare : brass band. (Drexler, Werner).
   Weinberger. Unpriced WMK/AGN (B74-50825)
World cup fanfare : military band. (Drexler, Werner).
   Weinberger. Unpriced UMMK/AGN (B74-50733)
World of your 100 best tunes requested by listeners to the
   popular BBC radio series devised and presented by Alan
   Keith, easy-to-play piano album, piano arrangements by
   James Burt
   Vol.4. (Keith, Alan). *Chappell. Unpriced* QPK/AAY
   (B74-50598)
World of your 100 best tunes requested by listeners to the
   popular BBC radio series
   Vol.1. (Keith, Alan). *Chappell. £0.50* QPK/AAY
   (B74-50599)
   Vol.2. (Keith, Alan). *Chappell. £0.50* QPK/AAY
   (B74-50600)
   Vol.3. (Keith, Alan). *Chappell. £0.95* QPK/AAY
   (B74-50601)
World's favorite contemporary music for all organs. (Grant,
   Lawrence). *Ashley : Phoenix. Unpriced* RK/AAY
   (B74-51200)
World's favorite preludes : offertories and postludes for the
   piano
   Vol.1. (Grant, Lawrence). *Ashley : Phoenix. Unpriced*
   QPK/AAY (B74-50596)
   Vol.2. (Grant, Lawrence). *Ashley : Phoenix. Unpriced*
   QPK/AAY (B74-50597)
World's favorite wedding music for piano. (Grant,
   Lawrence). *Ashley : Phoenix. Unpriced* QPK/KDD/AY
   (B74-50605)
World's favourite best known Debussy piano music.
   (Debussy, Claude). *Ashley : Phoenix. Unpriced* QPJ
   (B74-50587)
Wren, Christopher, *b.1936.* Johnny Cash - winners got scars
   too. *Abacus. £0.60* AKDW/GCW(P) (B74-11737)
                                 ISBN 0-349-13740-4
Wren, Christopher, *b.1936.* Winners got scars too. *See* Wren,
   Christopher, b.1936. Johnny Cash - winners got scars
   too.
Wright, Denis. Chanson de matin, Op.15, no.1: arr. Chanson
   de matin. Opus 15, no.1. (Elgar, *Sir* Edward, *bart*).
   Paxton. £1.25 WMK (B74-50824)
Wright, Francis. 5 divertimento for accordion. *Charnwood*
   Music. Unpriced RSPMJ (B74-51212)
Wright, Rosemary.
   Useful tunes for guitar
      No.1: Little brown jug : trad. and, Home on the range :
      trad. *Charnwood Music. Unpriced* TSPMK (B74-51278)

      No.2: The national anthem and Jingle bells : trad.
      Charnwood Music. Unpriced TSPMK (B74-51279)
      No.3: Minuet in G (from 'Notenbüchlein für Anna
      Magdelena Bach' 1725. *Charnwood Music. Unpriced*
      TSPMK (B74-51280)
      No.5: Hot cross buns : trad. and Auld lang syne : trad.
      Charnwood Music. Unpriced RSPMK (B74-51214)
Wyatt, *Sir* Thomas. A supplication : for SAB
   unaccompanied. (Stoker, Richard). *Ashdown. £0.12*
   EZDW (B74-50062)
Wyner, Yehudi.
   Psalm 143 : full chorus of mixed voices a cappella,
   SAATTB. *Associated Music. Unpriced* EZDR
   (B74-50051)
   Psalms and early songs. *Associated Music. Unpriced*
   KDH (B74-50097)
   Three short fantasias : for piano. *Associated Music.*
   Unpriced QPJ (B74-50593)
Yannatos, James.
   Three settings of E.E. Cummings
      1: Buffalo Bill's: TTBB a capella. *Associated Music.*
      Unpriced GEZDW (B74-50081)
      2: The rose: SSAA a capella. *Associated Music. Unpriced*
      FEZDW (B74-50076)
      3: In just- : SSATB a cappella. *Associated Music.*
      Unpriced EZDW (B74-50065)

You are Peter : brass accompaniment, 3 trumpets and
   trombone. (Tamblyn, William). *Boosey and Hawkes.*
   £0.40 EWNSDK (B74-50384)
Young, Andrew. Christmas day : SATB unacc.
   (Butterworth, Neil). *Banks. Unpriced* EZDP/LF
   (B74-50960)
Young, Douglas. Sir Patrick Spens. Vocal score. Sir Patrick
   Spens : chorus and orchestra, SATB. *Faber Music.*
   Unpriced DW (B74-50024)
Young, Percy Marshall. A concise history of music : from
   primitive times to the present. *E. Benn. £2.00* A(X)
   (B74-13103)   ISBN 0-510-37312-7
Young harpist. (Griffiths, Ann). *Adlais. Unpriced* TQ/AC
   (B74-51260)
Young World tripper books. Blackwood, Alan, *b.1932.* A
   trip to the concert. *36 Park St., W1Y 4DE : Nelson*
   Young World. £0.45 AM (B74-13709)
                                 ISBN 0-7238-0946-1
Zámečnik, Evžen. Twelve studies for violin : for technical
   problems in contemporary music. *Bärenreiter. £3.25*
   S/AF (B74-50659)
Zamfir, Gheorghe. Suites pour flûte de Pan. *Chappell.*
   Unpriced VRPG (B74-50758)
Zayde, Jascha. Let's play piano. *Experience Music :*
   Chappell. Unpriced Q/AC (B74-51124)
Zemanek, Vilem. My country. Vltava. My fatherland = Ma
   vlast : a cycle of symphonic poems
   No.2: Vltava. (Smetana, Bedřich). *Eulenburg. Unpriced*
   MMJ (B74-50507)
Zeraschi, Helmut. Drehorgelstücklein aus dem 18.
   Jahrhundert in Originalen, zubereitet für Flötlein sowie
   für Klavier oder andere Tasteninstrumente. *Peters.*
   Unpriced PWPK/AY(XF101) (B74-51122)
Zigeunerbaron. Selections: arr. The gypsy baron suite.
   (Strauss, Johann, *b.1825*). *Boosey and Hawkes. £15.00*
   MMK (B74-50143)
Zigeunerlieder = Gypsy songs. Op.103 : for four-part
   chorus of mixed voices with soprano and tenor solos and
   piano accompaniment. (Dodgson, Stephen). *Chappell.*
   Unpriced MMJ (B74-50504)
Ziguenerlieder = Gypsy songs. Op.103 : for four-part
   chorus of mixed voices with soprano and tenor solos and
   piano accompaniment. (Brahms, Johannes). *Schirmer.*
   Unpriced DW (B74-50357)
Zillertal : for B flat cornet or trumpet with piano
   accompaniment. (Simon, Frank). *Rubank : Novello.*
   Unpriced WRPJ (B74-51364)
Zillertal : for baritone with piano accompaniment. (Simon,
   Frank). *Rubank : Novello. Unpriced* WTZPJ
   (B74-51370)
Zillertal : for E flat or BB flat bass with piano
   accompaniment. (Simon, Frank). *Rubank : Novello.*
   Unpriced WXPJ (B74-51372)
Zils, Diethard. Oekumenische Beatmesse : Liebe ist nicht
   nur ein Wort. (Blarr, Oskar Gottlieb). *Bosse*
   Bärenreiter. £1.60 ELDE (B74-50372)
Zoephel, Klaus. Quintet for wind instruments. Quintett für
   Flöte, Oboe, Klarinette in B, Horn in F und Fagott.
   Peters. Unpriced VNR (B74-51312)
Zoo illogical : for solo voice, or voices in unison or octaves,
   with instrumental ensemble woodwind, brass &
   percussion, (optional piano). (Grundman, Clare). *Boosey*
   and Hawkes. Unpriced JE/NYHNMDE (B74-50450)
Zoo illogical : for solo voice, or voices in unison or octaves
   with piano. (Grundman, Clare). *Boosey and Hawkes.*
   Unpriced JDW (B74-50447)
Zoo illogical. *Vocal score.* Zoo illogical : for solo voice, or
   voices in unison or octaves with piano. (Grundman,
   Clare). *Boosey and Hawkes. Unpriced* JDW (B74-50447)

SUBJECT INDEX

4

Recorded vocal music: Books   AB/FD
Recorder   VS
Recorder & drum   VSPLXQ
Recorder, keyboard & percussion: Accompanying
    unison voices   JE/NYFS
Recorder (descant)   VSR
Recorder (descant), keyboard & percussion:
    Accompanying unison voices
    JE/NYFSR
Recorder (descant) & guitar   VSRPLTS
Recorder (tenor)   VST
Recorder (treble)   VSS
Recorders (4) & keyboard   VSNRPW
Recorders (4) & piano   VSNRQ
Recording: Books   A/F
Regimental marches: Military band
    UMMGM/KH
Religious cantatas   DE
Religious cantatas: Accompanied by brass sextet
    EWNQDE
Religious cantatas: Accompanied by guitar
    ETSDE
Religious cantatas: Accompanied by harps (3) &
    organ   ETQNSRDE
Religious cantatas: Accompanied by instruments
    ELDE
Religious cantatas: Accompanied by keyboard &
    percussion   ENYLDE
Religious cantatas: Accompanied by orchestra
    EMDE
Religious cantatas: Carols: Female voices,
    Children's voices: Accompanied by harp
    FE/TQDPDE
Religious cantatas: Female voices, Children's voices
    FDE
Religious cantatas: Female voices, Children's voices
    Unison   JFDE
Religious cantatas: Low voice: Accompanied by
    flute & piano   KFXE/VRPDE
Religious cantatas: Soprano voice: Accompanied by
    trumpet & organ   KFLE/WSPLRDE
Religious cantatas: Unaccompanied vocal octets
    JNEZAYDE
Religious cantatas: Unaccompanied works
    EZDE
Religious cantatas: Unison: Accompanied by wind
    & percussion nonet   JE/NYHNMDE
Religious choral music   DC
    Accompanied by brass sextet
      EWNQDC
    Accompanied by cello   ESSDC
    Accompanied by guitar   ETSDC
    Accompanied by harps (3) & organ
      ETQNSRDC
    Accompanied by instruments   ELDC
    Accompanied by keyboard & percussion
      ENYLDC
    Accompanied by orchestra   EMDC
    Accompanied by strings & keyboard
      ENXDC
    Books   AD/L
    Female voices, Children's voices   FDC
    Female voices, Children's voices: Unison
      JFDC
    Low voice: Accompanied by flute & piano
      KFXE/VRPDC
    Soprano voice: Accompanied by trumpet &
      organ   KFLE/WSPLRDC
    Unaccompanied vocal octets
      JNEZAYDC
    Unaccompanied works   EZDC
    Unison: Accompanied by wind & percussion
      nonet   JE/NYHNMDC
Religious music: Instrumental ensemble
    LN/L
Religious music: Motets, Anthems, Hymns, etc.
    DH
    Accompanied by brass band   EWMDH
    Accompanied by brass quartet
      EWNSDH
    Accompanied by brass septet
      ENYHXPNPDH
    Accompanied by flute & organ
      EVRPLRDH
    Accompanied by keyboard & percussion
      ENYLDH
    Accompanied by wind band   EUMDH
    Arrangements for flute quartet
      VRNSK/DH
    Arrangements for guitar solo
      TSPMK/DH
    Arrangements for organ   RK/DH
    Arrangements for recorder ensemble
      VSNK/DH
    Arrangements for recorder quartet
      VSNSK/DH
    Arrangements for recorder sextet
      VSNQK/DH
    Arrangements for trumpet & piano
      WSPK/DH
    Female voices, Children's voices   FDH
    Female voices, children's voices: Accompanied
      by harp & guitar   FE/TQPLTSDH
    Female voices, Children's voices: Unison
      JFDH
    Solo voice   KDH
    Solo voice: Accompanied by guitar
      KE/TSDH

Soprano voice   KFLDH
Soprano voices: Unison   JFLDH
Treble voices   FLDH
Unaccompanied female voices, children's voices
    FEZDH
Unaccompanied male voices   GEZDH
Unaccompanied soprano voices
    FLEZDH
Unaccompanied works   EZDH
Unaccompanied works: Unison
    JEZDH
Unison   JDH
Unison: Accompanied by guitar
    JE/TSDH
Vocal quintets   JNBDH
Religious musical plays for children: Vocal scores
    CN/L
Renn, Samuel: Books   AR/BC(YD/P)
Requiem Masses: Roman liturgy   DGKAV
Rhythm: Percussion instruments   X/NM
Ringing: Church bells: Books   AXSR/E
Rock 'n' roll: Songs: Solo voice: Books
    AKDW/HK
Rolling Stones: Books   AKDW/GB/E(P)
Roman liturgy: Accompanied by trombones &
    strings   ENVXUDFF
Roman liturgy: Choral works   DFF
Roman liturgy: Female voices, Children's voices
    FDFF
Roman liturgy: Organ   RDFF
Roman liturgy: Treble voices   FLDFF
Roman liturgy: Unaccompanied female voices,
    children's voices   FEZDFF
Roman liturgy: Unaccompanied male voices
    GEZDFF
Roman liturgy: Unaccompanied works
    EZDFF
Roman liturgy: Unison   JDFF
Rondos: Concertos: Symphony orchestra
    MMF/W
Rondos: Horn & piano   WTP/W
Rondos: Oboe & piano   VTP/W
Rounds: Female voices, children's voices: Accom-
    panied by percussion ensemble
    FE/XNDW/XC
Rounds: String orchestra   RXM/X
Royal College of Organists: Books
    AR/YC/VP/Q)
Rudiments of music: Books   A/M
Russia: Piano solos: Collections   QP/AYM

Sadler's Wells Opera Company: Books
    AC/E(YC/QB)
St. George's Chapel: Windsor: Organists: Books
    AR/E(YDEUW)
Sanctus: Ordinary of the Mass   DGE
Saxophone   VU
Saxophone (alto)   VUS
Saxophones (2) & piano   VUNTQ
Schoenberg, Arnold: Books   BSET
Schubert, Franz: Books   BSF
Scotland: Concerts: Piano   AQ(W/YDL)
Scotland: Dances: Collections for dancing: Piano
    solos   QPH/H/AYDL
Scotland: Folk music   A/G(YDL)
Scotland: Folk songs: Collections: Unaccompanied
    female voices, children's voices: Unison
    JFEZDW/G/AYDL
Sea: Songs: Books   ADW/KC
Secondary schools: Education: Books
    A(VK)
Secondary schools: Woodwind instruments
    AV/E(VK)
Secular cantatas   DX
Secular cantatas: Accompanied by clarinet &
    bassoon   EVVPLVWDX
Secular cantatas: Accompanied by flute & marimba
    FE/VRPLXTQSDX
Secular cantatas: Accompanied by orchestra
    EMDX
Secular cantatas: Books   ADX
Secular cantatas: Britten, B.: Books
    BBUADX
Secular cantatas: Female voices, Children's voices
    FDX
Secular cantatas: Female voices, Children's voices:
    Accompanied by orchestra   FE/MDX
Secular cantatas: Female voices, children's voices:
    Accompanied by string & percussion quintet
    FE/NYJNRDX
Secular cantatas: Solo voice   KDX
Secular cantatas: Solo voice: Accompanied by
    violin & piano   KGE/SPDX
Secular cantatas: Soprano voice: Accompanied by
    flute & percussion
    KFLE/NYHRDX
Secular cantatas: Soprano voice: Accompanied by
    orchestra   KFLE/MDX
Secular cantatas: Soprano voice: Accompanied by
    string quartet   KFLE/RXNSDX
Secular cantatas: Soprano voices   FLDX
Secular cantatas: Speaking chorus: Accompanied by
    percussion band   FHYE/XMDX
Secular cantatas: Unaccompanied male voices:
    Vocal sextet   JNGAZEZDX
Secular cantatas: Unaccompanied works
    EZDX
Secular cantatas: Unison   JDX

Secular choral music   DTZ
    Accompanied by clarinet & bassoon
      EVVPLVWDTZ
    Accompanied by double bass & accordion
      ESSPLRSDTZ
    Accompanied by flute & marimba
      FE/VRPLXTQSDTZ
    Accompanied by lute   ETWDTZ
    Accompanied by various instruments: Books
      AELDTZ
    Accompanied by wood-block   EXXDTZ
    Arrangements for brass band
      WMK/DTZ
    Arrangements for clarinet ensemble
      VVNK/DTZ
    Arrangements for descant recorder solo
      VSRPMK/DTZ
    Arrangements for electronic organ
      RPVK/DTZ
    Arrangements for guitar solo
      TSPMK/DTZ
    Arrangements for military band
      UMMK/DTZ
    Arrangements for organ   RK/DTZ
    Arrangements for piano duet, 4 hands
      QNVK/DTZ
    Arrangements for piano solo   QPK/DTZ
    Arrangements for plucked string instrument
      band   TMK/DTZ
    Arrangements for recorder duet
      VSNSK/DTZ
    Arrangements for string orchestra
      RXMK/DTZ
    Arrangements for symphony orchestra
      MMK/DTZ
    Arrangements for viol quartet
      STNSK/DTZ
    Arrangements for violin & piano
      SPK/DTZ
    Arrangements for wind band
      UMK/DTZ
    Arrangements for woodwind ensemble
      VNK/DTZ
    Books   ADTZ
    Britten, B.: Books   BBUADTZ
    Female voices, Children's voices
      FDTZ
    Female voices, Children's voices: Accompanied
      by orchestra   FE/MDTZ
    Female voices, children's voices: Accompanied
      by percussion ensemble   FE/XNDTZ
    Female voices, Children's voices: Unison
      JFDTZ
    Female voices, Children's voices: Unison:
      Accompanied by percussion band
      JFE/XMDTZ
    Female voices, Children's voices: Unison:
      Accompanied by strings & percussion
      JFE/NYJDTZ
    Speaking chorus: Accompanied by percussion
      band   FHYE/XMDTZ
    Treble voices: Unison: Accompanied by key-
      board & percussion
      JFLE/NYLDTZ
    Unaccompanied female voices, children's voices
      FEZDTZ
    Unaccompanied female voices, children's voices:
      Unison   JFEZDTZ
    Unaccompanied male voices   GEZDTZ
    Unaccompanied works   EZDTZ
    Unaccompanied works: Unison
      JEZDTZ
    Unison   JDTZ
    Unison: Accompanied by descant recorder,
      keyboard & percussion
      JE/NYFSRDTZ
    Unison: Accompanied by guitar
      JE/TSDTZ

Secular vocal music   KDTZ
    Accompanied by lute: Books
      AKE/TWDTZ
    Baritone voice   KGNDTZ
    Bass voice   KGXDTZ
    Books   AKDTZ
    Female voice, Child's voice duets: Vocal en-
      sembles   JNFEDTZ
    Female voices, children's voices: Accompanied
      by string & percussion quintet
      FE/NYJNRDTZ
    High voice   KFTDTZ
    High voice: Accompanied by clarinet
      KFTE/VVDTZ
    High voice: Accompanied by guitar
      KFTE/TSDTZ
    Low voice   KFXDTZ
    Middle voice   KFVDTZ
    Middle voice: Accompanied by guitar
      KFVE/TSDTZ
    Middle voice: Accompanied by orchestra
      KFVE/MDTZ
    Schubert, F.: Books   BSFAKDTZ
    Solo voice: Accompanied by Appalachian
      dulcimer   KE/TWTDTZ
    Solo voice: Accompanied by cello & piano
      KE/SRPDTZ
    Solo voice: Accompanied by guitar & piano
      KE/TSPDTZ

Solo voice: Accompanied by guitar ensemble
KE/TSNDTZ
Solo voice: Accompanied by harp
KE/TQDTZ
Solo voice: Accompanied by instrumental trio
KE/LNTDTZ
Solo voice: Accompanied by orchestra
KE/MDTZ
Solo voice: Accompanied by violin & piano
KGE/SPDTZ
Soprano voice KFLDTZ
Soprano voice: Accompanied by clarinet &
piano KFLE/VVPDTZ
Soprano voice: Accompanied by flute & per-
cussion KFLE/NYHRDTZ
Soprano voice: Accompanied by orchestra
KFLE/MDTZ
Soprano voice: Accompanied by string quartet
KFLE/RXNSDTZ
Soprano voice: Accompanied by woodwind,
string & keyboard sextet
KFLE/NUPNQDTZ
Unaccompanied male voices: Vocal sextet
JNGAZEZDTZ
Unaccompanied solo voice KEZDTZ
Septets: Brass & percussion: Accompanying choral
works ENYHXPNP
Septets: Wind & percussion NYHNP
Sequences: Proper of the Mass: Roman liturgy
DGKADD
Sequences: Proper of the Mass: Roman liturgy:
Accompanied by orchestra
EMDGKADD
Sequences: Proper of the Mass: Roman liturgy:
Unaccompanied works EZDGKADD
Serial music: Books A/PN
Sextets: Brass: Accompanying choral music
EWNQ
Sextets: Oboe, strings & keyboard NUTNQ
Sextets: Recorder VSNQ
Sextets: Trumpet, strings & keyboard
NUXSNQ
Sextets: Woodwind, strings & keyboard: Accom-
panying soprano voice
KFLE/NUPNQ
Sicilianos: Violin & piano SPHVQ
Sight reading: Piano playing Q/EG
Sight reading: Solo voice K/EG
Singers: Blues: Solo voice: Books
AKDW/HHW/E(M)
Singers: Country 'n' western songs: Books
AKDW/GCW/E(M)
Singers: Popular music: Books
AKDW/GB/E(M)
Singers: Rock 'n' roll: Songs: Solo voice: Books
AKDW/HK/E(M)
Singers: Soloists: Books AK/E(M)
Singers: Tenor voice: Books AKGH/E(M)
Singing games: Female voices, Children's voices:
Unison JFDW/GS
Singing: Solo voice: Books AK/E
Singing: Tenor voice: Books AKGH/E
Soft shoe dances: Double bass & piano
SSPHVPS
Solos, Unaccompanied: Accordion RSPM
Solos, Unaccompanied: Appalachian dulcimer
TWTTPM
Solos, Unaccompanied: Bassoon VWPM
Solos, Unaccompanied: Brass instruments
WPM
Solos, Unaccompanied: Cello SRPM
Solos, Unaccompanied: Clairsach TQCPM
Solos, Unaccompanied: Clarinet VVPM
Solos, Unaccompanied: Descant recorder
VSRPM
Solos, Unaccompanied: Double bass SSPM
Solos, Unaccompanied: Flute VRPM
Solos, Unaccompanied: Guitar TSPM
Solos, Unaccompanied: Instrumental music
LPM
Solos, Unaccompanied: Oboe VTPM
Solos, Unaccompanied: Tenor recorder
VSTPM
Solos, Unaccompanied: Trumpet WSPM
Solos, Unaccompanied: Tuba WVPM
Solos, Unaccompanied: Viola SQPM
Solos, Unaccompanied: Violin SPM
Solos, Unaccompanied: Voice KEZ
Solos: Keyboard instruments PWP
Solos: Organ R
Solos: Piano QP
Solos: Vocal music K
Solos: Vocal music: Books AK
Sonatas: Arrangements for flute & piano
VRPK/AE
Sonatas: Arrangements for treble recorder & piano
VSSPK/AE
Sonatas: Arrangements for unaccompanied guitar
TSPMK/AE
Sonatas: Arrangements for wind, strings & keyboard
trio NUNTK/LE
Sonatas: Arrangements for wind band
UMK/AE
Sonatas: Bassoon & piano VWPE
Sonatas: Cello & piano SRPE
Sonatas: Clarinet & piano VVPE
Sonatas: Clarinet (A) & piano VVQPE
Sonatas: Double bass & piano SSPE
Sonatas: Flute & piano VRPE

Sonatas: Flute solo VRPME
Sonatas: Oboe, string & keyboard trio
NUTNTE
Sonatas: Oboe & keyboard trio NWNTE
Sonatas: Oboe & piano VTPE
Sonatas: Oboes (2) & keyboard
VTNTPWE
Sonatas: Piano solos QPE
Sonatas: String & keyboard quintet
NXNRE
Sonatas: String orchestra RXME
Sonatas: String quartet RXNSE
Sonatas: Treble recorder & piano VSSPE
Sonatas: Treble recorders (2) & keyboard
VSSNTPWE
Sonatas: Trumpet, strings & keyboard quintet
NUXSNRE
Sonatas: Trumpet, strings & keyboard sextet
NUXSNQE
Sonatas: Trumpet & piano WSPE
Sonatas: Trumpet & string orchestra
RXMPWSE
Sonatas: Trumpet band WSME
Sonatas: Violin & piano SPE
Sonatas: Violin solos SPME
Sonatas: Wind, strings & keyboard nonet
NUNME
Sonatas: Wind, strings & keyboard quartet
NUNSE
Sonatas: Wind, strings & keyboard quintet
NUNRE
Sonatas: Wind & keyboard quintet NWNRE
Sonatas: Wind & strings quintet NVNRE
Sonatinas: Clarinet & piano VVPEM
Sonatinas: Flute & piano VRPEM
Sonatinas: Guitar & piano TSPEM
Sonatinas: Guitar solo TSPMEM
Sonatinas: Piano solo QPEM
Songs: Accompanied by double bass & accordion
ESSPLRSDW
Songs: Accompanied by various instruments
AELDW
Songs: Accompanied by wood-block
EXXDW
Songs: Arrangements for brass band
WMK/DW
Songs: Arrangements for clarinet ensemble
VVNK/DW
Songs: Arrangements for descant recorder solo
VSRPMK/DW
Songs: Arrangements for electronic organ
RPVK/DW
Songs: Arrangements for guitar solo
TSPMK/DW
Songs: Arrangements for military band
UMMK/DW
Songs: Arrangements for organ RK/DW
Songs: Arrangements for piano duet, 4 hands
QNVK/DW
Songs: Arrangements for piano solo
QPK/DW
Songs: Arrangements for plucked string instrument
band TMK/DW
Songs: Arrangements for string orchestra
RXMK/DW
Songs: Arrangements for symphony orchestra
MMK/DW
Songs: Arrangements for viol quartet
STNSK/DW
Songs: Arrangements for violin & piano
SPK/DW
Songs: Arrangements for wind band
UMK/DW
Songs: Arrangements for woodwind ensemble
VNK/DW
Songs: Baritone voice KGNDW
Songs: Bass voice KGXDW
Songs: Choral music DW
Songs: Choral music: Unaccompanied works
EZDW
Songs: Collected works of individual composers
KDW/AZ
Songs: Female voice duets: Vocal ensembles
JNFEDW
Songs: Female voices, Children's voices
FDW
Songs: Female voices, children's voices: Accom-
panied by percussion ensemble
FE/XNDW
Songs: Female voices, Children's voices: Unison
JFDW
Songs: Female voices, Children's voices: Unison:
Accompanied by percussion band
JFE/XMDW
Songs: Female voices, Children's voices: Unison:
Accompanied by string & percussion ensemble
JFE/NYJDW
Songs: High voice KFTDW
Songs: High voice: Accompanied by clarinet
KFTE/VVDW
Songs: Low voice KFXDW
Songs: Middle voice KFVDW
Songs: Middle voice: Accompanied by orchestra
KFVE/MDW
Songs: Musical literature ADW
Songs: Solo voice KDW
Songs: Solo voice: Accompanied by Appalachian
dulcimer KE/TWTDW

Songs: Solo voice: Accompanied by cello & piano
KE/SRPDW
Songs: Solo voice: Accompanied by guitar & piano
KE/TSPDW
Songs: Solo voice: Accompanied by guitar ensemble
KE/TSNDW
Songs: Solo voice: Accompanied by harp
KE/TQDW
Songs: Solo voice: Accompanied by instrumental
trio KE/LNTDW
Songs: Solo voice: Accompanied by lute: Books
AKE/TWDW
Songs: Solo voice: Accompanied by orchestra
KE/MDW
Songs: Solo voice: Books AKDW
Songs: Solo voice: Schubert, F.: Books
BSFAKDW
Songs: Soprano voice KFLDW
Songs: Soprano voice: Accompanied by clarinet &
piano KFLE/VVPDW
Songs: Soprano voice: Accompanied by woodwind,
string & keyboard sextet
KFLE/NUPNQDW
Songs: Treble voices: Unison: Accompanied by key-
board & percussion JFLE/NYLDW
Songs: Unaccompanied female voices, children's
voices FEZDW
Songs: Unaccompanied female voices, children's
voices: Unison JFEZDW
Songs: Unaccompanied male voices
GEZDW
Songs: Unaccompanied solo voice KEZDW
Songs: Unaccompanied works: Unison
JEZDW
Songs: Unison JDW
Songs: Unison: Accompanied by descant recorder,
keyboard & percussion
JE/NYFSRDW
Songs: Unison: Accompanied by guitar
JE/TSDW
Soprano voice KFL
Soprano voices: Choral works FL
Soprano voices: Unison JFL
Sousa, John Philip: Books BSK
South Africa: Books BZNR
Spain: Carols: Collections: Female voices,
Children's voices FDP/LF/AYK
Speaker KHY
Speakers: Female voices, Children's voices
FHY
Spirituals: Arrangements for electronic organ
RPVK/DW/LC
Spirituals: Female voices, Children's voices
FDW/LC
Spirituals: Unaccompanied female voices, children's
voices FEZDW/LC
Spirituals: Unaccompanied male voices
GEZDW/LC
Spirituals: Unaccompanied works
EZDW/LC
Stabat Mater: Proper of the Mass
EMDGKADD/LK
Stabat mater: sequences: Proper of the Mass: Un-
accompanied works EZDGKADD/LK
Stockhausen, Karlheinz: Books BSNK(N)
Stories: Comedians, The: Kabalevsky, D.: Books
BKDBAM/HMBN
Stories; Librettos: Musical plays ACMBN
Stories: Nutcracker, The: Books
BTDAM/HMBN
Stories: Peer Gynt: Grieg, E.: Books
BGTAM/JMBN
Stories: Swan Lake: Books BTDAM/HMBN
Stravinsky, Igor: Books BSV
String bass SS
String instruments RW
String instruments: Accompanying choral works
ERW
String instruments: Books ARW
String instruments: Haydn, J.: Books
BHEARX
String trio & string orchestra RXMPRXNT
Strings, trumpet & keyboard: Chamber music
NUXS
Strings, wind & keyboard: Chamber music
NU
Strings, wind & keyboard: Ensembles: Accompany-
ing soprano voice KFLE/NU
Strings, woodwind & keyboard: Ensembles: Accom-
panying soprano voice KFLE/NUP
Strings & keyboard: Accompanying choral music
ENX
Strings & keyboard: Chamber music NX
Strings & percussion: Ensembles: Accompanying
voices, children's voices
FE/NYJ
Strings & percussion: Ensembles: Accompanying
female voices, children's voices: Unison
JFE/NYJ
Strings & wind: Ensembles: Accompanying choral
music ENV
Strings & wind: Ensembles: Chamber music
NV
Strings & woodwind: Chamber music NVP
Suites: Arrangements for flute & piano
VRPK/AG
Suites: Arrangements for trumpet & piano
WSPK/AG

LIST OF MUSIC PUBLISHERS

While every effort has been made to check the information given in this list with the publishers concerned, the British Library cannot hold itself responsible for any errors or omissions.

ACUFF-ROSE Music Ltd. 16 St George St., London W.1. *Tel:* 01-629-0392. *Grams:* Acufrose London.

AFFILIATED MUSIC Publishers Ltd. 138 Charing Cross Rd, London WC2H OLD. *Tel:* 01-836-9351.

AMERICAN UNIVERSITY PUBLISHERS Group, Ltd. 70 Great Russell St., London WC1B 3BY. *Tel:* 01-405-0182. *Grams:* Amunpress.

ANTICO Edition. North Harton, Lustleigh, Newton Abbot, Devon TQ13 9SG. *Tel:* Lustleigh (064 77) 260.

ARNOLD. E.J. Arnold & Son Ltd. Butterley St., Leeds LS10 1AX.

ARS VIVA. 48 Great Marlborough St., London W1V 2BN.

ASCHERBURG, HOPWOOD AND CREW Ltd. 50 New Bond St., London W1A 2BR. *Tel:* 01-629-7600. *Grams:* Symphony London.

ASHDOWN. Edwin Ashdown, Ltd. 275-281 Cricklewood Broadway, London NW2 6QR. *Tel:* 01-450-5237.

ASHLEY-FIELDS Music Ltd. 61 Frith St., London W1V 5TA. *Tel:* 01-734-7462. *Grams:* Fieldmus London.

ASSOCIATED BOARD OF THE ROYAL SCHOOLS OF MUSIC. (Publications Dept,) 14 Bedford Sq., London WC1B 3JG. *Tel:* 01-636-6919. *Grams:* Musexam London WC1.

ASSOCIATED MUSIC Publishers Inc. c/o G. Schirmer Ltd, 140 Strand, London WC2R 1HH. *Tel:* 01-836-4011.

BANKS and Son (Music) Ltd. Stonegate, York.

BARENREITER Ltd. 32 Great Titchfield St., London W.1. *Tel:* 01-580-9008.

BAYLEY AND FERGUSON, Ltd. 65 Berkeley St., Glasgow C3. *Tel:* Central 7240. *Grams:* Bayley Glasgow.

B.B.C. *See* British Broadcasting Corporation.

BELWIN-MILLS Music, Ltd. 250 Purley Way, Croydon CR9 4QD. *Tel:* 01-681-0855. *Grams:* Belmilmus Croydon.

BERRY MUSIC Co. Ltd. 10 Denmark St., London WC2H 8LU. *Tel:* 01-836-1653.

BLOSSOM Music, Ltd. 139 Piccadilly, London W.1. *Tel:* 01-629-7211. *Grams:* Leedsmusik London W1.

BODLEY HEAD. The Bodley Head, Ltd. 9 Bow St., London WC2E 7AL. *Tel:* 01-836-9081. *Grams:* Bodleian London WC2.

BOOSEY AND HAWKES Music Publishers, Ltd. 295 Regent St., London W1A 1BR. *Tel:* 01-580-2060. *Grams:* Sonorous London W1. *Trade:* The Hyde, Edgware Rd, London NW9 6JN. *Tel:* 01-205-3861. *Grams:* Sonorous London NW9.

BOSWORTH and Co., Ltd. 14 Heddon St., London W1R 8DP. *Tel:* 01-734-0475. *Grams:* Bosedition London W1.

BOURNE MUSIC Ltd. 34/36 Maddox St., London W1R 9PD. *Tel:* 01-493-6412. *Grams:* Bournemusic London W1.

BREGMAN, VOCCO AND CONN, Ltd. 50 New Bond St., London W1A 1BR. *Tel:* 01-629-7600. *Grams:* Symphony London.

BREITKOPF AND HARTEL (London) Ltd. 8 Horse and Dolphin Yard, London W1V 7LG. *Tel:* 01-437-3342. *Grams:* Breitkopfs London W.1.

BRITISH AND CONTINENTAL Music Agencies, Ltd. 64 Dean St., London W.1. *Tel:* 01-437-7543.

BRITISH BROADCASTING CORPORATION. BBC Publications, 35 Marylebone High St., London W1M 4AA. *Tel:* 01-580-5577. *Grams:* Broadcasts London. *Telex:* 265781.

CAMBRIDGE UNIVERSITY PRESS. Bentley House, P.O. Box 92, 200 Euston Rd, London NW1 2DB. *Tel:* 01-387-5030. *Grams:* Cantabrigia London NW1. *Telex:* 27335. *Editorial and Production:* The Pitt Building, Trumpington St., Cambridge CB2 1RP. *Tel:* Cambridge 58331. *Grams:* Unipress Cambs. *Telex:* 817256.

CAMPBELL CONNELLY and Co., Ltd. 10 Denmark St., London W.C.2. *Tel:* 01-836-1653.

CARY. L.J. Cary and Co., Ltd. 50 New Bond St., London W1A 2BR. *Tel:* 01-629-7600. *Grams:* Symphony London W1.

CENTRAL COUNCIL OF CHURCH BELL RINGERS. c/o 'Monsal', Bredon, Tewkesbury, Glos. GL20 7LY.

CHAPPELL and Co., Ltd. 50 New Bond St., London W1A 1DR. *Tel:* 01-629-7600. *Grams:* Symphony London. *Telex:* 268403.

CHARNWOOD MUSIC Publishing Co. 5 University Rd, Leicester.

CHESTER. J. and W. Chester/Edition Wilhelm Hansen London Ltd. Eagle Court, London EC1M 5QD. *Tel:* 01-253-6947. *Grams:* Guarnerius London EC1.

CLIFFORD ESSEX Music Co. Ltd. 20 Earlham St., London W.C.2. *Tel:* 01-836-2810. *Grams:* Triomphe London WC2.

COLLIER MACMILLAN Publishers. Division of Cassell and Collier Macmillan Publishers Ltd, 35 Red Lion Sq., London WC1R 4SG. *Tel:* 01-242-6281.

Connelly, Campbell and Co., Ltd. *See* Campbell Connelly.

CONSTABLE and Co., Ltd. 10 Orange St., London WC2H 7EG. *Tel:* 01-930-0801. *Grams:* Dhagoba London WC2H 7EG. *Trade:* Tiptree, Essex. *Tel:* 0621-81-6362.

CRAMER. J.B. Cramer and Co., Ltd. 99 St Martin's Lane, London WC2N 4AZ. *Tel:* 01-240-1612.

CRANZ and Co. Ltd. Alderman's House, Bishopsgate, London E.C.2. *Tel:* 01-283-4266. *Grams:* Cranz Usually London.

Curwen. J. Curwen and Sons, Ltd. *See* Faber Music.

DANIEL. The C.W. Daniel Co. Ltd. 60 Muswell Rd, London N.10. *Tel:* 01-444-8650.

DAVID AND CHARLES (Publishers), Ltd. South Devon House, Railway Station, Newton Abbot, Devon TQ12 2BP. *Tel:* 0626-3521. *Telex:* 42904.

DE WOLFE, Ltd. 80-82 Wardour St., London W1V 3LF. *Tel:* 01-437-4933. *Grams:* Musicall London.

DICK JAMES MUSIC Ltd. 71 New Oxford St., London WC1A 1DP. *Tel:* 01-836-4864.

EFDS. *See* English Folk Dance and Song Society.

EGRET HOUSE. 93 Chancery La., London W.C.2.

ELKIN and Co., Ltd. Borough Green, Sevenoaks, Kent. *Tel:* 0732-88-3261. *Grams:* Novellos Sevenoaks.

EMERSON. June Emerson Wind Music. Windmill Farm, Ampleforth, York.

EMI MUSIC. 20 Manchester Sq., London W.1. *Tel:* 01-486-4488.

ENGLISH FOLK DANCE AND SONG SOCIETY. Cecil Sharp House, 2 Regent's Park Rd, London NW1 7AY. *Tel:* 01-485-2206.

EP PUBLISHING. EP Group of Companies. Bradford Rd, East Ardsley, Wakefield, Yorkshire. *Tel:* Wakefield 823971 (0924). *Grams:* Edpro Wakefield. *London Office:* 27 Maunsel St., London SW1P 2QS. *Tel:* 01-834-1067.

Essex, C. Clifford Essex Music Co. Ltd. *See* Clifford Essex.

ESSEX MUSIC Group. Essex House, 19/20 Poland St., London W1V 3DD. *Tel:* 01-734-8121. *Grams:* Sexmus London. *Trade:* Music Sales Ltd, 78 Newman St., London W.1.

EULENBURG. Ernst Eulenburg, Ltd. 48 Great Marlborough St., London W1V 2BN. *Tel:* 01-437-1246.

FABER MUSIC, Ltd. 38 Russell Sq., London WC1B 5DA. *Tel:* 01-636-1344. *Grams:* Fabbaf London WC1.

FAMOUS CHAPPELL, Ltd. 50 New Bond St., London W1A 2BR. *Tel:* 01-629-7600. *Grams:* Symphony London.

FELDMAN. B. Feldman and Co., Ltd. 1-6 Denmark Place, London WC2H 8NL. *Tel:* 01-836-6699. *Grams:* Humfriv London WC2.

FENETTE MUSIC. 138-140 Charing Cross Rd, London WC2H 0LD.

FORSYTH Brothers, Ltd. 190 Grays Inn Rd, London WC1X 8EW. *Tel:* 01-837-4768.

Fox. Sam Fox Publishing Co. (London) Ltd. *See* Sam Fox.

FRANCIS, DAY AND HUNTER, Ltd. 138 Charing Cross Rd, London WC2H 0LD. *Tel:* 01-836-6699. *Grams:* Arpeggio London WC2.

FRANK MUSIC Co, Ltd. 50 New Bond St., London W1A 2BR. *Tel:* 01-629-7600. *Grams:* Symphony London.

FREEMAN. H. Freeman, Ltd. 138 Charing Cross Rd, London WC2H 0LD. *Tel:* 01-836-6699.

GALLIARD, Ltd. 82 High Rd, London N2 9PW.

GLOCKEN Verlag, Ltd. 10-16 Rathbone St., London W1P 2BJ. *Tel:* 01-580-2827. *Grams:* Operetta London W1.

GOOD NEWS CRUSADE. 32a Fore St., St Austell, Cornwall PL25 5EP. *Tel:* St Austell 2716.

GRAHAM. Frank Graham. 6 Queen's Terrace, Newcastle upon Tyne 2. *Tel:* Newcastle upon Tyne 813067.

GWASG PRIFYSGOL CYMRU. *See* University of Wales Press.

Hansen. Edition Wilhelm Hansen London Ltd. *See* Chester.

HANSEN Publications Ltd. 218 Great Portland St., London W1N 6JH. *Tel:* 01-387-0851.

Hart. F. Pitman Hart and Co., Ltd. *See* Pitman Hart.

HINRICHSEN Edition Ltd. 10 Baches St., London N1 6DN. *Tel:* 01-253-1638. *Grams:* Musipeters London.

HORTON TRUST. 1 Sherbourne Rd, Great Horton, Bradford, West Yorkshire BD7 1RB. *Tel:* Bradford (0274) 26975. *Grams:* Hortrust Bradford.

HUGHES A'I FAB. (Hughes and Son) Publishers, Ltd. 29 Rivulet Rd, Wrexham, Clwyd. *Tel:* Wrexham 4340.

IMPERIA MUSIC Co. Ltd. 21 Denmark St., London W.C.2. *Tel:* 01-836-6699. *Grams:* Mauritunes London WC2.

INTER-ART Music Publishers. 10-16 Rathbone St., London W1P 2BJ. *Tel:* 01-580-2827. *Grams:* Operetta London W1.

James. Dick James Music Ltd. *See* Dick James Music.

KALMUS. Alfred A. Kalmus, Ltd. 2-3 Fareham St., London W1V 4DU. *Tel:* 01-437-5203. *Grams:* Alkamus London W1.

KEITH PROWSE MUSIC Publishing Co., Ltd. 21 Denmark St., London WC2H 8NE. *Tel:* 01-836-6699.

LEEDS MUSIC, Ltd. 230 Purley Way, Croydon CR9 4QD. *Tel:* 01-681-0855. *Grams:* Leedsmusik London.

LENGNICK. Alfred Lengnick and Co., Ltd. Purley Oaks Studios, 421a Brighton Rd, South Croydon, Surrey CR2 6YR. *Tel:* 01-660-7646.

LEONARD, GOULD AND BOLTTLER. 99 St Martin's Lane, London WC2N 4AZ. *Tel:* 01-240-1612.

LONDON PRO MUSICA. 42 Christchurch Ave., London N.W.6.

LONGMAN Group Ltd. Longman House, Burnt Mill, Harlow, Essex. *Tel:* Harlow 26721. *Trade:* Pinnacles, Harlow, Essex. *Tel:* Harlow 29655. *Grams:* 81259.

MORRIS. Edwin H. Morris and Co., Ltd. 50 New Bond St., London W1Y 9HA. *Tel:* 01-629-0576.

MOZART EDITION (Great Britain) Ltd. 199 Wardour St., London W1V 3FA. *Tel:* 01-734-3711.

MUSIC SALES Ltd. 78 Newman St., London W.1. *Tel:* 01-636-9033.

MUSICA RARA. 2 Great Marlborough St., London W.1. *Tel:* 01-437-1576.

MUSICA VIVA. 558 Galleywood Rd, Chelmsford, Essex CM2 8BX.

NATIONAL FEDERATION OF WOMEN'S INSTITUTES. 39 Eccleston St., London SW1W 9NT. *Tel:* 01-730-7212. *Grams:* Fedinsti London SW1.

NOVELLO and Co., Ltd. Borough Green, Sevenoaks, Kent TN15 8DT. *Tel:* 0732-88-3261. *Grams:* Novellos Sevenoaks.

OCTAVA Music Co., Ltd. *See* Weinberger.

OXFORD UNIVERSITY PRESS (Music Department). 44 Conduit St., London W1R ODE. *Tel:* 01-734-5364. *Grams:* Fulscore London W1.

PATERSON. Paterson's Publications, Ltd. 38 Wigmore St., London W1H OEX. *Tel:* 01-935-3551. *Grams:* Paterwia London W1.

PAXTON. Borough Green, Sevenoaks, Kent TN15 8DT.

PENGUIN Books, Ltd. Bath Rd, Harmondsworth, Middx. *Tel:* 01-759-1984. *Grams:* Penguinook West Drayton. *Telex:* 263130. *London office:* 17 Grosvenor Gardens, London S.W.1.

PETERS Edition. 10 Baches St., London N1 6DN. *Tel:* 01-253-1638. *Grams:* Musipeters London.

PHOENIX. 61 Frith St., London W1V 5TA.

PITMAN HART. F. Pitman Hart, and Co., Ltd. 99 St Martin's Lane, London WC2N 4AZ. *Tel:* 01-240-1612.

Pro Musica. *See* London Pro Musica.

Prowse. Keith Prowse Music Publishing Co. Ltd. *See* Keith Prowse Music.

R. SMITH and Co. Ltd. 210 Strand, London WC2R 1AP. *Tel:* 01-353-1166.

RAHTER. D. Rahter. Lyra House, 67 Belsize La., London N.W.3. *Tel:* 01-794-8038.

REGINA MUSIC Publishing Co., Ltd. Old Run Rd, Leeds LS10 2AA. *Tel:* Leeds 700527.

RICORDI. G. Ricordi and Co. (London), Ltd. The Bury, Church St., Chesham, Bucks HP5 1JG. *Tel:* Chesham 3311. *Grams:* Ricordi Chesham.

ROBBINS Music Corporation, Ltd. 138 Charing Cross Rd, London WC2H 0LD. *Tel:* 01-836-6699.

ROBERTON Publications. The Windmill, Wendover, Aylesbury, Bucks. HP22 6JJ. *Tel:* Wendover (0296) 623107.

ROYAL SCHOOL OF CHURCH MUSIC. Addington Palace, Croydon CR9 5AD. *Tel:* 01-654-7676. *Grams:* Cantoris Croydon.

ROYAL SCOTTISH COUNTRY DANCE SOCIETY. 12 Coates Cres., Edinburgh EH3 7AF. *Tel:* 031-225-3854.

SALVATIONIST PUBLISHING AND SUPPLIES, Ltd. 117 Judd St., London WC1H 9NN. *Tel:* 01-387-1656. *Grams:* Savingly London WC1.

SAM FOX Publishing Co. (London) Ltd. 21 Denmark St., London WC2H 8NE. *Tel:* 01-836-6699.

SCHAUER AND MAY. 67 Belsize La., London N.W.3. *Tel:* 01-794-8038.

SCHIRMER. G. Schirmer Ltd, (Music Publishers). 140 Strand, London WC2R 1HH. *Tel:* 01-836-4011.

SCHOFIELD AND SIMS, Ltd. 35 St John's Rd, Huddersfield, Yorkshire HD1 5DT. *Tel:* Huddersfield 30684. *Grams:* Schosims Huddersfield.

SCHOOLMASTER PUBLISHING Co. Ltd. Derbyshire House, Lower St., Kettering, Northants. NN16 8BB. *Tel:* 053687-3407.

SCHOTT and Co. Ltd. 48 Great Marlborough St., London W1V 2BN. *Tel:* 01-437-1246. *Grams:* Shotanco London.

SCHROEDER, A. A. Schroeder Music Publishing Co., Ltd. 15 Berkeley St., London W.1. *Tel:* 01-493-2506.

SCHROEDER AND GUNTHER Inc. c/o G. Schirmer Ltd., 140 Strand, London WC2R 1HH. *Tel:* 01-836-4011.

SIMROCK. N. Simrock. Lyra House, 67 Belsize Lane, London NW3 5AX. *Tel:* 01-794-8038.

Smith. R. Smith and Co. Ltd. *See* R. Smith.

SPARTA FLORIDA MUSIC Group Ltd. Suite 4, Carlton Tower Place, London S.W.1. *Tel:* 01-245-9339.

ST GREGORY PUBLISHING Co. 4 West Hill Rd, Hoddesdon, Herts. *Tel:* Hoddesdon 64483.

ST MARTINS PUBLICATIONS, Ltd. *No longer publishing.*

STAINER AND BELL Ltd. 82 High Rd, London N2 9PW. *Tel:* 01-444-9135.

STOCKWELL. Arthur H. Stockwell, Ltd. Elms Court, Ilfracombe, Devon EX34 8BA. *Tel:* 02716-2557. *Grams:* Stockwell, Ilfracombe.

STUDIO MUSIC Co. 89-91 Vicarage Rd, London NW10 2UA. *Tel:* 01-459-6194.

THAMES MUSIC. 39-41 New Bond St., London W.1. *Tel:* 01-499-5961.

THAMES Publishing. 14 Barlby Rd, London W10 6AR. *Tel:* 01-969-3579.

TOMUS Publications. Carne House, Parsons La., Bury, Lancs. BL9 0JT. *Tel:* 061-764-1099.

UNITED MUSIC Publishers Ltd. 1 Montague St., London WC1B 5BS. *Tel:* 01-636-5171.

UNIVERSAL EDITION (London), Ltd. 2 Fareham St., Dean St., London W1V 4DU. *Tel:* 01-437-5203. *Grams:* Alkamus London W1.

UNIVERSITY OF ILLINOIS PRESS. *See* American University Publishers.

UNIVERSITY OF TEXAS PRESS, Ltd. *See* American University Publishers.

UNIVERSITY OF WALES PRESS. Merthyr House, James St., Cardiff CF1 6EU. *Tel:* Cardiff 31919.

VANGUARD MUSIC Ltd. 19 Charing Cross Rd, London W.C.2. *Tel:* 01-839-3655.

WARREN AND PHILLIPS. 196 Grays Inn Rd, London WC1X 8EW.

WEINBERGER. Joseph Weinberger Ltd. 10-16 Rathbone St., London W1P 2BJ. *Tel:* 01-580-2827. *Grams:* Operetta London W1.

WISE Publications. 78 Newman St., London W.1. *Tel:* 01-636-0933.

WOLFE Publishing, Ltd. 10 Earlham St., London WC2H 9LP. *Tel:* 01-240-2935.

YORKE Edition. 8 Cecil Rd, London W3 ODA. *Tel:* 01-992-1068.